MATHEMATICS

6th Edition

4

Consultant:
Dr Yeap Ban Har

Authors:
Teh Keng Seng BSc, Dip Ed • Loh Cheng Yee 劳静仪 BSc, Dip Ed
Joseph Yeo MEd, PGDE (Distinction), BSc (Hons) • Ivy Chow MEd, PGDE, BSc

shinglee publishers pte ltd

SHINGLEE PUBLISHERS PTE LTD
120 Hillview Avenue #05-06/07
Kewalram Hillview Singapore 669594
Tel: 67601388 Fax: 67623247
email: info@shinglee.com.sg
http://www.shinglee.com.sg

First Published 1982
Reprinted 1983, 1984, 1985, 1986
Second Edition 1987
Reprinted 1987, 1988, 1989, 1990, 1991, 1992, 1993
Third Edition 1994
Reprinted 1994, 1995, 1996, 1997
Fourth Edition 1998
Reprinted 1999
Fifth Edition 2001
Reprinted 2002, 2003, 2004, 2005, 2006
Sixth Edition 2008, 2009

ISBN 978 981 237 355 7

Cover design by Dave Cheong

Printed in Singapore by Utopia Press Pte Ltd

PREFACE

New Syllabus Mathematics is a series of four books. These books follow the Mathematics Syllabus for Secondary Schools, implemented from 2007 by the Ministry of Education, Singapore. The whole series covers the complete syllabus for the Singapore-Cambridge GCE 'O' Level Mathematics.

The sixth edition of New Syllabus Mathematics retains the goals and objectives of the previous edition, but has been revised to meet the needs of the users of the fifth edition and to keep materials up-to-date as well as to give students a better understanding of the contents.

All topics are comprehensively dealt with to provide students with a firm grounding in the subject. Explanations of concepts and principles are precise and written clearly and concisely with supportive illustrations and examples. Examples and exercises have been carefully graded to aid students in progressing within and beyond each level. Those exercises marked with a ✶ either require more thinking or involve more calculations.

Numerous revision exercises are provided at appropriate intervals to enable students to recapitulate what they have learnt.

Some interesting features of this series include the following:

- an interesting introduction at the beginning of each chapter complete with photographs or graphics.
- brief specific instructional objectives for each chapter.
- **Just for fun** arouses the students' interests in studying mathematics.
- **Thinking Time** encourages students to think creatively and go even deeper into the topics.
- **Exploration** provides opportunities for students to learn actively and independently.
- **For your information** provides extra information on mathematicians, mathematical history and events etc.
- **Problem Solving Tips** provide suggestions to help students in their thinking processes. We also introduce problem solving heuristics and strategies systemically throughout the series.
- **Your Attention** alerts students to misconceptions.

CONTENTS

In this chapter, you will learn how to

- *draw cubic, reciprocal and exponential graphs;*
- *solve quadratic, cubic and exponential equations graphically.*

CHAPTER

1

Graphical Solution of Equations

Introduction

The photograph shows the decorative shapes of glass panels hanging from the ceiling of a function hall in a local hotel. Each part of the glass panel resembles a quadratic curve.

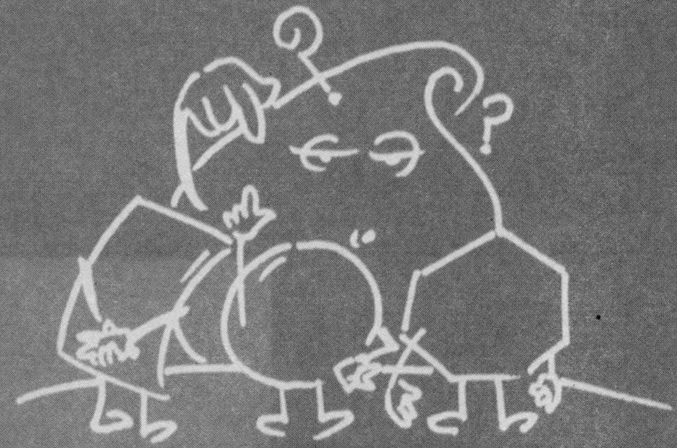

Graphs of Cubic Functions

In Book 2, we learnt how to draw graphs of linear and quadratic functions. Now, we will learn how to draw graphs of cubic, reciprocal and exponential functions.

Let's recall the steps for drawing a linear or quadratic graph.

(a) Choose a suitable scale for the x-axis and y-axis.
(b) Construct a table of x and y values for the equation.
(c) Plot the coordinates on the graph paper and join up the points.

Using the above steps, draw the graph of $y = x^3 - 15x + 5$ for values of x from -4 to 4. You have to join up the points to form a smooth curve. Alternatively, you may use the computer software, Graphmatica to draw the graph.

To use Graphmatica, first go to **view**, **graph paper** to select **rectangular**. Then go to **view** again to select **grid range**.

Do you get the graph as in Fig 1.1?

Use your graph to find

(a) the value of y when $x = 2.5$;
(b) the value of x when $y = 5$.

Compare your answers with your classmates.

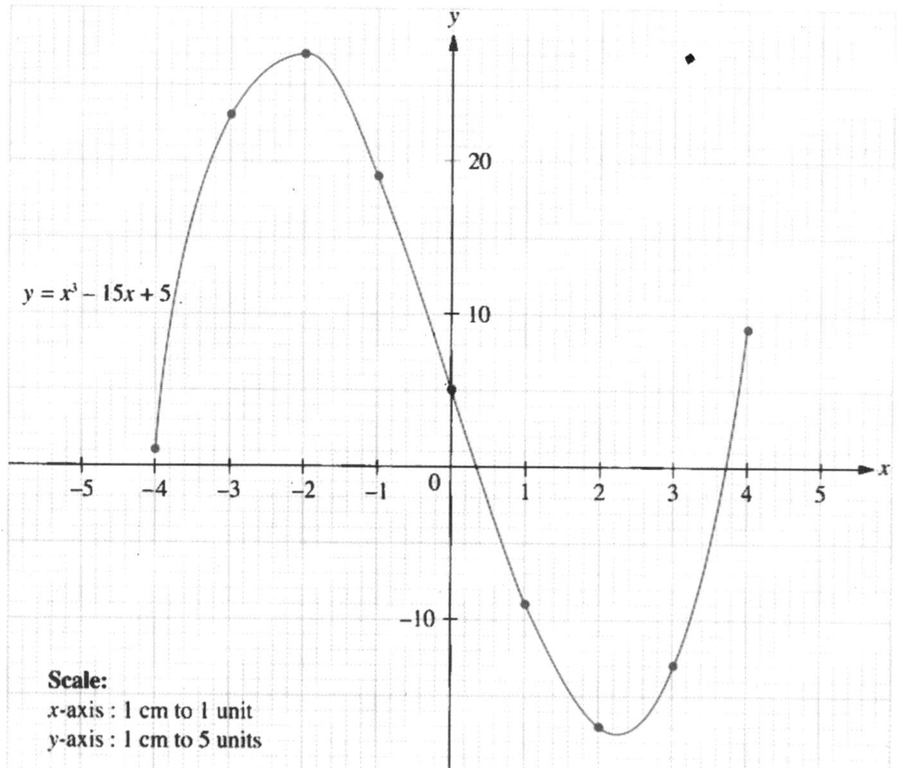

Fig. 1.1

Example 1

Draw the graph of $y = x^3 + 3$ and of $y = -x^3 - 3$ on the same axes, for values of x from −3 to 3 and use each graph to find

(a) *the value of y when $x = 1.5$;*
(b) *the value of x when $y = 20$.*

The table displaying values of x and y is shown below:

	−3	−2	−1	0	1	2	3
	−24	−5	2	3	4	11	30
	24	5	−2	−3	−4	−11	−30

The curves of $y = x^3 + 3$ and $y = -x^3 - 3$ are plotted as shown in Fig. 1.2.

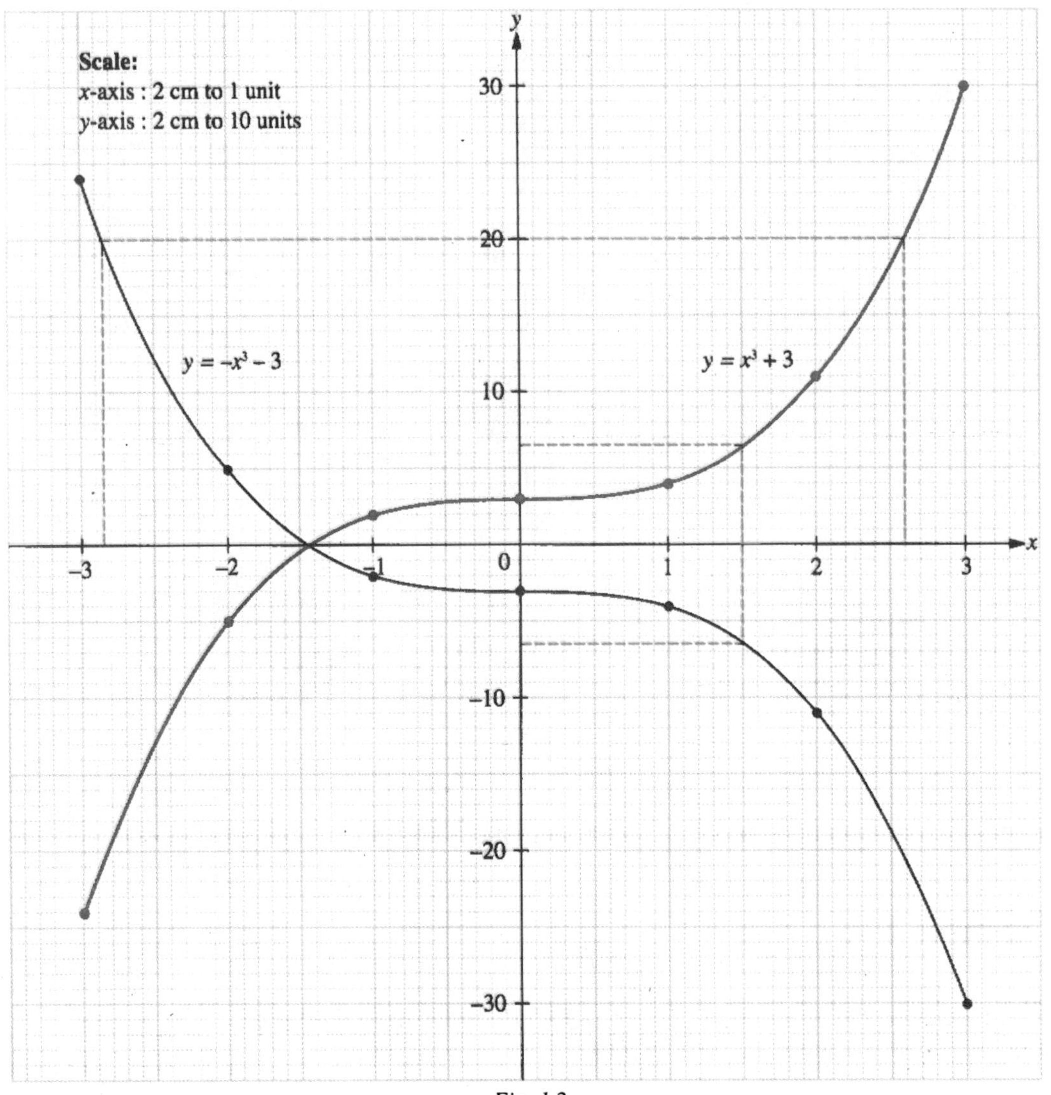

Fig. 1.2

From the graph,

for $y = x^3 + 3$,
(a) when $x = 1.5$, $y \approx 6.5$
(b) when $y = 20$, $x \approx 2.6$

for $y = -x^3 - 3$,
(a) when $x = 1.5$, $y \approx -6.5$
(b) when $y = 20$, $x \approx -2.85$

Graphs of Reciprocal Functions

The general form of a **reciprocal function** is $y = \frac{a}{x}$, where a is a real number and $a \neq 0$. The function $y = \frac{a}{x}$ is defined for all real values of x, except when $x = 0$.

Using the steps for drawing a graph, draw the graph of $y = \frac{1}{x}$. You have to join up the points to form a smooth curve, except for the break at $x = 0$. Alternatively, you may use the computer software, Graphmatica to draw the graph. Do you get the graph below?

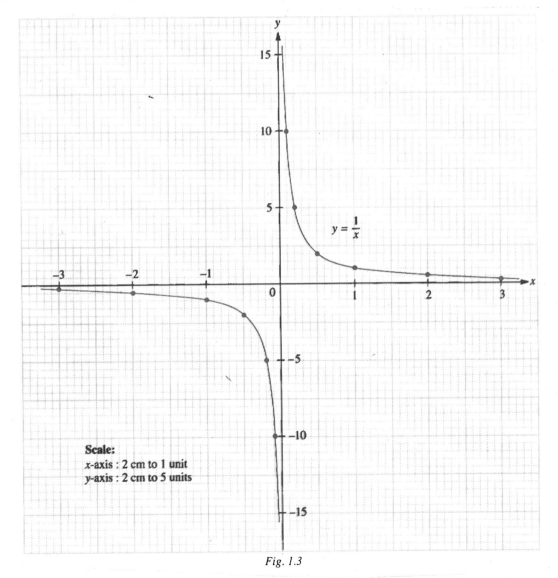

$y = \frac{1}{x}$

Scale:
x-axis : 2 cm to 1 unit
y-axis : 2 cm to 5 units

Fig. 1.3

Does the curve $y = \frac{1}{x}$ intersect the x-axis and y-axis? Why?

Observe the graph of $y = \frac{1}{x}$, we notice that:

(1) Although the graph occurs in two separate parts, it must be regarded as a single graph and not as two separate graphs.

(2) As the positive value of x increases, the value of y decreases. The curve gets very close to the x-axis but never touches it. As the positive value of x decreases, the value of y increases rapidly and it gets very close to the y-axis.

When x is negative, y becomes larger as x becomes smaller and when x gets very close to 0, y decreases rapidly. In other words, as x approaches zero, y approaches **infinity** (symbol: ∞).

(3) When $x = 0$, the function $y = \frac{1}{x}$ is not defined. This means that there is a break when $x = 0$.

(4) The two parts of the graph are mirror images of each other. The equations of the two mirror lines of symmetry are $y = x$ and $y = -x$.

Drawing graphs may seem complicated at first but after the plotting of tables and sketching, it becomes a much simpler process.

xample 2

Draw the graph of $y = \frac{6}{x}$ *for* $-5 \leqslant x \leqslant 5, x \neq 0$, *and use it to find*

(a) the value of y *when* $x \doteq 1.5$;

(b) the value of x *when* $y = -8$.

The table displaying values of x and y for $y = \frac{6}{x}$ is

	–5	–4	–3	–2	–1	–0.5	0.5	1	2	3	4	5
	–1.2	–1.5	–2	–3	–6	–12	12	6	3	2	1.5	1.2

The coordinates of the points are plotted as shown in Fig. 1.4.

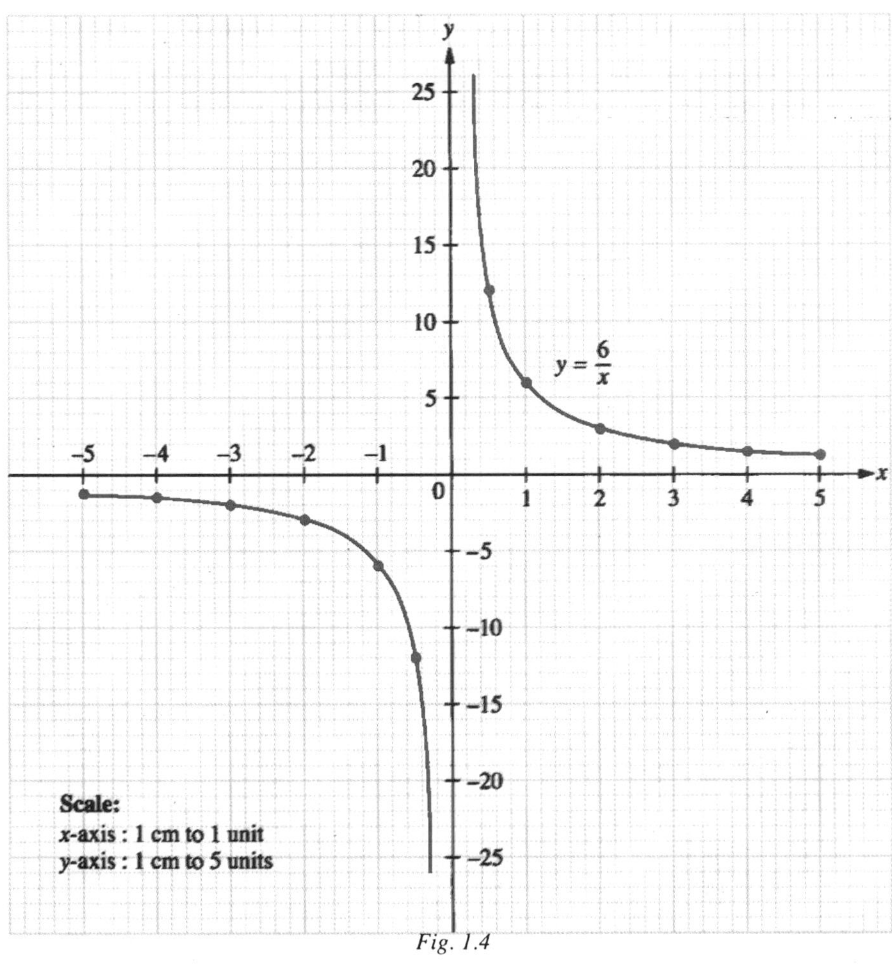

Fig. 1.4

From the graph,

(a) when $x = 1.5$, $y \approx 4$
(b) when $y = -8$, $x \approx -0.75$

Graphs of the Function $y = \frac{a}{x^2}$

We shall now learn about the graph of the function $y = \frac{a}{x^2}$, where a is a real number and $a \neq 0$. The function $y = \frac{a}{x^2}$ is defined for all real values of x, except when $x = 0$.

Using the steps for drawing graphs, draw the graph of $y = \frac{1}{x^2}$ for values of x between –4 and 4, except for $x = 0$. You have to join up the points to form a smooth curve except for the break at $x = 0$. Alternatively, you may use the computer software, Graphmatica to draw the graph. Did you get the following graph?

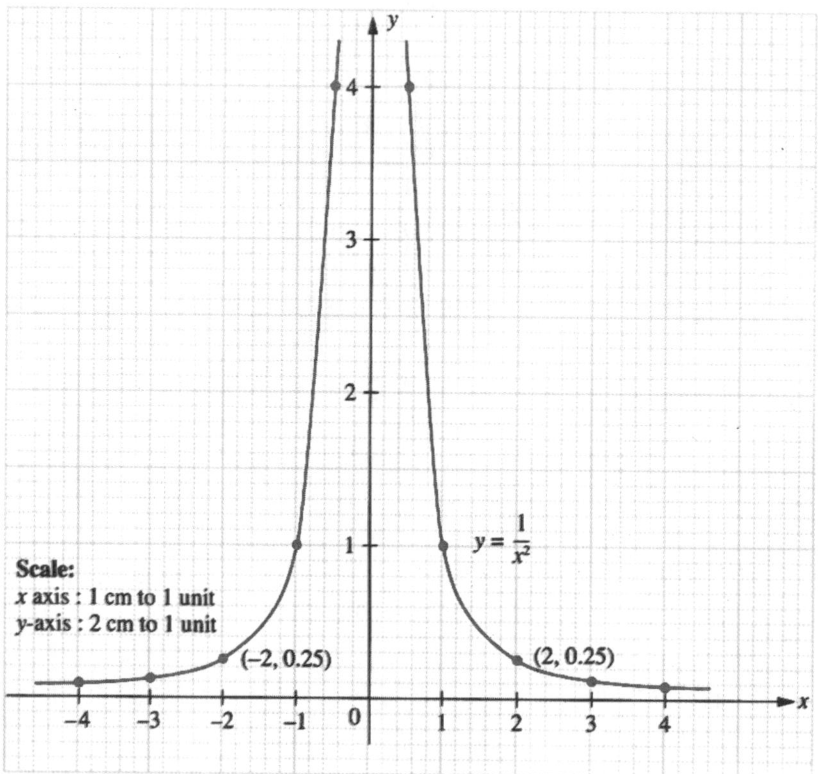

From Fig. 1.5,

(1) the function is made up of two parts and should be treated as a single graph;
(2) the values of y are always positive. Therefore the curve lies entirely above the x-axis;
(3) the curve is symmetrical about the y-axis and thus the y-axis is the line of symmetry;
(4) the function is not defined when $x = 0$.

Graphs of Exponential Functions

The general form of an **exponential function** is $y = a^x$, where a is a positive real number. The function $y = a^x$ is defined for all real values of x.

Using the steps for drawing graphs, draw the graph of $y = 3^x$. Alternatively, you may use the computer software, Graphmatica to draw the graph.

Did you get the following graph?

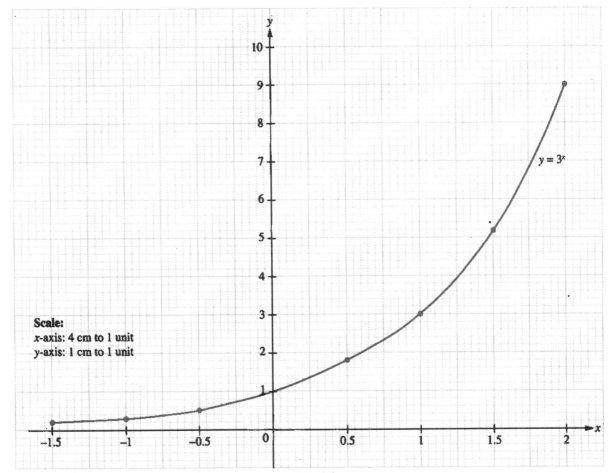

Scale:
x-axis: 4 cm to 1 unit
y-axis: 1 cm to 1 unit

$y = 3^x$

Fig. 1.6

Use your graph to estimate the value of (i) y when $x = 1.2$ and (ii) x when $y = 8$.
Compare your answers with your classmates.
Does the curve intersect the x-axis? Why?

From the graph of $y = 3^x$, we observe that:

(1) There is no negative value of y for all real values of x. Therefore the graph lies entirely above the x-axis.

(2) As the value for negative x increases, the value of y increases very slowly. As x increases its value in the positive range, the value of y increases very rapidly.

(3) The curve cuts the y-axis at (0, 1).

 xample 3

Given that $y = 2^x$, copy and complete the following table of values. Give all values of x and y correct to 1 decimal place where necessary.

	–1	–0.5	0	0.5	1	1.5	2	2.5
	0.5		1	1.4	2			

(a) Using a scale of 4 cm to represent 1 unit on the x-axis and 2 cm to represent 1 unit on the y-axis, draw the graph of $y = 2^x$ for $-1 \le x \le 2.5$.

(b) Use your graph to estimate the values of

(i) y when $x = -0.8$, 0.8 and 1.8;
(ii) x when $y = 0.8$, 2.6 and 4.6.

	–1	–0.5	0	0.5	1	1.5	2	2.5
	0.5	0.7	1	1.4	2	2.8	4	5.7

(a) The graph of $y = 2^x$ is shown in Fig. 1.7.

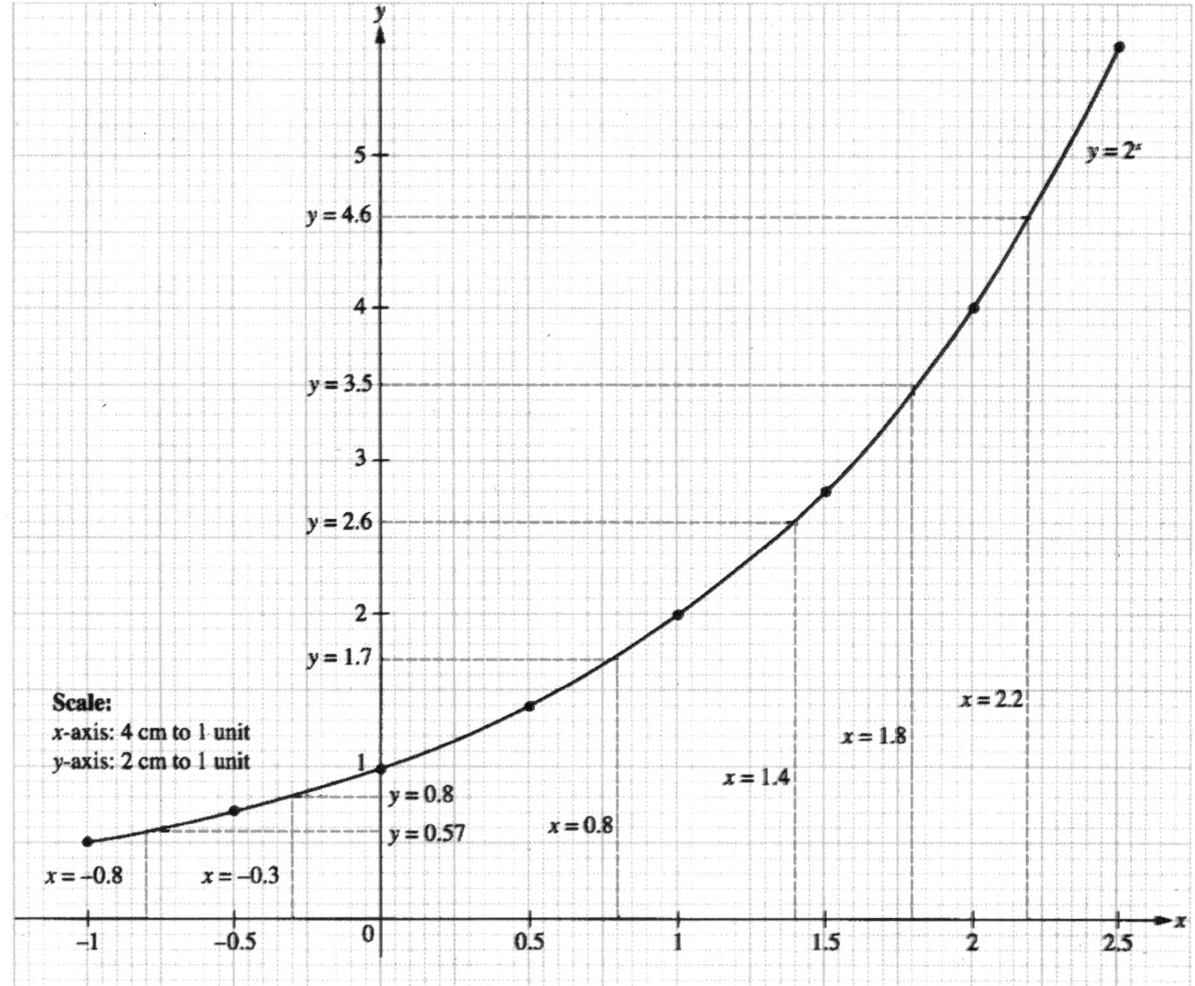

Fig. 1.7

(b) (i) When $x = -0.8$, $y \approx 0.57$;
when $x = 0.8$, $y \approx 1.7$;
when $x = 1.8$, $y \approx 3.5$.

(ii) When $y = 0.8$, $x \approx -0.3$;
when $y = 2.6$, $x \approx 1.4$;
when $y = 4.6$, $x \approx 2.2$.

1. Copy and complete the following table which gives values of $y = x^3$ for values of x between –3 and 3 inclusive.

x	–3	–2	–1	0	1	2	3
y		–8			1		27

Using 2 cm to represent 1 unit on the x-axis and 1 cm to represent 5 units on the y-axis, draw the graph of $y = x^3$. Use your graph to find

(a) the value of y when $x = 1.5$;
(b) the value of x when $y = -12$.

2. Copy and complete the following table which gives values of $y = x^3 - 5$ for values of x between –3 and 3 inclusive.

x	–3	–2	–1	0	1	2	3
y	–32		–6				22

Using 2 cm to represent 1 unit on the x-axis and 1 cm to represent 5 units on the y-axis, draw the graph of $y = x^3 - 5$. Use your graph to find

(a) the value of y when $x = -2.2$;
(b) the value of x when $y = 14$.

3. Copy and complete the following table which gives the values of $y = 3x - x^3$ for $-3 \leq x \leq 3$.

x	–3	–2	–1	0	1	2	3
y	18				2		–18

Using 2 cm to represent 1 unit on the x-axis and 1 cm to represent 5 units on the y-axis, draw the graph of $y = 3x - x^3$. Use your graph to find

(a) the value of y when $x = 1.7$;
(b) the values of x when $y = -6.6$.

4. Copy and complete the following table which gives values of $y = \frac{4}{x}$ for $\frac{1}{4} \le x \le 5$.

x	$\frac{1}{4}$	$\frac{1}{2}$	1	2	3	4	5
y	16			2		1	

Using 2 cm to represent 1 unit on the x-axis and 1 cm to represent 1 unit on the y-axis, draw the graph of $y = \frac{4}{x}$. Use your graph to find

(a) the value of y when $x = 3.6$;
(b) the value of x when $y = 1.5$.

5. Copy and complete the following table which gives the values of $y = \frac{10}{x^2}$ for $1 \leqslant x \leqslant 5$.

x	1	2	3	4	5
y	10			0.6	

Using 2 cm to represent 1 unit on both axes, draw the graph of $y = \frac{10}{x^2}$. Use your graph to find

(a) the value of y when $x = 2.8$;
(b) the value of x when $y = 4.4$.

6. Given that $y = -\frac{2}{x} - 1$, copy and complete the following table for $\frac{1}{2} \leqslant x \leqslant 4$.

x	$\frac{1}{2}$	1	1.5	2	3	4
y		–3		–2		

Taking 2 cm to represent 1 unit on the x and y-axis, plot the graph of $y = -\frac{2}{x} - 1$ for $\frac{1}{2} \leqslant x \leqslant 4$. Use your graph to find

(a) the value of y when $x = 2.5$;
(b) the value of x when $y = -1.6$.

7. Copy and complete the following table which gives the values of $y = 2 - \frac{3}{x^2}$ for $1 \leqslant x \leqslant 5$.

x	1	2	3	4	5
y		1.25	1.67		

Using 2 cm to represent 1 unit on the x-axis and 4 cm to represent 1 unit on the y-axis, draw the graph of $y = 2 - \frac{3}{x^2}$. Use your graph to find

(a) the value of y when $x = 1.5$;
(b) the value of x when $y = 1.5$.

8. **(a)** Copy and complete the following table which gives the values of $y = x^3 - 2x - 1$ for $-3 \leqslant x \leqslant 3$.

x	–3	–2	–1	0	1	2	3
y	–22		0			3	

Taking 2 cm to represent 1 unit on the x-axis and 2 cm to represent 5 units on the y-axis, draw the graph of $y = x^3 - 2x - 1$.

(b) Use your graph to find

(i) the values of x when $y = 0$, -10 and 15;
(ii) the values of y when $x = -2.5$, 0.5 and 2.2.

9. **(a)** Copy and complete the following table which gives the values of $y = x^3 - 6x^2 + 13x$ for values of x between 0 and 5 inclusive.

x	0	1	2	3	4	$4\frac{1}{2}$	5
y		8		12		$28\frac{1}{8}$	40

Using 2 cm to represent 1 unit on the x-axis and 2 cm to represent 5 units on the y-axis, draw the graph of $y = x^3 - 6x^2 + 13x$.

(b) Use your graph to find

(i) the values of y when $x = 1.5$, 3.5 and 4.45;
(ii) the values of x when $y = 7$, 15 and 22.

10. The table below shows some x and y values of $y = x - \frac{3}{x}$.

x	0.5	1	2	3	4	5	6
y	–5.5	–2	0.5	h	3.3	4.4	k

(a) Find the value of h and of k.
(b) Using 2 cm to represent 1 unit on both the x-axis and the y-axis, draw the graph of $y = x - \frac{3}{x}$ for $\frac{1}{2} \leqslant x \leqslant 6$. Use your graph to find

(i) the values of x when $y = -2.5$, 0 and 4.6;
(ii) the values of y when $x = 1.6$, 3.4 and 5.3.

11. (a) Copy and complete the following table which gives the values of $y = 16 + \frac{16}{x}$ for values of x between 1 and 6.

x	1	2	3	4	5	6
y	32		21.3			18.7

Using 2 cm to represent 1 unit on the x-axis and 2 cm to represent 5 units on the y-axis, draw the graph of $y = 16 + \frac{16}{x}$ for values of x between 1 and 6 inclusive.

(b) Use your graph to find

(i) the values of x when $y = 19$, 21 and 30;

(ii) the values of y when $x = 1.5$, 3.2 and 5.4.

12. Given that $y = 2 + 2^x$, copy and complete the following table of values:

x	−1	−0.5	0	1	1.5	2	2.5	3
y		2.7	3	4	4.8	6		10

(a) Using a scale of 4 cm for 1 unit on the x-axis and 2 cm for 1 unit on the y-axis, draw the graph of $y = 2 + 2^x$ for $-1 \leqslant x \leqslant 3$.

(b) Use your graph to find the values of

(i) y when $x = -0.7$ and 2.7;

(ii) x when $y = 5.3$ and 7.5.

13. (a) Given that $y = 2x + 2^x$, copy and complete the following table of values:

x	−1	−0.5	0	0.5	1	1.5	2	2.5	3
y	−1.5	−0.3	1		4		8		14

Using a scale of 4 cm for 1 unit on the x-axis and 1 cm for 1 unit on the y-axis, plot the graph of $y = 2x + 2^x$ for $-1 \leqslant x \leqslant 3$.

(b) Use your graph to find the values of

(i) y when $x = 0.7$ and 2.3;

(ii) x when $y = 1.5$ and 6.3.

Sketches of Some Important Graphs

The following are sketches of the functions with the form $y = ax^n$, where $n = -2, -1, 1, 2$ and 3.

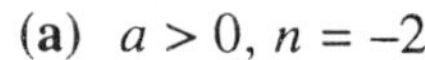

(a) $a > 0, n = -2$

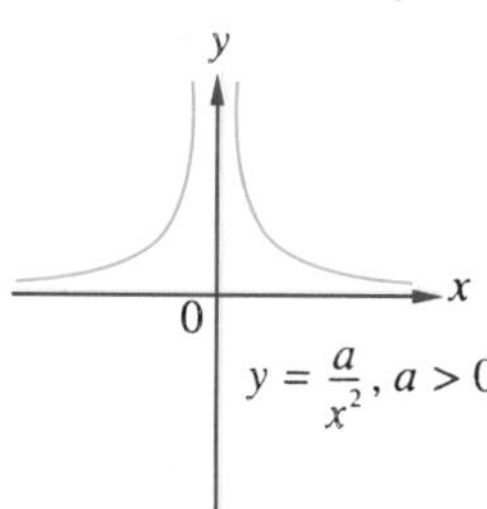

(b) $a < 0, n = -2$

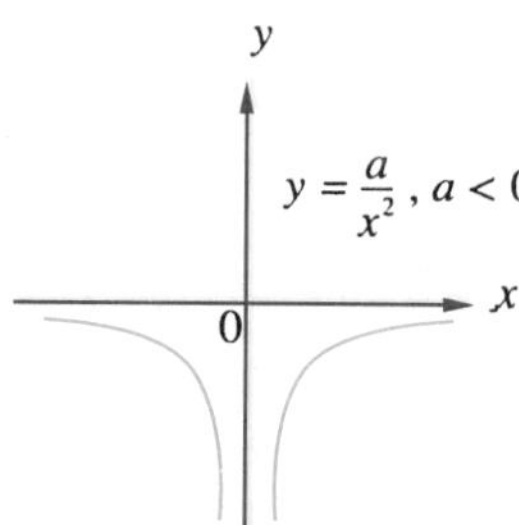

(c) $a > 0, n = -1$

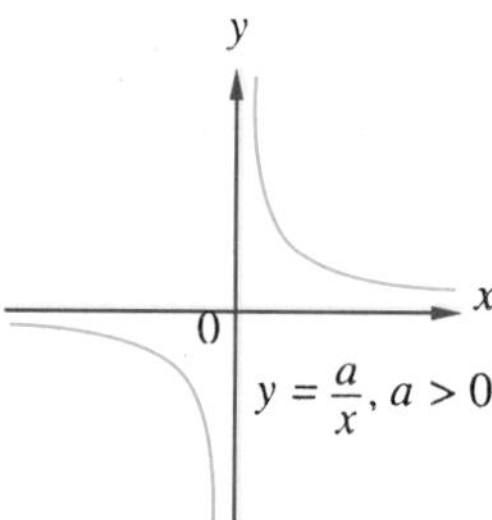

(d) $a < 0, n = -1$

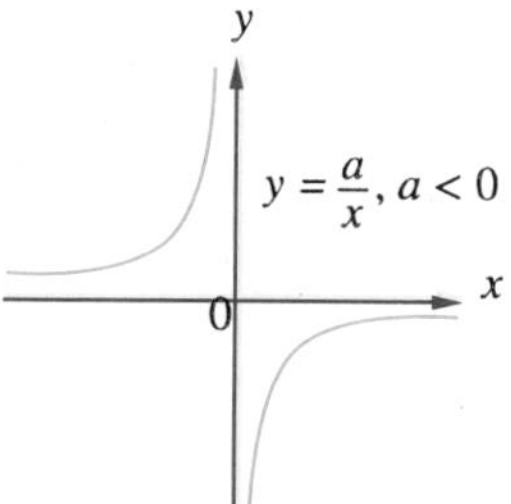

(e) $a > 0, n = 1$

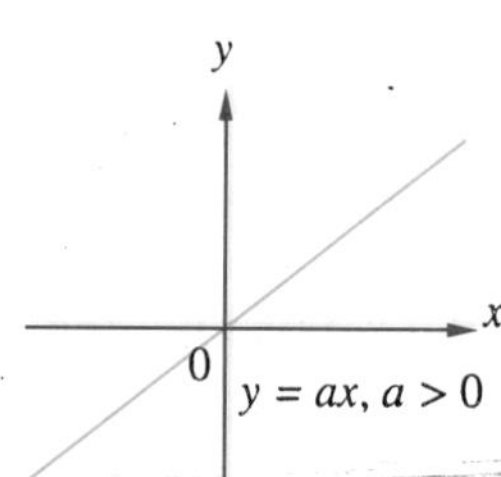

(f) $a < 0, n = 1$

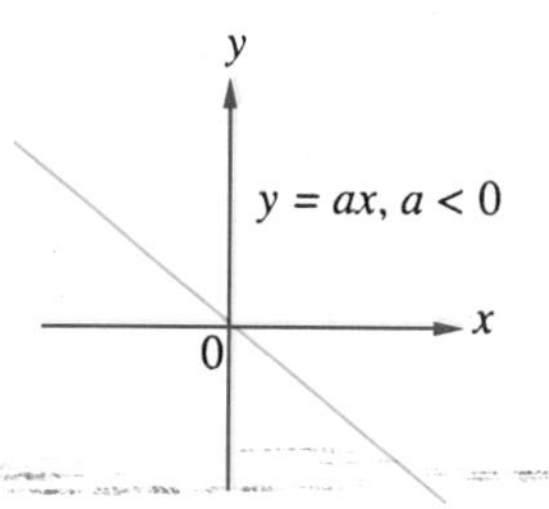

(g) $a > 0, n = 2$

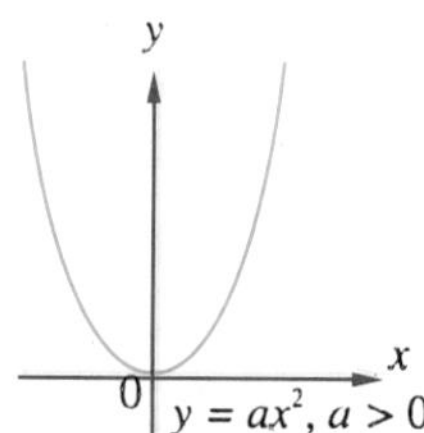

(h) $a < 0, n = 2$

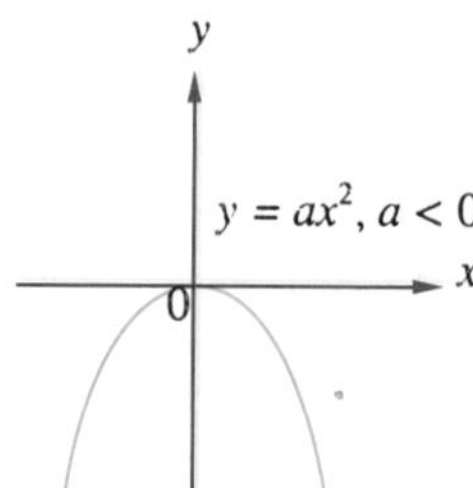

Before plotting a graph, it is useful to draw a table (if not given) of the values of x and y for a given range of x. Check if the range includes the end points. The table of values will help you to decide the correct scale to use for each axis.

The arch of our upper jaws can be described by the shapes of the graphs of some functions.

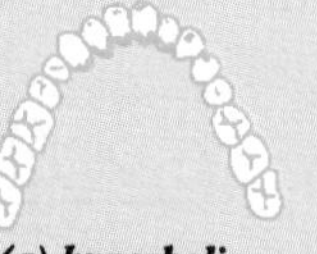

(a) hyperbolic

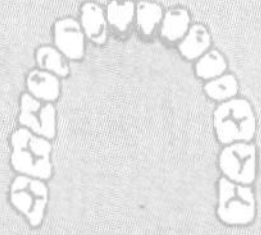

(b) parabolic

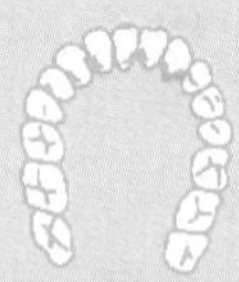

(c) elliptic

Which one of the above best describes the shape of your upper jaw? Find out yourself.

(i) $a > 0, n = 3$

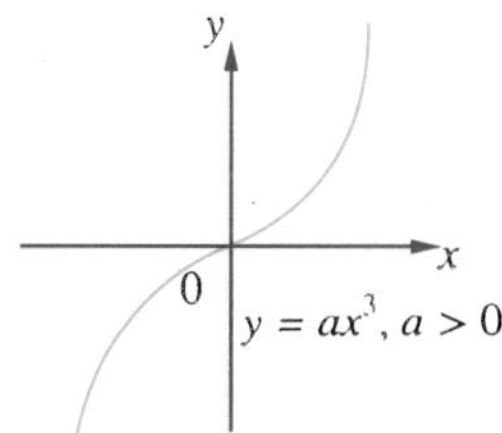

(j) $a < 0, n = 3$

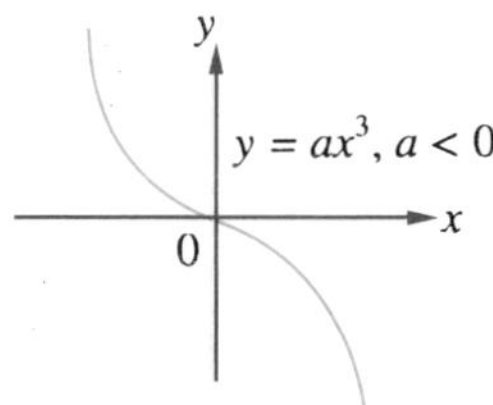

Sketching Graphs of Quadratic Functions

In Book 2, we learnt that graphs of the quadratic function, $y = ax^2$ where $a > 0$ has the shape

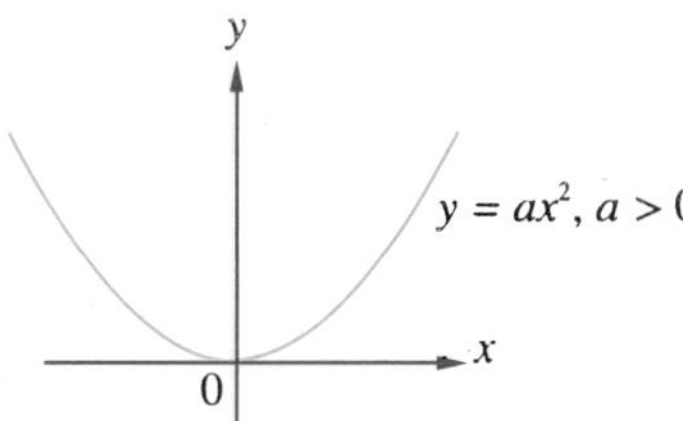

and $y = ax^2$ where $a < 0$ has the shape

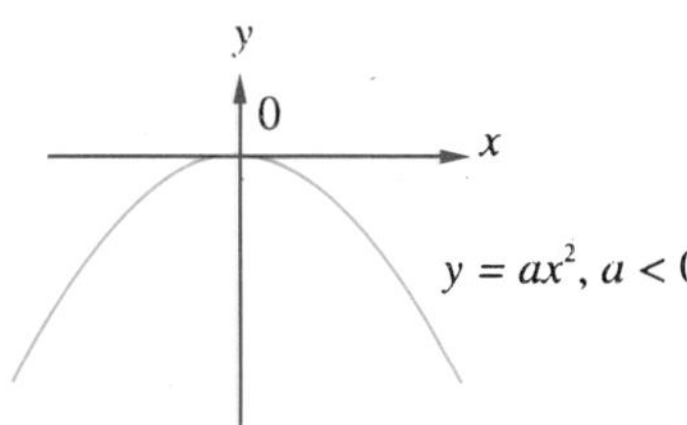

We shall now learn how to sketch graphs of quadratic functions of the form $y = \pm (x - a)(x - b)$ where a and b are constants.

Graphs of the form = ± (x–a)(x–*b*).

In this Exploration, we shall examine some sketches of the quadratic functions in the form of $y = (x - a)(x - b)$, where a and b are constants. The following steps are useful to guide you in exploring the shapes of the graphs of quadratic functions using Graphmatica.

1. For the curve $y = (x - 2)(x + 4)$, type $y = (x - 2)(x + 4)$ and press Enter to see the graph.
   (a) Is the shape ∪ or ∩?
   (b) Write down the coordinates of the points where the curve cuts the x-axis. Are they (2, 0) and (–4, 0)?
   (c) Write down the coordinates of the point where the curve cuts the y-axis.
   (d) What is the equation of the line of symmetry of the curve? Is it $x = -1$?
   (e) Write down the coordinates of the minimum point of the curve.

2. For the curve $y = -(x - 3)(x - 5)$, type $y = -(x - 3)(x - 5)$ and press Enter to see the graph.
   (a) Is the shape ∪ or ∩?
   (b) Write down the coordinates of the points where the curve cuts the x-axis. Are they (3, 0) and (5, 0)?
   (c) Write down the coordinates of the point where the curve cuts the y-axis.
   (d) What is the equation of the line of symmetry of the curve? Is it $x = 4$?
   (e) Write down the coordinates of the maximum point of the curve.

3. Repeat all the steps in 1 or 2 for each of the following curves.
   (i) $y = (x - 1)(x - 6)$
   (ii) $y = -(x - 4)(x + 5)$
   (iii) $y = -(x + 3)(x - 4)$
   (iv) $y = (x - 1)(x + 3)$

4. Based on your observation of the above curves, answer the following questions about the graph of $y = \pm (x - a)(x - b)$.
   (a) When will the shape of $y = \pm (x - a)(x - b)$ be ∪ or ∩?
   (b) What are the coordinates of the points where the curve cuts the x-axis?
   (c) What is the equation of the line of symmetry of the curve?

   Using the conclusions we get from the Exploration, we can sketch the graph of $y = \pm (x - a)(x - b)$, where a and b are constants.

xample 4

Sketch the graph of $y = (x - 1)(x - 5)$.

The coefficient of x^2 is 1 and the graph should take the shape of $\cup$.

When $y = 0$, $(x - 1)(x - 5) = 0$

$\therefore \quad x = 1$ or $x = 5$

When $x = 0$, $y = (0 - 1)(0 - 5) = 5$

Thus the graph will pass through (1, 0), (5, 0) and (0, 5).

Moreover, the line of symmetry of the graph should be $x = \dfrac{1 + 5}{2} = 3$, and the graph has a minimum point when $x = 3$.

When $x = 3$, $y = (3 - 1)(3 - 5) = 2(-2) = -4$

So the minimum point of the graph is (3, –4).

Based on the above analysis, we can sketch the graph as below:

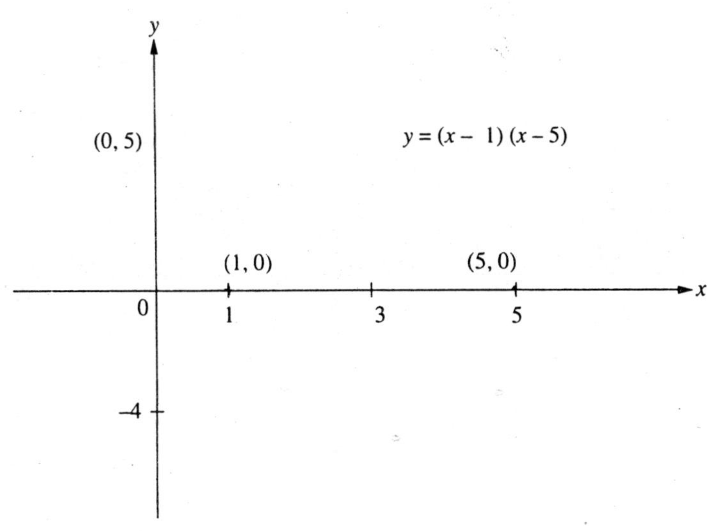

Example 5

Sketch the graph of $y = (3 - x)(x + 1)$.

Since $(3 - x)(x + 1) = -(x - 3)(x + 1)$, so the coefficient of x^2 is -1. The graph of $y = (3 - x)(x + 1)$ should take the shape of $\frown$.

When $y = 0$, $(3 - x)(x + 1) = 0$

$\therefore \quad x = 3$ or $x = -1$

When $x = 0$, $y = (3 - 0)(0 + 1) = 3$.

Thus the graph passes through $(-1, 0)$ $(3, 0)$ and $(0, 3)$

Moreover, the line of symmetry of the graph should be $x = \dfrac{3 + (-1)}{2} = 1$, and the graph of $y = (3 - x)(x + 1)$ has a maximum point when $x = 1$.

When $x = 1$, $y = (3 - 1)(1 + 1) = 2 \times 2 = 4$

So the maximum point of the graph is $(1, 4)$.

Based on the above analysis, we sketch the graph as below:

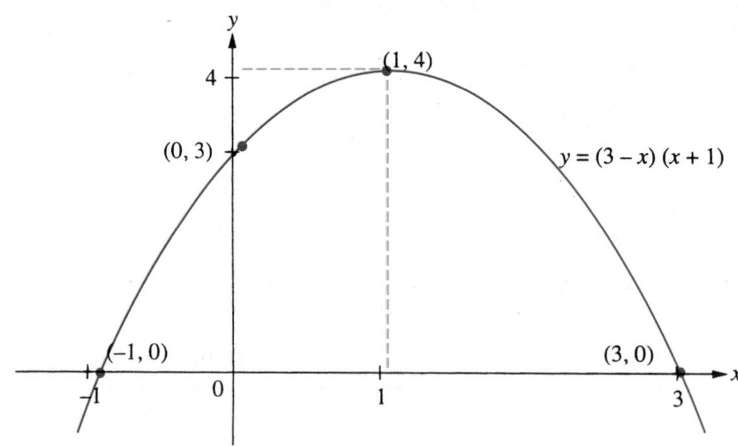

Graphs of the form $y = \pm (x - p)^2 + q$ where p and q are constants

In this Exploration, we will examine some sketches of the quadratic functions in the form of $y = \pm (x - p)^2 + q$, where p and q are constants, using IT open tools (for example **Graphmatica**).

1. For the curve $y = (x - 3)^2$, type $y = (x - 3)^2$ and press Enter to see the graph. Study the graph carefully and answer the following questions.
   (a) Is the shape ∪ or ∩?
   (b) Write down the coordinates of the points where the curve cuts the x-axis.
   (c) Write down the the coordinates of the point where the curve cuts the y-axis.
   (d) What is the equation of the line of symmetry of the curve?
   (e) Write down the coordinates of the minimum point of the curve.

2. Using your IT open tool, draw the graphs of
   (i) $y = (x - 3)^2 + 4$
   (ii) $y = (x - 3)^2 - 1$.
   and answer the same questions (a) – (e) in question 1.

Based on your observation and answers in questions 1 and 2, what can you conclude about the graph of $y = (x - p)^2 + q$?

(a) Is the graph ∪ or ∩ ?
(b) What is the line of symmetry of the graph?
(c) What is the minimum point of the graph?

3. Do the same as in question 1 for
   (i) $y = -(x + 2)^2$,
   (ii) $y = -(x + 2)^2 + 5$,
   (iii) $y = -(x + 2)^2 - 3$.

Based on your observations and answers in question 3, what can you conclude about the graph of $y = -(x - p)^2 + q$?

(a) Is the graph ∪ or ∩ ?
(b) What is the line of symmetry of the graph?
(c) What is the maximum point of the graph?

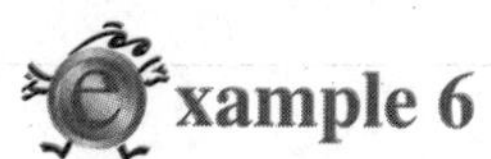

Example 6

Sketch the graph of $y = (x - 1)^2 + 4$.

The coefficient of x^2 is 1 and the graph will take the shape of $\cup$.

When $y = 0$, $(x - 1)^2 + 4 = 0$
$(x - 1)^2 = -4$ (no solution)
The curve will not cut the x-axis.

When $x = 0$, $y = (0 - 1)^2 + 4 = 5$

Notice that y is minimum when $(x - 1)^2$ is minimum, i.e. $(x - 1)^2 = 0$

$\therefore$ the minimum point occurs when $x = 1$
and $y = 0 + 4 = 4$.

Moreover the line of symmetry of the graph is $x = 1$.
Based on the above analysis, we can sketch the graph as below:

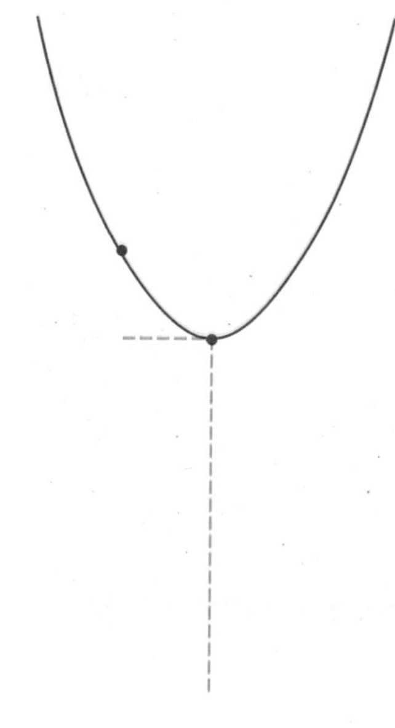

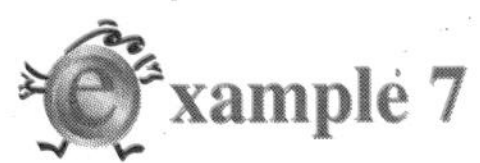

Example 7

Sketch the graph of $y = -(x - 1)^2 + 4$.

The coefficient of x^2 is -1 and the graph will take the shape of $\frown$.

When $y = 0$, $-(x - 1)^2 + 4 = 0$

$$(x - 1)^2 = 4$$

$$x - 1 = \pm 2$$

$$\therefore \quad x = 3 \text{ or } x = -1$$

When $x = 0$, $y = -(0 - 1)^2 + 4$

$$= -1 + 4$$

$$= 3$$

So the graph has a maximum point when $x = 1$ and $y = 4$.
Moreover, the line of symmetry of the graph is $x = 1$.
Based on the above analysis, we can sketch the graph as below:

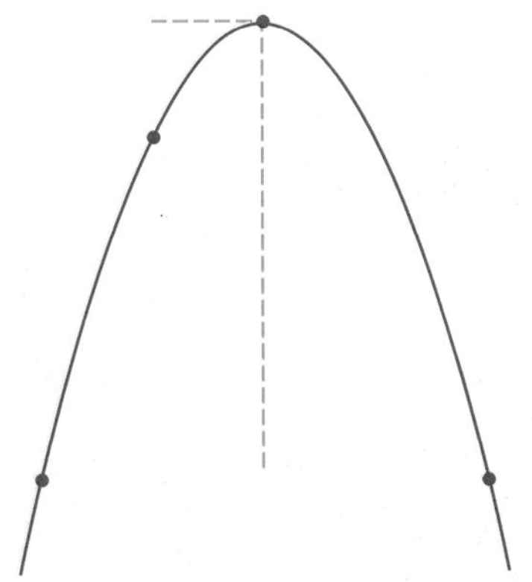

Graphical Solution of Quadratic Equations

A quadratic equation of the form $ax^2 + bx + c = 0$, where $a \neq 0$, can be solved by algebraic method which we learned in Book 3. We can also use **graphical method** to solve quadratic equations and simultaneous equations involving a linear equation and a quadratic equation.

Let's recall the steps to solve simultaneous equations graphically.

(i) Choose a suitable scale for both axes.
(ii) Construct a table of values for each equation.
(iii) Plot and draw the two straight lines using the tables of values.
(iv) From the graph, find the coordinates of the point of intersection which is the solution to the simultaneous equations.

Using the steps for solving simultaneous equations graphically or the computer software Graphmatica, draw the graphs of $y = x^2 - x - 6$ for $-4 \le x \le 4$ and $y = x + 2$ and use them to solve the simultaneous equations $y = x^2 - x - 6$ and $y = x + 2$.

Did you get the graph below?

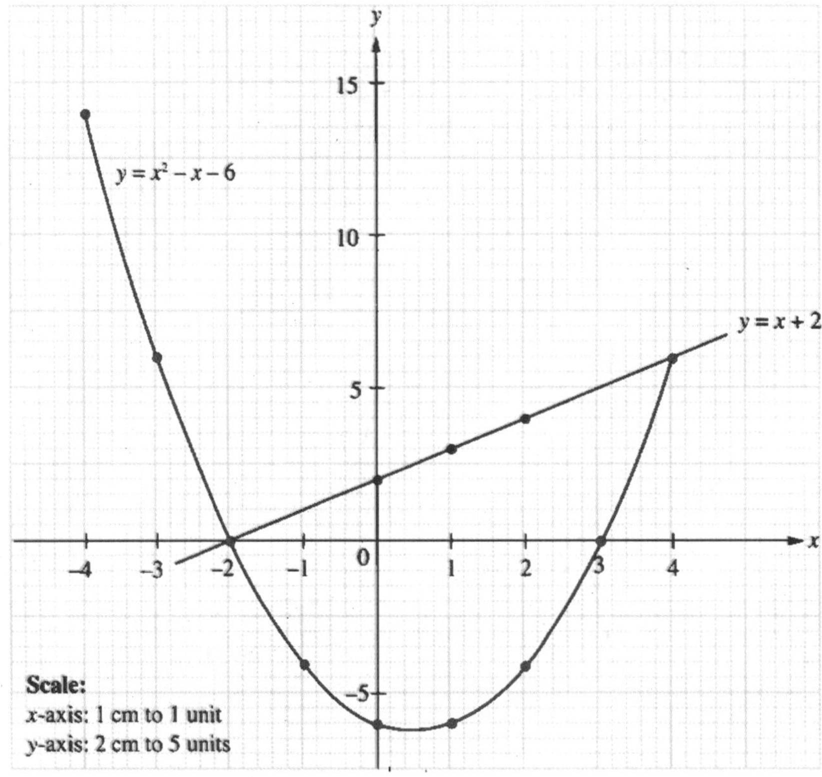

Fig. 1.8

How many points of intersection are there?
What are the solutions of the simultaneous equations?

Notice that the values $x = -2$ and $x = 4$ which we obtained graphically also satisfy the equation $x^2 - 2x - 8 = 0$. Why? Hence we can solve the equation $x^2 - x - 6 = x + 2$ or $x^2 - 2x - 8 = 0$ by finding the x-coordinates of the points of intersection of the graphs $y = x^2 - x - 6$ and $y = x + 2$.

xample 8

Draw the graph of $y = x^2 - 2x + 1$ for $-4 \leqslant x \leqslant 5$ and use it to solve the equation $x^2 - 2x + 1 = 10$. What is the least value of y? State the value of x when this occurs.

A table of values for $y = x^2 - 2x + 1$ is first constructed. The graph is then plotted accordingly, as shown in Fig. 1.9 below.

	–4	–3	–2	–1	0	1	2	3	4	5
	25	16	9	4	1	0	1	4	9	16

For greater accuracy, scales chosen are usually as large as possible.

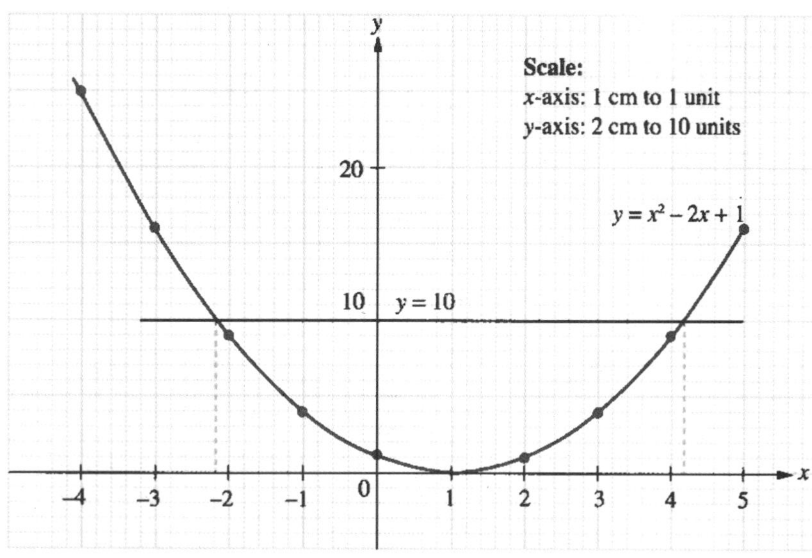

Fig. 1.9

The *solutions* to $x^2 - 2x + 1 = 10$ can be found by the *points of intersection* of the graph $y = x^2 - 2x + 1$ and $y = 10$. Thus $x \approx -2.2$ and $x \approx 4.2$ are the solutions to the equation $x^2 - 2x + 1 = 10$. From the graph, the least value of y is 0 and it occurs when $x = 1$.

Plot and draw the graph of $y = x^2$. Locate the points on the curve that have –3 and 4 as their x-coordinates. Join the two points by a straight line. What do you notice about the y-intercept of the line? Use other pairs of points on the curve. What do you notice?

xample 9

Draw the graph of $y = x^2 + x + 4$ for $-4 \leqslant x \leqslant 4$ and use it to solve the equation $x^2 + x + 4 = 0$. State the minimum value of y and the value of x when this occurs.

A table of values is constructed and the graph plotted as shown in Fig. 1.10.

−4	−3	−2	−1	0	1	2	3	4
16	10	6	4	4	6	10	16	24

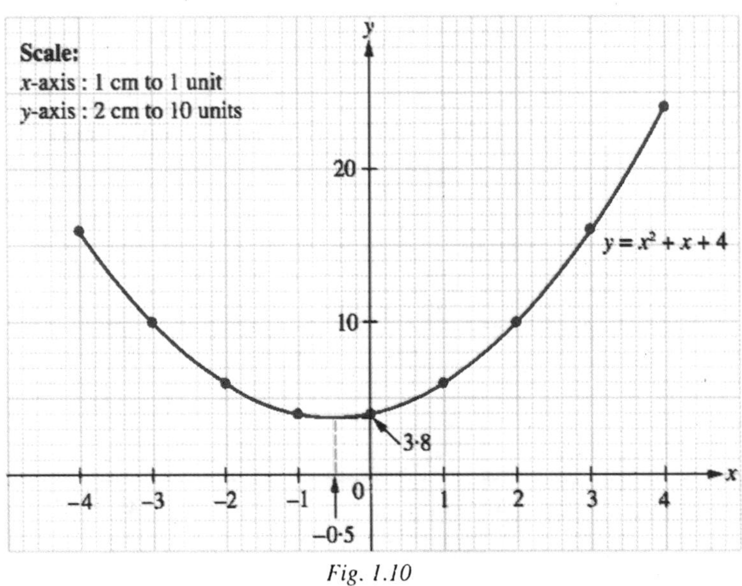

Fig. 1.10

The solution to $x^2 + x + 4 = 0$ can be obtained from the point of intersection of the curve $y = x^2 + x + 4$ and the line $y = 0$. Since the curve $y = x^2 + x + 4$ does not cut the line $y = 0$, i.e., the x-axis, there is no real solution to $x^2 + x + 4 = 0$.

From the graph, the minimum value of y is about 3.8 and it occurs when $x = -0.5$.

The accurate minimum value of y is 3.75. Can you explain why?

Let $a = b$.
Then $a^2 = ab$.

$$a^2 - b^2 = ab - b^2$$
$$(a + b)(a - b) = b(a - b)$$
$$a + b = b$$

Since $a = b$,
then $2b = b$,
$2 = 1$.

But is 2 equal to 1?
Where is the mistake?

Carl Friedrich Gauss, a German mathematician (1777–1855), is often considered to be the greatest mathematician of all time. He proved that every algebraic equation in one unknown has a root. This is known as the ***fundamental theorem of algebra****.*

Step 1 Open **Graphmatica**.

Step 2 For the curve $y = x^2 - 4x - 1$, type $y = x^2 - 4x - 1$ and press Enter to see the graph. At how many points does the graph cut the x-axis? Write down the solutions of the equation $x^2 - 4x - 1 = 0$.

Step 3 You can solve the equation $x^2 - 4x + 2 = 0$ by adding a straight line graph to the existing curve $y = x^2 - 4x - 1$. State the straight line graph that you need to plot to solve it.

Plot the straight line graph by keying in the equation of the line. Write down the solution(s) of the equation $x^2 - 4x + 2 = 0$.

[You can do this by selecting "**coord cursor**" from the tool bar and move the cursor to the point(s) of intersection of the two graphs. The bottom of the screen shows the coordinates where the cursor is placed. Clicking the mouse one more time will release this function.]

Step 4 To solve the equation $x^2 - 5x - 1 = 0$, what straight line graph must you add to the existing curve to solve it?

Plot the straight line graph by keying in the equation. State the solution(s) of the equation $x^2 - 5x - 1 = 0$.

Step 5 To solve the equation $3x^2 - 12x + 7 = 0$, what straight line graph must you add to the existing curve to solve it?

Plot the straight line graph by keying in the equation. State the solution(s) of the equation $3x^2 - 12x + 7 = 0$.

Step 6 To solve the equation $2x^2 - 7x + 3 = 0$, what curve must you add to the existing curve to solve it?

Plot the straight line graph by keying in the equation. State the solution(s) of the equation $2x^2 - 7x + 3 = 0$.

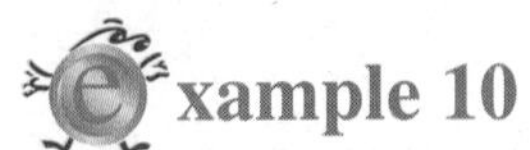

xample 10

Draw the graph of $y = 4x^2 - 4x - 15$ *for* $-3 \leqslant x \leqslant 4$. *By drawing suitable straight lines to the curve, solve the following equations:*

(a) $4x^2 - 4x - 15 = 0$ (b) $4x^2 - 4x - 15 = 20$
(c) $4x^2 - 4x - 25 = 0$ (d) $4x^2 - 6x - 20 = 0$
(e) $4x^2 - 3x + 3 = 0$

When there is no real solution to an equation, the roots of the equation are known to be complex, or imaginary, or simply, unreal.

A table of values is constructed as follows:

	−3	−2	−1	0	1	2	3	4
	33	9	−7	−15	−15	−7	9	33

The values are plotted as shown in Fig. 1.11.

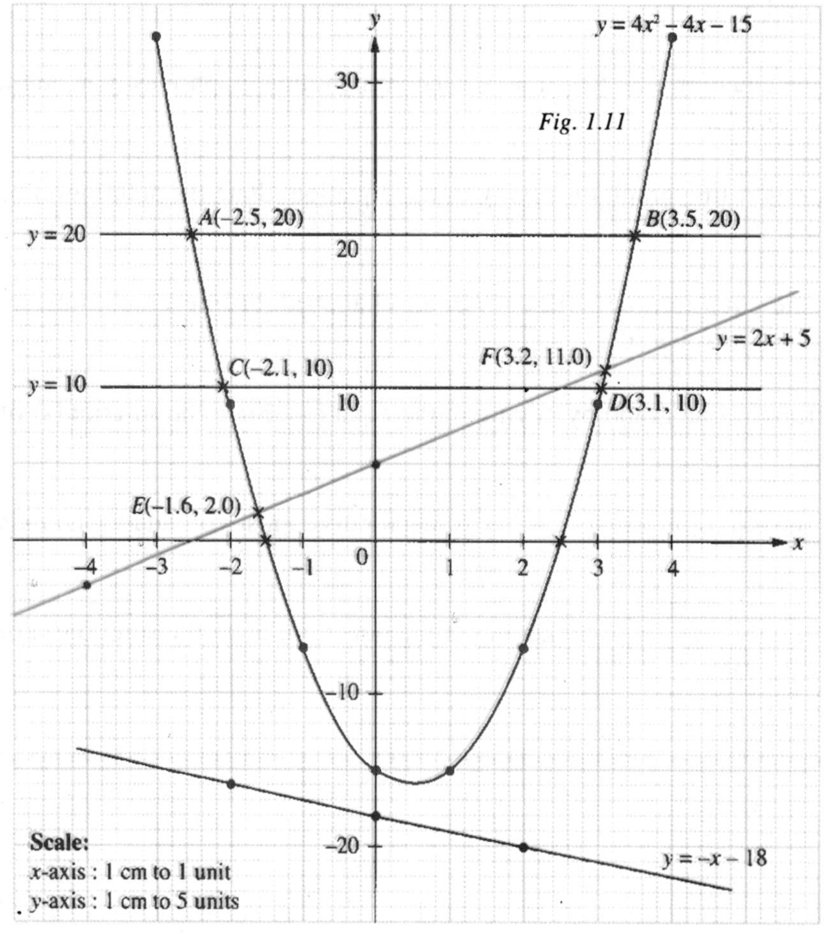

(a) The solution to $4x^2 - 4x - 15 = 0$ is derived from the points where the curve cuts the line $y = 0$, i.e., the x-axis. From the graph, the solutions of $4x^2 - 4x - 15 = 0$ are $x = -1.5$ and 2.5.

(b) The solution to $4x^2 - 4x - 15 = 20$ is obtained from the points of intersection, A and B, of the curve and the line $y = 20$. From the graph, $x = -2.5$ and 3.5.

(c) To solve the equation $4x^2 - 4x - 25 = 0$ graphically, we make the LHS of the equation equal to the function y, i.e., $4x^2 - 4x - 15$.

$4x^2 - 4x - 25 = 0$ can be written as
$4x^2 - 4x - 25 + 10 = 0 + 10$,
i.e., $4x^2 - 4x - 15 = 10$.

The solution to the above equation is found from the points of intersection of the curve and the line $y = 10$.

From the graph, it is seen that the line $y = 10$ cuts the curve at approximately $C(-2.1, 10)$ and $D(3.1, 10)$. Hence the solutions to $4x^2 - 4x - 25 = 0$ are $x \approx -2.1$ and 3.1.

(d) $4x^2 - 6x - 20 = 0$ can similarly be expressed as

$4x^2 - 6x + (2x) - 20 + (5) = 0 + (2x) + (5)$,
i.e. $4x^2 - 4x - 15 = 2x + 5$.

To find the solution, the points of intersection of $y = 4x^2 - 4x - 15$ and $y = 2x + 5$ must be located.

A table of values for $y = 2x + 5$ is constructed.

	-4	0	4
	-3	5	13

The straight line is drawn on the same graph and is found to intersect the curve approximately at $E(-1.6, 2.0)$ and $F(3.2, 11.0)$. Thus, the solutions to $4x^2 - 6x - 20 = 0$ are $x \approx -1.6$ and $x \approx 3.2$.

(e) $4x^2 - 3x + 3 = 0$ is written as

$$4x^2 - 3x - (x) + 3 - (18) = 0 - (x) - (18).$$

i.e. $$4x^2 - 4x - 15 = -x - 18.$$

The straight line function $y = -x - 18$ is plotted.

	-2	0	2
	-16	-18	-20

From the graph, it is seen that the line $y = -x - 18$ does not cut the curve $y = 4x^2 - 4x - 15$. Thus, there is no real solution to $4x^2 - 3x + 3 = 0$.

Evariste Galois (1811–1832), a French mathematician, developed a new branch of mathematics known as the group theory. This theory generalised an important result in algebra, i.e., there is no general solution to equations of the 5th degree.

Given that
$f(x) = (x + 1)(x - 2)(x - 3)$, solve $f(x) = 0$, $f(x) > 0$ and $f(x) < 0$.

Can you guess the shape of the curve of $y = f(x)$ on the coordinate plane?

1. Sketch the graph of each of the following functions.

   (a) $y = (x + 1)(x + 3)$
   (b) $y = (x - 2)(x + 4)$
   (c) $y = -(x + 1)(x - 5)$
   (d) $y = (3 - x)(x + 2)$

2. Sketch the graph of each of the following functions.

   (a) $y = x^2 + 2$
   (b) $y = -x^2 - 6$
   (c) $y = (x - 3)^2 + 1$
   (d) $y = -(x + 2)^2 + 3$

3. Using a scale of 2 cm to represent 1 unit on the x-axis and 1 cm to represent 1 unit on the y-axis, draw the graph of $y = x^2 + 2x - 8$ for $-5 \leq x \leq 3$. By adding a suitable straight line to your graph, solve each of the following equations graphically.

   (a) $x^2 + 2x - 8 = 0$,
   (b) $x^2 + 2x = 5$,
   (c) $x^2 = 8$,
   (d) $x^2 + 5x - 9 = 0$.

4. Using a scale of 2 cm to represent 1 unit on the x-axis and 1 cm to represent 1 unit on the y-axis, draw the graph of $y = 6 + x - x^2$ for $-3 \le x \le 4$. By adding a suitable straight line to your graph, solve each of the following equations graphically.

   (a) $6 + x - x^2 = 0$,
   (b) $6 + x - x^2 = 1$,
   (c) $6 + x - x^2 = -2$,
   (d) $2 - 3x - x^2 = 0$.

5. Draw the graph of $y = x^2$ for $-4 \le x \le 4$ by using a scale of 2 cm to represent 1 unit on the x-axis and 1 cm to represent 1 unit on the y-axis. By further plotting suitable straight lines on the graph, solve the following equations graphically if real roots do exist.

   (a) $x^2 - 4x + 3 = 0$
   (b) $x^2 - 7 = 0$
   (c) $x^2 + 5 = 0$
   (d) $x^2 - 2x + 5 = 0$
   (e) $x^2 + 3x - 1 = 0$

6. Plot the graph of $y = x^2 - 4x$ for $-2 \le x \le 6$ by using a scale of 2 cm to represent 1 unit on the x-axis and 1 cm to represent 1 unit on the y-axis. By further plotting suitable straight lines on the graph, find the real roots, where they exist, of the following equations.

   (a) $x^2 - 4x = 3$
   (b) $x^2 - 4x + 2 = 0$
   (c) $x^2 - 4x - 7 = 0$
   (d) $3x^2 - 12x + 10 = 0$
   (e) $2x^2 - 9x + 4 = 0$

7. Draw the graph of $y = (3 + 2x)(2 - x)$ for $-3 \le x \le 3$ by using a scale of 2 cm to represent 1 unit on the x-axis and 1 cm to represent 1 unit on the y-axis. Use your graph to find

   (a) the greatest value of y;
   (b) the solution to the equation $(3 + 2x)(2 - x) = 2$.

8. The perimeter of a rectangular lawn is 60 m and its diagonal is 25 m. If the length of the lawn is x m, show that $2x^2 - 60x + 275 = 0$.

   (a) Given that $y = 2x^2 - 60x + 275$ and that some corresponding values of x and y are shown in the table below, calculate the value of a and of b.

x	4	8	12	16	20	24	28
y	67	a	−157	−173	−125	−13	b

   (b) Using a scale of 2 cm to represent 4 units on the x-axis and 2 cm to represent 20 units on the y-axis, plot the graph of $y = 2x^2 - 60x + 275$. Use your graph to find the solution of the equation $2x^2 - 60x + 275 = 0$.

9. Using a scale of 2 cm to represent 1 unit on the x-axis and 2 cm to represent 5 units on the y-axis, draw the graph of $y = 2x^2 - 5x - 2$ for values of x from -2 to 5. Use your graph to find
   (a) the least value of y;
   (b) the solution of the equation $2x^2 - 5x - 2 = 0$,
   (c) the solution of the equation $2x^2 - 7x - 6 = 0$ by adding a suitable straight line to your graph.

10. Solve the following equations by graphical method. Choose a suitable scale for each of the graphs.
   (a) $x^2 - 5x - 4 = 0$,
   (b) $x^2 + x - 3 = 0$,
   (c) $x^2 + 7x = 0$.

1. The general form of a **reciprocal** function is $y = \frac{a}{x}$, where $a \neq 0$, $x \neq 0$. It consists of two separate curves.

2. The general form of an **exponential** function is $y = a^x$, where $a > 0$. The entire graph lies above the x-axis.

3. The solution(s) to a pair of simultaneous equations can be found by drawing their graphs on the same axes. The **point(s) of intersection** of these graphs gives the **solution(s)**

4. To find the solution to an equation $f(x) = 0$, plot the graph of $y = f(x)$. The points of intersection of the graph $y = f(x)$ and the x-axis, $y = 0$, give the roots of the equation $f(x) = 0$.

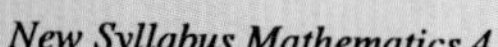

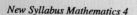

Review Examples 1

Example 1

The variables x and y are connected by the equation

$$y = \frac{1}{4}x^2 + \frac{8}{x} - 9$$

The following table shows some corresponding values of x and y.

	0.5	1	2	3	4	5	6	7
	h	–0.8	–4	k	–3	–1.2	1.3	4.4

(a) Calculate the value of h and of k, correct to one decimal place.

(b) Using a scale of 2 cm to represent 1 unit on the x-axis and 1 cm to represent 1 unit on the y-axis, draw the graph of $y = \frac{1}{4}x^2 + \frac{8}{x} - 9$*, for* $0.5 \le x \le 7$.

(c) Use your graph to find the minimum value of y in the given range.

(d) By drawing suitable straight lines to the graph, solve the following equations, giving your answer correct to one decimal place.

(i) $\frac{1}{4}x^2 + \frac{8}{x} = 6$

(ii) $\frac{1}{4}x^2 + \frac{8}{x} = x + 4$

(iii) $\frac{1}{4}x^2 + 2x = 15 - \frac{8}{x}$

Solution

(a) When $x = 0.5$, $y = \frac{1}{4}(0.5)^2 + \frac{8}{0.5} - 9 = 7.1$ (correct to 1 decimal place)

When $x = 3$, $y = \frac{1}{4}(3)^2 + \frac{8}{3} - 9 = -4.1$ (correct to 1 decimal place)

$\therefore \quad h = 7.1$ and $k = -4.1$

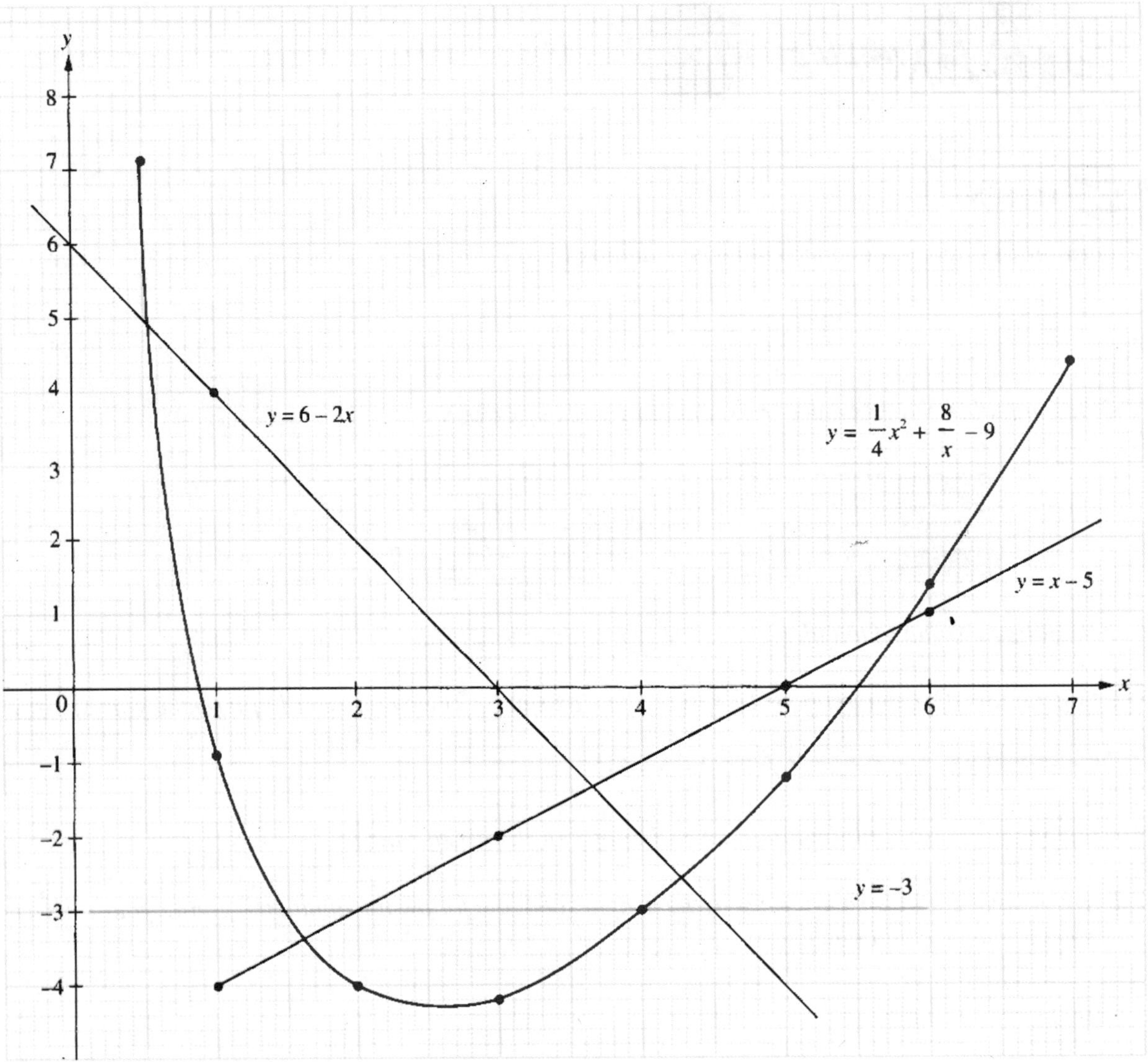

Fig. 1.12

(c) The mimimum value of $y = -4.2$

(d) (i) $\frac{1}{4}x^2 + \frac{8}{x} = 6$

$\therefore \quad \frac{1}{4}x^2 + \frac{8}{x} - 9 = 6 - 9 = -3$

Draw $y = -3$.

From the graph, the curve $y = \frac{1}{4}x^2 + \frac{8}{x} - 9$ meets $y = -3$ at $x = 1.6$ or 4

$\therefore$ the solution of $\frac{1}{4}x^2 + \frac{8}{x} = 6$ is $x = 1.5$ or 4.

(ii) $\frac{1}{4}x^2 + \frac{8}{x} = x + 4$

$\therefore \quad \frac{1}{4}x^2 + \frac{8}{x} - 9 = x + 4 - 9$

$= x - 5$

Draw $y = x - 5$

From the graph, the line $y = x - 5$ meets the curve $y = \frac{1}{4}x^2 + \frac{8}{x} - 9$ at $x = 1.6$ or 5.8

$\therefore$ the solution of $\frac{1}{4}x^2 + \frac{8}{x} = x + 4$ is $x = 1.6$ or 5.8.

(iii) $\frac{1}{4}x^2 + 2x = 15 - \frac{8}{x}$

$\therefore \quad \frac{1}{4}x^2 + \frac{8}{x} - 9 = 15 - 9 - 2x$

$= 6 - 2x$

Draw $y = 6 - 2x$.

From the graph, the line $y = 6 - 2x$ meets the curve $y = \frac{1}{4}x^2 + \frac{8}{x} - 9$ at $x = 0.6$ or 4.2

$\therefore$ the solution of $\frac{1}{4}x^2 + 2x = 15 - \frac{8}{x}$ is $x = 0.6$ or 4.2.

. **(a)** Copy and complete the following table which gives values of $y = x^3 - 3x - 10$. Draw the graph using a scale of 1 cm to represent 1 unit on the x-axis and 1 cm to represent 5 units on the y-axis.

x	–3	–2	–1	0	1	2	3	4
y	–28			–10			8	42

(b) Use your graph to find
(i) the value of y when $x = 1.8$;
(ii) the value of x when $y = 10$.

2. (a) Copy and complete the following table which gives values of $y = x(x - 2)(x + 2)$.

x	-3	-2	-1	0	1	2	3
y	-15	0		0	-3		

Using 2 cm to represent 1 unit on the x-axis and 2 cm to represent 5 units on the y-axis, draw the graph of $y = x(x - 2)(x + 2)$.

(b) Use your graph to find
(i) the value of y when $x = 1.4$;
(ii) the value of x when $y = 4.5$;
(iii) the solution to the equation $x(x - 2)(x + 2) = 0$

3. (a) Copy and complete the following table which gives values of

$y = 1 - 2x - \frac{1}{x}$.

x	-4	-3	-2	-1	-0.5	-0.25
y	9.3			4		5.5

Using 4 cm to represent 1 unit on the x-axis and 2 cm to represent 1 unit on the y-axis, draw the graph of

$y = 1 - 2x - \frac{1}{x}$,

(b) Use your graph to find
(i) the values of x when $y = 7$ and 9;
(ii) the values of y when $x = -0.75$, -2.5 and -3.75.

4. Copy and complete the following table which gives values of $y = 3^x - 2$.

x	-1.5	-1	-0.5	0	0.5	1	1.5	2
y	-1.8			-1			3.2	7

Give answers for y correct to 1 decimal place.
(a) By using a suitable scale, draw the graph of $y = 3^x - 2$ for $-1.5 \leq x \leq 2$.

(b) Use your graph to find the values of
(i) y when $x = -0.2$ and 1.2, correct to 1 decimal place;
(ii) x when $y = 0$ and 5, correct to 1 decimal place.

In a game called Tower of Hanoi, there are a number of discs of different diameters but with the same thickness on a rod A. You are to transfer all the discs from rod A to either rod B or C in the minimum number of moves using the following rules.

(1) Move only one disc at a time.
(2) A larger disc must never be on top of a smaller disc at any time.

A

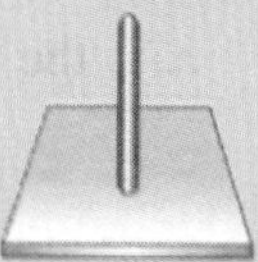

B

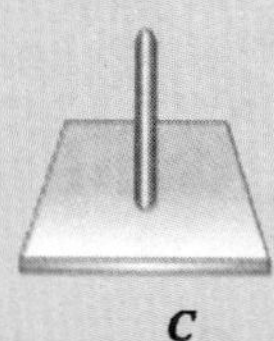

C

How many moves are needed when rod A consists of
(a) 2 discs
(b) 3 discs
(c) 4 discs
(d) 10 discs
(e) n discs?

Can you find a rule for the minimum number of moves when rod A consists of n discs?

5. Copy and complete the following table which gives values of $y = 3 - 2^x$.

x	–1	–0.5	0	0.5	1	1.5	2	3
y	2.5		2	1.6	1		–1	–5

Give answers for y correct to 1 decimal place.

(a) Using a scale of 4 cm for 1 unit on the x-axis and 2 cm for 1 unit on the y-axis, draw the graph of $y = 3 - 2^x$ for $-1 \le x \le 3$.

(b) Use your graph to determine, correct to 1 decimal place,

(i) the values of y when $x = 2.3$ and 0.3;

(ii) the values of x when $y = -3$ and 1.8.

6. A metal solid is made up of a cylinder and cube, and has a fixed height of 8 cm.

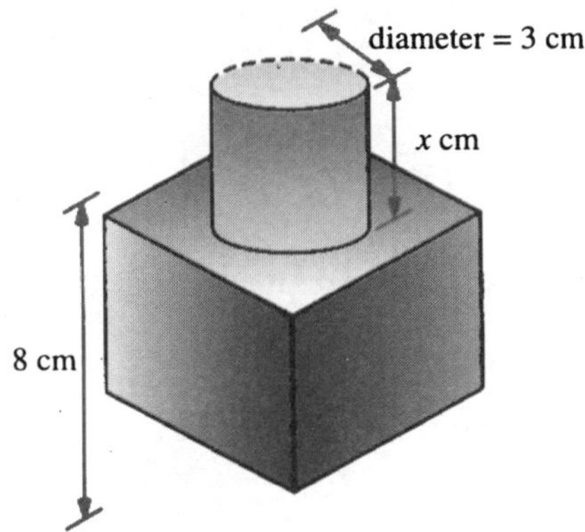

(a) Show that the total surface area of the solid can be given as $A = 6x^2 + (3\pi - 96)x + 384$.

(b) Copy and complete the following table of values. Give your answers correct to the nearest whole number. Hence draw the graph of A versus x.

x	1	2	3	4	5	6	7
A			178				

(c) The block is melted to form a solid cuboid of sides 3 cm, 5 cm and 3 cm. If the new solid is to have the same surface area as the old one, estimate the value of x by drawing a suitable straight line on the same axes.

7. Given that $\begin{pmatrix} y+3 \\ y \end{pmatrix} = \begin{pmatrix} 5 & -x-1 \\ x & 0 \end{pmatrix}\begin{pmatrix} x \\ -1 \end{pmatrix}$, solve for x graphically by using a scale of 2 cm to represent 1 unit on the x-axis and 1 cm to represent 1 unit on the y-axis for $-3 \le x \le 3$.

In this chapter, you will learn how to

- ***draw distance-time and speed-time graphs;***
- ***solve problems involving distance-time and speed-time graphs;***
- ***find the distance covered by a particle using the speed-time graph.***

CHAPTER

2

Further Graphs and Graphs Applied to Kinematics

Introduction

When we travel from one place to another, we often talk about time, speed and distance. When two motor car enthusiasts talk, they will usually bring up terms like acceleration and the time needed to reach a maximum speed. The study of moving objects in relation to distance, time, speed and acceleration without consideration of their causes is known as kinematics.

Linear Distance-Time Graphs

We have studied various forms of graphs and their applications to problems. We shall now look at some simple graphs as applied to kinematic problems involving distance-time and speed-time.

A cyclist starts a 50-km journey at 08 00. The table below is the distance-time chart of his journey.

	08 00	08 30	09 00	09 30	10 00	10 30
	0	10	20	20	35	50

Fig. 2.1 shows the graph of the cyclist's journey between 08 00 and 10 30. The graph can be divided into three parts: from 08 00 to 09 00, from 09 00 to 09 30 and from 09 30 to 10 30.

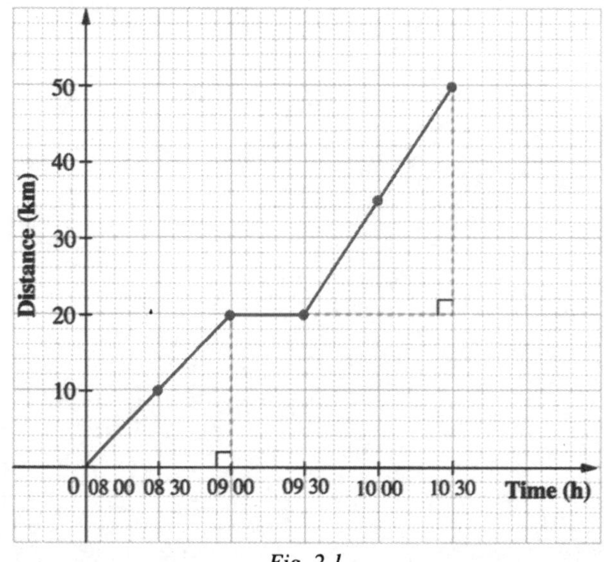

Fig. 2.1

In a distance-time graph, a straight line with positive or negative gradient represents constant speed and the gradient is the speed of the object.

Gradient of the first part of graph (from 08 00 to 09 00) $= \dfrac{20\text{ km}}{1\text{ h}}$

$= 20$ km/h.

Gradient of the third part of the graph (from 09 30 to 10 30) $= \dfrac{30\text{ km}}{1\text{ h}}$

$= 30$ km/h.

A horizontal line in a distance-time graph represents zero speed since the gradient is zero. Therefore, the object is at rest. The second part of the graph shows the cyclist at rest, i.e., 20 km from the starting point. He is actually at rest from 09 00 to 09 30.

The average speed of the whole motion is defined as $\dfrac{\text{total distance travelled}}{\text{total time taken}}$.

$\therefore$ average speed of cyclist $= \dfrac{50\text{ km}}{2\frac{1}{2}\text{ h}}$

$= 20$ km/h

Why is the average speed of the cyclist not $\dfrac{20 + 0 + 30}{3}$ km/h?

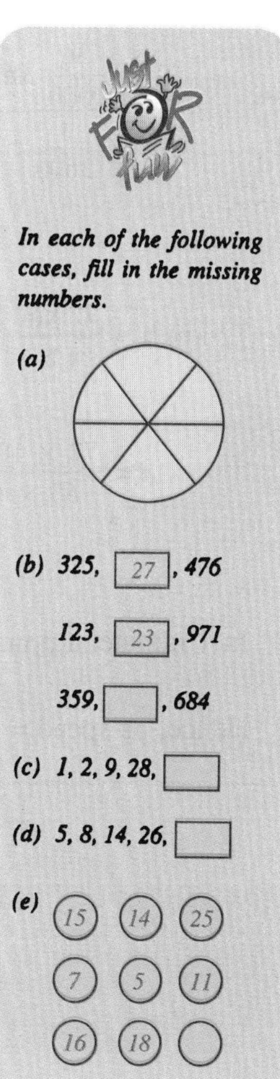

Just FOR fun
In each of the following cases, fill in the missing numbers.
(a)
(b) 325, 27, 476
123, 23, 971
359, , 684
(c) 1, 2, 9, 28,
(d) 5, 8, 14, 26,
(e)
15 14 25
7 5 11
16 18

xample 1

(a) Convert the speed 36 m/s into kilometres per hour.

(b) Convert the speed 72 km/h into metres per second.

(c) A wheel of radius 14 cm is turning at 30 revolutions per minute. Find the speed of a point on the rim of the wheel, giving your answer in m/s.

(Take π = 3.142)

(a) $36 \text{ m/s} = \dfrac{36 \text{ m}}{1 \text{ s}}$

$$= \dfrac{\frac{36}{1000} \text{ km}}{\frac{1}{3600} \text{ h}} = 129.6 \text{ km/h}$$

(b) $72 \text{ km/h} = \dfrac{72 \text{ km}}{1 \text{ h}}$

$$= \dfrac{72 \times 1000 \text{ m}}{60 \times 60 \text{ s}} = 20 \text{ m/s}$$

(c) In 1 minute, a point on the rim moves $30 \times 2 \times \pi \times 14$ cm.

Hence, its speed $= \dfrac{30 \times 2 \times 3.142 \times 14 \text{ cm}}{60 \text{ s}}$

$= 43.988$ cm/s

$= 0.440$ m/s (correct to 3 sig. fig.)

Mr Tan made a car journey from Singapore to Kuala Lumpur at an average speed of 80 km/h. On his return journey, his average speed was 90 km/h.

Mr Lee made the same journey from Singapore to Kuala Lumpur and back at an average speed of 85 km/h throughout.

Assume they travelled using the same route, would the time taken by Mr Lee and Mr Tan be the same? If not, who would have taken a longer time?

Gradient of a Curve

In Book 3, we learnt that when a straight line touches a circle at a single point A, the line is called the tangent to the circle at the point A.

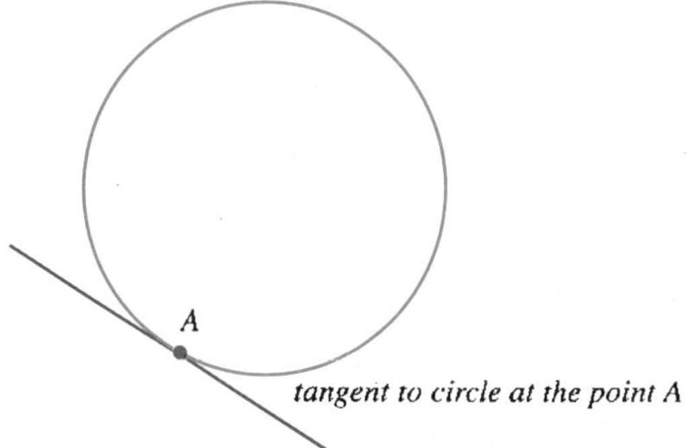

When a line l_1 touches the curve at P, l_1 is called the tangent to the curve at P. When a line l_2 touches the curve at Q, l_2 is called the tangent to the curve at Q, etc.

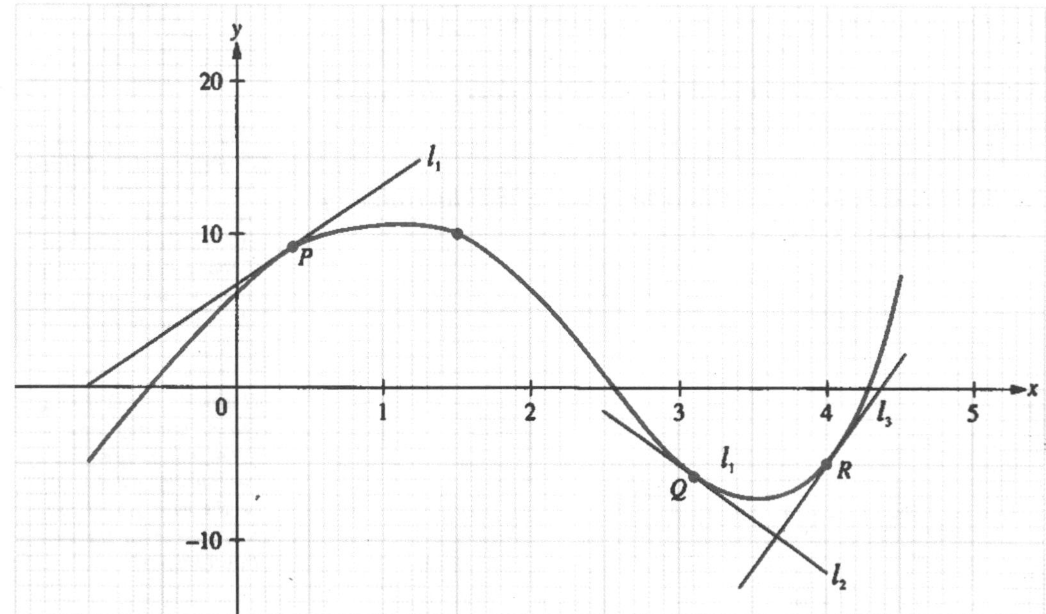

Fig. 2.2

The gradient of the curve at a point is defined as the gradient of the tangent to the curve at that point. Thus the gradient of the curve at P in Fig. 2.2 is equal to the gradient of the line l_1 and that the gradient of the curve at Q is equal to the gradient of the line l_2 etc.

The gradient of a curve at a point can be found by using calculus. This is taught in Additional Mathematics.

The variables x and y are connected by the equation $y = \frac{1}{2}(5x - x^2)$. *Corresponding values of x and y are given in the table below:*

	-1	0	1	2	$2\frac{1}{2}$	3	4	5
	a	0	2	3	b	3	2	0

(a) Calculate the values of a and b.

(b) Taking 2 cm to represent 1 unit on both axes, draw the graph of

$y = \frac{1}{2}(5x - x^2)$ for $-1 \leqslant x \leqslant 5$.

(c) By drawing a tangent, find the gradient of the curve at the point $x = 1$.

(d) Use your graph to estimate, correct to one decimal place, the values of x satisfying the equation $5x - x^2 - 1 = 0$.

(e) By drawing the line $2y = x + 2$ *on the same graph, find the range of values of x for which* $5x - x^2 > x + 2$.

Mrs Lim has decided to go to Johor Bahru for a shopping spree next Sunday. She can either take a train from Tanjong Pagar which is near to her house, or she can drive to Johor Bahru.

Draw a graph for a train journey and a separate graph for a car journey. What would be the most significant difference in the two travel graphs?

Solution

(a) When $x = -1$, $y = \frac{1}{2}[5(-1) - (-1)^2] = -3$

$\therefore \quad a = -3$

When $x = 2\frac{1}{2}$, $y = \frac{1}{2}\left[5\left(2\frac{1}{2}\right) - \left(2\frac{1}{2}\right)^2\right] = 3\frac{1}{8}$

$\therefore \quad b = 3\frac{1}{8}$

(b) The graph of $y = \frac{1}{2}(5x - x^2)$, for $-1 \leqslant x \leqslant 5$, is shown below:

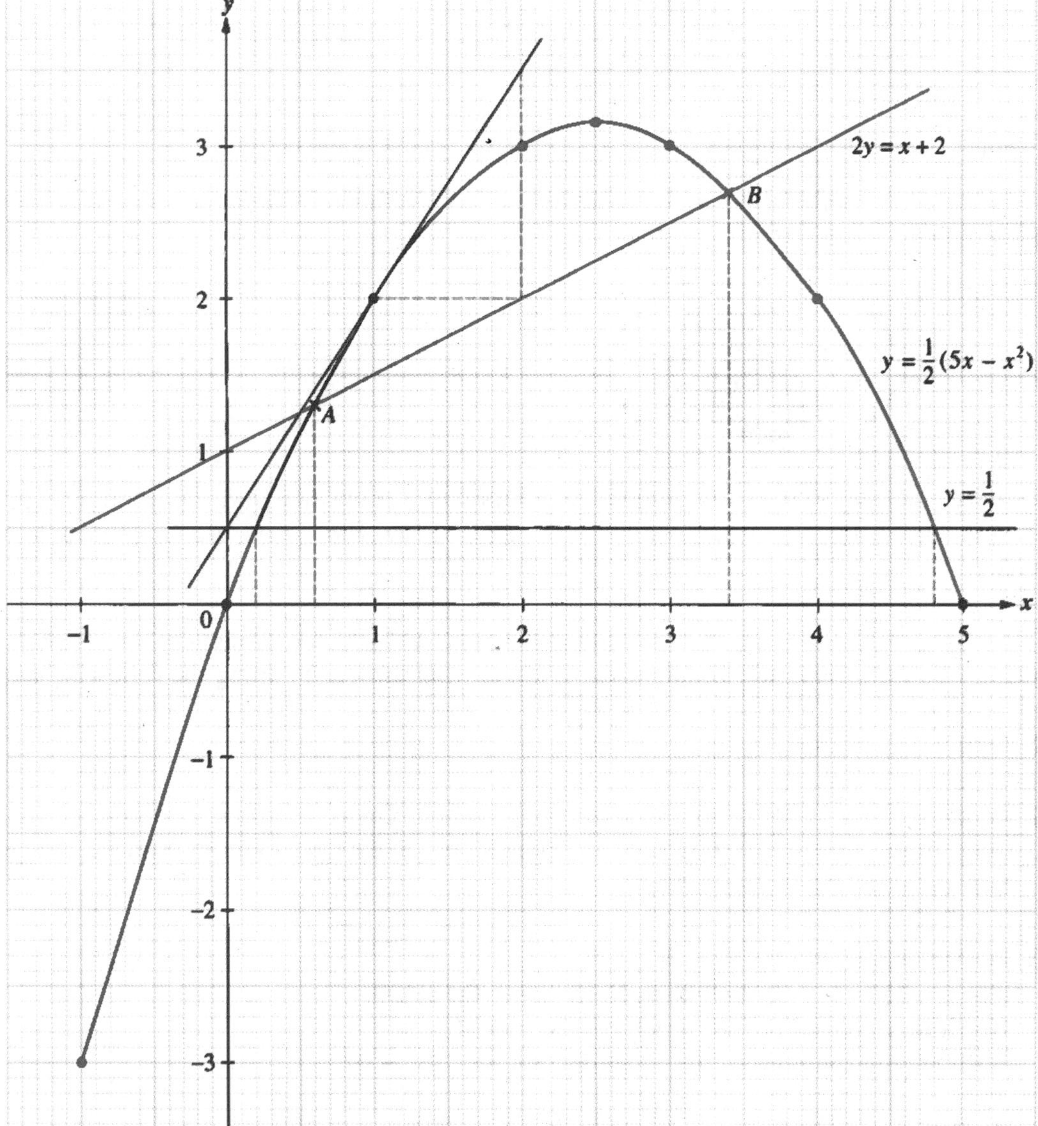

Fig. 2.3

(c) A tangent is drawn to the curve at the point $x = 1$. From the graph, the gradient $\approx \frac{1.5}{1} = 1.5$.

(d) $5x - x^2 - 1 = 0$

$$5x - x^2 = 1$$

$$\frac{1}{2}(5x - x^2) = \frac{1}{2}$$

The solution is given by the points of intersection of the curve and the line $y = \frac{1}{2}$.

From the graph, $x \approx 0.2$ or 4.8.

(e) The line $2y = x + 2$ intersects the curve at A and B.

$$5x - x^2 > x + 2$$

$$\frac{1}{2}(5x - x^2) > \frac{1}{2}(x + 2)$$

Thus the values of x for which $\frac{1}{2}(5x - x^2) > \frac{1}{2}(x + 2)$ occur in the region between A and B, where the curve is above the line. Hence, the range is approximately $0.6 < x < 3.4$.

It takes some practice to draw the tangent to a curve at a point and find the gradient. However, the gradient found using this method will only be approximate. For a start, use Graphmatica to check your answer.

Draw the curve $y = 15 + 4x - 2x^2$ on a piece of graph paper and find the gradient of the curve at $x = 0.5$ by drawing a tangent. Next, use Graphmatica to check your answer by doing the following steps:

Step 1 Open **Graphmatica**.

Step 2 Go to **Options**, **Graph Paper** to select **Rectangular**. Go to **View** to select **Grid Range**.. Select range from –3 to 10 for left to right and from 20 to –20 for top to bottom. You can change these later on to see the different effects.

Step 3 For the curve $y = 15 + 4x - 2x^2$,
type $y = 15 + 4x - 2x^2$ and press Enter to see the graph.
How many points does the graph cut the x-axis?
What are the solutions of the equation $15 + 4x - 2x^2 = 0$?

Step 4 To find the gradient of the curve $y = 15 + 4x - 2x^2$ at the point $x = 0.5$, select **Calculus** and **Draw Tangent**. Bring the cross cursor to the graph where $x = 0.5$ and click the mouse. What are the values of the coordinates and slope (i.e. the gradient) of the curve indicated at the bottom of the screen?

Step 5 To find the gradient of the curve $y = 15 + 4x - 2x^2$ at the point $x = -0.5$, select **Calculus** and **Draw Tangent**. Bring the cross cursor to the graph where $x = -0.5$ and click the mouse. What are the values of the coordinates and slope (i.e. the gradient) of the curve indicated at the bottom of the screen?

Step 6 Using the same method, find the gradient of the curve $y = 15 + 4x - 2x^2$ at the point where
(a) $x = 2.5$
(b) $x = -2.4$.

Practise more by finding the gradient of the curves below on graph paper and using Graphmatica to check your answers.

(i) $y = \frac{1}{9}(110 - x^2 - \frac{88}{x})$ at the point $x = 1.5$,

(ii) $y = 2^x + 1$ at the point $x = 1.5$.

Gradient of a Distance-Time Curve

We shall now study the applications of the *gradients of tangents* in kinematics.

When the distance-time graph is *a straight line*, the gradient measured is of that between any two points on the line. When the distance-time graph is *a curve*, the gradient at a point P is defined as the gradient of the tangent to the curve at the point P.

The gradient of the tangent at a point on a distance-time graph gives the speed at that particular point. It is also called the **instantaneous speed.**

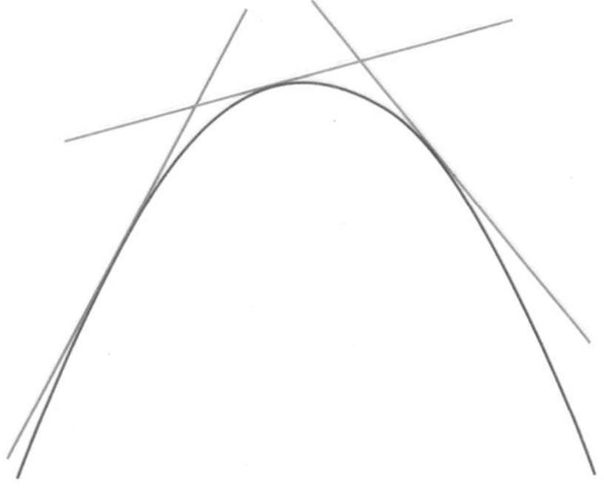

Fig. 2.4

The above figure shows the gradients of a curve at different parts of the curve.

Thus, the gradient of the tangent m_1 gives the gradient of the curve at P_1; the gradient of the tangent m_2 gives the gradient of the curve at P_2; and so on. Notice that the gradient of P_1 is greater than that at P_2. This implies that at P_1, *the body is moving faster* than at P_2. At P_3, the gradient is negative. This implies that *the body is moving in the opposite direction, i.e., back to its starting point.*

xample 3

A train started from A and travelled to a point 8 km from A. The following readings of the time (in minutes) since leaving A and the distance (in km) from A were taken .

	1	2	3	4	5	6	7	8
	0.3	1.1	2.3	4.8	6.8	7.4	7.8	8.0

Draw a graph of these values, using a scale of 2 cm for 2 minutes on the horizontal axis and a scale of 2 cm for 2 km on the vertical axis.

Use your graph
(a) to estimate the time taken to travel the first 4 km;
(b) to find, by drawing a tangent, the speed of the train in km/h, 5 minutes after leaving A.

The graph is shown in Fig. 2.5.

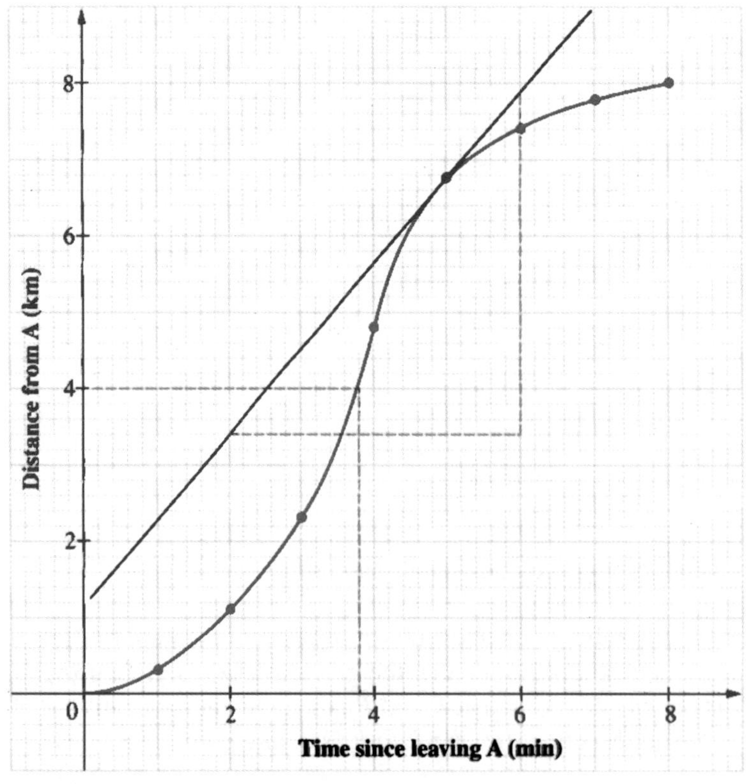

Fig. 2.5

The points on the graph are joined by a smooth curve instead of line segments as we assume that the train is not travelling at a constant speed.

(a) From the graph, the train takes approximately 3.8 minutes to travel the first 4 km.

(b) A tangent is drawn at the point 5 minutes after leaving A. The gradient of the tangent

$$\approx \frac{4.4 \text{ km}}{4 \text{ min}} = \left(4.4 \div \frac{4}{60}\right) \frac{\text{km}}{\text{h}}$$

$= 66$ km/h, which is the speed of the train at this point.

The graphical method of finding gradients yields only approximate results. A slight change in the drawing will give very different results.

1. Convert the following speeds into km/h:
(a) 24 m/s
(b) 18 m/s
(c) 40 m/s
(d) a m/s

2. Convert the following speeds into m/s:
(a) 16 km/h
(b) 32 km/h
(c) 45 km/h
(d) b km/h

3. The Sjoormen submarine in the Singapore Navy is capable of attaining a speed of 16 nautical miles an hour. Given that one nautical mile is equivalent to 1.852 km, express the speed of the Sjoormen submarine in
(a) km/h
(b) m/s

4. A cyclist set out at 09 00 for a destination 40 km away. He cycled at a speed of 15 km/h until 10 30. Then, he rested for half an hour before completing his journey at a speed of 20 km/h. Draw the distance-time graph to represent the journey and use your graph to estimate the time at which the cyclist reached his destination.

5. The BIONIX Infantry Fighting Vehicle developed by the Singapore Army is capable of attaining a maximum speed of 70 km/h. Express this speed in m/s.

6. A motorist travelled for 2 hours on a muddy road at an average speed of 30 km/h; then he travelled another 168 km in 3 hours on a dual-carriage way; and finally he travelled 114 km on an expressway at an average speed of 76 km/h. Calculate the
(a) distance he travelled on the muddy road;
(b) average speed on the dual-carriage way;
(c) time he spent on the expressway;
(d) average speed for the whole journey.

7. A bicycle wheel of diameter 70 cm is turning at 5 revolutions per second. Find the speed of a point on the rim of the wheel, giving your answers in km/h.

(Take $\pi = 3.142$)

8. A wheel of radius 40 cm is turning about a fixed axis through the centre of the wheel at a rate of 2 revolutions per minute. Calculate the

(a) angle through which the wheel turns in 10 seconds;
(b) distance moved by a point on the rim in 10 seconds.

9. A cyclist starts a 30-km journey at 09 00. He maintains an average speed of 20 km/h for the first three-quarter hour and then stops. Subsequently, he continues his journey at an average speed of 30 km/h, finally arriving at his destination at 11 20. Draw the distance-time graph and state, in minutes, the duration of his stop.

10. Use the travel graph for a train to find

(a) the time interval during which the train remained stationary;
(b) the average speed for the first two hours;
(c) the average speed for the last two hours.

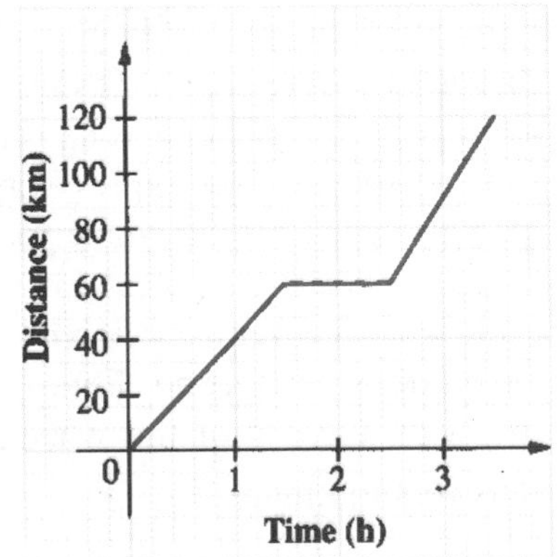

11. A motorist left town X at 08 00 for town Y, situated 120 km away, travelling at a constant speed of v km/h, so as to arrive at Y at 10 40. But, after travelling for 80 minutes, his car developed engine trouble and he had to stop for 30 minutes to repair it. Then he continued his journey at a speed of u km/h, so as to arrive at Y at 10 40.

(a) Sketch the distance-time graph of the car.
(b) Calculate the values of v and u.

12. A motorist set off from town A at 08 00 for town B, 70 km away. He drove at a speed of 45 km/h until his car broke down 1 hour later and he had to spend 30 minutes repairing it. Then he completed his journey at a speed of 20 km/h. Draw the distance-time graph to represent the journey and use your graph to estimate the motorist's time of arrival at town B.

13. Two men start moving towards each other at the same time. If they are originally 32 km apart and one is cycling at 20 km/h while the other is walking at 7 km/h, how long will it take them to pass each other? At what time will they be 5 km apart? Illustrate your answer using a distance-time graph.

14. At 09 00, A cycles to meet B, who is staying 20 km away. The cyclist travels at a steady speed of 18 km/h for half an hour. A is delayed for 20 minutes and then continues his journey at 8 km/h. At 09 00, B sets off from home on the same road to meet A and travels at 7 km/h. Draw the distance-time graph for the above information and find the time at which A and B meet. How far away are they from B's home?

15. The variables x and y are connected by the equation $y = (x + 2)(4 - x)$. Corresponding values of x and y are given in the table below:

x	−2	−1	0	1	2	3	4
y	0	p	8	9	q	r	0

(a) Find the values of p, q and r.
(b) Using a scale of 2 cm to represent 1 unit on both axes, draw the graph of $y = (x + 2)(4 - x)$ for $-2 \leqslant x \leqslant 4$.
(c) Use your graph to find the gradient of the curve at the point where $x = -1$ by drawing a tangent.
(d) By drawing a suitable straight line on your graph, find the solution of the equation $(x + 2)(4 - x) = x + 3$.
(e) Find the range of values of x for which

$$\frac{1}{2}(x + 2)(4 - x) > 4 - \frac{1}{2}x.$$

16. The variables x and y are connected by the equation $y = 12 + 10x - 3x^2$. Copy and complete the table of values for $y = 12 + 10x - 3x^2$.

x	−2	−1	0	1	2	3	4	5
y	−20		12	19	20			

(a) Using a scale of 2 cm to represent 1 unit on the x-axis and 2 cm to represent 5 units on the y-axis, draw the graph of $y = 12 + 10x - 3x^2$ for $-2 \leqslant x \leqslant 5$.
(b) Find the gradient of the curve at $x = 0$ and $x = 4$ by drawing two appropriate tangents.
(c) By drawing a suitable straight line on your graph, find the range of values of x for which $14 + 9x - 3x^2 \geqslant 0$.

17. A lift moves up from ground level to a 60-m level in 10 seconds, stops for 10 seconds and then descends to the ground in 10 seconds. The table shows the height of the lift on the upward and downward journeys, t seconds after leaving ground level:

t (s)	0	2	4	6	8	10	20	22	24	26	28	30
H (m)	0	3	16	44	57	60	60	57	44	16	3	0

(a) Plot a graph of H (m) against t (s) for values of t from 0 to 30. (Let 2 cm represent 5 seconds on the horizontal axis.)
(b) Find the gradient of the graph at $t = 8$ and explain briefly what this gradient represents.
(c) A man, waiting at the 40-m level, starts to go downstairs at $t = 15$. He moves at a steady speed of 2 m/s. From the graph, find the height at which the lift passes him.

18. A train left A for B, 7 km away. The table gives the time since leaving A and the distance from A.

Time (min)	0	2	4	6	8	10	12
Distance (km)	0	0.25	1.15	2.83	5.40	6.65	7.0

Plot the graph of the values. Take 1 cm to represent 1 minute horizontally and 2 cm to represent 1 km vertically. Estimate, from the graph, the speed of the train in km per minute when the train moved 6 km. Another train passed through B two minutes after the first train left A. It travelled towards A at a uniform speed of 60 km/h. On the same axes, plot the graph of this journey and, hence, determine the distance from A at which the trains pass each other.

19. A train started from A and travelled to a point B, 3 km away. The table below gives the time after the train left A and the distance from A.

Time (min)	0	1	2	3	4	5	6
Distance (km)	0	0.2	0.7	1.8	2.5	2.9	3.0

Using a scale of 2 cm to represent 1 minute on the horizontal axis and a scale of 4 cm to represent 1 km on the vertical axis, plot a graph using the given values. From your graph, find the

(a) approximate time taken to travel 1 km;

(b) gradient of the graph at a time of $1\frac{1}{2}$ minutes and explain briefly what this value represents;

(c) time taken to travel the last 1 km.

Speed-Time Graphs

We shall now look at another commonly used graph which is the **speed-time graph**. On a speed-time graph, the *speed* is represented on the *vertical* axis and the *time*, on the *horizontal* axis. Fig. 2.6 is a simple example of a body moving at constant speed.

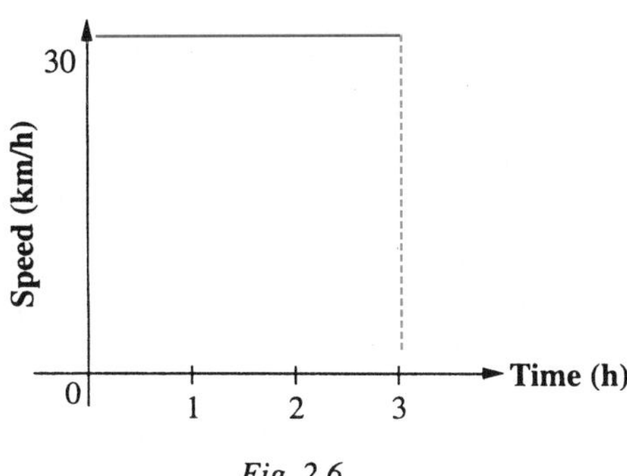

Fig. 2.6

If the direction in which an object moves is taken into consideration, then the graph obtained is called a velocity-time graph.

Do you remember how to represent constant speed on a distance-time graph? Draw the distance-time graph for the above speed-time graph. What do you notice about the area under the speed-time graph in relation to the distance-time graph?

Did you get the graph below?

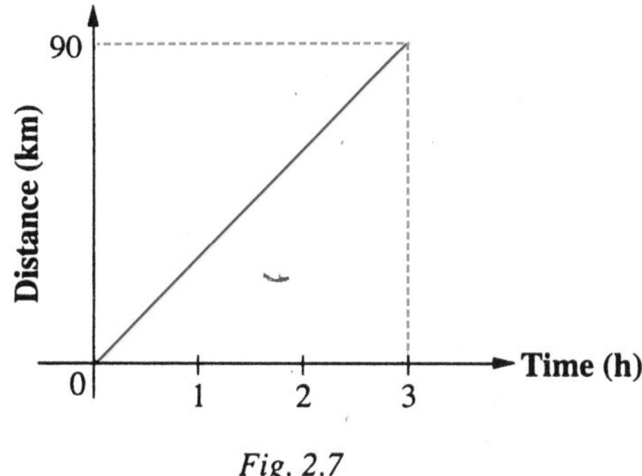

Fig. 2.7

If so, how do you calculate the distance travelled in the 3 hours? Notice that the area under the speed-time graph = 30 km/h × 3 h = 90 km. In fact, in all speed-time graphs, the distance covered is normally represented by the area under the graph.

Let's look at the speed-time graph for equation of the form $v = at$ where v represents speed and t represents time.

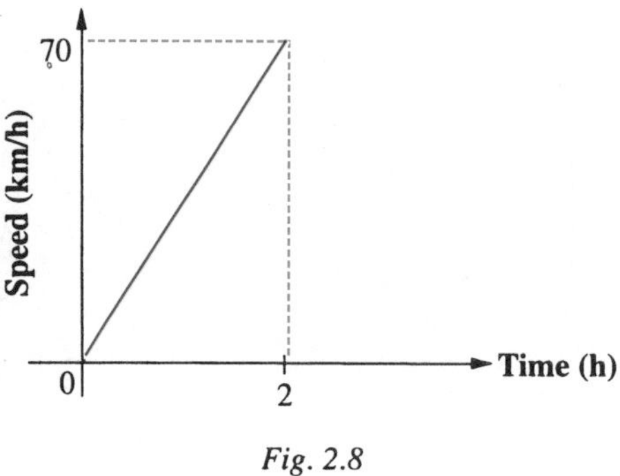

Fig. 2.8

Although Fig. 2.7 and Fig. 2.8 look similar, the first graph represents distance vs time whereas the second graph represents speed vs time.

The gradient of the speed-time graph shows the rate of change of speed. The rate of change of speed gives the magnitude of the **acceleration.** Acceleration is the measure of how fast the speed is increasing or decreasing over time. Fig. 2.8 shows that the object is moving at constant acceleration. When the speed decreases over time, the acceleration is negative and is known as **deceleration** **retardation** In this case, the object tends to slow down. What does the speed-time graph of a decelerating object look like?

In general,

(a) the gradient of the distance-time graph is the speed of the object,
(b) the gradient of the speed-time graph is the acceleration of the object,
(c) the area under the speed-time graph is the distance travelled by the object.

The distance-time graph of an object moving at constant acceleration is a quadratic curve. Draw the distance-time graph for Fig. 2.8 by finding the area under the speed-time graph for various times, e.g. $t = 0, 0.5, 1, 2$.

xample 4

The graph shows the speed of a body over a period of 10 seconds. Find

(a) the acceleration during the first 2 seconds;
(b) the total distance travelled during the first 2 seconds;
(c) the average speed during the 10 seconds.

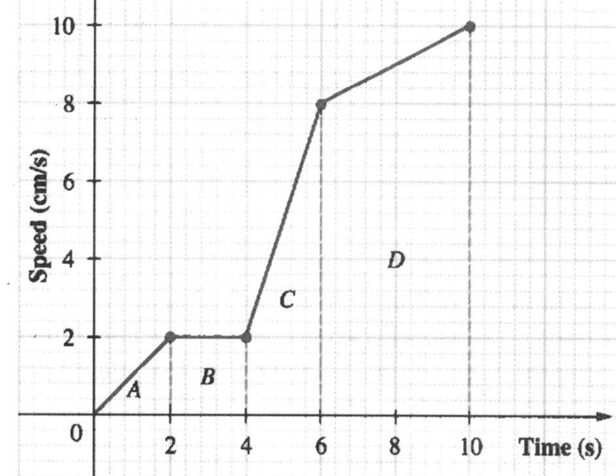

Fig. 2.9

Solution

(a) During the first 2 seconds,

$$\text{acceleration} = \frac{(2 - 0)\text{ cm/s}}{(2 - 0)\text{ s}} = \frac{2\text{ cm/s}}{2\text{ s}}$$

$$= 1\text{ cm/s}^2$$

(b) Distance travelled during the first 2 seconds is the area under the graph from $t = 0$ to $t = 2$.

$\therefore$ distance travelled $= \frac{1}{2} \times 2\text{ cm/s} \times 2\text{ s} = 2\text{ cm}$

(c) Distance travelled during the 10 seconds is the area under the graph for the 10 seconds.

$\therefore$ distance travelled = **(Area of *A*) + (Area of *B*) + (Area of *C*) + (Area of *D*)**

Distance travelled in the first 2 s = **Area of *A*** $= \frac{1}{2} \times 2 \times 2 = 2$ cm

Distance travelled from 2 s to 4 s = **Area of *B*** $= 2 \times 2 = 4$ cm

Distance travelled from 4 s to 6 s = **Area of *C*** $= \frac{1}{2}(2 + 8) \times 2 = 10$ cm

Distance travelled from 6 s to 10 s = **Area of *D*** $= \frac{1}{2}(8 + 10) \times 4 = 36$ cm

$\therefore$ total distance travelled $= 2 + 4 + 10 + 36 = 52$ cm

$$\text{Average speed} = \frac{\text{total distance}}{\text{total time}} = \frac{52}{10}$$

$$= 5.2\text{ cm/s}$$

xample 5

A particle moves along a straight line AB so that, after t seconds, its speed, v m/s, in the direction AB is given by

$$v = 3t^2 - 15t + 20.$$

The corresponding values of t and v are given in the table below:

	0	*1*	*2*	*3*	*4*	*5*
	20	*8*	*2*	*k*	*8*	*h*

Calculate the values of k and h.
Taking 2 cm to represent 1 second on the horizontal axis and 2 cm to represent 5 m/s on the vertical axis, draw the graph of $v = 3t^2 - 15t + 20$ *for the range* $0 \leqslant t \leqslant 5$. *Use your graph to estimate*

(a) the value of t when the speed is 10 m/s;
(b) the time at which the acceleration is zero;
(c) the gradient at t = 4, and explain what this value represents;
(d) the time interval when the speed is less than 15 m/s.

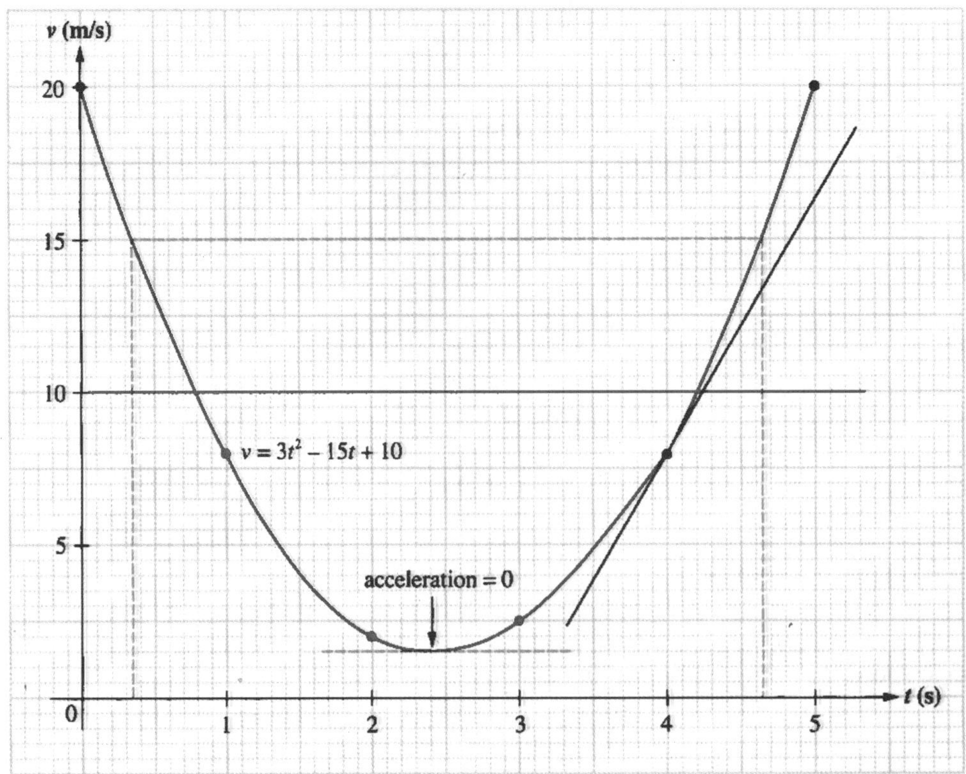

Fig. 2.10

When $t = 3$, $v = 3(3)^2 - 15(3) + 20 = 2$.
$\therefore \quad k = 2$

When $t = 5$, $v = 3(5)^2 - 15(5) + 20 = 20$.
$\therefore \quad h = 20$

(a) From the graph, $t \approx 0.8$ or 4.2 when speed = 10 m/s.

(b) The acceleration is zero when the gradient of the curve is zero. From the graph, the acceleration is zero at $t \approx 2.4$.

(c) A tangent is drawn at the point $t = 4$. From the graph,

$$\text{gradient of the tangent} = \frac{14.0 \text{ m/s}}{1.7 \text{ s}} \approx 8.2 \text{ m/s}^2$$

(The gradient of the tangent of the speed-time graph gives the acceleration of the particle at that instant.)

(d) The time interval for which the speed is less than 15 m/s is $0.35 < t < 4.65$.

Suppose a car moves up the slope of a hill at an average speed of 30 km/h. At what speed must the car go back down the slope in order to achieve an average speed of 60 km/h for the whole journey?

JOURNAL WRITING

The diagram shows the speed-time graph of a bus ferrying workers from their quarters to a factory. Based on the information given by the graph, make up a story about the journey and share it with your class.

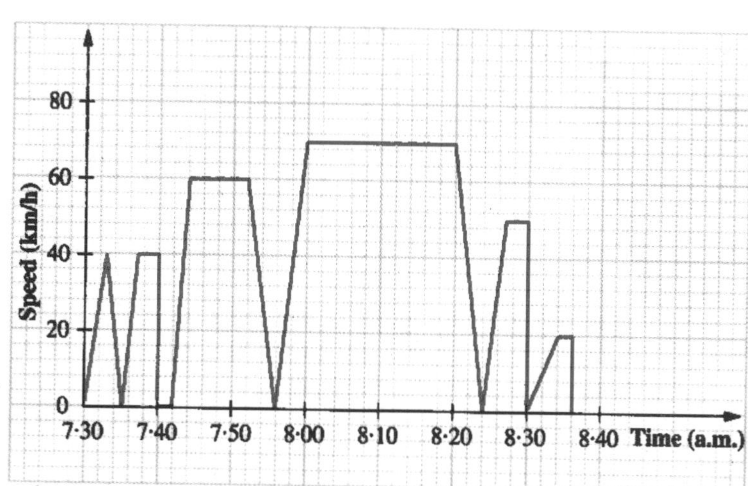

Graphs in Practical Situations

Fig. 2.11 shows three containers, each of which contains liquid of height h cm and the liquids are of the same volume. Each container is being filled with liquid at a constant rate from a tap. The containers are initially empty. The graph which shows the height of the liquid as the container is being filled, is shown beside the container.

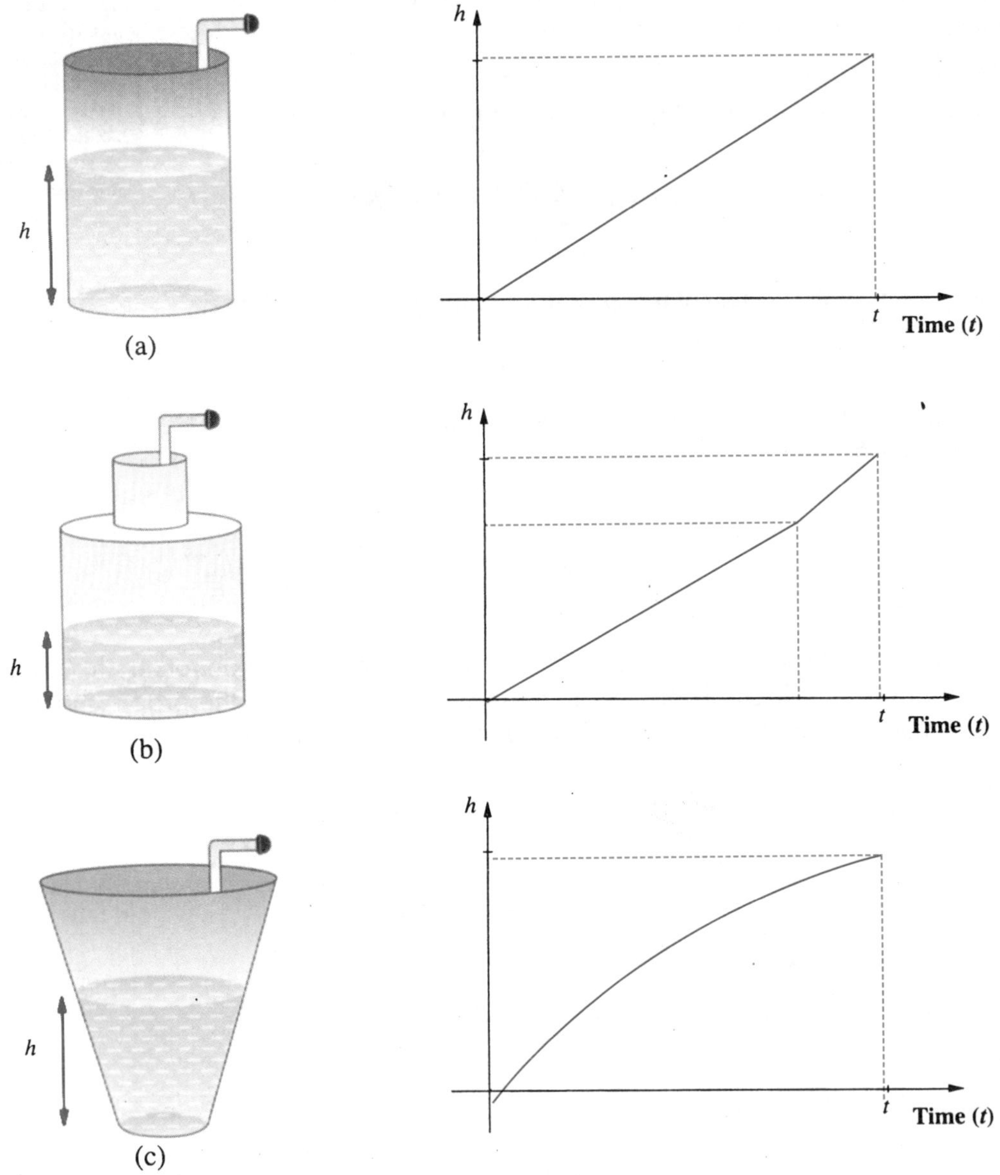

Fig. 2.11

In Fig. 2.11 (a), the graph is a straight line with constant gradient as the water level rises uniformly. Can you explain the significance of the graph for Fig. 2.11 (b) and why the graph in Fig. 2.11 (c) is a curve?

1. The diagram shows the speed-time graph of a car.

   Calculate
   (a) its acceleration during the first 2 seconds;
   (b) the distance travelled during the first 4 seconds;
   (c) the average speed for the whole journey.

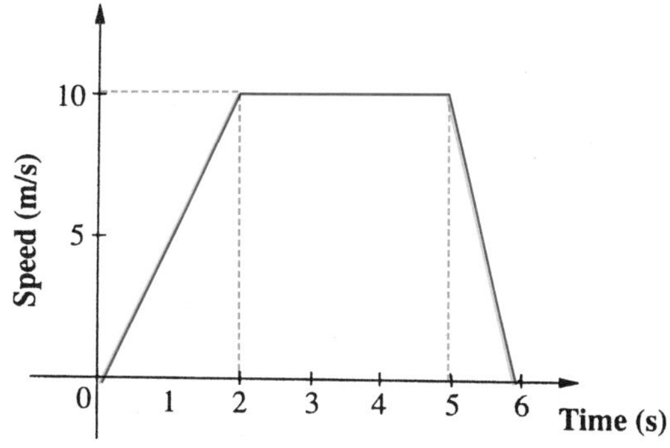

2. The diagram shows the speed-time graph of a particle over a period of 6 seconds.

   Calculate
   (a) its acceleration during the first two seconds;
   (b) the greatest acceleration;
   (c) the total distance moved;
   (d) the average speed of the particle.

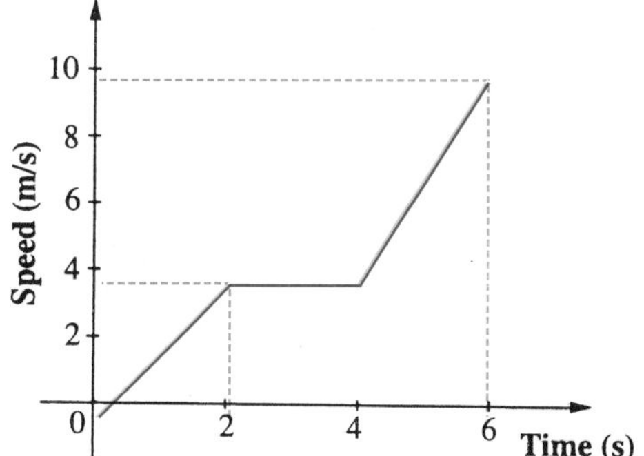

3. The diagram is the speed time graph of a particle which travels at a constant speed of 36 m/s and then slows down at a rate of 12 m/s^2, coming to rest at time t seconds.

   Calculate the
   (a) value of t;
   (b) average speed for the whole journey.

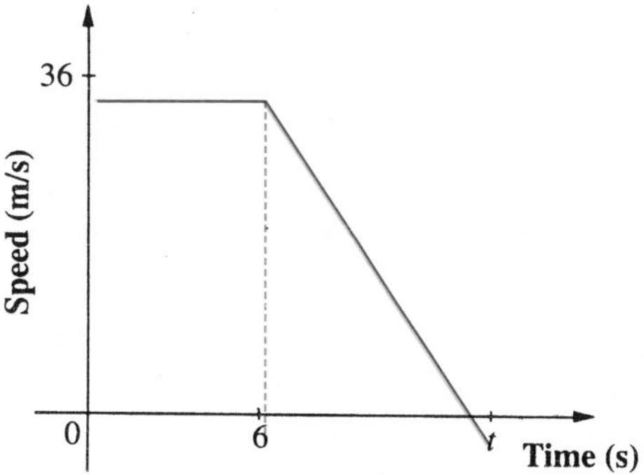

4. The graph shows the speed v m/s of a car after t s.
   (a) What does the gradient of OA represent?
   (b) What is the speed of the car when $t = 15$?
   (c) How far does the car travel between $t = 30$ and $t = 60$?

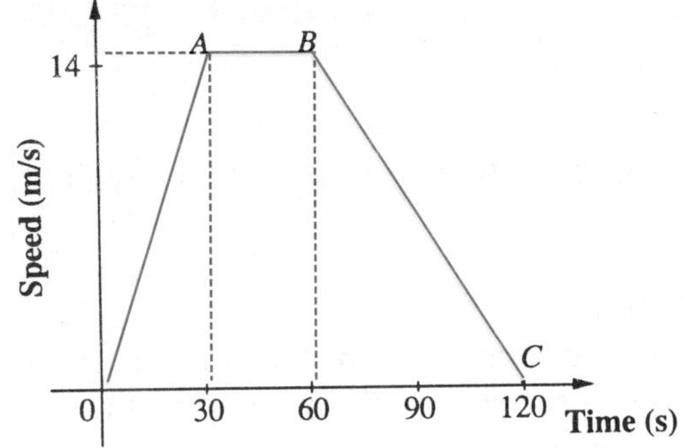

5. The graph shows the speed of a body during a period of 6 seconds. Find
   (a) its acceleration during the first 2 seconds;
   (b) the total distance travelled during the 6 seconds;
   (c) the average speed during the 6 seconds.

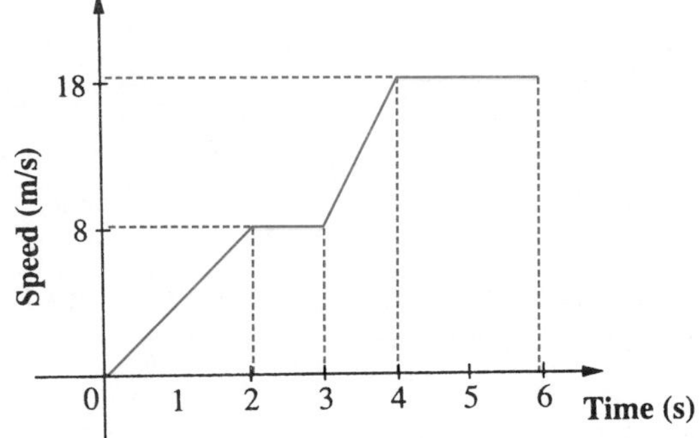

6. The graph illustrates the speed of a car in kilometres per hour during a period of 25 minutes. Find
   (a) the total distance travelled, in kilometres, over the 25 minutes;
   (b) the average speed, in km/h, during the 25 minutes.

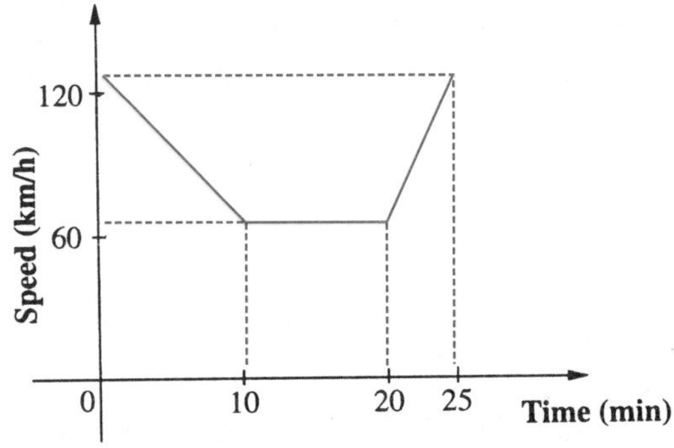

7. The diagram shows the speed-time graph of a train.
   (a) Calculate the acceleration of the train during the first 20 seconds.
   (b) Calculate the distance the train travels from rest before it begins to decelerate.
   (c) Given that the train decelerates at 0.75 m/s^2, calculate the time taken for the whole journey.

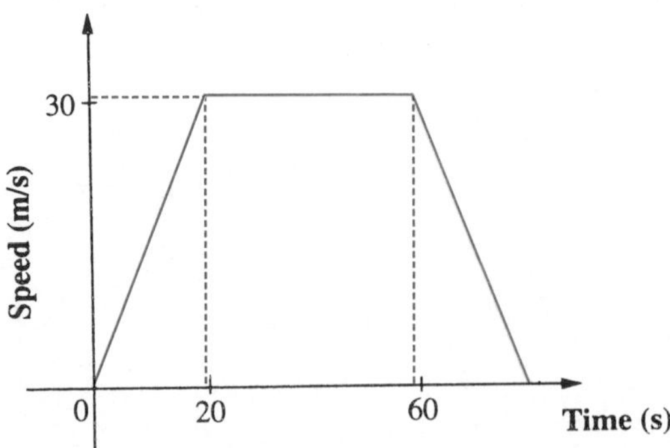

8. The diagram below shows three containers, each of height 8 cm. They have a fixed volume and varying area of cross-section as shown below.

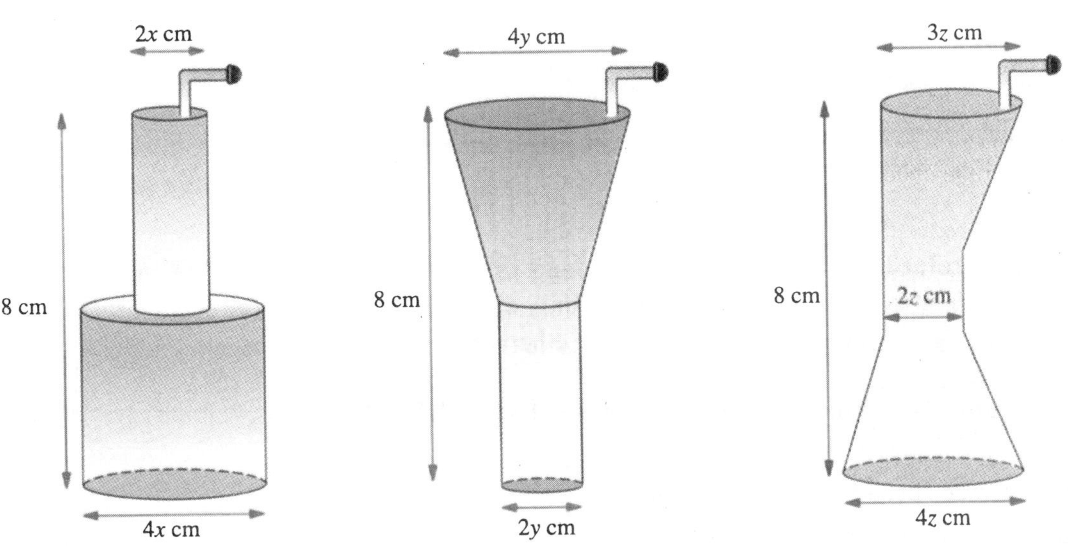

A tap is used to fill each of the containers at a constant rate. Draw a sketch of the graph of the height of water level against time, given that it takes 60 seconds to fill each of the containers. Use a scale of 1 cm to represent 5 seconds on the horizontal axis and 1 cm to represent a height of 1 cm on the vertical axis.

9. A particle travels at a constant speed of 6 m/s for 24 seconds and then slows down to rest in the next 3 seconds. Sketch the speed-time graph for the motion and calculate the

(a) retardation in the last 3 seconds;
(b) total distance covered in the whole duration.

10. An electric train accelerates uniformly from rest to reach 14 m/s in 10 seconds. Sketch a speed-time graph for the motion. What is the total distance covered?

11. A train starts from rest and accelerates at a uniform rate for 45 seconds, at the end of which it is travelling at a speed of 30 m/s. It then travels at this constant speed. Sketch a speed-time graph and calculate the

(a) speed after 10 seconds;
(b) total distance covered in the first 2 minutes.

12. A car travels 63 km in $1\frac{1}{2}$ hours and then travels at a constant speed of 36 km/h for the next $1\frac{1}{2}$ hours. It is then brought to rest uniformly for a further $\frac{1}{2}$ hour. Calculate the

(a) average speed for the first $1\frac{1}{2}$ hours;
(b) total distance covered;
(c) average speed for the whole journey.

13. A car is retarded uniformly from a speed of 32 m/s to a speed of 24 m/s in a time of 24 seconds. It is then brought to rest uniformly after a further 4 seconds. Sketch the speed-time graph for the motion of the car. Hence, or otherwise, calculate the

(a) retardation of the car during the first 24 seconds;
(b) total distance covered;
(c) average speed for the whole journey;
(d) speed of the car after 25 seconds.

14. The speed of an object, v m/s, at time t seconds from the start is given by $v = 6 + 2t$. Sketch the speed-time graph and calculate the

(a) speed when $t = 3$;
(b) acceleration;
(c) average speed during the first 4 seconds;
(d) average speed during the fourth second.

15. The speed of a body, v m/s, after time t seconds is given in the following table:

t (s)	0	2	4	6	8	10	12
v (m/s)	0	2	7	12	19	28	42

Using a scale of 1 cm to represent 1 second on the horizontal axis and 1 cm to represent 5 m/s on the vertical axis, plot the graph of v against t for values of t from 0 to 12.

(a) By drawing two tangents, find the accleration of the body when $t = 4$ and $t = 10$.
(b) Estimate the speed of the body at $t = 5$ and $t = 11$.

16. A body starts from a point A and moves towards a point Q, which it reaches after 7 seconds. The velocity v cm/s after t seconds is given in the table below:

t (s)	0	1	2	3	4	5	6	7
v (cm/s)	0	3	7	15	15	7	3	0

Using a scale of 2 cm to represent 1 second on the horizontal axis and a scale of 2 cm to represent 2 cm/s on the vertical axis, draw the graph of v against t for $0 \leqslant t \leqslant 7$.

(a) By drawing a tangent, find the acceleration of the body at $t = 2$ and $t = 6$.

(b) Estimate the time at which the acceleration of the body is zero.

1. Average speed $= \dfrac{\text{total distance travelled}}{\text{total time taken}}$.

2. The gradient of a distance-time graph gives the instantaneous speed of a particle.

3. The gradient of a speed-time graph gives the instantaneous acceleration of a particle.

4. The area under a speed-time graph gives the distance travelled.

xample 1

The graph shows the speed-time graph of a moving object over a given time.

Given that the distance covered in the first 8 seconds is 80 metres, the total distance covered in the first k seconds is 400 metres and that the deceleration during the last part of the journey is 2 m/s^2,

(a) calculate
   (i) the maximum speed v m/s,
   (ii) the acceleration for the first 8 seconds,
   (iii) the value of k and of h.

(b) sketch the distance-time graph and the acceleration-time graph.

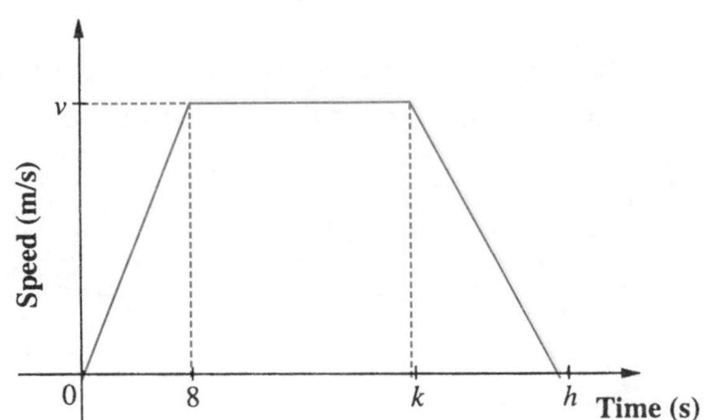

Fig. 2.12

(a) (i) We have $\frac{1}{2} \times 8 \times v = 80$

$$v = 20 \text{ m/s}$$

(ii) Acceleration $= \frac{20 \text{ m/s}}{8 \text{ s}} = 2.5 \text{ m/s}^2$

(iii) $80 + 20(k - 8) = 400$

$$4 + k - 8 = 20$$

$$\therefore \quad k = 24$$

$$\frac{20}{h - k} = 2$$

$$\therefore \quad 20 = 2(h - 24)$$

$$h = 10 + 24 = 34$$

Distance moved in the last part of the journey $= \frac{1}{2} \times (34 - 24) \times 20 = 100$ m

(b)

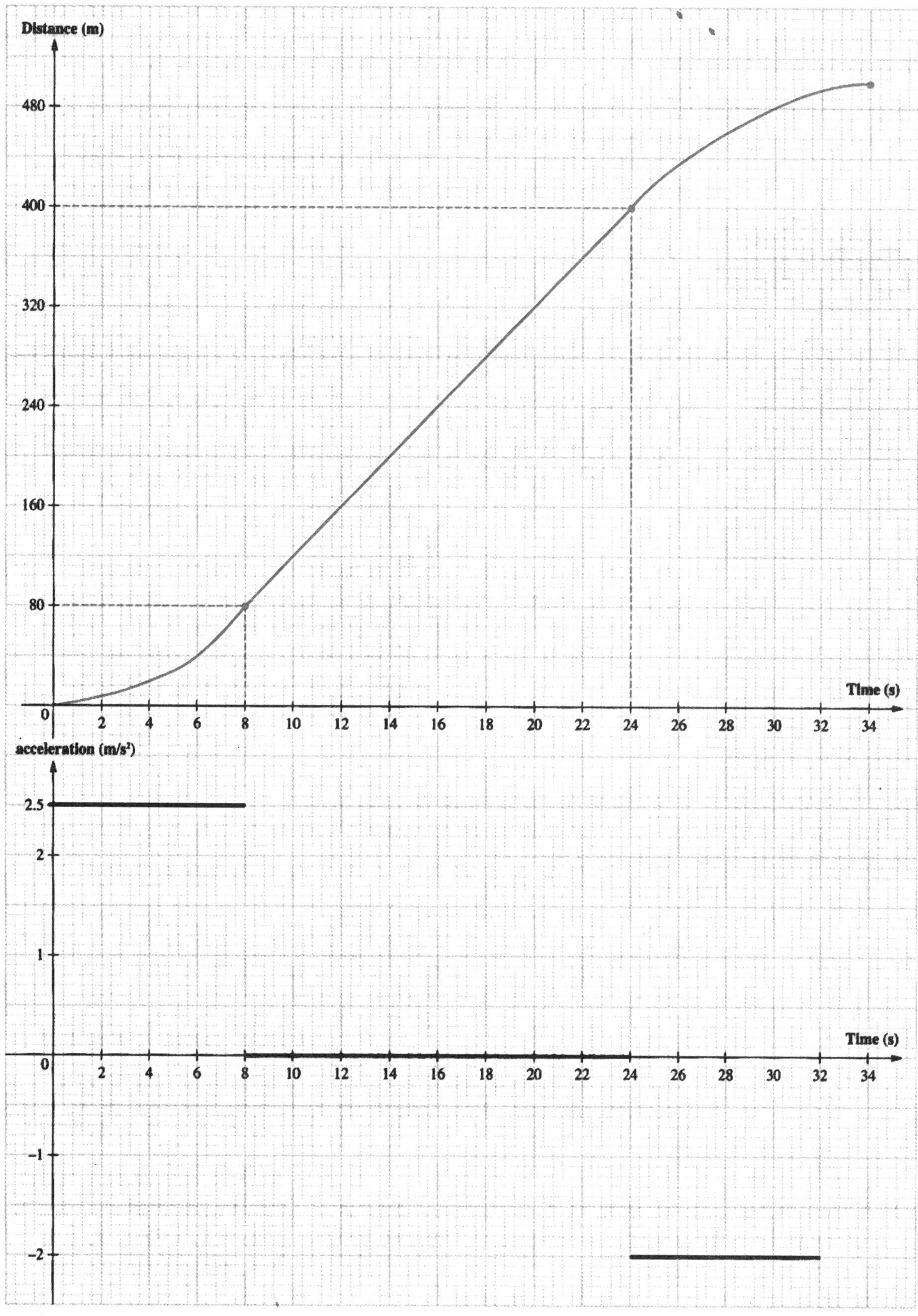

Distance (m)
480
400
320
240
160
80
0
Time (s)
2 4 6 8 10 12 14 16 18 20 22 24 26 28 30 32 34
acceleration (m/s²)
2.5
2
1
0
−1
−2
Time (s)
2 4 6 8 10 12 14 16 18 20 22 24 26 28 30 32 34

From the distance-time graph, we notice that for the first part of the journey, the distance increases slowly at the beginning and the rate of increase picks up as time approaches 8 seconds. The second part of the journey is a straight line and during the last part of the journey, the distance increases slowly as time approaches 34 seconds.

For the acceleration-time graph, we notice that the graph consists of three separate sections, all of which are horizontal lines, i.e. the acceleration is constant.

1. The diagram shows the distance-time graph of a motorist after leaving a starting point. Using the graph, find
   (a) its speed during the first 20 minutes;
   (b) its speed during the last 40 minutes;
   (c) the average speed for the whole journey.

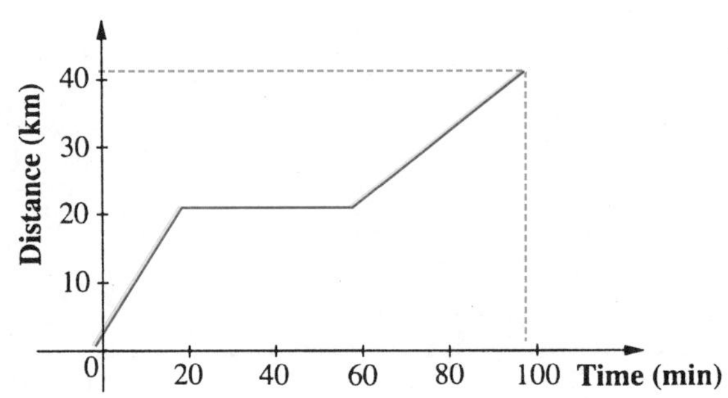

2. The diagram shows the travel graph of a train. Find
   (a) the time interval during which the train is stationary;
   (b) the greatest speed at which it travelled;
   (c) the average speed for the whole journey.

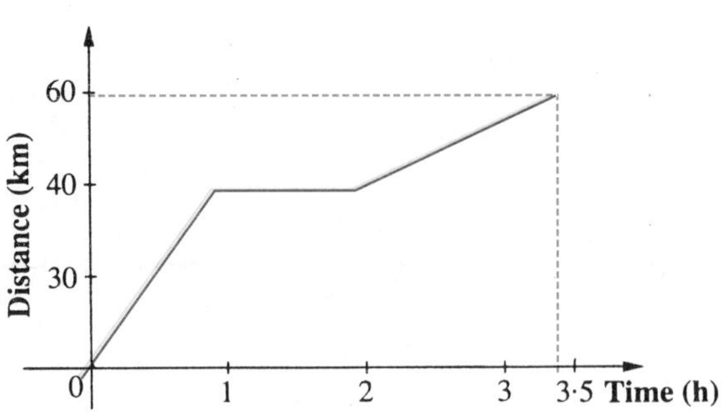

3. A wheel of radius 28 cm is turning at 40 revolutions per minute. Calculate the speed of a point on the rim of the wheel, giving your answer in metres per minute. (Take $\pi = 3.142$)

4. The F-16 Falcon aircraft is a major defence force in the Singapore Airforce. The advanced aircraft is capable of attaining a speed equivalent to twice the speed of sound (i.e. 2 Mac). If the speed of sound is 330 m/s, express the speed of the F-16 Falcon in km/h.

5. A car travelled from X to Y in 20 minutes at a constant speed of 45 km/h. Then, after stopping for 30 minutes, the car returned from Y to X at a constant speed of 60 km/h. Draw the distance-time graph of the car. Find, from your graph,
   (a) the distance between X and Y;
   (b) the time taken for the return journey.

A man with a dog, a rabbit and a piece of lettuce arrives at a river crossing and wants to cross the river. There is a small boat for him to use. However the boat can only take him and either the dog, the rabbit or the lettuce.

He does not dare leave the dog alone with the rabbit or the rabbit alone with the lettuce for the dog would attack the rabbit and the rabbit would eat the lettuce.

Can you help the man to arrange a way to transport himself and all his belongings safely across the river?

6. A bus leaves a town P for another town Q at time 13 00 and travels at 60 km/h. A car travelling at 80 km/h leaves P by the same route an hour later. Using a horizontal scale of 2 cm for 1 hour and a vertical scale of 2 cm for 100 km, draw the distance-time graphs and find, graphically, when the car overtakes the bus. If the bus arrives at Q half an hour later than the car, find, graphically or otherwise, the distance from P to Q.

7. A motorist, travelling at a constant speed, leaves A at 11 00, intending to arrive at B, 100 km away, at 13 00. Half an hour later, one of the tyres of his vehicle has a puncture and the motorist is delayed for 18 minutes. How fast must he then proceed in order to reach B on time? At what time will he meet a cyclist who leaves B at 11 45 for A, travelling at a constant speed of 20 km/h? Illustrate your answer by using a distance-time graph.

8. An object travels along a straight line AB such that at time t seconds, the speed v m/s in the direction AB is given by $v = 50 + 9t - 2t^2$.

   Corresponding values of t and v are given in the table below.

t	0	1	2	3	4	5	6	7
v	50	57	60	59	a	b	32	15

   Calculate the values of a and b.

   Using 2 cm to represent 1 second on the horizontal axis and 2 cm to represent 10 m/s on the vertical axis, draw the graph of $v = 50 + 9t - 2t^2$ for $0 \leqslant t \leqslant 7$.

   Use your graph to find the
   (a) value of t when $v = 20$;
   (b) value of t when the acceleration is zero;
   (c) acceleration when $t = 1$.

9. The variables x and y are connected by the equation $y = x - 2 + \frac{3}{x}$. Copy and complete the table of values for this equation.

x	0.5	1	1.5	2	2.5	3	3.5	4
y	4.5	2		1.5	1.7		2.36	2.75

(a) Using a scale of 4 cm to represent 1 unit on both axes, draw the graph of $y = x - 2 + \frac{3}{x}$ for $0.5 \leqslant x \leqslant 4$.
(b) State the minimum value of y and the corresponding value of x.
(c) Find the range of values of x for which $y < 2.2$.
(d) By drawing a tangent, find the gradient of the graph at the point $x = 3$.
(e) By drawing a straight line, find the value of x for which $2x + \frac{3}{x} = 8$.

10. The following is a table of values for the graph of $y = 2x + \frac{12}{x} - 8$:

x	1	1.5	2	2.5	3	4	5	6
y	6	3	2	1.8	2	a	b	6

(a) Calculate the values of a and b.
(b) Using a scale of 2 cm to represent 1 unit on both axes, plot the graph of $y = 2x + \frac{12}{x} - 8$ for $1 \leqslant x \leqslant 6$.
(c) Use your graph to solve the equation $2x + \frac{12}{x} = 12$.
(d) Find the range of values of x for which $2x + \frac{12}{x} \leqslant 10 + \frac{1}{2}x$.
(e) By drawing a tangent, find the gradient of the graph at the point where $x = 4$.

11. A particle moves along a straight line AB so that, after t seconds, the speed v m/s in the direction AB is given by $v = 2t^2 - 8t + 8$.

Corresponding values of t and v are given in the table below:

t	0	1	2	3	4	5	6	7
v	8	2	h	2	8	18	32	k

Calculate the values of h and k.

Taking 2 cm to represent 1 second on the horizontal axis and 2 cm to represent 10 m/s on the vertical axis, draw the graph of $v = 2t^2 - 8t + 8$ for $0 \leqslant t \leqslant 7$.

Use your graph to find approximately, the
(a) values of t when the speed is 10 m/s;
(b) time at which the acceleration is zero;
(c) gradient of the curve at $t = 1$ and $t = 5$. What does this gradient represent?

12. Car A travelling at a steady speed of 10 metres per second passes a stationary car, B. Two seconds later, car B starts to accelerate uniformly for 6 seconds (that is, its speed increases at a uniform rate during the interval of 6 seconds) and reaches a speed of 15 metres per second. It then continues with this speed until it overtakes car A.

On the same axes, using a horizontal scale of 1 cm for 1 second and a vertical scale of 2 cm for 5 m/s, draw the speed-time graphs for both cars A and B. Find the

(a) acceleration of car B;
(b) distance travelled by car B when it reaches the same speed as a car A.

The diagram below shows a row of ten coins, comprising five 50-cent coins and five 20-cent coins.

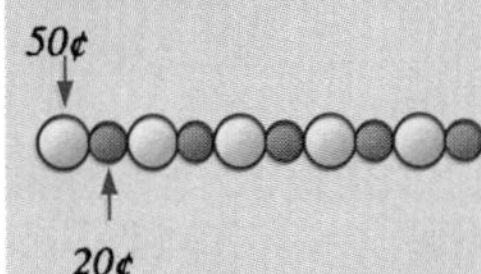

You are to get all the 50-cent coins to the right end and all the 20-cent coins to the left end. If you are allowed only to move the coins by interchanging the positions of any two neighbouring coins, how many moves will you have to make?

How many moves do you have to make if you start with ten 50-cent coins and ten 20-cent coins arranged in the same way?

13.

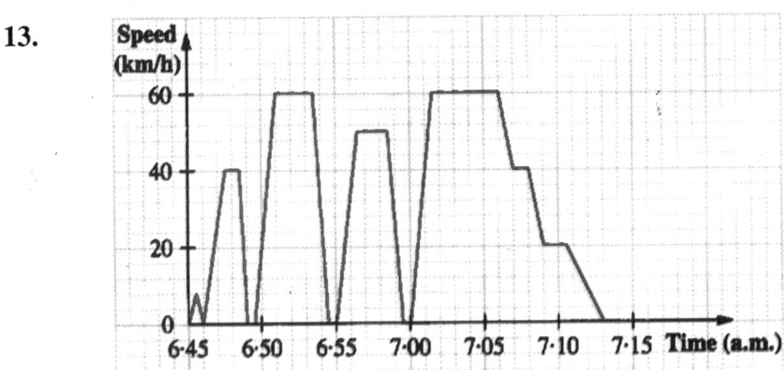

The graph shows the speed of Mrs Ong's car on her way to school. Use the graph to answer the following questions:

(a) How fast was Mrs Ong driving at 7.05 a.m.?
(b) Where do you think Mrs Ong was, from 6.45 a.m. to 6.46 a.m.? Why did Mrs Ong drive so slowly at that time?
(c) At what time did Mrs Ong reach her school?
(d) How many times did Mrs Ong stop on her way to school? Why do you think she made those stops?
(e) Why do you think Mrs Ong slowed down from 7.06 a.m. onwards?

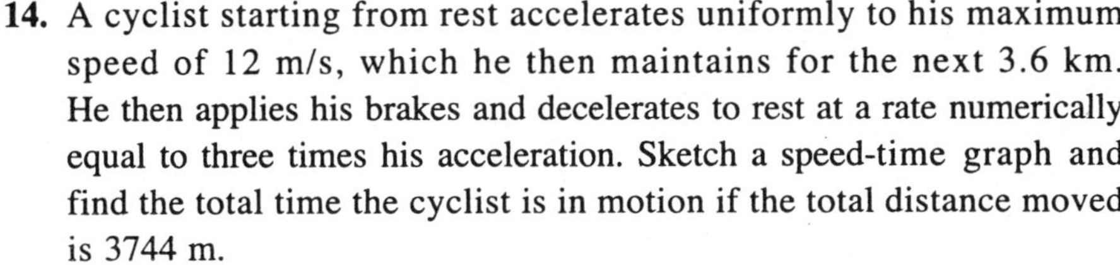

14. A cyclist starting from rest accelerates uniformly to his maximum speed of 12 m/s, which he then maintains for the next 3.6 km. He then applies his brakes and decelerates to rest at a rate numerically equal to three times his acceleration. Sketch a speed-time graph and find the total time the cyclist is in motion if the total distance moved is 3744 m.

15. A particle is projected vertically upwards from the ground with a speed of 80 m/s. Sketch the speed-time graph and find the total time of flight. (Take the acceleration due to gravity to be 10 m/s^2.)

16. The diagram shows a speed-time graph of a particle moving in a straight line. Describe the motion of the particle as it passes through O, A, B, C, D and E.

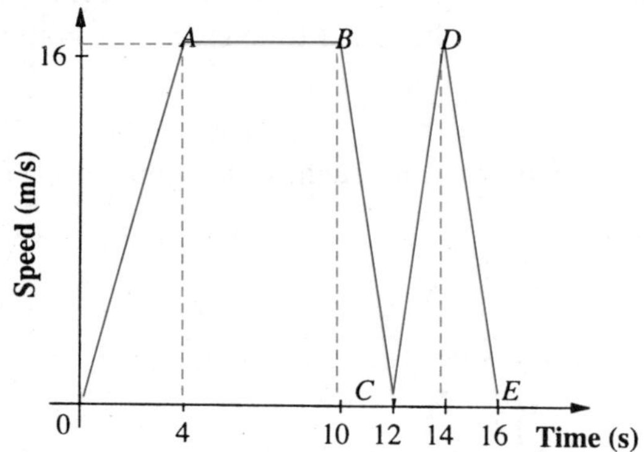

17. The diagram shows the speed-time graph of a bus and a car. The bus accelerates from rest to a speed of 15 m/s in a time of 8 seconds. It then continues to travel at this constant speed.

(a) Find the speed of the bus after 6 seconds.
(b) Find the distance travelled by the bus in 26 seconds.
(c) A car starts from the same place as the bus but 8 seconds later, and accelerates uniformly. After the bus has travelled for 26 seconds, the car just overtakes the bus. Calculate the speed of the car at this instant.

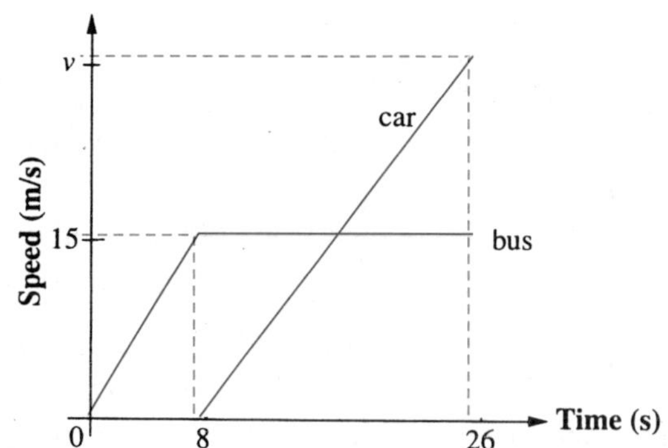

18. A cyclist travels at a constant speed of 5 m/s for 20 seconds. He then slows down at a constant rate for 40 seconds until he stops for rest.

(a) On the axes below, draw the speed-time graph for the journey of the cyclist.

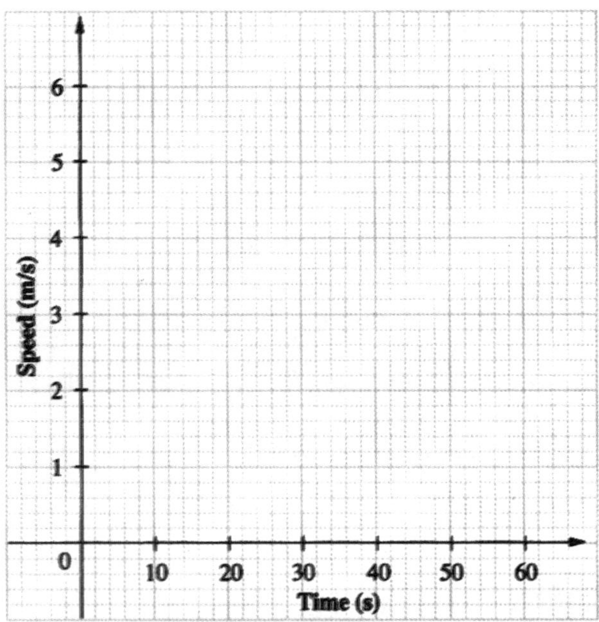

(b) Calculate the rate at which the cyclist was slowing down during the last 40 seconds.

(c) Calculate the distance travelled by the cyclist during the first 60 seconds.

In this chapter, you will learn how to

- *represent vector quantities using the notation $\overrightarrow{AB}$ or* **a**;
- *represent vector quantities by directed line segments;*
- *represent the magnitude of a vector using the notation* $|\overrightarrow{AB}|$ *or* $|\mathbf{a}|$;
- *find the magnitude of a vector;*
- *find the sum, difference and scalar multiples of vectors;*
- *manipulate vectors expressed in column vector form* $\begin{pmatrix} x \\ y \end{pmatrix}$;
- *express a vector in terms of two non-parallel coplanar vectors;*
- *express a vector in terms of position vectors;*
- *solve problems involving vectors.*

CHAPTER

3

Vectors in Two Dimensions

Introduction

The picture shows a sign post erected outside the airport in Christchurch, New Zealand. Each panel provides two pieces of information, the direction and the distance, of a place from the post. The two pieces of information together give us an idea of what a vector quantity is.

Scalar and Vector Quantities

Consider the following statements:

(a) The area of the triangle is 20 cm^2.

(b) The car takes 3 hours to complete the journey.

(c) The ship sails 8 km from P to Q on a bearing of 075°.

(d) The plane is flying due north at 750 km/h.

(e) Move the desk 5 m to the right.

1. In what ways are the first two statements different from the last three statements?

2. In statements (a) and (b), do 20 cm^2 and 3 hours completely describe the area of the triangle and the duration of the journey, respectively?

3. Will a ship sailing 8 km on a bearing of 075° get to the same place as one sailing 8 km on a bearing of 255°?

4. Will a plane flying north at 750 km/h get to the same place as one flying east at 750 km/h?

5. Will a desk that is moved 5 m to the right end up at the same place as one that is moved 5 m to the left?

6. Can we say that the first two statements involve quantities, which are completely described by their magnitudes alone?

7. Do you agree that the last three statements involve quantities which have both magnitudes and directions?

Quantities which have only magnitudes, such as area and time, are called **scalar** quantities. Quantities which have both **magnitudes** and **directions** are called **vector** quantities. The movement or the *displacement* of the ship from P to Q, the *velocity* (speed and direction) of the plane and the *translation* of the desk are examples of vector quantities.

Terminologies and Notations of Vectors

A vector can be represented by a **directed line segment**, whose *direction* is that of the vector and whose *length* represents the magnitude of the vector.

The displacement of the ship from P to Q in statement (c) given earlier is denoted by $\overrightarrow{PQ}$ and represented by the directed line segment shown in Fig. 3.1 (a) below. It has length PQ and direction given by the arrow from P to Q. In the notation $\overrightarrow{PQ}$, the order of the letters is important. It indicates that P is the **initial** or **starting point** and Q is the **terminal** or **ending point** of $\overrightarrow{PQ}$.

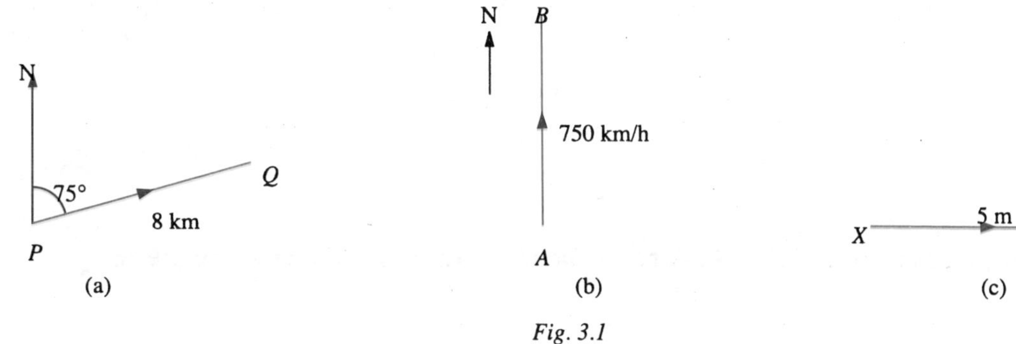

Fig. 3.1

The velocity of the plane in statement (d) is denoted by $\overrightarrow{AB}$ and represented by the directed line segment shown in Fig. 3.1(b).

The translation of the desk in statement (e) is denoted by $\overrightarrow{XY}$ and represented by the directed line segment shown in Fig. 3.1(c).

A vector can also be denoted by a single letter in bold typeface. In Fig. 3.2, the vector $\overrightarrow{AB}$ is denoted by **a**. In written work, it is more convenient to use $\underset{\sim}{a}$.

The **magnitude** of a vector is the length of the corresponding line segment. In Fig. 3.2, the magnitude of $\overrightarrow{AB}$, denoted by $|\overrightarrow{AB}|$ or $|\mathbf{a}|$, is the length of the line segment AB, i.e.

$$|\overrightarrow{AB}| = \text{length of } AB.$$

In written work, it is more convenient to use $|\underset{\sim}{a}|$.

B

A a

Fig. 3.2

Equal Vectors

When the desk in statement (e) (on page 75) is moved, every point of the desk is moved 5 m to the right. Fig. 3.3 shows the displacements of the four corners of the top of the desk.

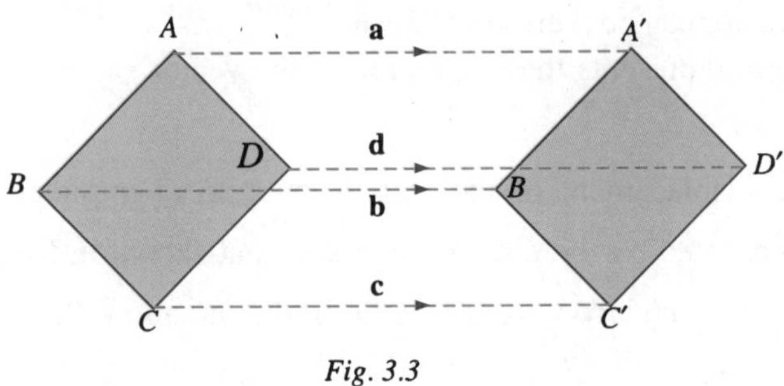

Fig. 3.3

The vectors $\overrightarrow{AA'} = \mathbf{a}$, $\overrightarrow{BB'} = \mathbf{b}$, $\overrightarrow{CC'} = \mathbf{c}$ and $\overrightarrow{DD'} = \mathbf{d}$ represent the displacements of the corners A, B, C and D of the desk.

These vectors **a**, **b**, **c** and **d** have the same magnitude and the same direction. They are **equal** vectors, i.e.

$$\mathbf{a} = \mathbf{b} = \mathbf{c} = \mathbf{d}.$$

Any one of these vectors can be used to describe the displacement or the translation of the desk.

Two vectors are equal if they have the same magnitude and the same direction.

In Fig. 3.4, $\overrightarrow{AB}$, $\overrightarrow{CD}$, **p**, **q** and **r** have the same magnitude; and $\overrightarrow{AB}$, $\overrightarrow{CD}$, **p** and **s** have the same direction. Which vectors are equal? Why?

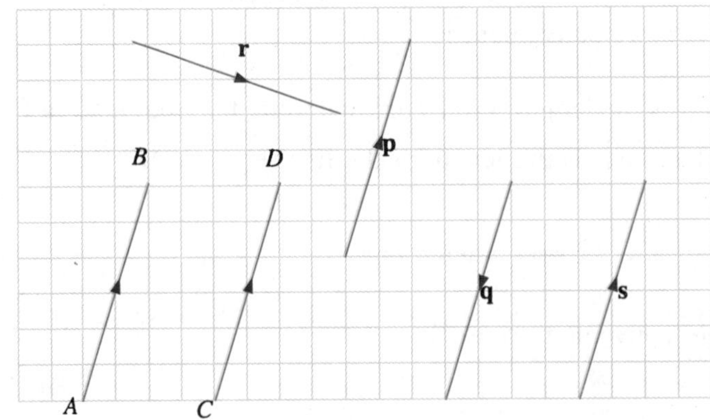

Fig. 3.4

Vectors Which are Opposite

On its return journey, the ship in statement (c) (on page 75) sails 8 km from Q to P on a bearing of 255°. The vector $\overrightarrow{QP}$ in Fig. 3.5 gives the displacement of the ship from Q to P. $\overrightarrow{QP}$ is opposite in direction to $\overrightarrow{PQ}$ but has the same magnitude. We write,

$$\overrightarrow{PQ} = -\overrightarrow{QP} \text{ or } \overrightarrow{QP} = -\overrightarrow{PQ} \text{ or } \mathbf{a} = -(-\mathbf{a}).$$

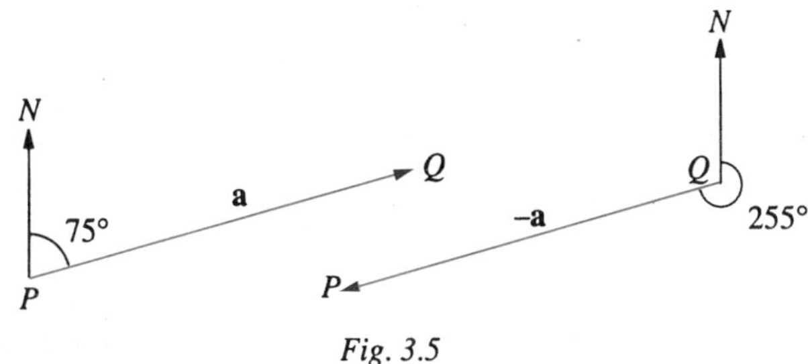

Fig. 3.5

Your Attention

$\overrightarrow{PQ}$ and $\overrightarrow{QP}$ are in different directions but we have to be more specific here: we say they are in opposite directions.

In general, a negative sign reverses the direction of a vector, $-\mathbf{a}$ is the vector that is negative to vector $\mathbf{a}$. The vectors $\mathbf{a}$ and $-\mathbf{a}$ have the same magnitude, but they are in opposite directions.

Column Vectors

Fig. 3.6 shows the translation of $\triangle ABC$ to $\triangle A'B'C'$. The translation, represented by the vector $\overrightarrow{AA'}$, $\overrightarrow{BB'}$, or $\overrightarrow{CC'}$, can also be achieved by moving $\triangle ABC$ 5 units to the right and 2 units up. We write

$$\overrightarrow{AA'} = \overrightarrow{BB'} = \overrightarrow{CC'} = \begin{pmatrix} 5 \\ 2 \end{pmatrix}.$$

$\begin{pmatrix} 5 \\ 2 \end{pmatrix}$ is called a **column vector**. 5 and 2 are called the **components** of the vector $\begin{pmatrix} 5 \\ 2 \end{pmatrix}$.

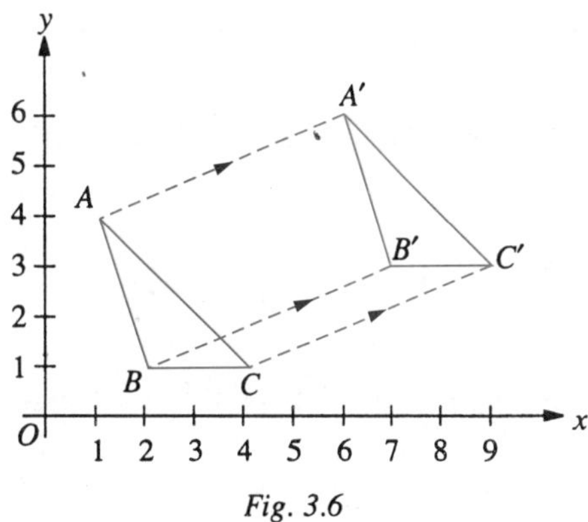

Fig. 3.6

Example 1

In Fig. 3.7, $\overrightarrow{PQ} = \begin{pmatrix} 2 \\ -5 \end{pmatrix}$*. Express each of the following as a column vector and then write down its negative vector.*

(a) $\overrightarrow{RS}$ *(b)* $\overrightarrow{TU}$

(c) $\overrightarrow{VW}$ *(d)* $\overrightarrow{XY}$

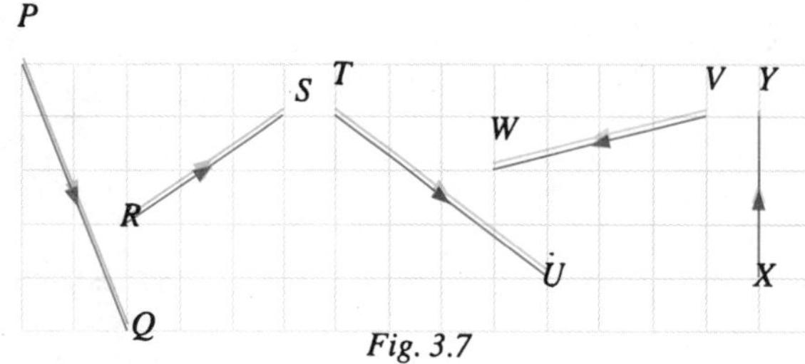

Fig. 3.7

(a) $\overrightarrow{RS} = \begin{pmatrix} 3 \\ 2 \end{pmatrix}$ (3 units to the right of R, 2 units up.)

The negative of $\overrightarrow{RS}$ is $\overrightarrow{SR} = -\overrightarrow{RS} = -\begin{pmatrix} 3 \\ 2 \end{pmatrix} = \begin{pmatrix} -3 \\ -2 \end{pmatrix}$.

(b) $\overrightarrow{TU} = \begin{pmatrix} 4 \\ -3 \end{pmatrix}$ (4 units to the right of T, 3 units down.)

The negative of $\overrightarrow{TU}$ is $\overrightarrow{UT} = -\overrightarrow{TU} = -\begin{pmatrix} 4 \\ -3 \end{pmatrix} = \begin{pmatrix} -4 \\ 3 \end{pmatrix}$.

(c) $\overrightarrow{VW} = \begin{pmatrix} -4 \\ -1 \end{pmatrix}$ (4 units to the left of V, 1 unit down.)

The negative of $\overrightarrow{VW}$ is $\overrightarrow{WV} = -\overrightarrow{VW} = -\begin{pmatrix} -4 \\ -1 \end{pmatrix} = \begin{pmatrix} 4 \\ 1 \end{pmatrix}$.

(d) $\overrightarrow{XY} = \begin{pmatrix} 0 \\ 3 \end{pmatrix}$ (3 units up from X.)

The negative of $\overrightarrow{XY}$ is $\overrightarrow{YX} = -\overrightarrow{XY} = -\begin{pmatrix} 0 \\ 3 \end{pmatrix} = \begin{pmatrix} 0 \\ -3 \end{pmatrix}$.

Anthony wants to go to three different places, the mountains (M), the village market (V) and the river (R) as shown in the map.

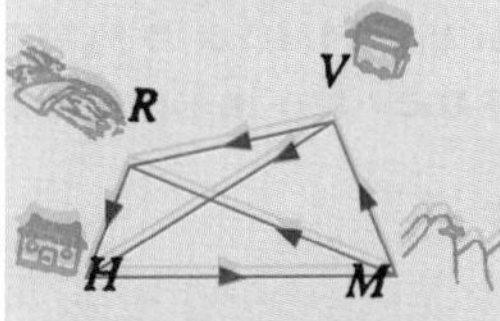

If he can visit these places in only two given sequences, i.e.

Route A : H → M → V → R → H

or Route B : H → M → R → V → H,

find out which is the shorter route for Anthony to travel.

The magnitude of a column vector $\mathbf{a} = \begin{pmatrix} x \\ y \end{pmatrix}$, is given by

$$|\mathbf{a}| = \sqrt{x^2 + y^2}$$

using Pythagoras' theorem (see Fig. 3.8).

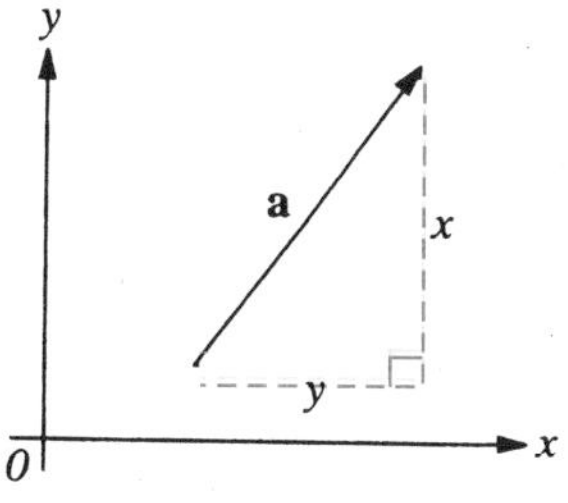

Fig. 3.8

example 2

Express each of the vectors in the diagram as a column vector and find its magnitude.

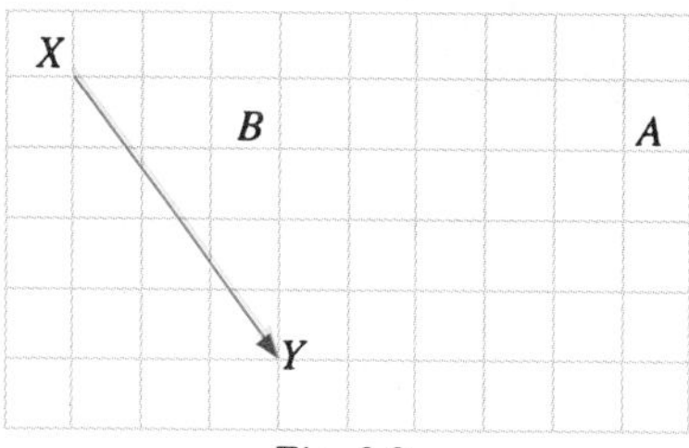

Fig. 3.9

Solution

$\overrightarrow{XY} = \begin{pmatrix} 3 \\ -4 \end{pmatrix}$ and $|\overrightarrow{XY}| = \sqrt{3^2 + (-4)^2} = \sqrt{25} = 5$ units

$\overrightarrow{AB} = \begin{pmatrix} -5 \\ 0 \end{pmatrix}$ and $|\overrightarrow{AB}| = \sqrt{(-5)^2 + 0^2} = \sqrt{25} = 5$ units

For horizontal vectors $\begin{pmatrix} x \\ 0 \end{pmatrix}$, the magnitude is just the numerical absolute value of x or $|x|$. In Example 2 above, $\overrightarrow{AB} = \begin{pmatrix} -5 \\ 0 \end{pmatrix}$, so $|\overrightarrow{AB}| = 5$ units.

For vertical vectors $\begin{pmatrix} 0 \\ y \end{pmatrix}$, the magnitude is the numerical value of y.

*The **numerical** or **absolute** value of x, $|x|$, is just the value without its sign. e.g. the numerical value of -5 is $|-5| = 5$, and the numerical value of 7 is $|7| = 7$.*

We have seen earlier that two vectors **a** and **b** are **equal** if and only if they have the same magnitude and the same direction.

> In general, if $\begin{pmatrix} p \\ q \end{pmatrix} = \begin{pmatrix} r \\ s \end{pmatrix}$, then $p = r$ and $q = s$.

In Fig. 3.10, $\mathbf{a} = \begin{pmatrix} 4 \\ 2 \end{pmatrix}$ and $\mathbf{b} = \begin{pmatrix} 4 \\ 2 \end{pmatrix}$, so **a** and **b** are equal vectors.

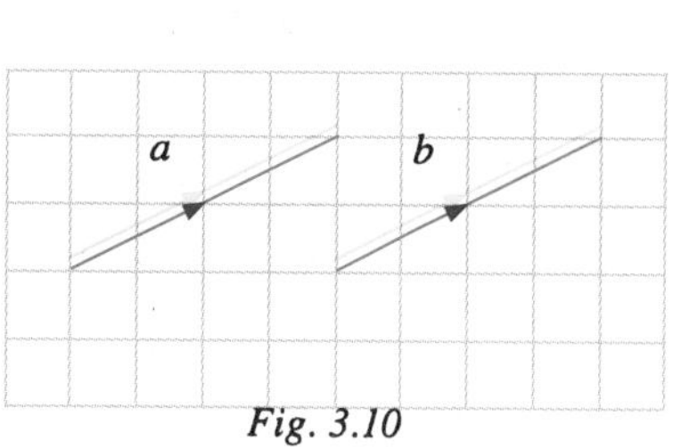

Fig. 3.10

Example 3

The column vectors **a** *and* **b** *are such that* $\mathbf{a} = \begin{pmatrix} 10 - p \\ 4 - q \end{pmatrix}$, *and* $\mathbf{b} = \begin{pmatrix} p + 2 \\ q - 5 \end{pmatrix}$.

(a) Given that $\mathbf{a} = \mathbf{b}$,

(i) find the values of p and q,

(ii) show that $|\mathbf{a}| = |\mathbf{b}| = \frac{\sqrt{145}}{2}$.

(b) Given that $|\mathbf{a}| = |\mathbf{b}|$, *express q in terms of p.*

(a) (i) $\mathbf{a} = \mathbf{b}$

$$\begin{pmatrix} 10 - p \\ 4 - q \end{pmatrix} = \begin{pmatrix} p + 2 \\ q - 5 \end{pmatrix}$$

$$\therefore \quad 10 - p = p + 2 \quad \text{and} \quad 4 - q = q - 5$$

$$p = 4 \quad \text{and} \quad q = 4\frac{1}{2}$$

(ii) $\mathbf{a} = \mathbf{b} = \begin{pmatrix} 6 \\ -\frac{1}{2} \end{pmatrix}$

$$|\mathbf{a}| = |\mathbf{b}| = \sqrt{6^2 + \left(-\frac{1}{2}\right)^2}$$

$$= \sqrt{36 + \frac{1}{4}} = \frac{\sqrt{145}}{2}$$

(b) $|\mathbf{a}| = |\mathbf{b}|$

$$\sqrt{(10 - p)^2 + (4 - q)^2} = \sqrt{(p + 2)^2 + (q - 5)^2}$$

$$\therefore \quad 100 - 20p + p^2 + 16 - 8q + q^2 = p^2 + 4p + 4 + q^2 - 10q + 25$$

$$2q = 24p - 87$$

$$\text{i.e.} \quad q = \frac{24p - 87}{2}$$

Example 4

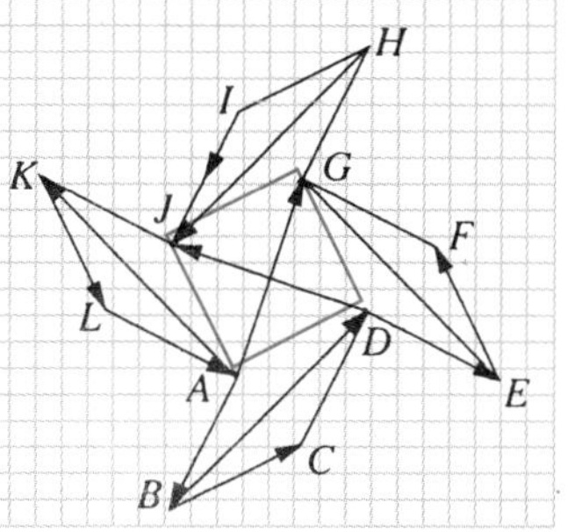

Fig. 3.11

The figure consists of a square and four identical rhombuses.

(a) (i) Explain why $\overrightarrow{AB} = \overrightarrow{IJ}$.

(ii) Name two other vectors that are equal to $\overrightarrow{AB}$.

(b) Name all the vectors that are equal to

(i) $\overrightarrow{KL}$, *(ii)* $\overrightarrow{DE}$,

(iii) $\overrightarrow{BC}$, *(iv)* $\overrightarrow{AK}$.

(c) Give a reason why $\overrightarrow{AG} \neq \overrightarrow{DJ}$.

(d) The line segments BD and HJ have the same length and are parallel. Explain why $\overrightarrow{BD} \neq \overrightarrow{HJ}$.

(e) Give a vector that has the same magnitude but opposite direction to

(i) $\overrightarrow{BC}$, *(ii)* $\overrightarrow{EF}$, *(iii)* $\overrightarrow{LA}$.

(a) (i) $\overrightarrow{AB} = \overrightarrow{IJ}$ because $AB = IJ$ and $\overrightarrow{AB}$ and $\overrightarrow{IJ}$ are in the same direction.

(ii) $\overrightarrow{DC}$ and $\overrightarrow{HG}$ are equal to $\overrightarrow{AB}$.

(b) (i) $\overrightarrow{KL} = \overrightarrow{JA} = \overrightarrow{GD} = \overrightarrow{FE}$

(ii) $\overrightarrow{DE} = \overrightarrow{GF} = \overrightarrow{KJ} = \overrightarrow{LA}$

(iii) $\overrightarrow{BC} = \overrightarrow{AD} = \overrightarrow{JG} = \overrightarrow{IH}$

(iv) $\overrightarrow{AK} = \overrightarrow{EG}$

(c) $\overrightarrow{AG}$ and $\overrightarrow{DJ}$ are in different directions.

(d) $\overrightarrow{BD}$ and $\overrightarrow{HJ}$ are in *opposite* directions.

(e) (i) $\overrightarrow{DA}$ (ii) $\overrightarrow{GD}$ (iii) $\overrightarrow{ED}$

In (d), DO NOT say the two vectors are not parallel. In fact, they are parallel but are in different directions.

Example 5

ABCD is a parallelogram. Given that $\overrightarrow{AB} = \begin{pmatrix} 7 \\ 0 \end{pmatrix}$ *and* $\overrightarrow{BC} = \begin{pmatrix} -3 \\ 4 \end{pmatrix}$,

(a) find the value of $|\overrightarrow{AB}|$,

(b) express each of the following as a column vector:

(i) $\overrightarrow{DC}$, *(ii)* $\overrightarrow{DA}$.

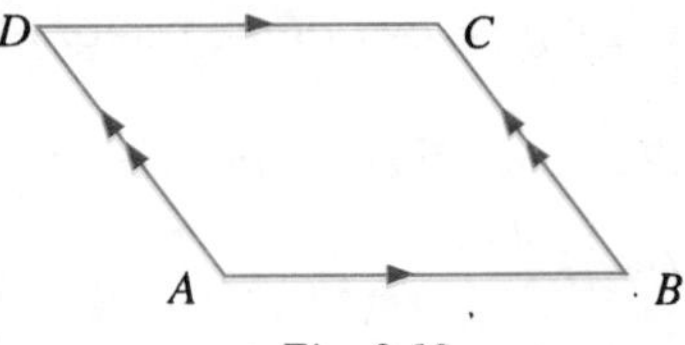

Fig. 3.12

(a) $|\overrightarrow{AB}| = 7$ units

(b) (i) $\overrightarrow{DC} = \overrightarrow{AB} = \begin{pmatrix} 7 \\ 0 \end{pmatrix}$ (ii) $\overrightarrow{DA} = \overrightarrow{CB} = -\overrightarrow{BC}$

$$= -\begin{pmatrix} -3 \\ 4 \end{pmatrix} = \begin{pmatrix} 3 \\ -4 \end{pmatrix}$$

1. Write down the column vectors represented by $\overrightarrow{AB}$, $\overrightarrow{BA}$, $\overrightarrow{CD}$, $\overrightarrow{DC}$, $\overrightarrow{EF}$ and $\overrightarrow{FE}$.

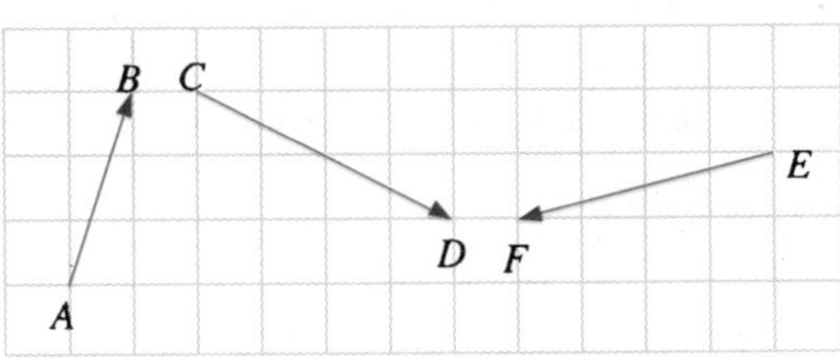

Fig. 3.13

2. Write down the vectors which are equal. In each case, express the equal vectors as a column vector.

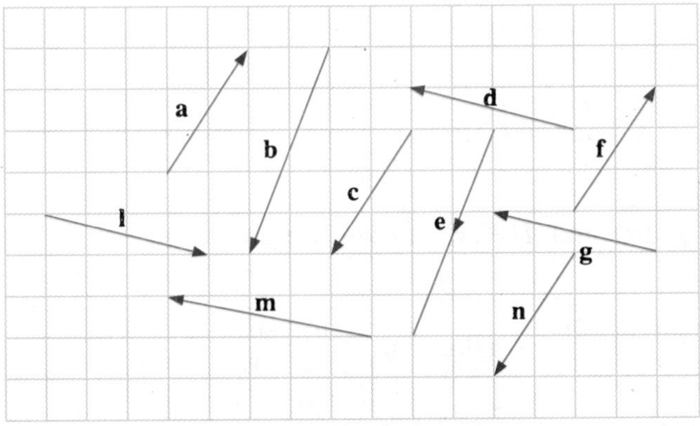

Fig. 3.14

3. Write down the *negatives* of the vectors:

(a) $\begin{pmatrix} 4 \\ 3 \end{pmatrix}$ **(b)** $\begin{pmatrix} -2 \\ 5 \end{pmatrix}$ **(c)** $\begin{pmatrix} 7 \\ -9 \end{pmatrix}$ **(d)** $\begin{pmatrix} -1 \\ -3 \end{pmatrix}$ **(e)** $\begin{pmatrix} p \\ q \end{pmatrix}$

4. On a sheet of squared or graph paper, draw representations of the vectors:

(a) $\begin{pmatrix} 3 \\ 4 \end{pmatrix}$ **(b)** $\begin{pmatrix} -2 \\ 5 \end{pmatrix}$ **(c)** $\begin{pmatrix} -1 \\ -2 \end{pmatrix}$ **(d)** $\begin{pmatrix} 0 \\ 3 \end{pmatrix}$ **(e)** $\begin{pmatrix} -3 \\ 0 \end{pmatrix}$

5. Find the magnitude of each of the following vectors, leaving the answer in square root form where necessary.

(a) $\begin{pmatrix} 5 \\ -12 \end{pmatrix}$ **(b)** $\begin{pmatrix} -6 \\ 8 \end{pmatrix}$ **(c)** $\begin{pmatrix} 5 \\ 2 \end{pmatrix}$ **(d)** $\begin{pmatrix} -7 \\ -1 \end{pmatrix}$ **(e)** $\begin{pmatrix} 0 \\ -3 \end{pmatrix}$

6. Given that $\overrightarrow{XY} = \begin{pmatrix} p \\ -2 \end{pmatrix}$, find the possible values of p such that $|\overrightarrow{XY}| = 5$ units.

7. Given that $\overrightarrow{AB} = \begin{pmatrix} -5 \\ 0 \end{pmatrix}$ and $\overrightarrow{PQ} = \begin{pmatrix} t \\ -3 \end{pmatrix}$, find

(a) $|\overrightarrow{AB}|$,

(b) two possible values of t if $|\overrightarrow{AB}| = |\overrightarrow{PQ}|$.

8. Given that $\mathbf{a} = \begin{pmatrix} 12 \\ 5 \end{pmatrix}$ and $\mathbf{b} = \begin{pmatrix} s \\ 0 \end{pmatrix}$, where s is positive, find the value of s such that $|\mathbf{a}| = |\mathbf{b}|$.

9. Given that $\overrightarrow{AB} = \begin{pmatrix} -4 \\ 2 \end{pmatrix}$ and $\overrightarrow{CD} = \begin{pmatrix} p \\ -12 \end{pmatrix}$, find

(a) $|\overrightarrow{AB}|$,

(b) the positive value of p if $|\overrightarrow{CD}| = 3|\overrightarrow{AB}|$.

10. Given that $\overrightarrow{PQ} = \begin{pmatrix} 13 \\ 0 \end{pmatrix}$ and $\overrightarrow{RS} = \begin{pmatrix} -5 \\ 12 \end{pmatrix}$, show that $|\overrightarrow{PQ}| = |\overrightarrow{RS}|$. Explain why $\overrightarrow{PQ} \neq \overrightarrow{RS}$ although $|\overrightarrow{PQ}| = |\overrightarrow{RS}|$.

11. If $\mathbf{u} = \begin{pmatrix} 5 \\ s \end{pmatrix}$, $\mathbf{v} = \begin{pmatrix} s - 2t \\ -3 \end{pmatrix}$ and $\mathbf{u} = \mathbf{v}$, find the values of s and t.

12. If $\mathbf{a} = \begin{pmatrix} p + q \\ p \end{pmatrix}$, $\mathbf{b} = \begin{pmatrix} 3 \\ q + 1 \end{pmatrix}$ and $\mathbf{a} = \mathbf{b}$, find the values of p and q.

13. **(a)** Name all the vectors in Fig. 3.15 that are equal to:

(i) $\overrightarrow{IJ}$ **(ii)** $\overrightarrow{AJ}$

(iii) $\overrightarrow{HI}$ **(iv)** $\overrightarrow{BC}$

(v) $\overrightarrow{AK}$ **(vi)** $\overrightarrow{LB}$

(b) Name a negative vector of

(i) $\overrightarrow{JH}$;   **(ii)** $\overrightarrow{AB}$;

(iii) $\overrightarrow{AJ}$.

(c) Explain why

(i) $\overrightarrow{AB} \neq \overrightarrow{DE}$;   **(ii)** $\overrightarrow{AK} \neq \overrightarrow{AB}$.

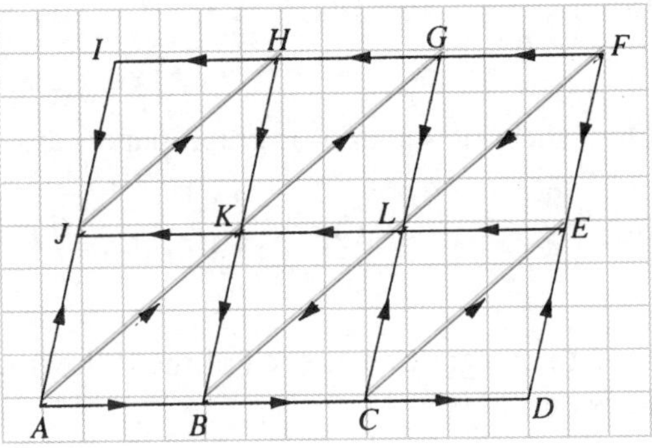
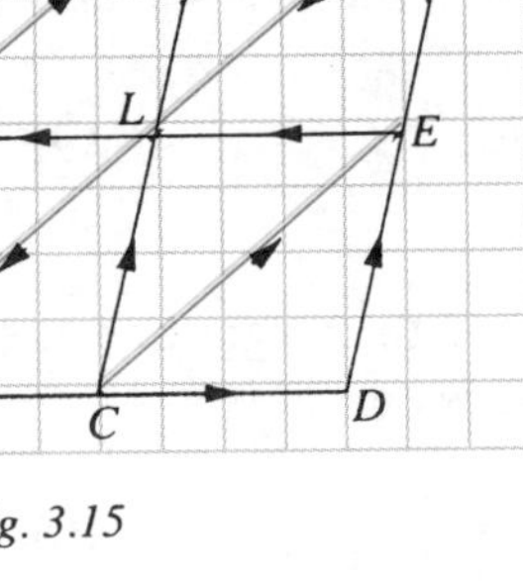

Fig. 3.15

14. Copy and complete the equalities below in each of the diagrams **(a)** – **(d)**. The first equality in **(a)** and **(b)** have been done for you.

(a)

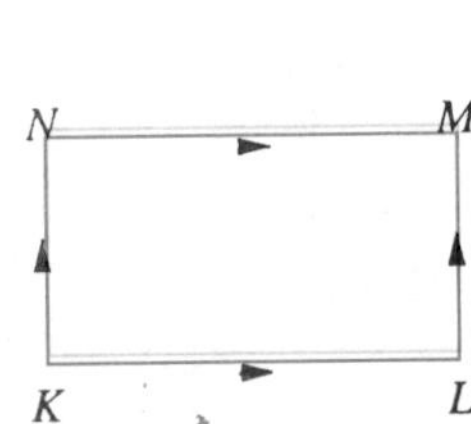

Fig. 3.16a

(b)

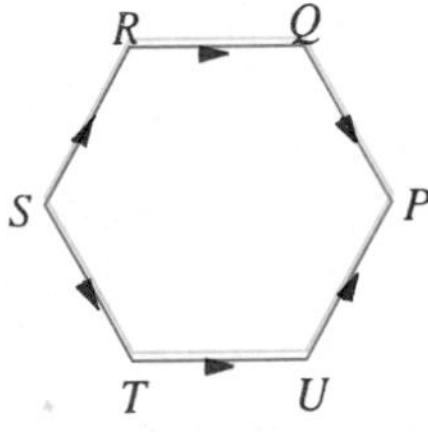

Fig. 3.16b

(c)

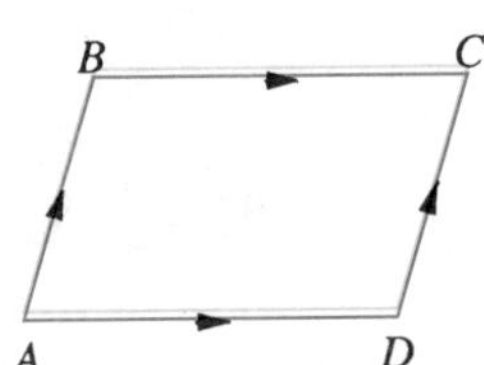

Fig. 3.16c

(d)

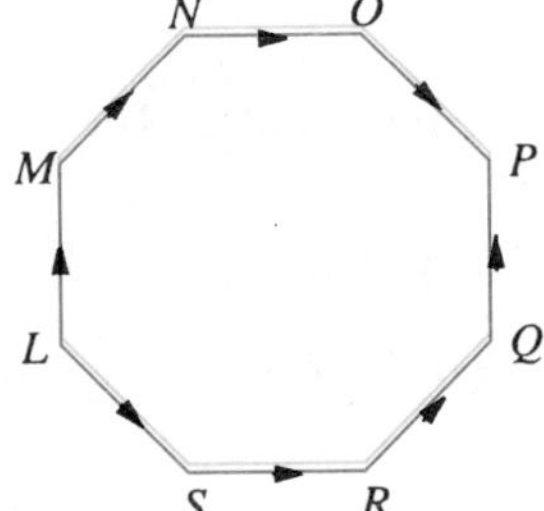

Fig. 3.16d

(a) $\overrightarrow{KN} = \overrightarrow{LM}$

$\overrightarrow{NM} =$

(b) $\overrightarrow{SR} = \overrightarrow{UP}$

$\overrightarrow{RQ} =$

$\overrightarrow{QP} =$

(c) $\overrightarrow{AB} =$

$\overrightarrow{BC} =$

(d) $\overrightarrow{LM} =$

$\overrightarrow{MN} =$

$\overrightarrow{NO} =$

$\overrightarrow{OP} =$

15. Fig. 3.17 shows the positions of the points P, A and B where $\overrightarrow{AB} = \begin{pmatrix} 3 \\ 1 \end{pmatrix}$.

(a) Express $\overrightarrow{PB}$ as a column vector.

(b) Q is a point such that $ABQP$ is a parallelogram. Express $\overrightarrow{BQ}$ as a column vector.

(c) R is a point such that $ABPR$ is a parallelogram. Express $\overrightarrow{PR}$ as a column vector.

(d) Do the two vectors $\overrightarrow{PQ}$ and $\overrightarrow{PR}$ have the same magnitude? Is $\overrightarrow{PQ} = \overrightarrow{PR}$? Why or why not?

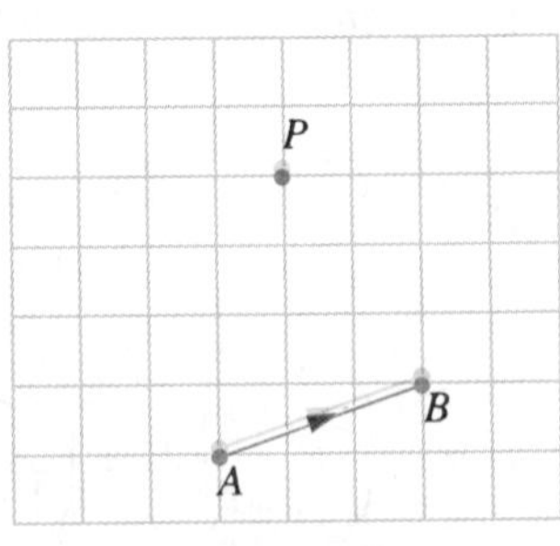

Fig. 3.17

Addition of Vectors

Fig. 3.18 shows the translation of a point, from P to Q, followed by another translation from Q to R.

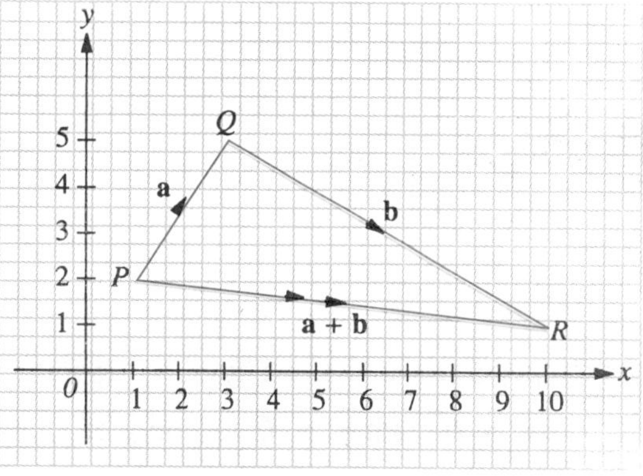

Fig. 3.18

The first translation is described by the vector

$$\overrightarrow{PQ} = \mathbf{a} = \begin{pmatrix} 2 \\ 3 \end{pmatrix}$$

and the second translation is described by the vector

$$\overrightarrow{QR} = \mathbf{b} = \begin{pmatrix} 7 \\ -4 \end{pmatrix}$$

Is there a single translation that will move the point from P to R directly? In Fig. 3.18, the translation of the body from P to R directly is described by the vector $\overrightarrow{PR}$.

We write algebraically:

$$\overrightarrow{PQ} + \overrightarrow{QR} = \overrightarrow{PR} \quad \text{or} \quad \overrightarrow{PR} = \mathbf{a} + \mathbf{b}.$$

start — P of $\overrightarrow{PQ}$; end — R of $\overrightarrow{PR}$; end (Q of $\overrightarrow{PQ}$) and start (Q of $\overrightarrow{QR}$):

must be the same point for addition of vectors

In column vector form, we write

$$\overrightarrow{PQ} + \overrightarrow{QR} = \begin{pmatrix} 2 \\ 3 \end{pmatrix} + \begin{pmatrix} 7 \\ -4 \end{pmatrix} = \begin{pmatrix} 9 \\ -1 \end{pmatrix} = \overrightarrow{PR}.$$

Thus, the vector $\overrightarrow{PR}$ can be written as the *sum* of the two vectors $\overrightarrow{PQ}$ and $\overrightarrow{QR}$, i.e.

$$\overrightarrow{PR} = \overrightarrow{PQ} + \overrightarrow{QR}$$

start — P of $\overrightarrow{PR}$; end — R of $\overrightarrow{PR}$; start — P of $\overrightarrow{PQ}$; end (Q of $\overrightarrow{PQ}$) and start (Q of $\overrightarrow{QR}$); end — R of $\overrightarrow{QR}$

must be the same point for addition of vectors

xample 6

Find the sum of the two given vectors **a** *and* **b**.

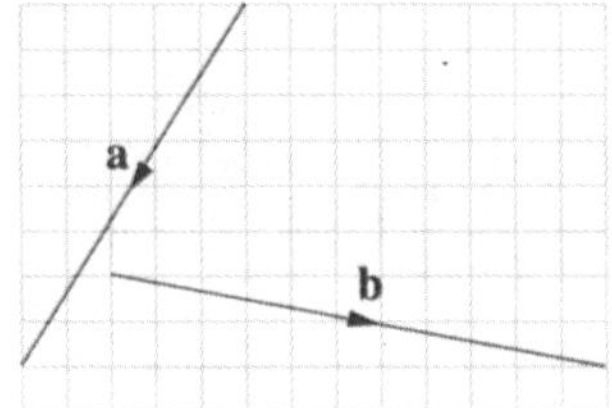

Fig. 3.19

Method 1

Copy the vector $\overrightarrow{AB} = \mathbf{a}$ on a sheet of squared or graph paper. From the end point B, draw the vector $\overrightarrow{BC} = \mathbf{b}$. Join A to C to complete the triangle. Insert a double arrow which points from A to C. $\overrightarrow{AC}$ represents the sum of **a** and **b**, i.e. $\overrightarrow{AC} = \mathbf{a} + \mathbf{b}$. This process is called the **Triangle Law of Vector Addition**.

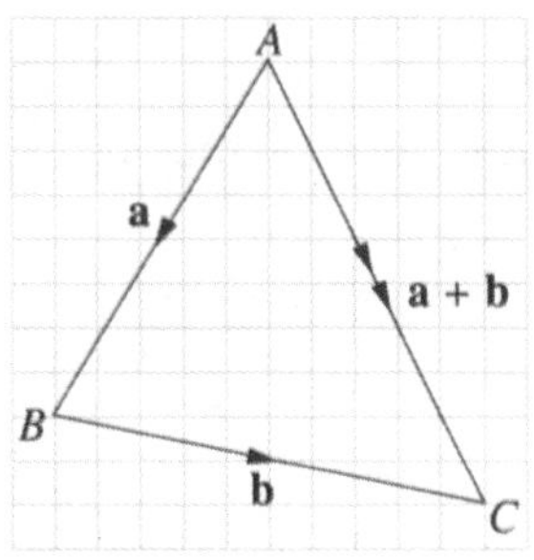

Fig. 3.19(a)

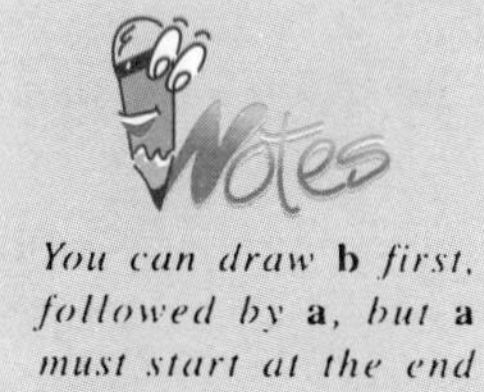

You can draw **b** *first, followed by* **a**, *but* **a** *must start at the end point of* **b**.

Method 2

Copy the vector $\overrightarrow{AB} = \mathbf{a}$. From the starting point A, draw the vector $\overrightarrow{AD} = \mathbf{b}$. Complete the parallelogram $ABCD$ and then draw the diagonal AC. Draw in a double arrow which points away from A to C. $\overrightarrow{AC}$ represents the sum of **a** and **b**. i.e. $\overrightarrow{AC} = \mathbf{a} + \mathbf{b}$. This process is called the **Parallelogram Law of Vector Addition**.

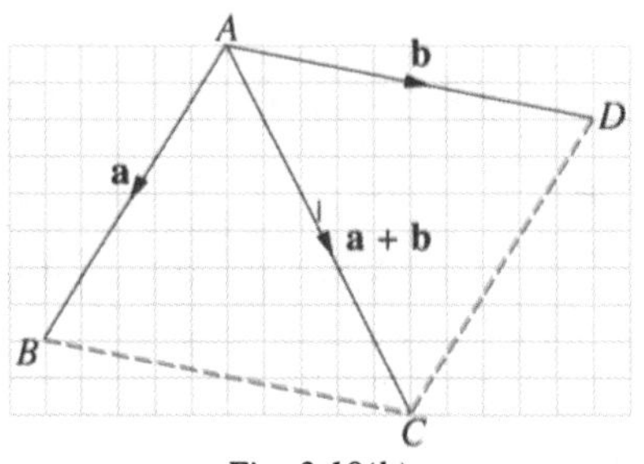

Fig. 3.19(b)

In practice, it is easier to use the Triangle Law of Vector Addition. However, if the question has already drawn a parallelogram, it may be easier to just use the Parallelogram Law of Vector Addition.

Both methods give the same vector $\overrightarrow{AC} = \mathbf{a} + \mathbf{b}$.

The difference is how you draw the two vectors **a** and **b**:

For the *Triangle Law of Vector Addition*, you must draw the second vector **b** after the first vector **a**, i.e. where the first vector **a** *ends*, the second vector **b** *starts*.

For the *Parallelogram Law of Vector Addition*, you must draw both vectors **a** and **b** from the *same starting point*. Notice that the vector **a** + **b** also have the same starting point.

Example 7

Copy on a sheet of squared or graph paper the directed line segments $\overrightarrow{PQ}$, $\overrightarrow{RS}$ *and* $\overrightarrow{VW}$ *shown in Fig. 3.20 to represent* **u**, **v** *and* **s** *respectively. Find the sum of the following vectors using graphical method:*

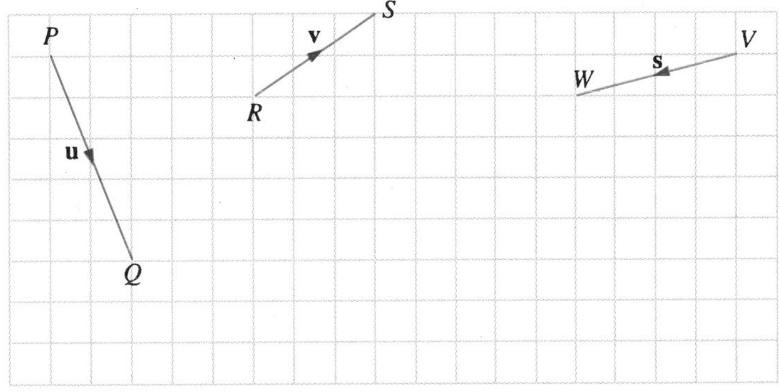

Fig. 3.20

(a) the two vectors **u** *and* **v**;

(b) the two vectors **u** *and* **s**.

In each case, write the vector sum in column vector form.

(a) $\overrightarrow{XZ} = \mathbf{u} + \mathbf{v} = \begin{pmatrix} 5 \\ -3 \end{pmatrix}$

(b) $\overrightarrow{LN} = \mathbf{u} + \mathbf{s} = \begin{pmatrix} -2 \\ -6 \end{pmatrix}$

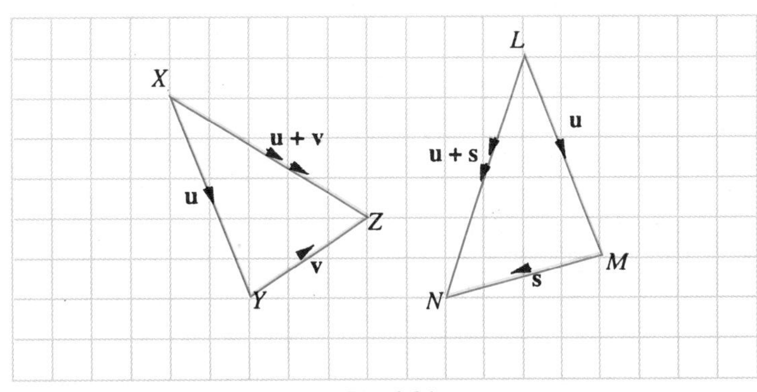

Fig. 3.21

From Fig. 3.20, since $\mathbf{u} = \begin{pmatrix} 2 \\ -5 \end{pmatrix}$, $\mathbf{v} = \begin{pmatrix} 3 \\ 2 \end{pmatrix}$ and $\mathbf{s} = \begin{pmatrix} -4 \\ -1 \end{pmatrix}$, then

$\mathbf{u} + \mathbf{v} = \begin{pmatrix} 2 \\ -5 \end{pmatrix} + \begin{pmatrix} 3 \\ 2 \end{pmatrix} = \begin{pmatrix} 5 \\ -3 \end{pmatrix}$, and $\mathbf{u} + \mathbf{s} = \begin{pmatrix} 2 \\ -5 \end{pmatrix} + \begin{pmatrix} -4 \\ -1 \end{pmatrix} = \begin{pmatrix} -2 \\ -6 \end{pmatrix}$.

In general, for any two column vectors $\mathbf{a} = \begin{pmatrix} p \\ q \end{pmatrix}$ **and** $\mathbf{b} = \begin{pmatrix} r \\ s \end{pmatrix}$, $\mathbf{a} + \mathbf{b} = \begin{pmatrix} p \\ q \end{pmatrix} + \begin{pmatrix} r \\ s \end{pmatrix} = \begin{pmatrix} p + r \\ q + s \end{pmatrix}$.

xample 8

Illustrate graphically the following vector sums using the vectors given in Fig. 3.22:

(a) **a** + **b** *(b)* **b** + **a**

(c) (**a** + **b**) + **c** *(d)* **a** + (**b** + **c**)

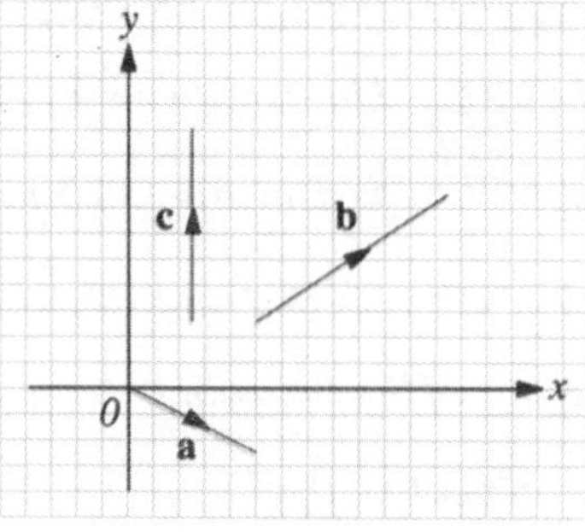

Fig. 3.22

(a)

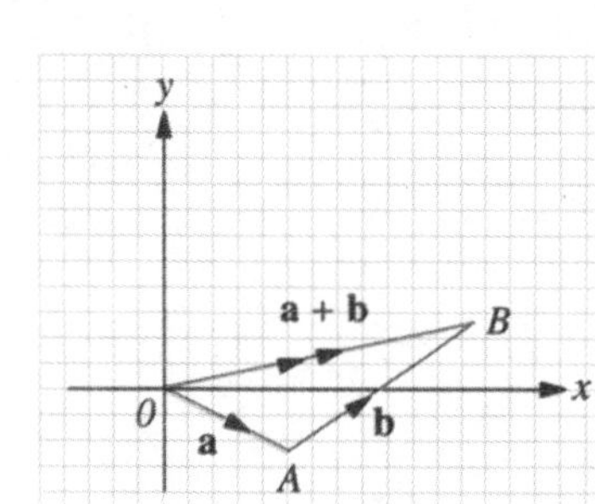

(b)

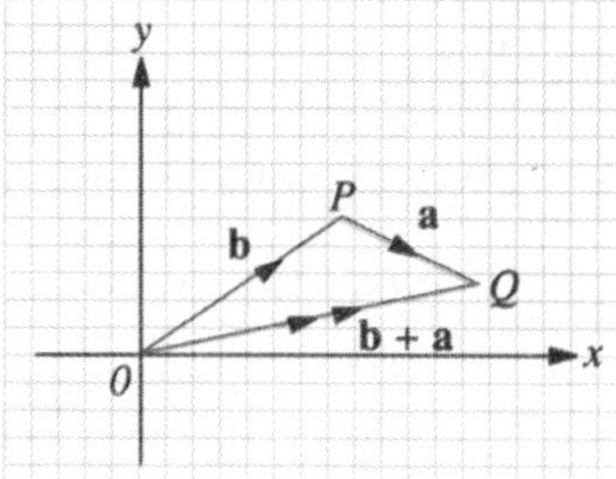

(c)

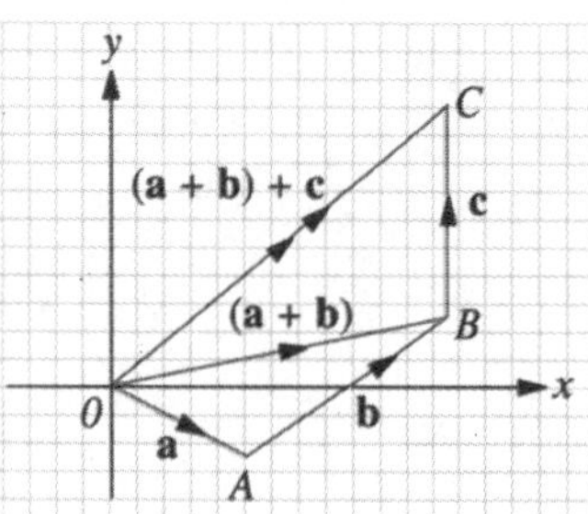

(d)

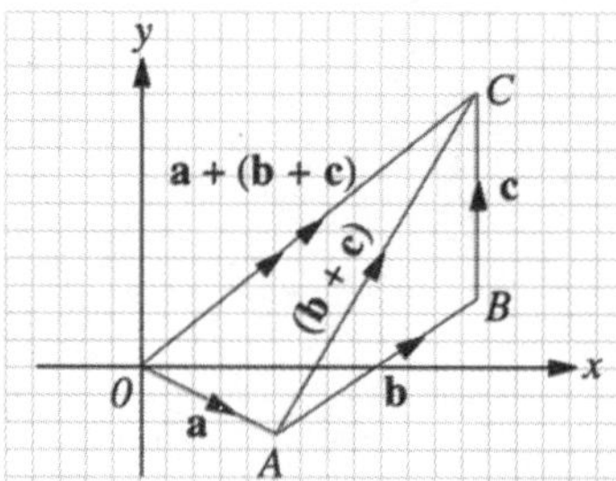

From part (a) and (b), we have

$$\mathbf{a} + \mathbf{b} = \mathbf{b} + \mathbf{a} \quad \text{or} \quad \begin{pmatrix} 2 \\ -1 \end{pmatrix} + \begin{pmatrix} 3 \\ 2 \end{pmatrix} = \begin{pmatrix} 3 \\ 2 \end{pmatrix} + \begin{pmatrix} 2 \\ -1 \end{pmatrix} = \begin{pmatrix} 5 \\ 1 \end{pmatrix}$$

and we say that vector addition is **commutative**.

From part (c) and (d), we have

$$(\mathbf{a} + \mathbf{b}) + \mathbf{c} = \mathbf{a} + (\mathbf{b} + \mathbf{c}) \quad \text{or} \quad \left[\begin{pmatrix} 2 \\ -1 \end{pmatrix} + \begin{pmatrix} 3 \\ 2 \end{pmatrix}\right] + \begin{pmatrix} 0 \\ 3 \end{pmatrix} = \begin{pmatrix} 2 \\ -1 \end{pmatrix} + \left[\begin{pmatrix} 3 \\ 2 \end{pmatrix} + \begin{pmatrix} 0 \\ 3 \end{pmatrix}\right] = \begin{pmatrix} 5 \\ 4 \end{pmatrix}$$

and we say that vector addition is **associative**.

Example 9

ABCD is a quadrilateral. Simplify

(a) $\overrightarrow{AB} + \overrightarrow{BC}$,

(b) $\overrightarrow{AD} + \overrightarrow{DB}$,

(c) $\overrightarrow{AC} + \overrightarrow{CB} + \overrightarrow{BD}$.

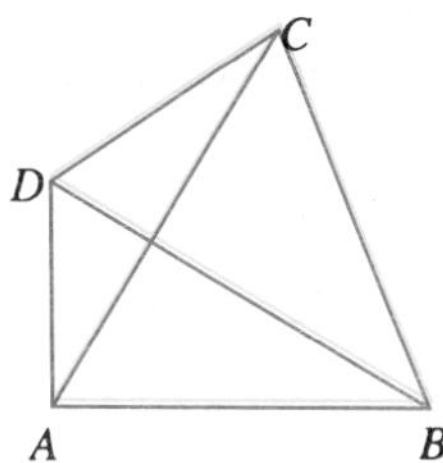

Fig. 3.23

(a) $\overrightarrow{AB} + \overrightarrow{BC} = \overrightarrow{AC}$ (Triangle Law)

(b) $\overrightarrow{AD} + \overrightarrow{DB} = \overrightarrow{AB}$ (Triangle Law)

(c) $\overrightarrow{AC} + \overrightarrow{CB} + \overrightarrow{BD}$

$= (\overrightarrow{AC} + \overrightarrow{CB}) + \overrightarrow{BD}$ (Associative Law)

$= \overrightarrow{AB} + \overrightarrow{BD}$ (Triangle Law)

$= \overrightarrow{AD}$ (Triangle Law)

The principle of adding two vectors can be extended to any number of vectors.

In the figure below,

$\overrightarrow{AB} + \overrightarrow{BC} + \overrightarrow{CD}$ *or*

$\begin{pmatrix} 0 \\ 3 \end{pmatrix} + \begin{pmatrix} 5 \\ 1 \end{pmatrix} + \begin{pmatrix} -2 \\ -5 \end{pmatrix} = \begin{pmatrix} 3 \\ -1 \end{pmatrix}$

$= \overrightarrow{AD}$

i.e. $\overrightarrow{AD}$ is the result of the addition of all three vectors.

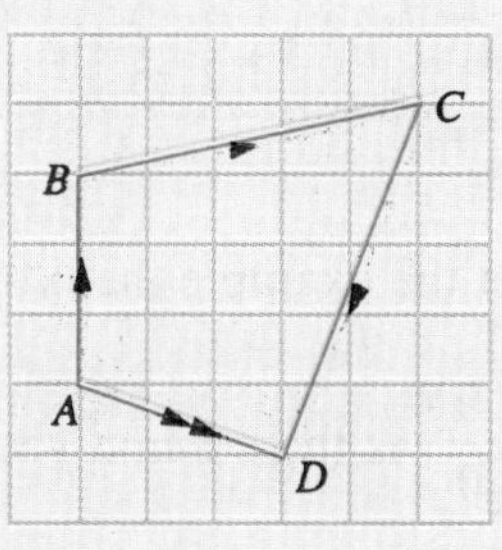

Zero Vectors

In Fig. 3.5, the two vectors $\overrightarrow{PQ}$ and $\overrightarrow{QP}$ represent the journey of a ship from P to Q, followed by the return journey from Q to P. The result of the whole journey is a zero displacement of the ship from P. Thus

$$\overrightarrow{PQ} + \overrightarrow{QP} = \mathbf{0}.$$

0 is called the **zero** vector.

Simplify the following:

(a) $\begin{pmatrix} 5 \\ -2 \end{pmatrix} + \begin{pmatrix} -5 \\ 2 \end{pmatrix}$ *(b)* $\begin{pmatrix} 3 \\ 1 \end{pmatrix} + \begin{pmatrix} -3 \\ -1 \end{pmatrix}$ *(c)* $\begin{pmatrix} 2 \\ 3 \end{pmatrix} + \begin{pmatrix} -2 \\ -3 \end{pmatrix}$

(a) $\begin{pmatrix} 5 \\ -2 \end{pmatrix} + \begin{pmatrix} -5 \\ 2 \end{pmatrix} = \begin{pmatrix} 0 \\ 0 \end{pmatrix}$ (b) $\begin{pmatrix} 3 \\ 1 \end{pmatrix} + \begin{pmatrix} -3 \\ -1 \end{pmatrix} = \begin{pmatrix} 0 \\ 0 \end{pmatrix}$ (c) $\begin{pmatrix} 2 \\ 3 \end{pmatrix} + \begin{pmatrix} -2 \\ -3 \end{pmatrix} = \begin{pmatrix} 0 \\ 0 \end{pmatrix}$

In the example that you have just seen,

$\begin{pmatrix} 0 \\ 0 \end{pmatrix}$ is the column vector form of the **zero** vector **0**.

$\begin{pmatrix} -5 \\ 2 \end{pmatrix}$, $\begin{pmatrix} -3 \\ -1 \end{pmatrix}$ and $\begin{pmatrix} -2 \\ -3 \end{pmatrix}$ are *negatives* of $\begin{pmatrix} 5 \\ -2 \end{pmatrix}$, $\begin{pmatrix} 3 \\ 1 \end{pmatrix}$ and $\begin{pmatrix} 2 \\ 3 \end{pmatrix}$ respectively.

In general, for any vector **a**, there is always a vector **–a** that is equal in magnitude but opposite in direction such that

$$\mathbf{a} + (-\mathbf{a}) = \mathbf{0} = (-\mathbf{a}) + \mathbf{a}.$$

Subtraction of Vectors

The difference of two vectors **a** and **b**, denoted by **a** – **b**, is the sum of **a** and –**b**, i.e.

$$\mathbf{a} - \mathbf{b} = \mathbf{a} + (-\mathbf{b}).$$

Example 11

Fig. 3.24 shows two given vectors **a** *and* **b**. *Find* **a** – **b** *using graphical method.*

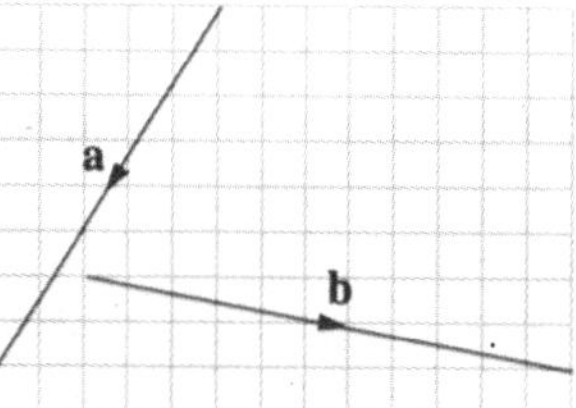

Fig. 3.24

Method 1: a – b = a + (– b)

Copy the vector $\overrightarrow{AB} = \mathbf{b}$ on a sheet of squared or graph paper. From the end point B, draw the vector $\overrightarrow{BC} = -\mathbf{b}$. Join A to C to complete the triangle. Insert a double arrow which points from A to C. Then

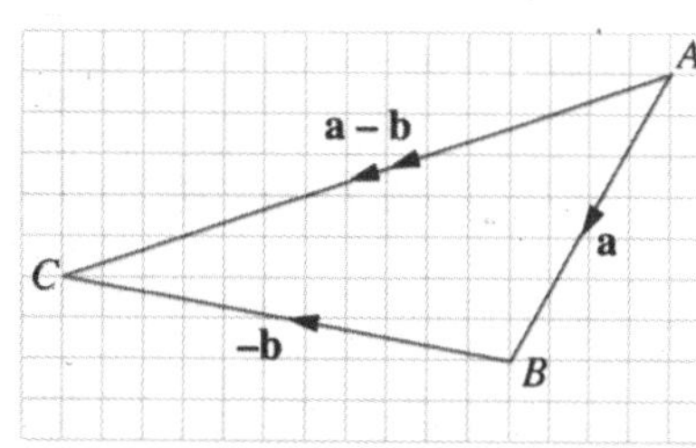

Fig. 3.24(a)

$$\overrightarrow{AC} = \mathbf{a} + (-\mathbf{b}) = \mathbf{a} - \mathbf{b}.$$

Method 2: Triangle Law of Vector Subtraction

Copy the vector $\overrightarrow{AB} = \mathbf{a}$ on a sheet of squared or graph paper. From the starting point A, draw the vector triangle. Insert a double arrow which points from C to B. Then

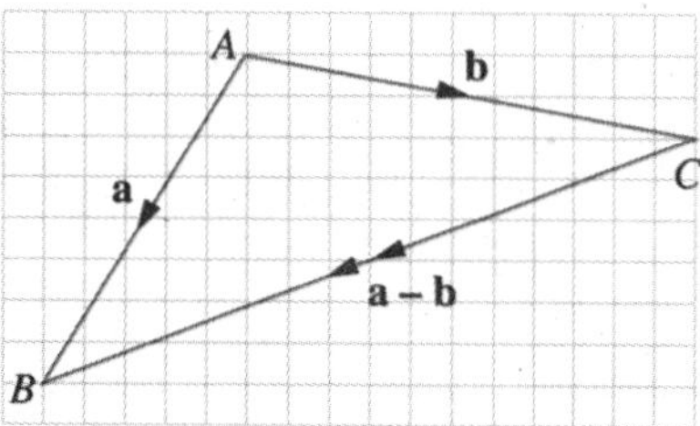

Fig. 3.24(b)

Notes

In most questions with diagrams, the diagram will look like Fig. 3.24(b). So you must learn how to use Method 2 to obtain **a – b** *fast. Moreover, you can get the vector* **b – a** *directly from Fig. 3.24(b) but not from Fig. 3.24(a) (see Fig. 3.24(c)).*

$$\overrightarrow{AC} + \overrightarrow{CB} = \overrightarrow{AB} \text{ (Triangle Law of Vector \textbf{Addition})}$$

$$\mathbf{b} + \overrightarrow{CB} = \mathbf{a}$$

$$\overrightarrow{CB} = \mathbf{a} - \mathbf{b}$$

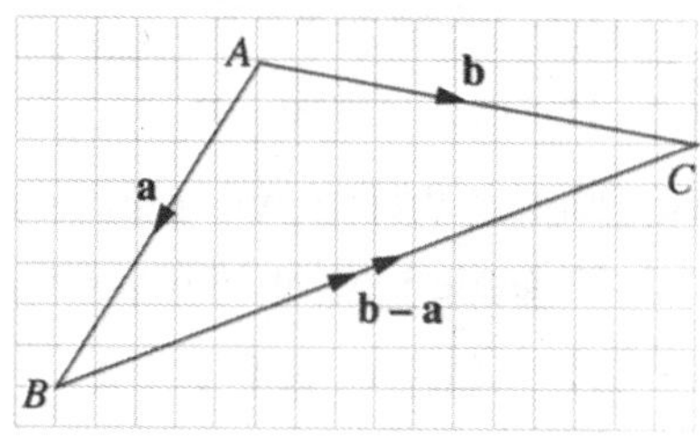

Fig. 3.24(c)

This process is called the **Triangle Law of Vector Subtraction**.

To summarise,

> For the *Triangle Law of Vector Subtraction*, you must draw both vectors **a** and **b** from the *same starting point.*

To determine the direction of **a** – **b** or **b** – **a**, just remember 'end minus start':

(i) **a** – **b**
end start

So the arrow starts from **b** and ends at **a**:

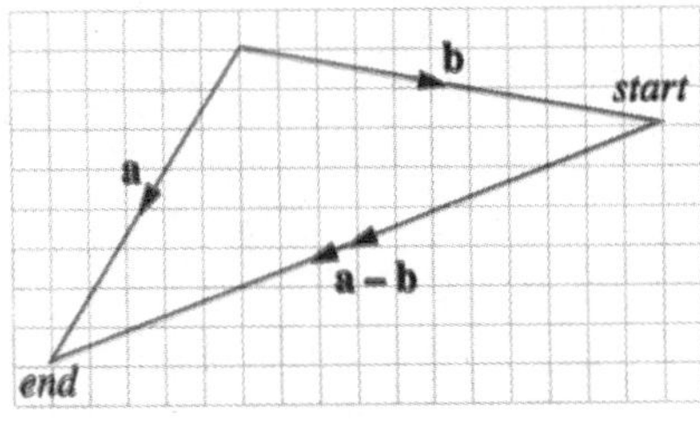

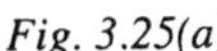
Fig. 3.25(a)

(ii) **b** – **a**
end start

So the arrow starts from **a** and ends at **b**:

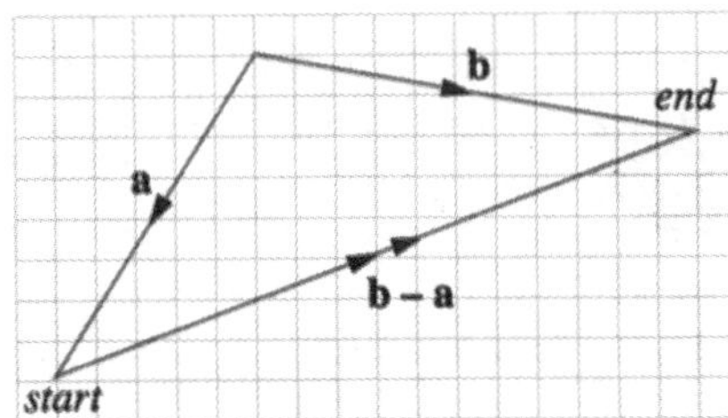

Fig. 3.25(b)

Example 12

Find the vector that is represented by the double arrow in each of the diagrams below:

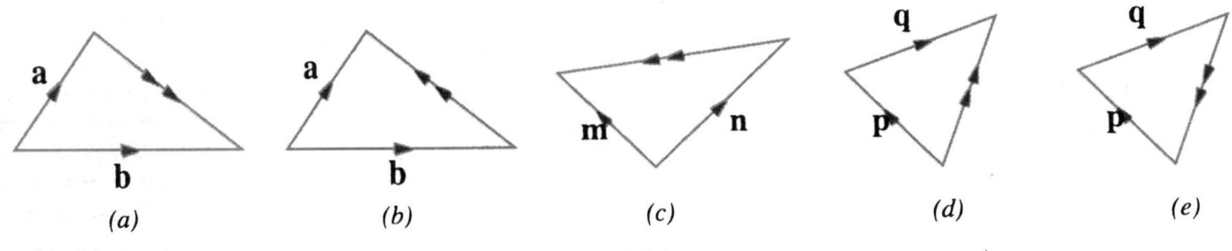

Fig. 3.26

(a) The vector is **b** – **a**
end start

(b) The vector is **a** – **b**

(c) The vector is **m** – **n**

(d) Notice that **p** and **q** do **not** start from the same point but **q** starts where **p** ends. So this is the Triangle Law of Vector **Addition**.

$\therefore$ the vector is **p** + **q**

(e) The vector is –(**p** + **q**) = – **p** – **q**

Example 13

OACB is a parallelogram where $\overrightarrow{OA} = \mathbf{a}$ *and* $\overrightarrow{OB} = \mathbf{b}$.

Express the following vectors in terms of **a** *and* **b**.

(a) $\overrightarrow{BC}$ *(b)* $\overrightarrow{OC}$ *(c)* $\overrightarrow{AB}$ *(d)* $\overrightarrow{BA}$

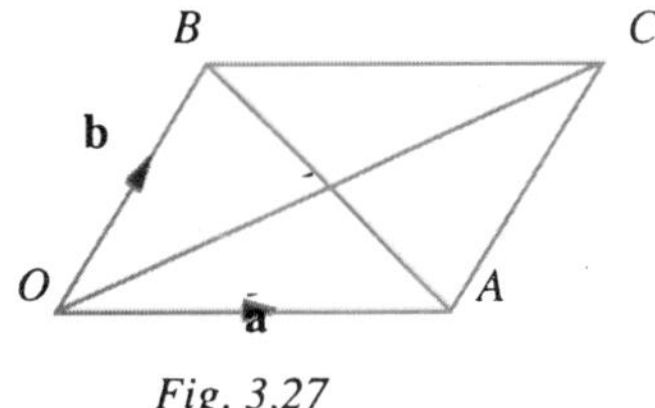

Fig. 3.27

(a) $\overrightarrow{BC} = \overrightarrow{OA} = \mathbf{a}$

(b) $\overrightarrow{OC} = \mathbf{a} + \mathbf{b}$ (Parallelogram Law of Vector Addition)

or $\overrightarrow{OC} = \overrightarrow{OB} + \overrightarrow{BC} = \mathbf{a} + \mathbf{b}$ (Triangle Law of Vector Addition)

(c) $\overrightarrow{AB} = \mathbf{b} - \mathbf{a}$ (Triangle Law of Vector Subtraction)

$\overrightarrow{BA} = \mathbf{a} - \mathbf{b}$ (Triangle Law of Vector Subtraction)

Notice that $\overrightarrow{OC}$ *and* $\overrightarrow{AB}$ *are diagonals of the parallelogram. One diagonal represents vector addition,* $\mathbf{a} + \mathbf{b}$*, and the other diagonal represents vector subtraction,* $\mathbf{a} - \mathbf{b}$ *or* $\mathbf{b} - \mathbf{a}$*, depending on which direction.*

For addition of vectors, we have seen on page 86 that:

$$\overrightarrow{PQ} + \overrightarrow{QR} = \overrightarrow{PR}$$

start, end, start, end, start, end

must be the same

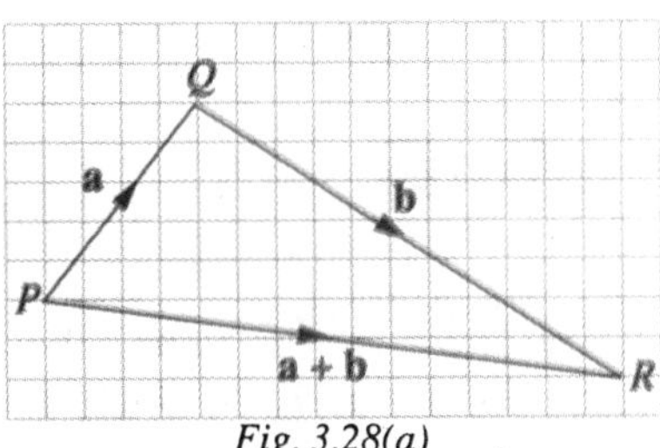

Fig. 3.28(a)

For subtraction of vectors, we have seen on page 92 that:

$$\overrightarrow{CB} = \mathbf{a} - \mathbf{b} = \overrightarrow{AB} - \overrightarrow{AC}.$$

So $\overrightarrow{AB} - \overrightarrow{AC} = \overrightarrow{CB}$

end, start, start, end

must be the same

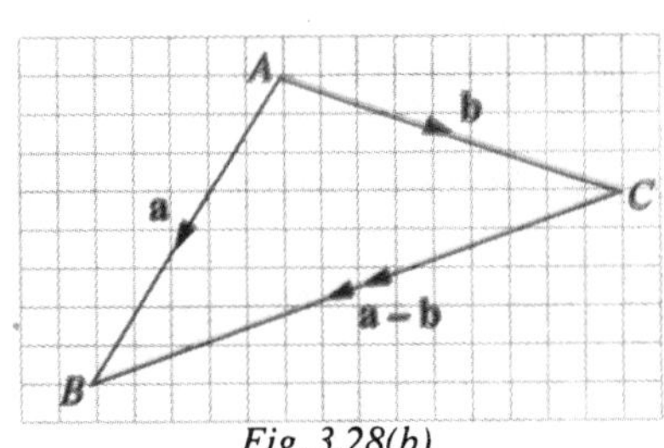

Fig. 3.28(b)

Notice it still has the same idea of 'end minus start'.

Simplify the following if possible.

(a) $\overrightarrow{PR} + \overrightarrow{RQ}$ *(b)* $\overrightarrow{PQ} - \overrightarrow{PR}$

(c) $\overrightarrow{PR} - \overrightarrow{PQ}$ *(d)* $\overrightarrow{PQ} - \overrightarrow{QR}$

(a) $\overrightarrow{PR} + \overrightarrow{RQ} = \overrightarrow{PQ}$

Check these are the same

(b) $\overrightarrow{PQ} - \overrightarrow{PR} = \overrightarrow{RQ}$ (start at R)

end start start end

Check these are the same

or $\overrightarrow{PQ} - \overrightarrow{PR} = \overrightarrow{PQ} + \overrightarrow{RP} = \overrightarrow{RP} + \overrightarrow{PQ} = \overrightarrow{RQ}$

(c) $\overrightarrow{PR} - \overrightarrow{PQ} = \overrightarrow{QR}$ (start at Q)

end start

(d) $\overrightarrow{PQ} - \overrightarrow{QR}$

These are the same. This is not addition, so we cannot simplify this further using P, Q and R.

In the diagram, PQTS is a quadrilateral and PQRS is a parallelogram.

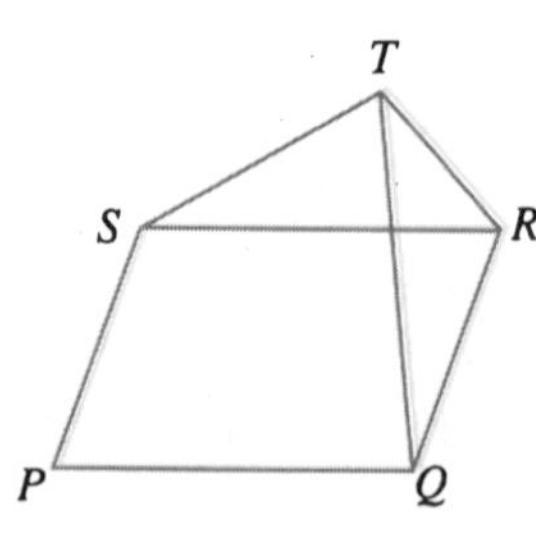

Fig. 3.29

(a) Simplify the following.

(i) $\overrightarrow{PQ} - \overrightarrow{PS}$ *(ii)* $\overrightarrow{PQ} + \overrightarrow{RS} + \overrightarrow{TR} - \overrightarrow{QR}$

(b) Find a vector which can replace **x** *in each of the following equations.*

$\overrightarrow{SR} + \mathbf{x} = \overrightarrow{ST}$ (ii) $\mathbf{x} - \overrightarrow{QP} = \overrightarrow{SQ}$

Solution

(a) (i) $\overrightarrow{PQ} - \overrightarrow{PS} = \overrightarrow{SQ}$ (Triangle Law of Vector Subtraction)

(ii) $\overrightarrow{PQ} + \overrightarrow{RS} + \overrightarrow{TR} - \overrightarrow{QR} = \overrightarrow{PQ} + \overrightarrow{QP} + \overrightarrow{TR} - \overrightarrow{QR}$ (equal vectors: $\overrightarrow{RS} = \overrightarrow{QP}$)

$= \mathbf{0} + \overrightarrow{TR} - \overrightarrow{QR}$ ($\overrightarrow{PQ} + \overrightarrow{QP} = \mathbf{0}$)

$= \overrightarrow{TR} + \overrightarrow{RQ}$ (opposite vector: $\overrightarrow{RQ} = -\overrightarrow{QR}$)

$= \overrightarrow{TQ}$ (Triangle Law of Vector Addition)

(b) (i) $\overrightarrow{SR} + \mathbf{x} = \overrightarrow{ST}$

$\therefore \quad \mathbf{x} = \overrightarrow{ST} - \overrightarrow{SR} = \overrightarrow{RT}$ (Triangle Law of Vector Subtraction)

(ii) $\mathbf{x} - \overrightarrow{QP} = \overrightarrow{SQ}$

$\therefore \quad \mathbf{x} = \overrightarrow{SQ} + \overrightarrow{QP} = \overrightarrow{SP}$ (Triangle Law of Vector Addition)

In Example 11, $\mathbf{a} = \begin{pmatrix} -5 \\ -8 \end{pmatrix}$ and $\mathbf{b} = \begin{pmatrix} 11 \\ -2 \end{pmatrix}$. Then $-\mathbf{b} = \begin{pmatrix} -11 \\ 2 \end{pmatrix}$.

So $$\mathbf{a} - \mathbf{b} = \mathbf{a} + (-\mathbf{b}) = \begin{pmatrix} -5 \\ -8 \end{pmatrix} + \begin{pmatrix} -11 \\ 2 \end{pmatrix} = \begin{pmatrix} -16 \\ --6 \end{pmatrix}$$

But we can also perform the subtraction directly:

$$\mathbf{a} - \mathbf{b} = \begin{pmatrix} -5 \\ -8 \end{pmatrix} - \begin{pmatrix} 11 \\ -2 \end{pmatrix} = \begin{pmatrix} -5 - 11 \\ -8 - (-2) \end{pmatrix} = \begin{pmatrix} -16 \\ -6 \end{pmatrix}$$

In general,

for any two column vectors, $\mathbf{a} = \begin{pmatrix} p \\ q \end{pmatrix}$ and $\mathbf{b} = \begin{pmatrix} r \\ s \end{pmatrix}$, $\mathbf{a} - \mathbf{b} = \begin{pmatrix} p \\ q \end{pmatrix} - \begin{pmatrix} r \\ s \end{pmatrix} = \begin{pmatrix} p - r \\ q - s \end{pmatrix}$.

Example 16

(a) Simplify $\begin{pmatrix} -4 \\ 6 \end{pmatrix} - \begin{pmatrix} 2 \\ 3 \end{pmatrix} - \begin{pmatrix} -7 \\ 1 \end{pmatrix}$.

(b) If $\mathbf{u} = \begin{pmatrix} 9 \\ 4 \end{pmatrix}$, $\mathbf{v} = \begin{pmatrix} -2 \\ 5 \end{pmatrix}$ *and* $\mathbf{w} = \begin{pmatrix} 3 \\ -1 \end{pmatrix}$, *express* $-\mathbf{u} + \mathbf{v} - \mathbf{w}$ *as a column vector.*

(a) $\begin{pmatrix} -4 \\ 6 \end{pmatrix} - \begin{pmatrix} 2 \\ 3 \end{pmatrix} - \begin{pmatrix} -7 \\ 1 \end{pmatrix} = \begin{pmatrix} -6 \\ 3 \end{pmatrix} - \begin{pmatrix} -7 \\ 1 \end{pmatrix}$

do this first $= \begin{pmatrix} 1 \\ 2 \end{pmatrix}$

or simply $\begin{pmatrix} -4 \\ 6 \end{pmatrix} - \begin{pmatrix} 2 \\ 3 \end{pmatrix} - \begin{pmatrix} -7 \\ 1 \end{pmatrix} = \begin{pmatrix} -4 - 2 - (-7) \\ 6 - 3 - 1 \end{pmatrix}$

$= \begin{pmatrix} 1 \\ 2 \end{pmatrix}$

(b) $-\mathbf{u} + \mathbf{v} - \mathbf{w} = -\begin{pmatrix} 9 \\ 4 \end{pmatrix} + \begin{pmatrix} -2 \\ 5 \end{pmatrix} - \begin{pmatrix} 3 \\ -1 \end{pmatrix}$

$= \begin{pmatrix} -14 \\ 2 \end{pmatrix}$

xample 17

Find the values of x and y in each of the following equations:

(a) $\begin{pmatrix} x \\ y \end{pmatrix} + \begin{pmatrix} 5 \\ -2 \end{pmatrix} = \begin{pmatrix} 2 \\ -3 \end{pmatrix}$

(b) $\begin{pmatrix} 4 \\ y \end{pmatrix} + \begin{pmatrix} x \\ 2 \end{pmatrix} = \begin{pmatrix} 5 \\ x \end{pmatrix}$

(c) $\begin{pmatrix} 2 \\ 3x \end{pmatrix} - \begin{pmatrix} x - 2y \\ -1 \end{pmatrix} = \begin{pmatrix} 3 \\ 10 \end{pmatrix}$

(a) $\begin{pmatrix} x \\ y \end{pmatrix} + \begin{pmatrix} 5 \\ -2 \end{pmatrix} = \begin{pmatrix} 2 \\ -3 \end{pmatrix}$

$$\begin{pmatrix} x \\ y \end{pmatrix} = \begin{pmatrix} 2 \\ -3 \end{pmatrix} - \begin{pmatrix} 5 \\ -2 \end{pmatrix}$$

$$= \begin{pmatrix} -3 \\ -1 \end{pmatrix}$$

$\therefore \quad x = -3$ and $y = -1$

(b) $\begin{pmatrix} 4 \\ y \end{pmatrix} + \begin{pmatrix} x \\ 2 \end{pmatrix} = \begin{pmatrix} 5 \\ x \end{pmatrix}$

$$\begin{pmatrix} 4 + x \\ y + 2 \end{pmatrix} = \begin{pmatrix} 5 \\ x \end{pmatrix}$$

$\therefore \quad 4 + x = 5$ and $y + 2 = x$

$4 + x = 5$

$x = 1$

$\therefore \quad y + 2 = 1$

$y = -1$

(c) $\begin{pmatrix} 2 \\ 3x \end{pmatrix} - \begin{pmatrix} x - 2y \\ -1 \end{pmatrix} = \begin{pmatrix} 3 \\ 10 \end{pmatrix}$

$$\begin{pmatrix} 2 - x + 2y \\ 3x + 1 \end{pmatrix} = \begin{pmatrix} 3 \\ 10 \end{pmatrix}$$

$\therefore \quad 3x + 1 = 10$ and $2 - x + 2y = 3$

i.e. $x = 3$ and $2 - 3 + 2y = 3$

i.e $2y = 4$

$\therefore \quad y = 2$

1. The figure below shows the vectors **a**, **b** and **c**. On a sheet of squared or graph paper,

   (a) draw a triangle ABC with $\overrightarrow{AB} = \mathbf{a}$ and $\overrightarrow{BC} = \mathbf{b}$ to show the addition of these vectors;

   (b) draw a triangle DEF with $\overrightarrow{DE} = \mathbf{b}$ and $\overrightarrow{EF} = \mathbf{c}$ to show the addition of these vectors;

   (c) draw a parallelogram $KMNL$ with $\overrightarrow{MN} = \mathbf{a}$ and $\overrightarrow{MK} = \mathbf{b}$, and name the directed line segment which represents $\mathbf{a} + \mathbf{b}$.

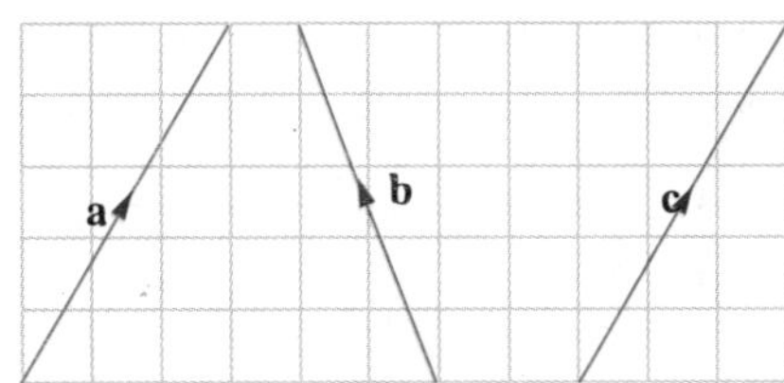

Fig. 3.30

2. The figure below shows the vectors **u**, **v** and **r**. On a sheet of squared or graph paper, draw appropriate triangles to illustrate the following vector additions:

   (a) $\mathbf{u} + \mathbf{v}$,

   (b) $\mathbf{u} + \mathbf{r}$,

   (c) $\mathbf{v} + \mathbf{r}$.

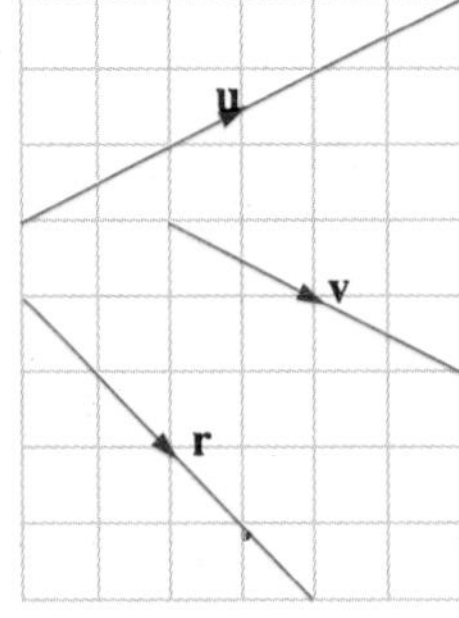

Fig. 3.31

In each case, write the vector sum in column vector form.

3. Simplify the following.

   (a) $\begin{pmatrix} 4 \\ 3 \end{pmatrix} + \begin{pmatrix} 2 \\ 5 \end{pmatrix}$ (b) $\begin{pmatrix} 2 \\ -3 \end{pmatrix} + \begin{pmatrix} 3 \\ 4 \end{pmatrix}$

   (c) $\begin{pmatrix} -2 \\ 6 \end{pmatrix} + \begin{pmatrix} -1 \\ -3 \end{pmatrix}$ (d) $\begin{pmatrix} 3 \\ 0 \end{pmatrix} + \begin{pmatrix} -2 \\ 7 \end{pmatrix}$

4. If $\mathbf{u} = \begin{pmatrix} 3 \\ 5 \end{pmatrix}$, $\mathbf{v} = \begin{pmatrix} 7 \\ 4 \end{pmatrix}$, $\mathbf{w} = \begin{pmatrix} -5 \\ 2 \end{pmatrix}$, express in column vector form:

   (a) $\mathbf{u} + \mathbf{v}$

   (b) $\mathbf{v} + \mathbf{u}$

   (c) $(\mathbf{u} + \mathbf{v}) + \mathbf{w}$

   (d) $\mathbf{u} + (\mathbf{v} + \mathbf{w})$

   Which two laws do the answers illustrate?

5. $PQRS$ is a quadilateral. Simplify the following.

   (a) $\overrightarrow{PT} + \overrightarrow{TR}$

   (b) $\overrightarrow{SQ} + \overrightarrow{QR}$

   (c) $\overrightarrow{ST} + \overrightarrow{TR}$

   (d) $\overrightarrow{SQ} + \overrightarrow{QT}$

   (e) $\overrightarrow{PS} + \overrightarrow{SQ} + \overrightarrow{QR}$

   (f) $\overrightarrow{RQ} + \overrightarrow{QT} + \overrightarrow{TP} + \overrightarrow{PS}$

Fig. 3.32

6. $ABCD$ is a quadrilateral. Simplify the following.

   (a) $\overrightarrow{AD} + \overrightarrow{DC}$

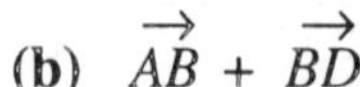

   (b) $\overrightarrow{AB} + \overrightarrow{BD}$

   (c) $\overrightarrow{AC} + \overrightarrow{CB} + \overrightarrow{BD}$

   (d) $\overrightarrow{AB} + \overrightarrow{BC} + \overrightarrow{CA}$

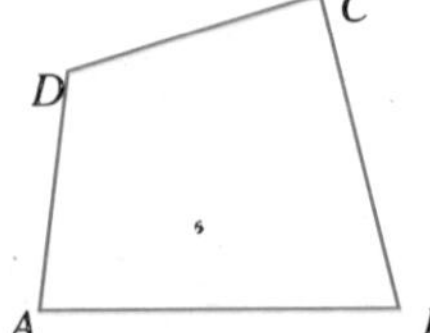

Fig. 3.33

7. Copy and complete the following:

(a) $\begin{pmatrix} 3 \\ \end{pmatrix} + \begin{pmatrix} \\ -9 \end{pmatrix} = \begin{pmatrix} 0 \\ 0 \end{pmatrix}$

(b) $\begin{pmatrix} 5 \\ -7 \end{pmatrix} + \begin{pmatrix} \\ \end{pmatrix} = \begin{pmatrix} 0 \\ 0 \end{pmatrix}$

(c) $\begin{pmatrix} x \\ -y \end{pmatrix} + \begin{pmatrix} \\ \end{pmatrix} = \begin{pmatrix} 0 \\ 0 \end{pmatrix}$

8. The figure below shows the vectors **a**, **b** and **c**. On a sheet of squared or graph paper,

(a) draw a triangle ABC with $\overrightarrow{AB}$ = **a** and $\overrightarrow{BC}$ = **b** to show the subtraction of vectors: **a** – **b**;

(b) draw a triangle DEF with $\overrightarrow{DE}$ = **a** and $\overrightarrow{DF}$ = **b** to show the subtraction of vectors: **a** – **b**;

(c) draw a triangle PQR with $\overrightarrow{PQ}$ = **a** and $\overrightarrow{PR}$ = **c** to show the subtraction of vectors: **a** – **c**.

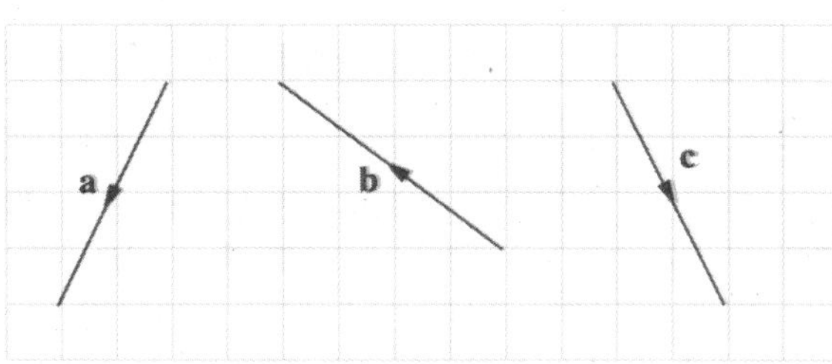

Fig. 3.34

9. Find the vector that is marked with double arrows in each of the diagrams below:

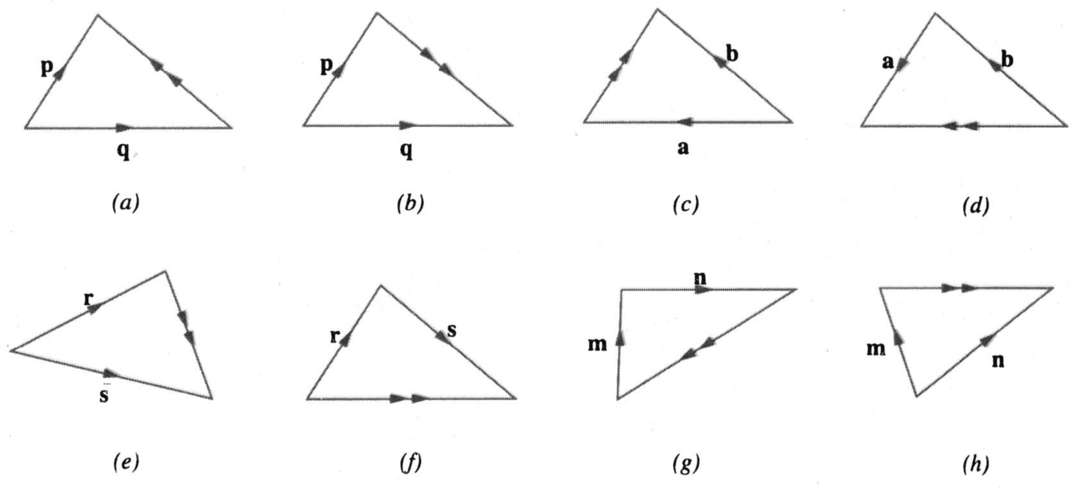

Fig. 3.35

10. Simplify the following if possible:

(a) $\vec{AB} + \vec{BC}$ (b) $\vec{PQ} + \vec{PR}$

(c) $\vec{AB} - \vec{AC}$ (d) $\vec{PQ} - \vec{PR}$

(e) $\vec{MN} - \vec{MQ}$ (f) $\vec{NM} - \vec{NQ}$

(g) $\vec{DE} - \vec{FE}$ (h) $\vec{DE} - \vec{DF}$

11. *PQRS* is a parallelogram. *O* is the point of intersection of its diagonals.

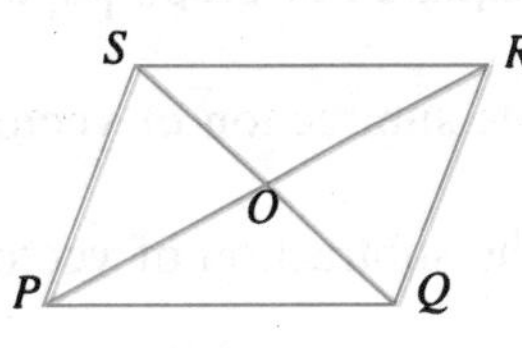

Fig. 3.36

(a) Simplify

(i) $\vec{PQ} + \vec{PS}$;

(ii) $\vec{RO} - \vec{QO}$;

(iii) $\vec{PR} - \vec{SR} + \vec{SQ}$.

(b) Find a vector which can replace **x** in each of the following equations.

(i) $\vec{SO} + \mathbf{x} = \vec{SP}$

(ii) $\vec{PO} + \mathbf{x} = \vec{PR}$

(iii) $\mathbf{x} + \vec{SQ} = \vec{RQ}$

(iv) $\vec{PR} + \mathbf{x} = \mathbf{0}$

(v) $\vec{PQ} + \mathbf{x} + \vec{RS} = \vec{PS}$

(vi) $\vec{QR} + \vec{RS} + \mathbf{x} = \vec{PS}$

(c) If $\vec{PQ} = \mathbf{a}$ and $\vec{PS} = \mathbf{b}$, find in terms of **a** and/or **b**:

(i) $\vec{SR}$; (ii) $\vec{PR}$; (iii) $\vec{SQ}$.

12. In Fig. 3.37, the diagonals of *PQRS* intersect at *K*. Find, for each of the following equations, a vector which can replace **u**.

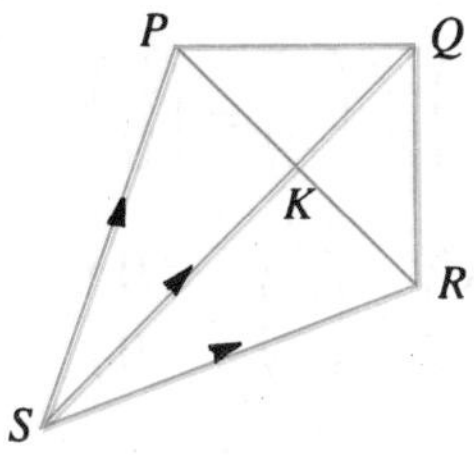

Fig. 3.37

(a) $\vec{SK} + \mathbf{u} = \mathbf{0}$

(b) $\vec{SP} + \vec{PQ} = \mathbf{u} = \mathbf{0}$

(c) $\vec{PS} + \vec{SK} + \vec{KR} = \mathbf{u}$

(d) $\vec{PK} + (-\vec{SK}) = \mathbf{u}$

(e) $\vec{PS} + (-\vec{RS}) = \mathbf{u}$

(f) $\vec{PQ} + \vec{QR} + (-\vec{PR}) = \mathbf{u}$

13. Find **x** in each of the following cases. (Refer to Fig. 3.38.)

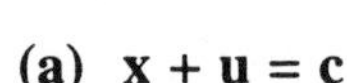

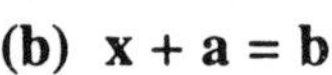

(a) $\mathbf{x} + \mathbf{u} = \mathbf{c}$

(b) $\mathbf{x} + \mathbf{a} = \mathbf{b}$

(c) $\mathbf{x} + \mathbf{c} = \mathbf{b}$

(d) $\mathbf{x} - \mathbf{b} = \mathbf{u}$

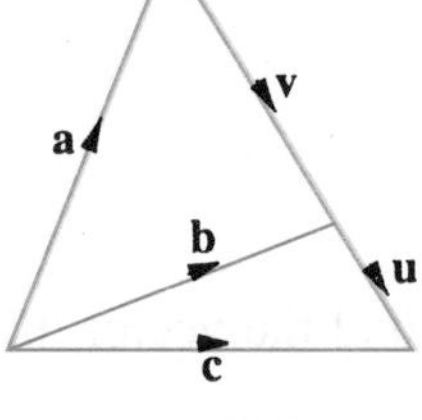

Fig. 3.38

14. Simplify the following:

(a) $\begin{pmatrix} 5 \\ 3 \end{pmatrix} - \begin{pmatrix} 2 \\ 1 \end{pmatrix}$

(b) $\begin{pmatrix} -1 \\ 4 \end{pmatrix} - \begin{pmatrix} -5 \\ -2 \end{pmatrix}$

(c) $\begin{pmatrix} -1 \\ 2 \end{pmatrix} - \begin{pmatrix} -3 \\ 2 \end{pmatrix}$

(d) $\begin{pmatrix} 8 \\ -2 \end{pmatrix} - \begin{pmatrix} -1 \\ -2 \end{pmatrix}$

15. Simplify:

(a) $\begin{pmatrix} 2 \\ 3 \end{pmatrix} + \begin{pmatrix} 4 \\ -1 \end{pmatrix} - \begin{pmatrix} 3 \\ 5 \end{pmatrix}$

(b) $\begin{pmatrix} -1 \\ 2 \end{pmatrix} - \begin{pmatrix} 4 \\ 5 \end{pmatrix} + \begin{pmatrix} 3 \\ -2 \end{pmatrix}$

(c) $\begin{pmatrix} 4 \\ 3 \end{pmatrix} - \begin{pmatrix} 1 \\ 2 \end{pmatrix} - \begin{pmatrix} -3 \\ 5 \end{pmatrix}$

16. If $\mathbf{u} = \begin{pmatrix} 7 \\ 2 \end{pmatrix}$, $\mathbf{v} = \begin{pmatrix} -1 \\ 4 \end{pmatrix}$ and $\mathbf{w} = \begin{pmatrix} -2 \\ -3 \end{pmatrix}$, express as column vectors:

(a) $\mathbf{u} + \mathbf{v} - \mathbf{w}$
(b) $\mathbf{u} - \mathbf{v} + \mathbf{w}$
(c) $\mathbf{u} - \mathbf{v} - \mathbf{w}$

17. If $\mathbf{a} = \begin{pmatrix} 4 \\ 3 \end{pmatrix}$, $\mathbf{b} = \begin{pmatrix} 2 \\ 1 \end{pmatrix}$ and $\mathbf{c} = \begin{pmatrix} -3 \\ 1 \end{pmatrix}$, express as column vectors:

(a) $\mathbf{a} - \mathbf{b}$
(b) $\mathbf{b} - \mathbf{c}$
(c) $\mathbf{a} - (\mathbf{b} + \mathbf{c})$
(d) $\mathbf{a} - (\mathbf{b} - \mathbf{c})$

18. Given that $\mathbf{u} = \begin{pmatrix} a \\ b \end{pmatrix}$ and $\mathbf{v} = \begin{pmatrix} c \\ d \end{pmatrix}$, if $\mathbf{u} = \mathbf{v}$, what can be said about a, b, c and d?

19. Find the values of a and b in each of the following equations:

(a) $\begin{pmatrix} a \\ b \end{pmatrix} + \begin{pmatrix} -2 \\ 3 \end{pmatrix} = \begin{pmatrix} 5 \\ 2 \end{pmatrix}$

(b) $\begin{pmatrix} 5 \\ -2 \end{pmatrix} + \begin{pmatrix} a \\ b \end{pmatrix} = \begin{pmatrix} 7 \\ -3 \end{pmatrix}$

(c) $\begin{pmatrix} a \\ b \end{pmatrix} + \begin{pmatrix} -1 \\ -4 \end{pmatrix} = \begin{pmatrix} 0 \\ 0 \end{pmatrix}$

20. Find $\mathbf{u}$ in column vector form in each of the following:

(a) $\mathbf{u} + \begin{pmatrix} 3 \\ 2 \end{pmatrix} = \begin{pmatrix} 7 \\ 1 \end{pmatrix}$

(b) $\mathbf{u} - \begin{pmatrix} -1 \\ 2 \end{pmatrix} = \begin{pmatrix} 1 \\ 4 \end{pmatrix}$

(c) $\begin{pmatrix} -1 \\ 3 \end{pmatrix} - \mathbf{u} = \begin{pmatrix} 4 \\ 1 \end{pmatrix}$

21. Find the values of x and y in the following equations:

(a) $\begin{pmatrix} x \\ 3 \end{pmatrix} + \begin{pmatrix} 1 \\ 2 \end{pmatrix} = \begin{pmatrix} 4 \\ y \end{pmatrix}$

(b) $\begin{pmatrix} 3 \\ y \end{pmatrix} + \begin{pmatrix} x \\ 4 \end{pmatrix} = \begin{pmatrix} -1 \\ -2 \end{pmatrix}$

(c) $\begin{pmatrix} x \\ -2 \end{pmatrix} + \begin{pmatrix} 3 \\ y \end{pmatrix} = \begin{pmatrix} -1 \\ 4 \end{pmatrix}$

(d) $\begin{pmatrix} 2x \\ 5 \end{pmatrix} - \begin{pmatrix} y - 3 \\ 3y \end{pmatrix} = \begin{pmatrix} 4 \\ -10 \end{pmatrix}$

Scalar Multiple of a Vector

Refer to Fig. 3.39.

(1) Is vector **u** parallel to vectors **a** and **b**?

(2) What can you say about the direction and magnitude of **a** when compared to those of **u**?

(3) Can we write **a** = **u** + **u** + **u** = 3**u**?

(4) What about the direction and magnitude of **b** when compared to those of **u**?

(5) Do you agree that **b** = (–**u**) + (–**u**) = –2**u**?

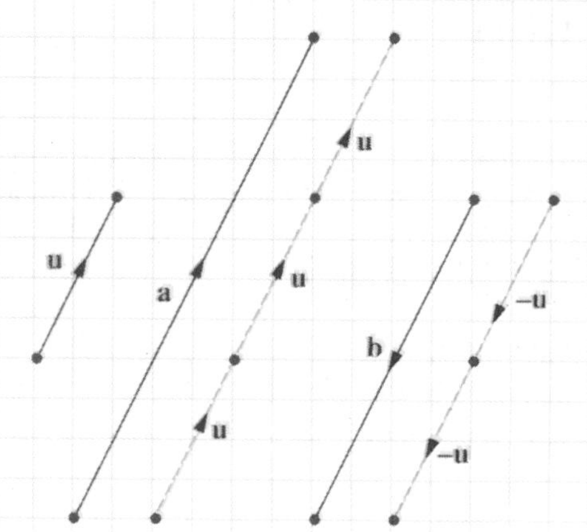

Fig. 3.39

3**u** and –2**u** are said to be scalar multiples of **u**.
In terms of column vectors, we have

$$\mathbf{u} = \begin{pmatrix} 2 \\ 4 \end{pmatrix},\ \mathbf{a} = \begin{pmatrix} 6 \\ 12 \end{pmatrix} = 3\begin{pmatrix} 2 \\ 4 \end{pmatrix} = 3\mathbf{u} \quad \text{and} \quad \mathbf{b} = \begin{pmatrix} -4 \\ -8 \end{pmatrix} = -2\begin{pmatrix} 2 \\ 4 \end{pmatrix} = -2\mathbf{u}.$$

In general,

(a) $k\mathbf{a}$ is called a scalar multiple of **a** if $k \neq 0$ and $\mathbf{a} \neq \mathbf{0}$.

(b) the magnitude of $k\mathbf{a}$ is $|k|$ times the magnitude of **a**, i.e $|k\mathbf{a}| = |k|\,|\mathbf{a}|$,

(c) when (i) $k > 0$, $k\mathbf{a}$ is in the same direction as **a**, when (ii) $k < 0$, $k\mathbf{a}$ is in the opposite direction as **a**.

Your Attention

|k| is the numerical or absolute value of k. Refer to marginal note on page 80 for further explanation. |a| is the magnitude of the vector a. See page 76.

Also, from the Exploration above, we know that

> If $\mathbf{b} = k\mathbf{a}$, where $k \neq 0$ is a scalar and $\mathbf{a} \neq \mathbf{0}$, then
> (i) **b** is parallel to **a**,
> (ii) **b** has a magnitude $|k|$ times the magnitude of **a**.
>
> Conversely, if **a** and **b** are parallel vectors, where $\mathbf{a} \neq \mathbf{0}$ and $\mathbf{b} \neq \mathbf{0}$, then
> (i) $\mathbf{a} = k\mathbf{b}$ for some scalar $k \neq 0$, or
> (ii) $\mathbf{b} = k\mathbf{a}$ for some scalar $k \neq 0$.

In Fig. 3.40, $\mathbf{a} = \begin{pmatrix} -1 \\ 2 \end{pmatrix}$ and $\mathbf{b} = \begin{pmatrix} -2 \\ 4 \end{pmatrix} = 2\begin{pmatrix} -1 \\ 2 \end{pmatrix} = 2\mathbf{a}$

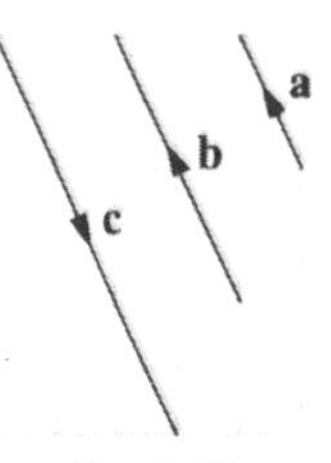

Fig. 3.40

Since $\mathbf{b} = 2\mathbf{a}$, then **b** is parallel to **a** and in the same direction as **a**, and the magnitude of **b** is 2 times the magnitude of **a**. This implies that **c** is also parallel to **a** but in the opposite direction as **a**, and the magnitude of **c** is $|-3| = 3$ times the magnitude of **a**.

Also, $\mathbf{c} = \begin{pmatrix} 3 \\ -6 \end{pmatrix} = -3\begin{pmatrix} -1 \\ 2 \end{pmatrix} = -3\mathbf{a}$.

Example 18

(a) State which of the following pairs of vectors are parallel.

(i) $\begin{pmatrix} 6 \\ 3 \end{pmatrix}, \begin{pmatrix} 2 \\ 1 \end{pmatrix}$ (ii) $\begin{pmatrix} 3 \\ -2 \end{pmatrix}, \begin{pmatrix} -12 \\ 8 \end{pmatrix}$

(iii) $\begin{pmatrix} 4 \\ 15 \end{pmatrix}, \begin{pmatrix} 2 \\ 5 \end{pmatrix}$ (iv) $\begin{pmatrix} 3 \\ 6 \end{pmatrix}, \begin{pmatrix} 4 \\ 8 \end{pmatrix}$

(b) Write down 2 vectors that are parallel to $\begin{pmatrix} 2 \\ -3 \end{pmatrix}$*, one in the same direction, and one in the opposite direction.*

(a) (i) Observe $\begin{pmatrix} 6 \\ 3 \end{pmatrix} = 3\begin{pmatrix} 2 \\ 1 \end{pmatrix}$.

$\therefore$ $\begin{pmatrix} 6 \\ 3 \end{pmatrix}$ and $\begin{pmatrix} 2 \\ 1 \end{pmatrix}$ are parallel.

(ii) Observe $\begin{pmatrix} -12 \\ 8 \end{pmatrix} = -4\begin{pmatrix} 3 \\ -2 \end{pmatrix}$.

$\therefore$ $\begin{pmatrix} 3 \\ -2 \end{pmatrix}$ and $\begin{pmatrix} -12 \\ 8 \end{pmatrix}$ are parallel.

(iii) Observe that $4 = 2 \times 2$, but $15 = 3 \times 5$. $2 \neq 3$, so it is impossible to find a k such that $\begin{pmatrix} 4 \\ 15 \end{pmatrix} = k\begin{pmatrix} 2 \\ 5 \end{pmatrix}$.

So $\begin{pmatrix} 4 \\ 15 \end{pmatrix}$ and $\begin{pmatrix} 2 \\ 5 \end{pmatrix}$ are not parallel.

(iv) Observe $\begin{pmatrix} 4 \\ 8 \end{pmatrix} = \frac{4}{3}\begin{pmatrix} 3 \\ 6 \end{pmatrix}$.

$\therefore$ $\begin{pmatrix} 3 \\ 6 \end{pmatrix}$ and $\begin{pmatrix} 4 \\ 8 \end{pmatrix}$ are parallel.

Observe:

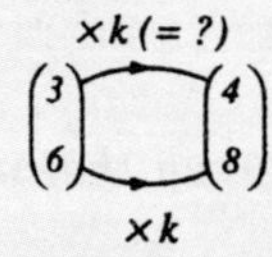

To obtain k, ask yourself: $3 \times ? = 4$

So $k = \frac{4}{3}$.

Then check: $6 \times \frac{4}{3} = 8$.

So $\begin{pmatrix} 3 \\ 6 \end{pmatrix} \times \frac{4}{3} = \begin{pmatrix} 4 \\ 8 \end{pmatrix}$

i.e. $\begin{pmatrix} 4 \\ 8 \end{pmatrix} = \frac{4}{3}\begin{pmatrix} 3 \\ 6 \end{pmatrix}$.

(b) A vector in the same direction as $\begin{pmatrix} 2 \\ -3 \end{pmatrix}$ is $2\begin{pmatrix} 2 \\ -3 \end{pmatrix} = \begin{pmatrix} 4 \\ -6 \end{pmatrix}$.

A vector in the opposition direction as $\begin{pmatrix} 2 \\ -3 \end{pmatrix}$ is $-\begin{pmatrix} 2 \\ -3 \end{pmatrix} = \begin{pmatrix} -2 \\ 3 \end{pmatrix}$.

xample 19

Given that $\begin{pmatrix} 4 \\ -3 \end{pmatrix}$ and $\begin{pmatrix} 12 \\ p \end{pmatrix}$ are parallel vectors, find the value of p.

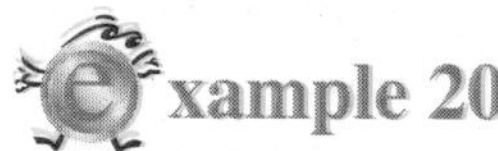

Method 1:

Since $\begin{pmatrix} 4 \\ -3 \end{pmatrix}$ and $\begin{pmatrix} 12 \\ p \end{pmatrix}$ are parallel, let $\begin{pmatrix} 12 \\ p \end{pmatrix} = k\begin{pmatrix} 4 \\ -3 \end{pmatrix} = \begin{pmatrix} 4k \\ -3k \end{pmatrix}$, where k is a scalar.

Then $12 = 4k$ and $p = -3k$.
So $k = 3$ and $p = -3 \times 3 = -9$.

In general,

> for any two non-zero vectors **a** and **b**, $\mathbf{a} = k\mathbf{b} \Rightarrow$ **a** and **b** are parallel where $k \neq 0$.

xample 20

*It is given that $\mathbf{u} = \begin{pmatrix} -15 \\ 8 \end{pmatrix}$. If $\mathbf{u} = k\mathbf{v}$ where k is a positive constant and $|\mathbf{v}| = 51$, find the value of k. Hence find **v**.*

Since $\mathbf{u} = k\mathbf{v}$, $|\mathbf{u}| = k|\mathbf{v}|$ (*where* $k > 0$)

i.e. $\sqrt{(-15)^2 + 8^2} = k \times 51$

$17 = 51k$

$\therefore \quad k = \frac{17}{51} = \frac{1}{3}$

Then $\mathbf{u} = \frac{1}{3}\mathbf{v}$ implies $\mathbf{v} = 3\mathbf{u} = 3\begin{pmatrix} -15 \\ 8 \end{pmatrix} = \begin{pmatrix} -45 \\ 24 \end{pmatrix}$.

Example 21

(a) *If* $\mathbf{u} = \begin{pmatrix} 1 \\ 2 \end{pmatrix}$, $\mathbf{v} = \begin{pmatrix} -2 \\ 1 \end{pmatrix}$ *and* $\mathbf{w} = \begin{pmatrix} 3 \\ -4 \end{pmatrix}$, *find a single column vector to represent the following.*

(i) $\mathbf{u} + 3\mathbf{v}$ (ii) $3\mathbf{u} - 2\mathbf{v} - \mathbf{w}$

(b) (i) *If* $\mathbf{a} = \begin{pmatrix} x \\ y \end{pmatrix}$, $\mathbf{b} = \begin{pmatrix} 2 \\ -3 \end{pmatrix}$ *and* $2\mathbf{a} + \mathbf{b} = \begin{pmatrix} 5 \\ 3 \end{pmatrix}$, *find the values of x and y.*

(ii) *If* $\mathbf{u} = \begin{pmatrix} x \\ 4 \end{pmatrix}$, $\mathbf{v} = \begin{pmatrix} -5 \\ y \end{pmatrix}$ *and* $\mathbf{u} - 2\mathbf{v} = \begin{pmatrix} 7 \\ 8 \end{pmatrix}$, *find the values of x and y.*

(a) (i)
$$\mathbf{u} + 3\mathbf{v} = \begin{pmatrix} 1 \\ 2 \end{pmatrix} + 3\begin{pmatrix} -2 \\ 1 \end{pmatrix} = \begin{pmatrix} 1 \\ 2 \end{pmatrix} + \begin{pmatrix} -6 \\ 3 \end{pmatrix} = \begin{pmatrix} -5 \\ 5 \end{pmatrix}$$

(ii)
$$3\mathbf{u} - 2\mathbf{v} - \mathbf{w} = 3\begin{pmatrix} 1 \\ 2 \end{pmatrix} - 2\begin{pmatrix} -2 \\ 1 \end{pmatrix} - \begin{pmatrix} 3 \\ -4 \end{pmatrix} = \begin{pmatrix} 3 \\ 6 \end{pmatrix} - \begin{pmatrix} -4 \\ 2 \end{pmatrix} - \begin{pmatrix} 3 \\ -4 \end{pmatrix} = \begin{pmatrix} 4 \\ 8 \end{pmatrix}$$

(b) (i)
$$2\mathbf{a} + \mathbf{b} = \begin{pmatrix} 5 \\ 3 \end{pmatrix}$$
$$2\mathbf{a} + \begin{pmatrix} 2 \\ -3 \end{pmatrix} = \begin{pmatrix} 5 \\ 3 \end{pmatrix}$$
$$2\mathbf{a} = \begin{pmatrix} 5 \\ 3 \end{pmatrix} - \begin{pmatrix} 2 \\ -3 \end{pmatrix} = \begin{pmatrix} 3 \\ 6 \end{pmatrix}$$
$$\mathbf{a} = \frac{1}{2}\begin{pmatrix} 3 \\ 6 \end{pmatrix} = \begin{pmatrix} 1\frac{1}{2} \\ 3 \end{pmatrix}$$

(ii)
$$\mathbf{u} - 2\mathbf{v} = \begin{pmatrix} 7 \\ 8 \end{pmatrix}$$
$$\begin{pmatrix} x \\ 4 \end{pmatrix} - 2\begin{pmatrix} -5 \\ y \end{pmatrix} = \begin{pmatrix} 7 \\ 8 \end{pmatrix}$$
$$\begin{pmatrix} x + 10 \\ 4 - 2y \end{pmatrix} = \begin{pmatrix} 7 \\ 8 \end{pmatrix}$$

$\therefore$ $x + 10 = 7$ and $4 - 2y = 8$

i.e. $x = -3$ and $y = -2$.

xample 22

Given that $\mathbf{a} = \begin{pmatrix} 2 \\ 1 \end{pmatrix}$ *and* $\mathbf{b} = \begin{pmatrix} 1 \\ -1 \end{pmatrix}$, *illustrate each of the following on a sheet of squared or graph paper. Hence write down as column vectors.*

(a) $\mathbf{a} + 2\mathbf{b}$ *(b)* $2\mathbf{a} + 3\mathbf{b}$ *(c)* $3\mathbf{a} - 2\mathbf{b}$

(a) For Triangle Law of Vector Addition, the second vector $2\mathbf{b}$ must start where the first vector $\mathbf{a}$ ends. From the diagram, $\mathbf{a} + 2\mathbf{b} = \begin{pmatrix} 4 \\ -1 \end{pmatrix}$.

To draw the vector $2\mathbf{b}$, draw the vector $\mathbf{b}$ first, followed by another vector $\mathbf{b}$.

Check: $\mathbf{a} + 2\mathbf{b} = \begin{pmatrix} 2 \\ 1 \end{pmatrix} + 2\begin{pmatrix} 1 \\ -1 \end{pmatrix} = \begin{pmatrix} 2 \\ 1 \end{pmatrix} + \begin{pmatrix} 2 \\ -2 \end{pmatrix} = \begin{pmatrix} 4 \\ -1 \end{pmatrix}$.

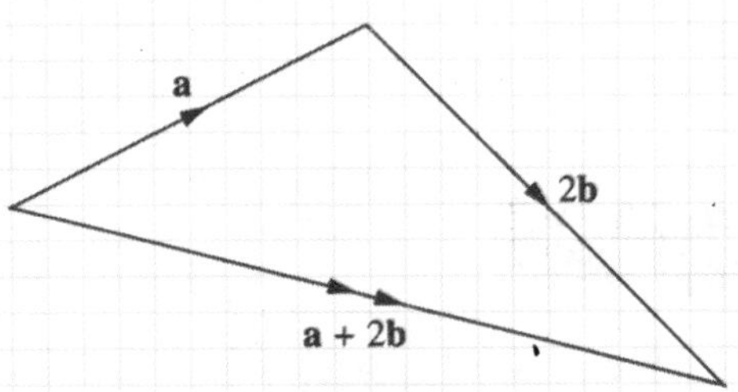

Fig. 3.41(a)

(b) For Triangle Law of Vector Addition, the second vector $3\mathbf{b}$ must start where the first vector $2\mathbf{a}$ ends. From the diagram,

$2\mathbf{a} + 3\mathbf{b} = \begin{pmatrix} 7 \\ -1 \end{pmatrix}$.

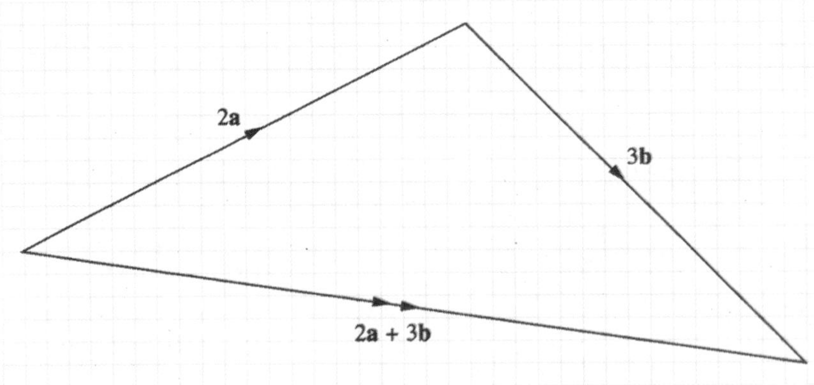

Fig. 3.41(b)

Check: $2\mathbf{a} + 3\mathbf{b} = 2\begin{pmatrix} 2 \\ 1 \end{pmatrix} + 3\begin{pmatrix} 1 \\ -1 \end{pmatrix} = \begin{pmatrix} 4 \\ 2 \end{pmatrix} + \begin{pmatrix} 3 \\ -3 \end{pmatrix} = \begin{pmatrix} 7 \\ -1 \end{pmatrix}$.

(c) For Triangle Law of Vector Subtraction, both vectors 3**a** and 2**b** must start from the **same** point.

To determine the direction of 3**a** – 2**b**, recall 'end minus start' (see page 93). From the diagram,

$3\mathbf{a} - 2\mathbf{b} = \begin{pmatrix} 4 \\ 5 \end{pmatrix}$.

Check: $3\mathbf{a} - 2\mathbf{b} = 3\begin{pmatrix} 2 \\ 1 \end{pmatrix} - 2\begin{pmatrix} 1 \\ -1 \end{pmatrix}$

$= \begin{pmatrix} 6 \\ 3 \end{pmatrix} - \begin{pmatrix} 2 \\ -2 \end{pmatrix}$

$= \begin{pmatrix} 4 \\ 5 \end{pmatrix}$.

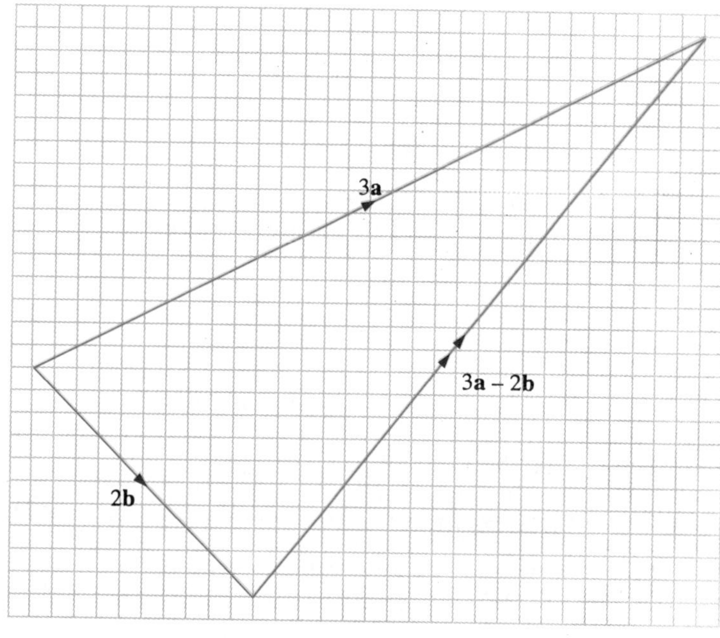

Fig. 3.41(c)

Exercise 3c

1. Study the diagram and draw vectors (on a sheet of squared paper) equal to

   (a) $3\mathbf{a}$ (b) $-2\mathbf{a}$ (c) $1\frac{2}{3}\mathbf{b}$

   (d) $-\mathbf{b}$ (e) $1\frac{1}{2}\mathbf{c}$ (f) $-\frac{1}{2}\mathbf{c}$

   (g) $1\frac{1}{2}\mathbf{c}$ (h) $1\frac{1}{3}\mathbf{d}$

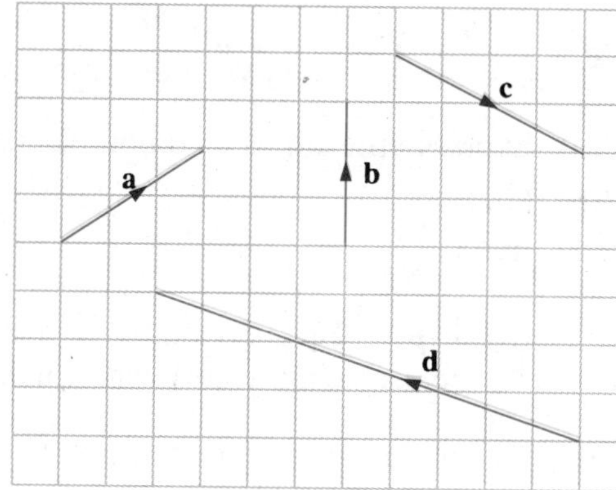

Fig. 3.42

2. State which of the following pairs of vectors are parallel.

   (a) $\begin{pmatrix} 3 \\ 1 \end{pmatrix}, \begin{pmatrix} 9 \\ 3 \end{pmatrix}$ (b) $\begin{pmatrix} 2 \\ 5 \end{pmatrix}, \begin{pmatrix} -2 \\ -5 \end{pmatrix}$

   (c) $\begin{pmatrix} 10 \\ 4 \end{pmatrix}, \begin{pmatrix} 5 \\ 3 \end{pmatrix}$ (d) $\begin{pmatrix} 12 \\ 9 \end{pmatrix}, \begin{pmatrix} 8 \\ 6 \end{pmatrix}$

   (e) $\begin{pmatrix} -3 \\ -21 \end{pmatrix}, \begin{pmatrix} 1 \\ 7 \end{pmatrix}$ (f) $\begin{pmatrix} 4 \\ -9 \end{pmatrix}, \begin{pmatrix} -4 \\ 9 \end{pmatrix}$

3. For each of the following vectors, write down *direction.*

   (a) $\begin{pmatrix} 2 \\ 1 \end{pmatrix}$ (b) $\begin{pmatrix} -3 \\ -2 \end{pmatrix}$ (c) $\begin{pmatrix} 8 \\ -5 \end{pmatrix}$

   (d) $\begin{pmatrix} -7 \\ 4 \end{pmatrix}$ (e) $\begin{pmatrix} -\frac{1}{2} \\ 2 \end{pmatrix}$ (f) $\begin{pmatrix} 3 \\ \frac{2}{3} \end{pmatrix}$

4. Given that $\begin{pmatrix} 5 \\ 2 \end{pmatrix}$ and $\begin{pmatrix} 20 \\ p \end{pmatrix}$ are parallel vectors, find the value of p.

5. Given that $\begin{pmatrix} 8 \\ -6 \end{pmatrix}$ and $\begin{pmatrix} 2 \\ p \end{pmatrix}$ are parallel vectors, find the value of p.

6. Given that $\begin{pmatrix} h \\ 12 \end{pmatrix}$ and $\begin{pmatrix} 3 \\ -9 \end{pmatrix}$ are parallel vectors, find the value of h.

7. If $\begin{pmatrix} a \\ b \end{pmatrix}$ and $\begin{pmatrix} c \\ d \end{pmatrix}$ are two parallel vectors, explain why $\frac{a}{c} = \frac{b}{d}$.

8. It is given that $\mathbf{u} = \begin{pmatrix} 4 \\ -3 \end{pmatrix}$ and $|\mathbf{v}| = 20$. If $\mathbf{u} = k\mathbf{v}$ where k is a positive constant, find the value of k. Hence find $\mathbf{v}$.

9. It is given that $\mathbf{p} = \begin{pmatrix} -12 \\ 5 \end{pmatrix}$ and $|\mathbf{q}| = 32.5$. If $\mathbf{p} = t\mathbf{q}$ where t is a positive constant, find the value of t. Hence find $\mathbf{q}$.

10. It is given that $\mathbf{a} = \begin{pmatrix} 7 \\ 14 \end{pmatrix}$ and $|\mathbf{b}| = 50$. If $\mathbf{a} = h\mathbf{b}$ where h is a negative constant, find the value of h. Hence find $\mathbf{b}$.

11. If $\mathbf{u} = \begin{pmatrix} -2 \\ 3 \end{pmatrix}$, $\mathbf{v} = \begin{pmatrix} 4 \\ 1 \end{pmatrix}$ and $\mathbf{w} = \begin{pmatrix} 6 \\ 2 \end{pmatrix}$, find a single column vector for each of the following:

(a) $\mathbf{u} - 2\mathbf{v}$

(b) $3\mathbf{u} + \mathbf{v}$

(c) $2\mathbf{u} - \mathbf{v} + 3\mathbf{w}$

(d) $-2\mathbf{u} + 3\mathbf{v} - \mathbf{w}$

(e) $-5\mathbf{u} - 2\mathbf{v} + \frac{1}{2}\mathbf{w}$

(f) $-4\mathbf{u} + 7\mathbf{v} - 2\mathbf{w}$

12. If $\overrightarrow{PQ} = \begin{pmatrix} 6 \\ 12 \end{pmatrix}$, $\overrightarrow{RS} = \begin{pmatrix} -12 \\ 3 \end{pmatrix}$ and $\overrightarrow{TU} = \begin{pmatrix} 5 \\ -15 \end{pmatrix}$, evaluate the following:

(a) $\frac{1}{3}\overrightarrow{PQ}$

(b) $\overrightarrow{PQ} + 2\overrightarrow{RS}$

(c) $3\overrightarrow{RS} + 2\overrightarrow{TU} - \overrightarrow{PQ}$

(d) $\frac{2}{3}\overrightarrow{PQ} - \frac{1}{3}\overrightarrow{RS} - \frac{3}{5}\overrightarrow{TU}$

13. For each of the following, find the values of x and y.

(a) $\mathbf{a} = \begin{pmatrix} x \\ y \end{pmatrix}$, $\mathbf{b} = \begin{pmatrix} 3 \\ 4 \end{pmatrix}$ and $\mathbf{a} + 2\mathbf{b} = \begin{pmatrix} 8 \\ 9 \end{pmatrix}$.

(b) $\mathbf{u} = \begin{pmatrix} 2 \\ y \end{pmatrix}$, $\mathbf{v} = \begin{pmatrix} x \\ 2 \end{pmatrix}$ and $4\mathbf{u} + \mathbf{v} = 2\begin{pmatrix} \frac{1}{2} \\ 9 \end{pmatrix}$.

(c) $\mathbf{p} = \begin{pmatrix} x \\ 5 \end{pmatrix}$, $\mathbf{q} = \begin{pmatrix} 6 \\ y \end{pmatrix}$ and $5\mathbf{p} - 2\mathbf{q} = \begin{pmatrix} 3 \\ 23 \end{pmatrix}$.

14. $\mathbf{p} = \begin{pmatrix} 5 \\ -12 \end{pmatrix}$, $\mathbf{q} = \begin{pmatrix} 2 \\ 3 \end{pmatrix}$, $\mathbf{r} = \begin{pmatrix} 20 \\ m \end{pmatrix}$.

(a) Express $2\mathbf{p} + 3\mathbf{q}$ as a column vector.

(b) Find

(i) $|\mathbf{p}|$,

(ii) $|-\mathbf{p} + 2\mathbf{q}|$, giving your answers correct to the nearest whole number.

(c) Given that $\mathbf{r}$ is parallel to $\mathbf{p}$, write down the value of m.

15. Given that $\overrightarrow{AB} = \begin{pmatrix} -3 \\ 5 \end{pmatrix}$, $\overrightarrow{CD} = \begin{pmatrix} 1 \\ 4 \end{pmatrix}$, $\overrightarrow{EF} = \begin{pmatrix} k \\ 7.5 \end{pmatrix}$ and $\overrightarrow{PQ} = \begin{pmatrix} \frac{1}{4} \\ 1 \end{pmatrix}$,

(a) express as a column vector $2\overrightarrow{AB} + 5\overrightarrow{CD}$;

(b) find the value of k if $\overrightarrow{EF}$ is parallel to $\overrightarrow{AB}$;

(c) explain why $\overrightarrow{PQ}$ is parallel to $\overrightarrow{CD}$.

16. Given that $\mathbf{a} = \begin{pmatrix} -1 \\ 1 \end{pmatrix}$ and $\mathbf{b} = \begin{pmatrix} 1 \\ 2 \end{pmatrix}$, illustrate each of the following on a sheet of squared paper:

(a) $2\mathbf{a} + \mathbf{b}$

(b) $3\mathbf{a} + 2\mathbf{b}$

(c) $\mathbf{a} - 2\mathbf{b}$

(d) $2\mathbf{a} - 3\mathbf{b}$

(e) $4\mathbf{a} + 3\mathbf{b}$

(f) $-3\mathbf{a} + 4\mathbf{b}$

Expression of a Given Vector in Terms of Two Vectors

We know that the result of adding two vectors is a vector. Can we do the reverse? That is, can we express a vector as the sum of two vectors?

Fig. 3.43(a) shows 2 non-parallel vectors **u** *and* **v**.

Express $\overrightarrow{AB}$ *and* $\overrightarrow{PQ}$ *in terms of* **u** *and* **v**.

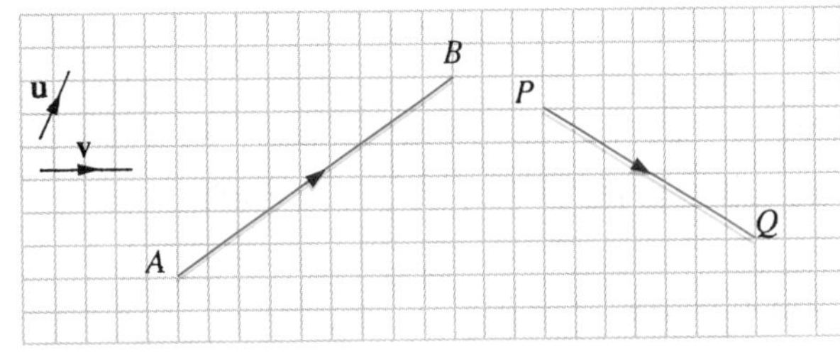

Fig. 3.43(a)

To express $\overrightarrow{AB}$ in terms of **u** and **v**, we start from the point A and draw a line parallel to **u** (see Fig. 3.43(b)). Then we draw a line from B parallel to **v** (this line must go in the opposite direction as **v** in order to intersect the first line). Call the point of intersection of the 2 lines C.

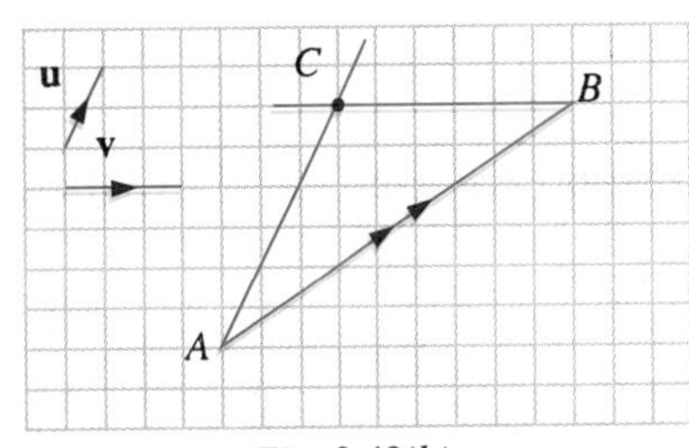

Fig. 3.43(b)

From the diagram, $\overrightarrow{AC} = 3\mathbf{u}$ and $\overrightarrow{CB} = 2\mathbf{v}$ (see Fig. 3.43(c)).

$\therefore \quad \overrightarrow{AB} = 3\mathbf{u} + 2\mathbf{v}$

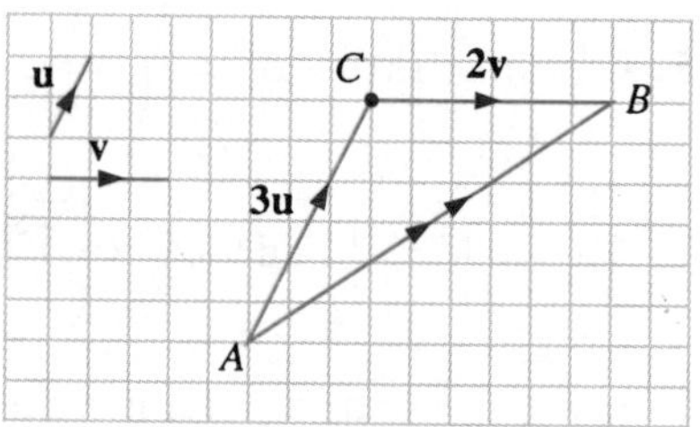

Fig. 3.43(c)

Alternatively, you can start from the point A and draw a line parallel to $\mathbf{v}$ first (see Fig. 2.43(d)). Then draw a line from B parallel to $\mathbf{u}$. From the diagram, $\overrightarrow{AC} = 2\mathbf{v}$ and $\overrightarrow{CB} = 3\mathbf{u}$.

$\therefore \quad \overrightarrow{AB} = 2\mathbf{v} + 3\mathbf{u} = 3\mathbf{u} + 2\mathbf{v}$

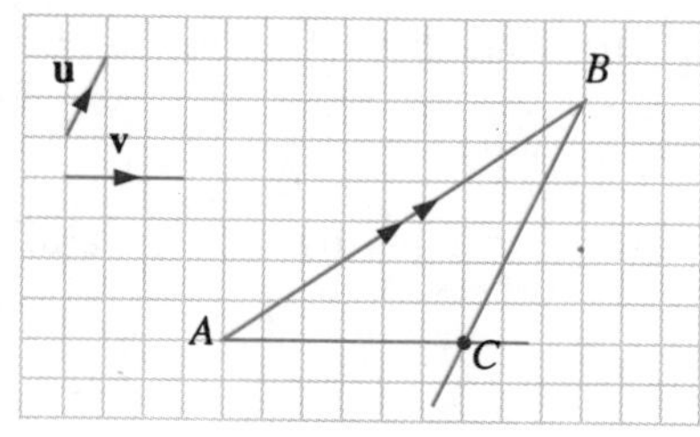

Fig. 3.43(d)

To express $\overrightarrow{PQ}$ in terms of $\mathbf{u}$ and $\mathbf{v}$, we start from P and draw a line parallel to $\mathbf{u}$ (see Fig. 3.43(e)). Then we draw a line from Q parallel to $\mathbf{v}$.

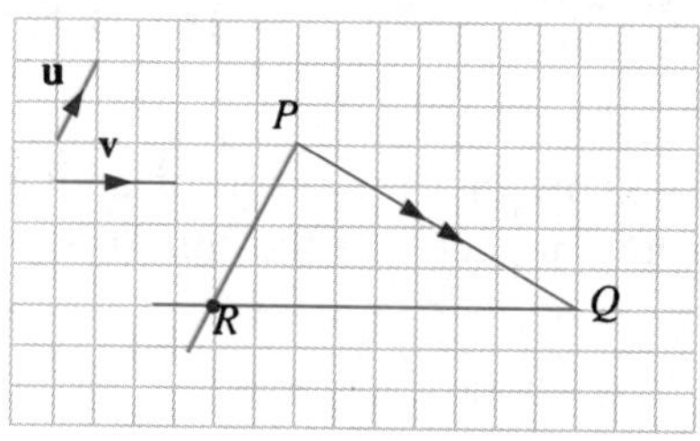

Fig. 3.43(e)

Call the point of intersection of the 2 lines R. From the diagram, $\overrightarrow{PR} = -2\mathbf{u}$ and $\overrightarrow{RQ} = 3\mathbf{v}$ (see Fig. 3.43(f)).

$\therefore \quad \overrightarrow{PQ} = -2\mathbf{u} + 3\mathbf{v}$ (or $3\mathbf{v} - 2\mathbf{u}$)

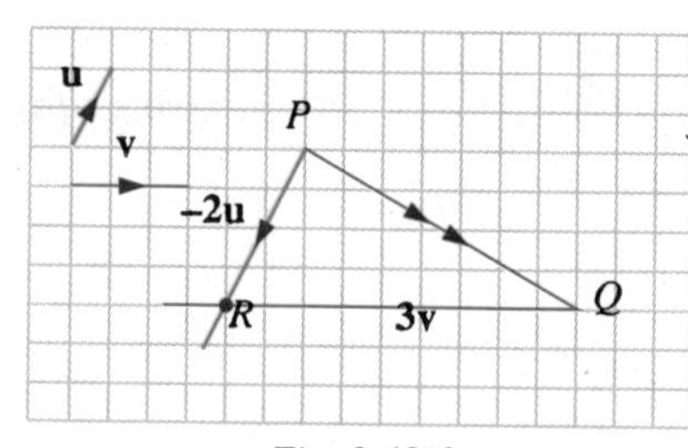

Fig. 3.43(f)

We observe from the above dicussion that there is only one way to write the vector $\overrightarrow{AB}$ in terms of $\mathbf{u}$ and $\mathbf{v}$, i.e. $\overrightarrow{AB} = 3\mathbf{u} + 2\mathbf{v}$.

We can also write $\overrightarrow{AB} = 2\mathbf{v} + 3\mathbf{u}$ but the order is not important.

Example 23

In the diagram, SPQR is a parallelogram. The point U, on SR, is such that $SU = \frac{2}{5}SR$. *The lines PS and QU, when produced, meet at T.* $\overrightarrow{PQ} = 10\mathbf{a}$ *and* $\overrightarrow{PS} = 5\mathbf{b}$.

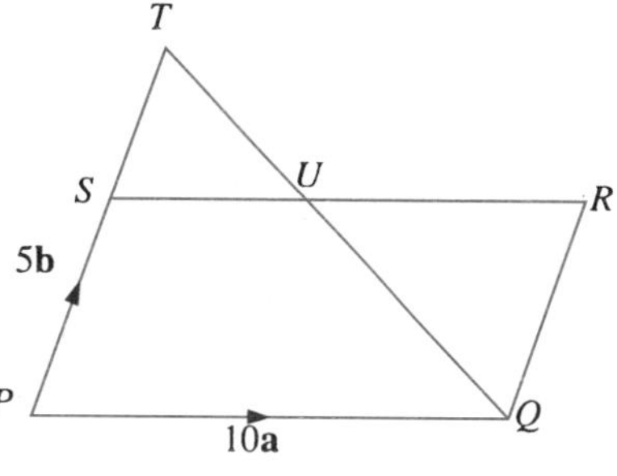

Fig. 3.44

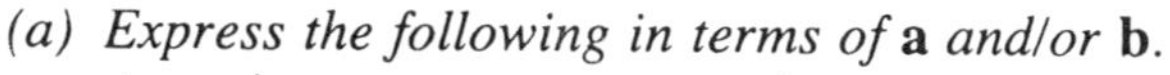

(a) Express the following in terms of **a** *and/or* **b**.

(i) $\overrightarrow{PR}$ *(ii)* $\overrightarrow{UR}$ *(iii)* $\overrightarrow{TU}$

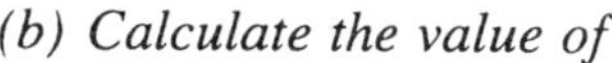

(b) Calculate the value of

(i) $\frac{TU}{UQ}$, *(ii)* $\frac{\text{area of } \Delta TSU}{\text{area of } \Delta QRU}$

(a) (i) $\overrightarrow{PR} = \overrightarrow{PQ} + \overrightarrow{QR} = \overrightarrow{PQ} + \overrightarrow{PS}$

$= 10\mathbf{a} + 5\mathbf{b}$

or $\overrightarrow{PR} = \overrightarrow{PQ} + \overrightarrow{PS}$ (Parallelogram Law of Vector Addition)

$= 10\mathbf{a} + 5\mathbf{b}$

(ii) $SU = \frac{2}{5} SR \Rightarrow \frac{SU}{SR} = \frac{2}{5}$

$\therefore$ UR = 3 parts (see Fig. 3.44(a)).

S —2— U —3— R (total 5)

Fig. 3.44(a)

$\frac{UR}{SR} = \frac{3}{5} \Rightarrow \overrightarrow{UR} = \frac{3}{5}\overrightarrow{SR} = \frac{3}{5}\overrightarrow{PQ} = \frac{3}{5}(10\mathbf{a}) = 6\mathbf{a}$

(iii) $\triangle TSU$ and $\triangle TPQ$ are similar.

$\frac{TU}{TQ} = \frac{SU}{PQ} = \frac{2}{5}$

$\therefore$ UQ = 3 parts (see Fig. 3.44(b)).

T —2— U —3— Q (total 5)

Fig. 3.44(b)

$\therefore \frac{TU}{UQ} = \frac{2}{3}$

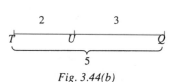

$TU = \frac{2}{3}(\overrightarrow{UR} + \overrightarrow{RQ})$

$= \frac{2}{3}(\overrightarrow{UR} - \overrightarrow{PS})$

$= \frac{2}{3}(6\mathbf{a} - 5\mathbf{b})$

Notes

ΔTSU and ΔTPQ are similar because the following angles are the same:

$T\hat{S}U = T\hat{P}Q$ *(corr. ∡s)*

$S\hat{T}U = P\hat{T}Q$ *(same ∡s)*

(b) (i) From (a)(iii), $\frac{TU}{UQ} = \frac{2}{3}$

(ii) $\triangle TSU$ and $\triangle QRU$ are similar.

$$\therefore \quad \frac{\text{area of } \Delta TSU}{\text{area of } \Delta QRU} = \left(\frac{TU}{QU}\right)^2$$

$$= \left(\frac{2}{3}\right)^2$$

$$= \frac{4}{9}$$

ΔTSU ***and*** ΔQRU ***are similar because***

$T\hat{U}S = Q\hat{U}R$ *(vert. opp. ∡s)*

$T\hat{S}U = Q\hat{R}U$ *(alt. ∡s)*

Since the two triangles are similar, we can use the formula:

$$\frac{A_2}{A_1} = \left(\frac{l_2}{l_1}\right)^2.$$

Example 24

PQRS is a parallelogram and M is the midpoint of SR. PS is produced to T so that PS = ST. PM is produced to N and RT = 3RN. $\overrightarrow{PQ} = 2\mathbf{a}$ *and* $\overrightarrow{QR} = 2\mathbf{b}$.

(a) Express, as simply as possible, in terms of **a** *and/or* **b**,

(i) $\overrightarrow{ST}$; *(ii)* $\overrightarrow{TR}$; *(iii)* $\overrightarrow{TN}$.

(b) Show that $\overrightarrow{PN} = \frac{4}{3}(\mathbf{a} + 2\mathbf{b})$.

(c) Express $\overrightarrow{PM}$, *as simply as possible, in terms of* **a** *and* **b**.

(d) Calculate the value of *(i)* $\frac{PM}{PN}$;

(ii) $\frac{\text{area of } \Delta MTP}{\text{area of } \Delta MTN}$.

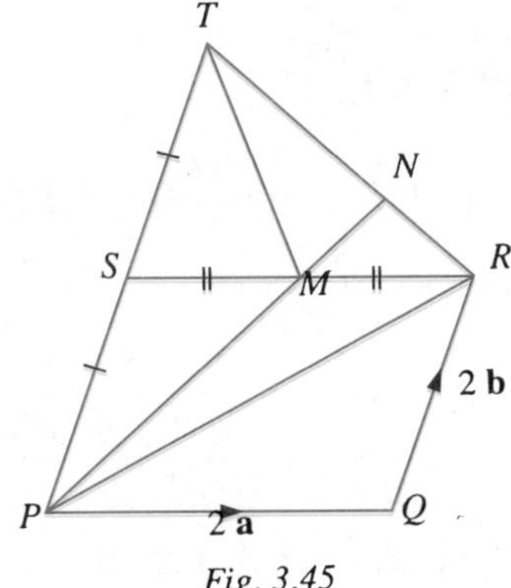

Fig. 3.45

(a) (i) $\overrightarrow{ST} = \overrightarrow{PS} = \overrightarrow{QR} = 2\mathbf{b}$

(ii) $\overrightarrow{SR} = \overrightarrow{PQ} = 2\mathbf{a}$

$$\overrightarrow{TR} = \overrightarrow{TS} + \overrightarrow{SR}$$

$$= -\overrightarrow{ST} + \overrightarrow{PQ}$$

$$= 2\mathbf{a} - 2\mathbf{b}$$

(iii) $RT = 3RN \Rightarrow \dfrac{RT}{RN} = \dfrac{3}{1}$

$\therefore \quad \dfrac{TN}{TR} = \dfrac{2}{3} \Rightarrow \overrightarrow{TN} = \dfrac{2}{3}\overrightarrow{TR}$

$$= \frac{2}{3}(2\mathbf{a} - 2\mathbf{b})$$

$$= \frac{4}{3}(\mathbf{a} - \mathbf{b})$$

Fig. 3.45(a)

(b) $\overrightarrow{PN} = \overrightarrow{PT} + \overrightarrow{TN} = 2\overrightarrow{ST} + \overrightarrow{TN}$

$$= 2(2\mathbf{b}) + \frac{4}{3}(\mathbf{a} - \mathbf{b})$$

$$= \frac{4}{3}\mathbf{a} + \frac{8}{3}\mathbf{b}$$

$$= \frac{4}{3}(\mathbf{a} + 2\mathbf{b})$$

(c) $\overrightarrow{PM} = \overrightarrow{PS} + \overrightarrow{SM} = \overrightarrow{PS} + \dfrac{1}{2}\overrightarrow{SR}$

$$= 2\mathbf{b} + \frac{1}{2}(2\mathbf{a})$$

$$= \mathbf{a} + 2\mathbf{b}$$

(d) (i) $\overrightarrow{PN} = \dfrac{4}{3}(\mathbf{a} + 2\mathbf{b}) = \dfrac{4}{3}\overrightarrow{PM}$

$\therefore \quad \overrightarrow{PN} = \dfrac{4}{3}\overrightarrow{PM} \Rightarrow \dfrac{PM}{PN} = \dfrac{3}{4}$

(ii) $\dfrac{PM}{PN} = \dfrac{3}{4} \Rightarrow \dfrac{PM}{MN} = \dfrac{3}{1} = 3$ (see Fig. 3.45(b))

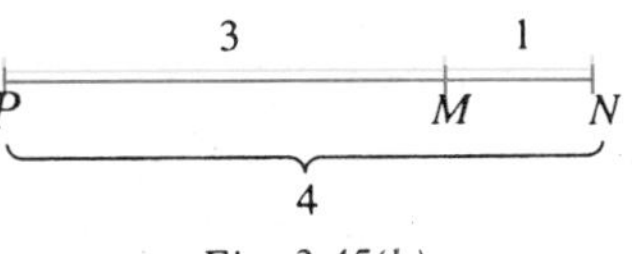

Fig. 3.45(b)

Since $\triangle MTP$ and $\triangle MTN$ have the same height (call it h), then

$$\frac{\text{area of } \triangle MTP}{\text{area of } \triangle MTN} = \frac{\frac{1}{2} PM \times h}{\frac{1}{2} MN \times h} = \frac{PM}{MN} = 3$$

1. Fig. 3.46 shows 2 non-parallel vectors **u** and **v**. Using the square grid below, express $\overrightarrow{AB}$, $\overrightarrow{MN}$ and $\overrightarrow{PQ}$ in terms of **u** and **v**.

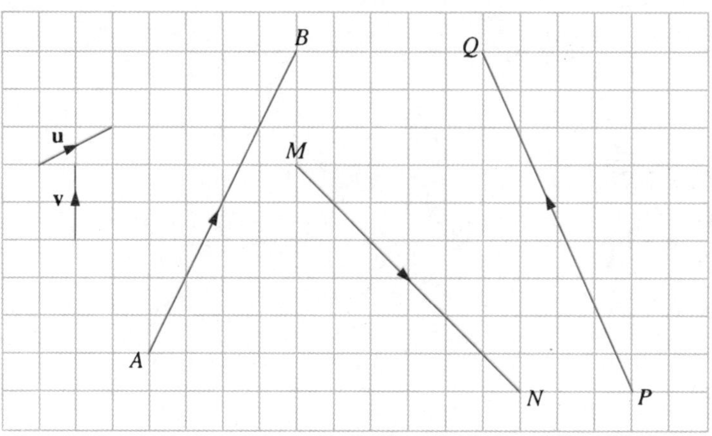

Fig. 3.46

2. Fig. 3.47 shows 2 non-parallel vectors **a** and **b**. Using the square grid below, express $\overrightarrow{LM}$, $\overrightarrow{PR}$, $\overrightarrow{ST}$ and $\overrightarrow{XY}$ in terms of **a** and **b**.

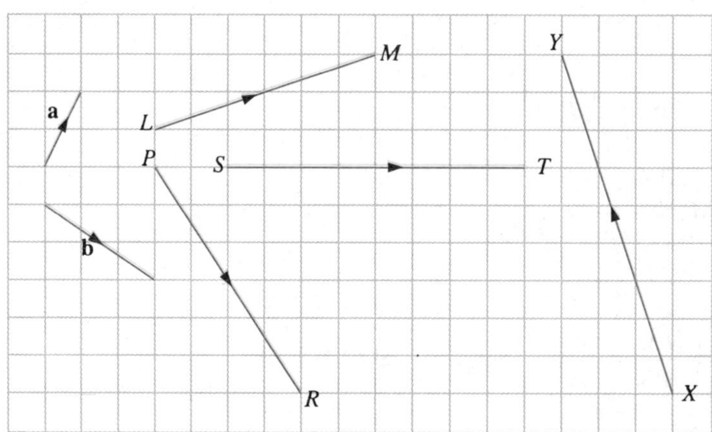

Fig. 3.47

3. In the diagram, $PQRS$ is a parallelogram. M is the mid-point of PQ, and N is on SR such that $SR = 3SN$. Given that $\overrightarrow{PS} = \mathbf{a}$ and $\overrightarrow{PM} = 2\mathbf{b}$, express in terms of **a** and **b**,

(a) $\overrightarrow{MR}$, (b) $\overrightarrow{RN}$, (c) $\overrightarrow{NM}$.

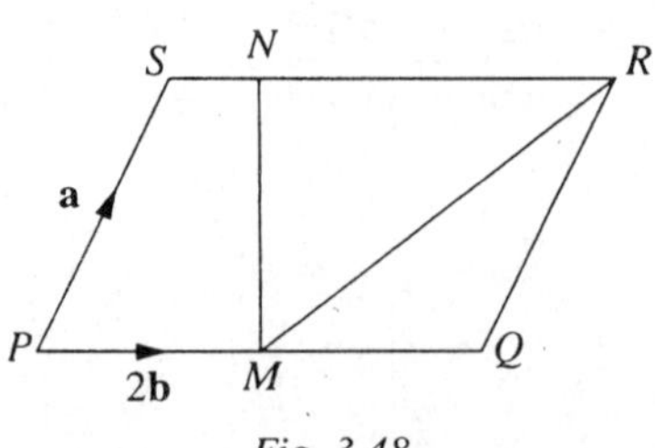

Fig. 3.48

4. $ABCD$ is a parallelogram with M as the mid-point of BC. If $\overrightarrow{AB} = \mathbf{p}$ and $\overrightarrow{AD} = \mathbf{q}$, express in terms of $\mathbf{p}$ and/or $\mathbf{q}$,

(a) $\overrightarrow{CM}$,

(b) $\overrightarrow{DB}$,

(c) $\overrightarrow{AM}$,

(d) $\overrightarrow{MD}$.

Fig. 3.49

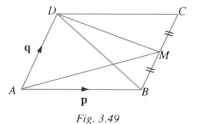

5. In the diagram, D is a point on BC such that $BD = 3DC$. Given that $\overrightarrow{BA} = \mathbf{p}$ and $\overrightarrow{BD} = \mathbf{q}$, express in terms of $\mathbf{p}$ and/or $\mathbf{q}$,

(a) $\overrightarrow{BC}$;

(b) $\overrightarrow{AD}$;

(c) $\overrightarrow{CA}$.

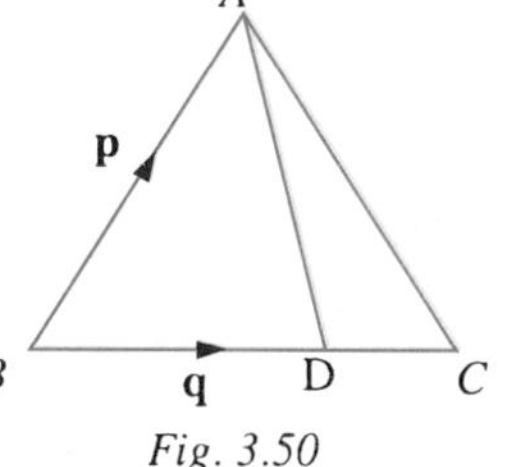

Fig. 3.50

6. In the diagram, if $\overrightarrow{AB} = \mathbf{u}$, $\overrightarrow{AC} = \mathbf{v}$, and M and N are the mid-points of AB and AC respectively, express in terms of $\mathbf{u}$ and $\mathbf{v}$,

(a) $\overrightarrow{BC}$,

(b) $\overrightarrow{AM}$,

(c) $\overrightarrow{AN}$,

(d) $\overrightarrow{MN}$.

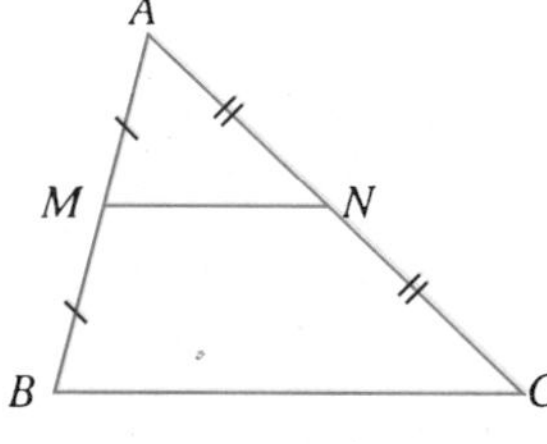

Fig. 3.51

What can you say about $\overrightarrow{BC}$ and $\overrightarrow{MN}$?

7. In the diagram, $\overrightarrow{AB} = \mathbf{u}$, $\overrightarrow{AC} = \mathbf{v}$, $\overrightarrow{CD} = \frac{3}{2}\mathbf{u}$, and $\overrightarrow{BE} = \frac{2}{5}\overrightarrow{BC}$. Express in terms of $\mathbf{u}$ and $\mathbf{v}$,

(a) $\overrightarrow{BC}$,

(b) $\overrightarrow{BE}$;

(c) $\overrightarrow{AD}$,

(d) $\overrightarrow{AE}$,

(e) $\overrightarrow{BD}$.

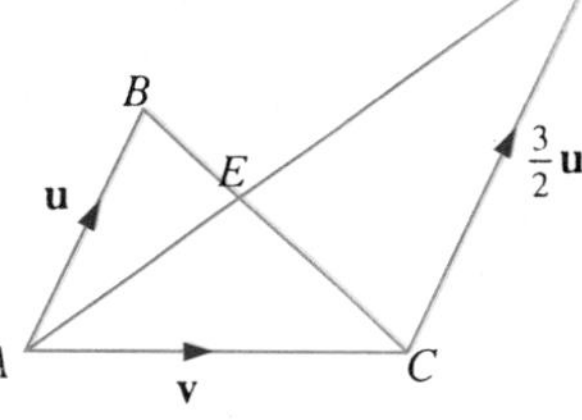

Fig. 3.52

8. In the diagram, $ABCD$ is a trapezium with $AD \mathbin{//} BC$ and $AD = \frac{2}{3}BC$. P and Q are points on AB and DC respectively such that P is the mid-point of AB and $DQ = \frac{1}{4}\overrightarrow{DC}$.

Given that $\overrightarrow{AB} = \mathbf{u}$ and $\overrightarrow{AD} = \mathbf{v}$, express in terms of $\mathbf{u}$ and $\mathbf{v}$,

(a) $\overrightarrow{AC}$,

(b) $\overrightarrow{DC}$,

(c) $\overrightarrow{AQ}$,

(d) $\overrightarrow{PQ}$.

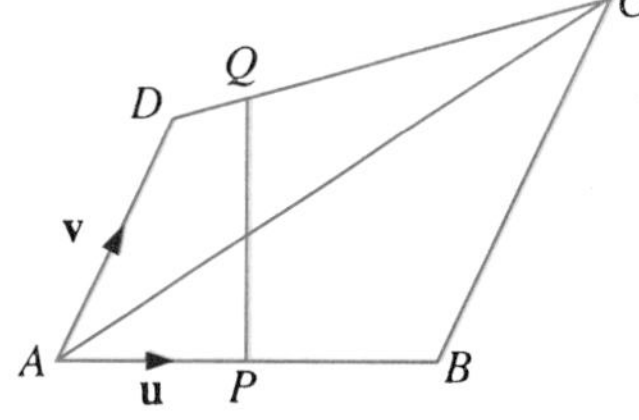

Fig. 3.53

9. $PQRS$ is a parallelogram. $\overrightarrow{BQ} = 2\overrightarrow{RB}$, $\overrightarrow{AR} = \frac{1}{3}\overrightarrow{SR}$, $\overrightarrow{PS} = \mathbf{a}$ and $\overrightarrow{PQ} = \mathbf{b}$.

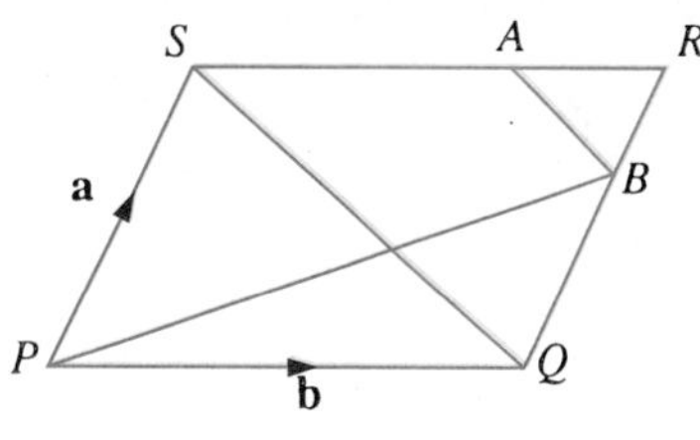

Fig. 3.54

(a) Express in terms of **a** and/or **b**,

(i) $\overrightarrow{SA}$, (ii) $\overrightarrow{QB}$, (iii) $\overrightarrow{PB}$,

(iv) $\overrightarrow{QS}$, (v) $\overrightarrow{BA}$.

(b) Calculate the value of

(i) $\frac{BA}{QS}$;

(ii) $\frac{\text{area of } \Delta ABR}{\text{area of } PQRS}$

10. In the diagram, T is the point of intersection of the diagonals of the quadrilateral $PQRS$. $\overrightarrow{PR} = 3\overrightarrow{PT}$, $\overrightarrow{PS} = 5\mathbf{b}$, $\overrightarrow{PQ} = 4\mathbf{a} + \mathbf{b}$ and $\overrightarrow{PR} = 3\mathbf{a} + 12\mathbf{b}$.

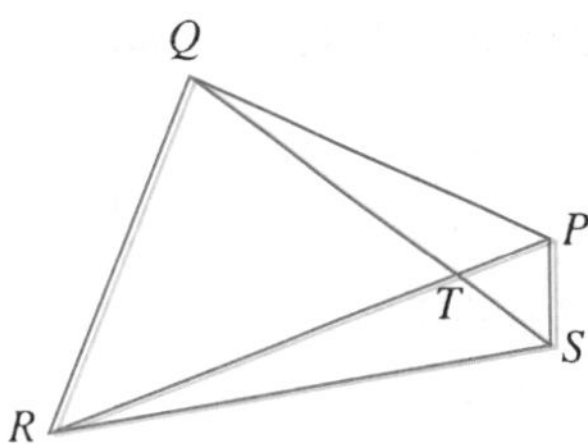

Fig. 3.55

(a) Express, as simply as possible, in terms of **a** and **b**,

(i) $\overrightarrow{RS}$, (ii) $\overrightarrow{RT}$, (iii) $\overrightarrow{RQ}$.

(b) Show that $\overrightarrow{QT} = 3(\mathbf{b} - \mathbf{a})$.

(c) Express $\overrightarrow{QS}$ as simply as possible, in terms of **a** and **b**.

(d) Calculate the value of

(i) $\frac{QT}{QS}$;

(ii) $\frac{\text{area of } \Delta PQT}{\text{area of } \Delta PQS}$;

(iii) $\frac{\text{area of } \Delta PQT}{\text{area of } \Delta RQT}$.

11. In triangle PQR, the point N on PR is such that $PN = \frac{2}{3}PR$. M is the mid-point of PQ, L is the mid-point of MN, and PL produced meets RQ at K. $4\overrightarrow{RK} = 3\overrightarrow{KQ}$, $\overrightarrow{PL} = \frac{7}{12}\overrightarrow{PK}$, $\overrightarrow{PN} = 2\mathbf{a}$ and $\overrightarrow{PM} = 2\mathbf{b}$.

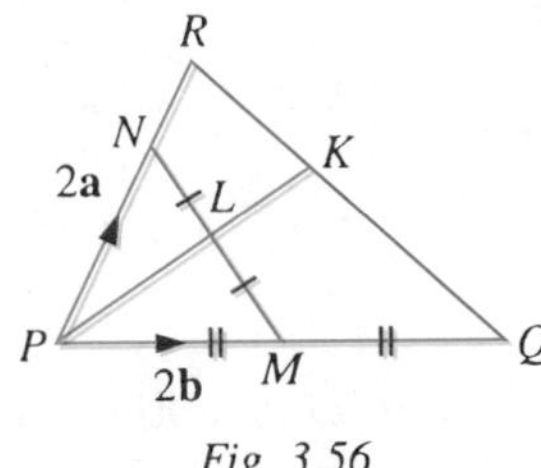

Fig. 3.56

(a) Express, as simply as possible, in terms of **a** and/or **b**,

(i) $\overrightarrow{NM}$, (ii) $\overrightarrow{NL}$, (iii) $\overrightarrow{PK}$,

(iv) $\overrightarrow{PR}$, (v) $\overrightarrow{PQ}$.

(b) Express $\overrightarrow{RQ}$ as simply as possible, in terms of **a** and **b**.

(c) Calculate the value of $\frac{KR}{QR}$.

(d) Show that $\overrightarrow{KR} = \frac{3}{7}(3\mathbf{a} - 4\mathbf{b})$.

(e) Calculate the value of

(i) $\frac{\text{area of } \Delta PKR}{\text{area of } \Delta PQR}$;

(ii) $\frac{\text{area of } \Delta PKN}{\text{area of } \Delta PQR}$.

Position Vectors

When we are considering the location of points in a plane, it is useful to refer to their positions relative to a fixed point O.

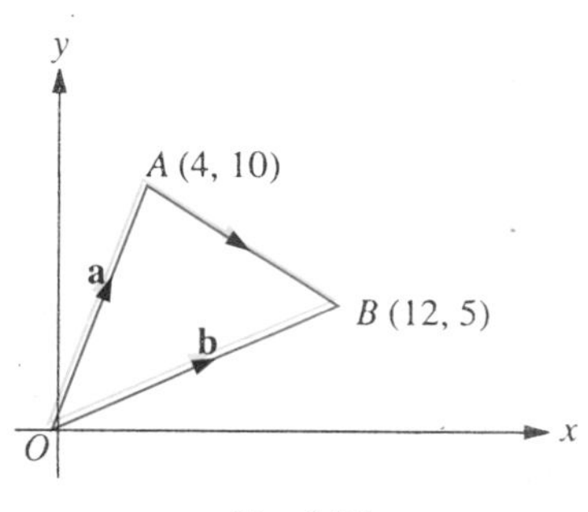

Fig. 3.57

In Fig. 3.57, the displacement vector $\overrightarrow{OA}$ describes the position of A relative to the origin O. $\overrightarrow{OA}$ is called the **position vector** of A relative to O.

Similarly, $\overrightarrow{OB}$ is the position vector of B relative to O.

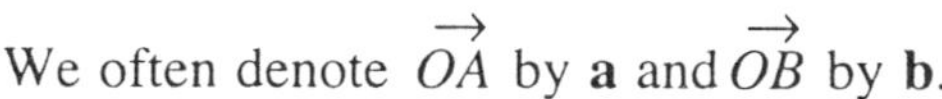

We often denote $\overrightarrow{OA}$ by **a** and $\overrightarrow{OB}$ by **b**.

In Fig 3.57, the vector $\overrightarrow{AB}$ can be expressed in terms of position vectors $\overrightarrow{OA}$ and $\overrightarrow{OB}$ as follows:

$$\overrightarrow{OA} + \overrightarrow{AB} = \overrightarrow{OB} \qquad \text{(Triangle Law of Vector Addition)}$$

$$\therefore \quad \underset{\text{start end}}{\overrightarrow{AB}} = \underset{\text{end}}{\overrightarrow{OB}} - \underset{\text{start}}{\overrightarrow{OA}} = \underset{\text{end}}{\mathbf{b}} - \underset{\text{start}}{\mathbf{a}}$$

(Recall: 'end minus start' for Triangle Law of Vector Subtraction)

In Fig. 3.57, the coordinates of A and B are (4, 10) and (12, 5) respectively. So

$$\overrightarrow{OA} = \mathbf{a} = \begin{pmatrix} 4 \\ 10 \end{pmatrix}, \ \overrightarrow{OB} = \mathbf{b} = \begin{pmatrix} 12 \\ 5 \end{pmatrix} \text{ and } \overrightarrow{AB} = \mathbf{b} - \mathbf{a} = \begin{pmatrix} 12 \\ 5 \end{pmatrix} - \begin{pmatrix} 4 \\ 10 \end{pmatrix} = \begin{pmatrix} 8 \\ -5 \end{pmatrix}$$

In general,

> **the position vector of $P(x, y)$ is $\overrightarrow{OP} = \begin{pmatrix} x \\ y \end{pmatrix}$. A vector $\overrightarrow{PQ}$ can be expressed in terms of position vectors as follows:**
>
> **$\overrightarrow{PQ} = \overrightarrow{OQ} - \overrightarrow{OP} = \mathbf{q} - \mathbf{p}$**

xample 25

(a) Write down the position vectors of A(2, 3) and B(4, 1). Hence express $\overrightarrow{AB}$ as a column vector.

(b) P is the point (2, −3) and $\overrightarrow{PQ} = \begin{pmatrix} 4 \\ -1 \end{pmatrix}$. Find the coordinates of Q and the gradient of PQ. What is the relationship between $\overrightarrow{PQ}$ and the gradient of PQ?

(a) The position vector of $A(2, 3)$ is $\overrightarrow{OA} = \begin{pmatrix} 2 \\ 3 \end{pmatrix}$.

The position vector of $B(4, 1)$ is $\overrightarrow{OB} = \begin{pmatrix} 4 \\ 1 \end{pmatrix}$.

$$\therefore \quad \underset{\text{start end}}{\overrightarrow{AB}} = \underset{\text{end}}{\overrightarrow{OB}} - \underset{\text{start}}{\overrightarrow{OA}} = \begin{pmatrix} 4 \\ 1 \end{pmatrix} - \begin{pmatrix} 2 \\ 3 \end{pmatrix} = \begin{pmatrix} 2 \\ -2 \end{pmatrix}.$$

(b) $\overrightarrow{PQ} = \overrightarrow{OQ} - \overrightarrow{OP} = \begin{pmatrix} 4 \\ -1 \end{pmatrix}$

$$\therefore \quad \overrightarrow{OQ} - \begin{pmatrix} 2 \\ -3 \end{pmatrix} = \begin{pmatrix} 4 \\ -1 \end{pmatrix}$$

i.e. $$\overrightarrow{OQ} = \begin{pmatrix} 4 \\ -1 \end{pmatrix} + \begin{pmatrix} 2 \\ -3 \end{pmatrix} = \begin{pmatrix} 6 \\ -4 \end{pmatrix}.$$

$\therefore$ the coordinates of Q are (6, −4).

$$\text{Gradient of } PQ = \frac{y_2 - y_1}{x_2 - x_1}$$

$$= \frac{-4 - (-3)}{6 - 2}$$

$$= -\frac{1}{4}$$

The relationship between $\overrightarrow{PQ}$ and the gradient of PQ is as follows:

$$\overrightarrow{PQ} = \begin{pmatrix} x \\ y \end{pmatrix} \Rightarrow \text{gradient of } PQ = \frac{y}{x}.$$

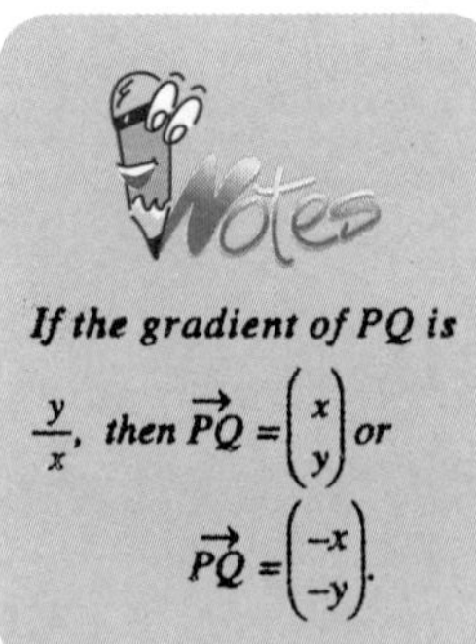
Notes
If the gradient of PQ is $\frac{y}{x}$, then $\overrightarrow{PQ} = \begin{pmatrix} x \\ y \end{pmatrix}$ or $\overrightarrow{PQ} = \begin{pmatrix} -x \\ -y \end{pmatrix}$.

Example 26

In Fig. 3.58, the coordinates of P, Q, and S are (1, 2), (7, 3) and (4, 7) respectively. Find the coordinates of R if PQRS is a parallelogram.

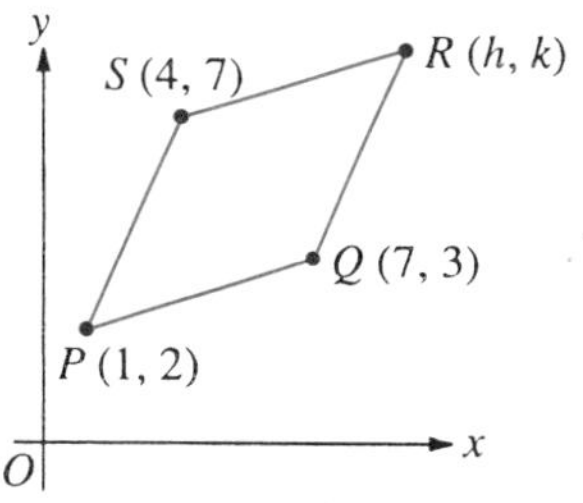

Fig. 3.58

Since $PQRS$ is a parallelogram,

$$\overrightarrow{SR} = \overrightarrow{PQ} = \begin{pmatrix}7\\3\end{pmatrix} - \begin{pmatrix}1\\2\end{pmatrix} = \begin{pmatrix}6\\1\end{pmatrix}.$$

So $\overrightarrow{OR} = \overrightarrow{OS} + \overrightarrow{SR} = \begin{pmatrix}4\\7\end{pmatrix} + \begin{pmatrix}6\\1\end{pmatrix} = \begin{pmatrix}10\\8\end{pmatrix},$

$\therefore$ the coordinates of R are (10, 8).

Example 27

*The point X in Fig. 3.59 lies on the straight line AC such that $AX = \frac{1}{4}AC$. With respect to the origin O, the position vector of A is 16**p** and the position vector of C is 16**q**. Express the following in terms of **p** and **q**.*

(a) $\overrightarrow{AC}$ *(b)* $\overrightarrow{AX}$ *(c)* $\overrightarrow{OX}$

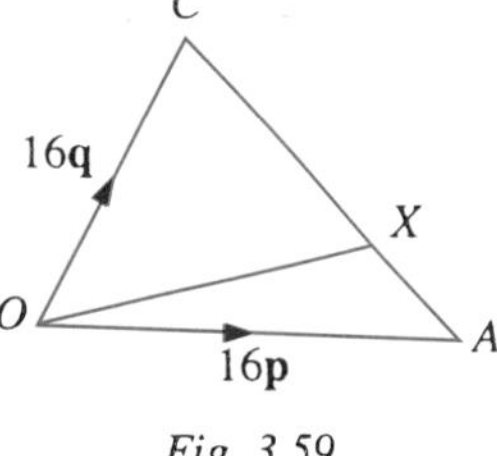

Fig. 3.59

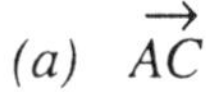

(a) $\overrightarrow{AC} = \overrightarrow{OC} - \overrightarrow{OA}$
$= 16\mathbf{q} - 16\mathbf{p}$

(b) $AX = \frac{1}{4}AC \Rightarrow \overrightarrow{AX} = \frac{1}{4}\overrightarrow{AC}$

$\therefore \quad \overrightarrow{AX} = \frac{1}{4}(16\mathbf{q} - 16\mathbf{p})$
$= 4\mathbf{q} - 4\mathbf{p}$

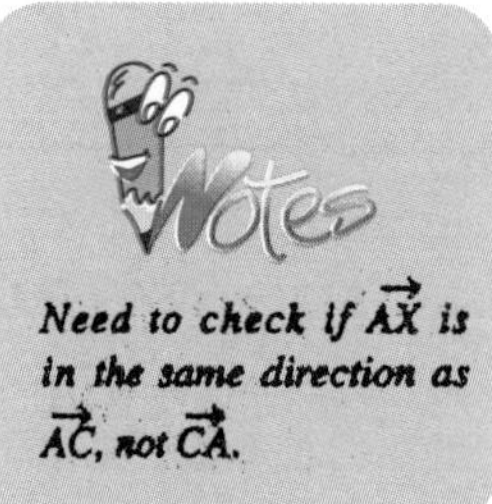

Notes
Need to check if AX is in the same direction as AC, not CA.

(c) $\overrightarrow{OX} = \overrightarrow{OA} + \overrightarrow{AX}$
$= 16\mathbf{p} + 4\mathbf{q} - 4\mathbf{p}$
$= 12\mathbf{p} + 4\mathbf{q}$

example 28

In Fig. 3.60, OABC is a parallelogram. X is a point on AB such that AX : XB = 1 : 2 and Y is the mid-point of BC. $\overrightarrow{OA} = 6\mathbf{p}$ *and* $\overrightarrow{OC} = 6\mathbf{q}$. *Express the following in terms of* **p** *and/or* **q**.

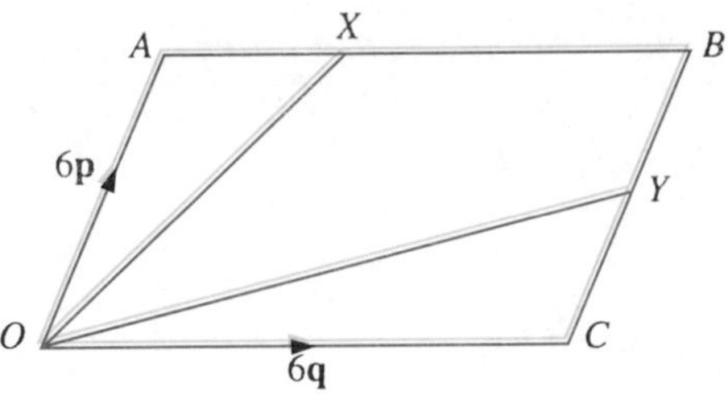

Fig. 3.60

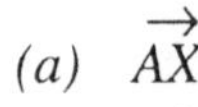
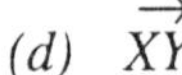

(a) $\overrightarrow{AX}$ *(b)* $\overrightarrow{OX}$ *(c)* $\overrightarrow{OY}$

(d) $\overrightarrow{XY}$ *(e)* $\overrightarrow{AY}$

Solution

(a) $AX : XB = 1 : 2 \Rightarrow \dfrac{AX}{AB} = \dfrac{1}{3}$ (see Fig. 3.61)

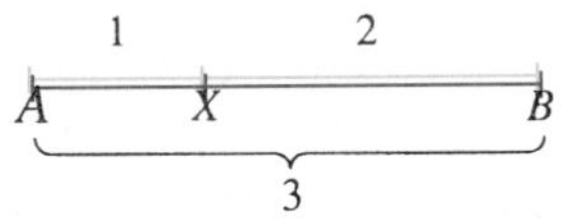

$\therefore \quad \overrightarrow{AX} = \dfrac{1}{3}\overrightarrow{AB} = \dfrac{1}{3}\overrightarrow{OC} = \dfrac{1}{3}(6\mathbf{q}) = 2\mathbf{q}$

1 2 A X B 3

Fig. 3.61

(b) $\overrightarrow{OX} = \overrightarrow{OA} + \overrightarrow{AX} = 6\mathbf{p} + 2\mathbf{q}$

(c) $\overrightarrow{OY} = \overrightarrow{OC} + \overrightarrow{CY} = \overrightarrow{OC} + \dfrac{1}{2}\overrightarrow{CB} = \overrightarrow{OC} + \dfrac{1}{2}\overrightarrow{OA}$

$= 6\mathbf{q} + \dfrac{1}{2}(6\mathbf{p}) = 6\mathbf{q} + 3\mathbf{p}$

(d) $\overrightarrow{XY} = \overrightarrow{OY} - \overrightarrow{OX}$

$= 6\mathbf{q} + 3\mathbf{p} - (6\mathbf{p} + 2\mathbf{q})$

$= 4\mathbf{q} - 3\mathbf{p}$

(e) $\overrightarrow{AY} = \overrightarrow{OY} - \overrightarrow{OA}$

$= 6\mathbf{q} + 3\mathbf{p} - 6\mathbf{p}$

$= 6\mathbf{q} - 3\mathbf{p}$

Example 29

In Fig. 3.62, $\overrightarrow{OU}$ *and* $\overrightarrow{OV}$ *represent the vectors 15***u** *and 15***v** *respectively.* $\overrightarrow{OA} = \frac{1}{3}\overrightarrow{OU}$ *and* $\overrightarrow{OB} = \frac{1}{3}\overrightarrow{OV}$. *Find the vectors* $\overrightarrow{AB}$ *and* $\overrightarrow{UV}$ *in terms of* **u** *and* **v**. *Given that* $\overrightarrow{AX} = \frac{1}{5}\overrightarrow{AV}$, *express the vectors* $\overrightarrow{VA}$, $\overrightarrow{UX}$ *and* $\overrightarrow{XB}$ *in terms of* **u** *and* **v**.

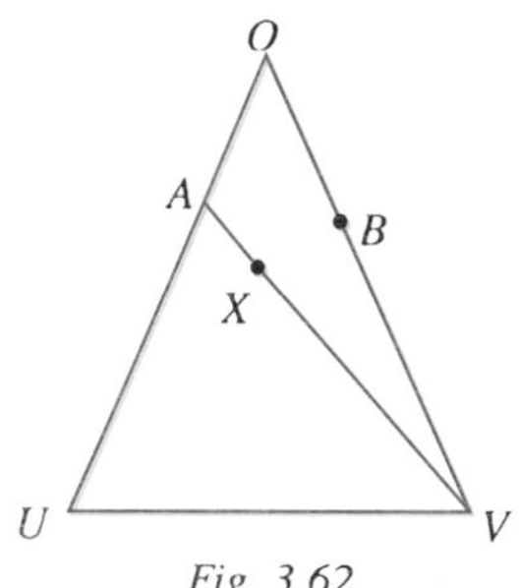

Fig. 3.62

$\overrightarrow{OU} = 15\mathbf{u}$, $\overrightarrow{OV} = 15\mathbf{v}$, $\overrightarrow{OA} = \frac{1}{3}\overrightarrow{OU} = \frac{1}{3}(15\mathbf{u}) = 5\mathbf{u}$,

$\overrightarrow{OB} = \frac{1}{3}\overrightarrow{OV} = \frac{1}{3}(15\mathbf{v}) = 5\mathbf{v}$

$\therefore \quad \overrightarrow{AB} = \overrightarrow{OB} - \overrightarrow{OA} = 5\mathbf{v} - 5\mathbf{u}$

$\overrightarrow{UV} = \overrightarrow{OV} - \overrightarrow{OU} = 15\mathbf{v} - 15\mathbf{u}$

Given $\overrightarrow{AX} = \frac{1}{5}\overrightarrow{AV}$, then $\overrightarrow{OX} - \overrightarrow{OA} = \frac{1}{5}(\overrightarrow{OV} - \overrightarrow{OA})$

$$\overrightarrow{OX} - 5\mathbf{u} = \frac{1}{5}(15\mathbf{v} - 5\mathbf{u})$$

$$= 3\mathbf{v} - \mathbf{u}$$

$$\overrightarrow{OX} = 4\mathbf{u} + 3\mathbf{v}$$

$\therefore \quad \overrightarrow{VA} = \overrightarrow{OA} - \overrightarrow{OV} = 5\mathbf{u} - 15\mathbf{v}$

$\overrightarrow{UX} = \overrightarrow{OX} - \overrightarrow{OU} = 4\mathbf{u} + 3\mathbf{v} - 15\mathbf{u} = 3\mathbf{v} - 11\mathbf{u}$

$\overrightarrow{XB} = \overrightarrow{OB} - \overrightarrow{OX} = 5\mathbf{v} - 4\mathbf{u} - 3\mathbf{v} = 2\mathbf{v} - 4\mathbf{u}$

This question can be solved ***without*** *even looking at the diagram. The trick is to express everything in terms of position vectors. For example, given* $\overrightarrow{AX} = \frac{1}{5}\overrightarrow{AV}$, *we just break the equation down into position vectors.*

1. Write down the position vectors of the following points as column vectors.

   (a) $A(4, 7)$
   (b) $B(-2, 5)$
   (c) $C(6, -1)$
   (d) $D(-4, -9)$

2. If P, Q and R are the points $(3, -2)$, $(2, -4)$ and $(2, 3)$ respectively, express the following as column vectors.

   (a) $\overrightarrow{PQ}$ (b) $\overrightarrow{QR}$

   (c) $\overrightarrow{RP}$

3. If L, M and N are the points $(2, 2)$, $(4, 7)$ and $(8, 1)$ respectively, express the following as column vectors.

   (a) $\overrightarrow{NM}$ (b) $\overrightarrow{LM}$

   (c) $\overrightarrow{LN}$

4. P is the point $(-1, 3)$, $\overrightarrow{PQ} = \begin{pmatrix} -2 \\ 5 \end{pmatrix}$ and $\overrightarrow{PR} = \begin{pmatrix} 0 \\ 7 \end{pmatrix}$.

   (a) Find the coordinates of Q and R.
   (b) Find the gradient of QR and the vector $\overrightarrow{QR}$.

5. A, B, C and D are four points such that A is $(-5, 3)$, C is $(7, 4)$, $\overrightarrow{AB} = \begin{pmatrix} 6 \\ 1 \end{pmatrix}$ and $\overrightarrow{AD} = \begin{pmatrix} 8 \\ -9 \end{pmatrix}$. Find

   (a) the coordinates of B and D,
   (b) the vectors $\overrightarrow{BC}$ and $\overrightarrow{CD}$.

6. $\overrightarrow{AB} = \begin{pmatrix} 9 \\ -15 \end{pmatrix}$ and $\overrightarrow{CD} = \frac{2}{3}\overrightarrow{AB}$.

   (a) Express $\overrightarrow{CD}$ as a column vector.

   (b) Given that A is the point $(-2, 7)$, find the coordinates of the point B.

   (c) Given that D is the point $(8, -5)$, find the coordinates of the point C.

7. Two points A and B have position vectors $\mathbf{a}$ and $\mathbf{b}$ respectively, relative to the origin O.

   Given that A is the point $(7, 4)$ and $\overrightarrow{AB} = \begin{pmatrix} -3 \\ 2 \end{pmatrix}$, find

   (a) $\mathbf{b}$,

   (b) the coordinates of the point C, such that $\overrightarrow{OC} = \overrightarrow{BA}$.

8. L is the point $(-3, 2)$ and M is $(t, 6)$.

   (a) Express $\overrightarrow{LM}$ as a column vector.

   (b) If $\overrightarrow{LM}$ is parallel to $\mathbf{p} = \begin{pmatrix} 8 \\ 1 \end{pmatrix}$, find the value of t.

   (c) If instead, $|\overrightarrow{LM}| = |\mathbf{p}|$, find the two possible values of t.

9. The coordinates of P, Q and R are $(1, 0)$, $(4, 2)$ and $(5, 4)$ respectively. Use a vector method to determine the coordinates of S if

   (a) $PQRS$ is a parallelogram,

   (b) $PRQS$ is a parallelogram.

10. Given that A is the point $(1, 2)$, $\overrightarrow{AB} = \begin{pmatrix} 4 \\ -5 \end{pmatrix}$, $\overrightarrow{AC} = \begin{pmatrix} 6 \\ 3 \end{pmatrix}$ and that M is the mid-point of $\overrightarrow{BC}$, find

(a) $\overrightarrow{BC}$;

(b) $\overrightarrow{AM}$;

(c) the coordinates of the point D such that $ABCD$ is a parallelogram.

11. In the diagram, $\overrightarrow{OA} = \mathbf{a}$, $\overrightarrow{OB} = \mathbf{b}$ and M is the mid-point of OA. Find $\overrightarrow{BM}$ in terms of $\mathbf{a}$ and $\mathbf{b}$.

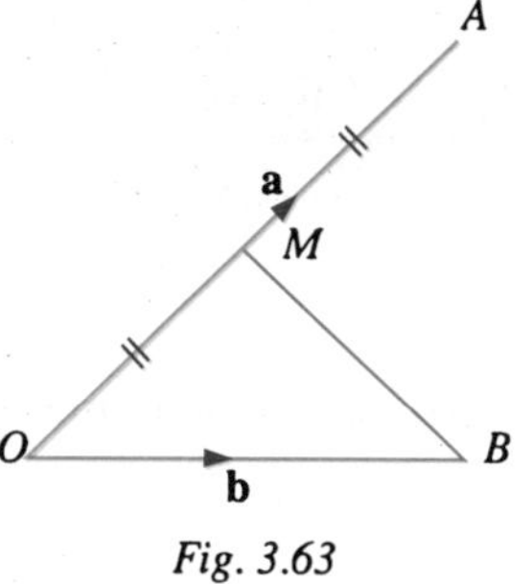

Fig. 3.63

12. In the diagram, M is the mid-point of OA and $BP = 3PM$. Given that the position vectors of A and B relative to O are $\mathbf{a}$ and $\mathbf{b}$ respectively, find the position vector of P relative to O.

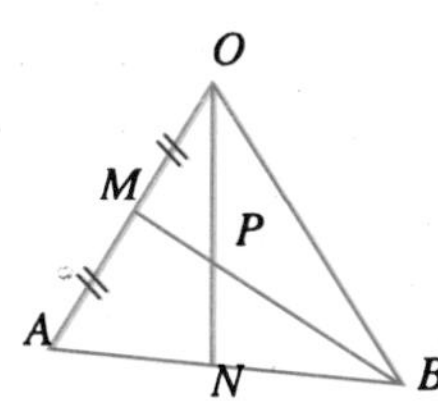

Fig. 3.64

13. Given that $\overrightarrow{OA} = \mathbf{a}$, $\overrightarrow{OB} = \mathbf{b}$ and $\overrightarrow{AC} = \frac{2}{3}\overrightarrow{CB}$, find $\overrightarrow{OC}$ in terms of $\mathbf{a}$ and $\mathbf{b}$.

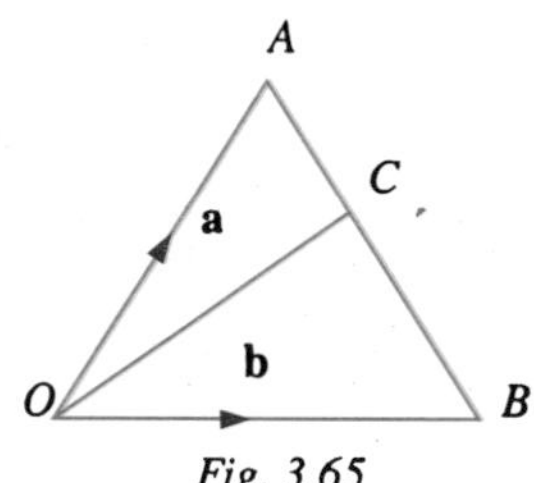

Fig. 3.65

14. $OPQR$ is a parallelogram. The point A on PR is such that $\overrightarrow{AR} = \frac{3}{4}\overrightarrow{PR}$. The point B on PQ is such that $\overrightarrow{PB} = \frac{1}{3}\overrightarrow{PQ}$. Given that $\overrightarrow{OP} = 15\mathbf{a}$ and $\overrightarrow{OR} = 15\mathbf{b}$, express the following vectors in terms of $\mathbf{a}$ and $\mathbf{b}$.

(a) $\overrightarrow{PR}$

(b) $\overrightarrow{PA}$

(c) $\overrightarrow{OA}$

(d) $\overrightarrow{OB}$

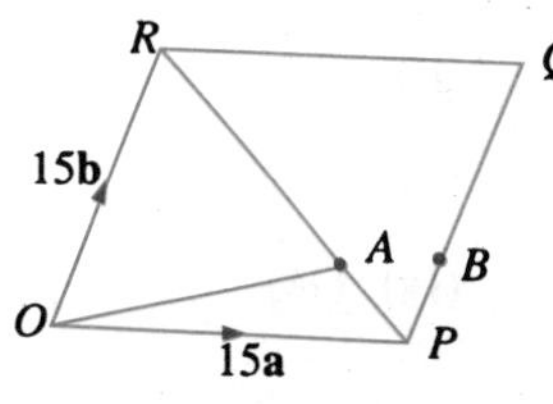

Fig. 3.66

15. $OPQR$ is a parallelogram and X is the mid-point of QR. OR is produced to S so that $\overrightarrow{OR} = \frac{1}{2}\overrightarrow{RS}$. Given that $\overrightarrow{OP} = 4\mathbf{a}$ and $\overrightarrow{PQ} = 4\mathbf{b}$, express the following vectors in terms of $\mathbf{a}$ and $\mathbf{b}$, giving your answers in the simplest form.

(a) $\overrightarrow{OQ}$

(b) $\overrightarrow{OX}$

(c) $\overrightarrow{QS}$

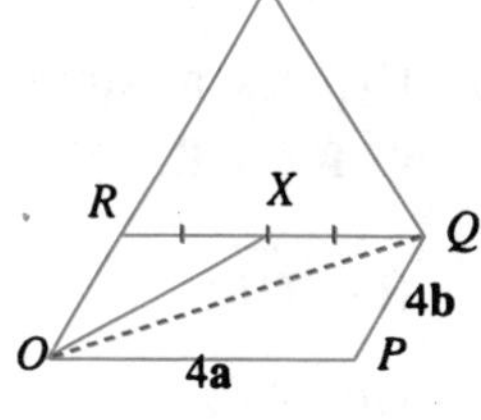

Fig. 3.67

16. OPA and OQC are straight lines and PC intersects QA at B. Given that $\overrightarrow{OQ} = \frac{2}{3}\overrightarrow{QC}$, $\frac{PB}{BC} = \frac{1}{3}$, $\overrightarrow{OP} = 8\mathbf{p}$ and $\overrightarrow{OQ} = 8\mathbf{q}$, express the following vectors as simply as possible in terms of $\mathbf{p}$ and $\mathbf{q}$.

(a) $\overrightarrow{PC}$

(b) $\overrightarrow{PB}$

(c) $\overrightarrow{OB}$

(d) $\overrightarrow{QB}$

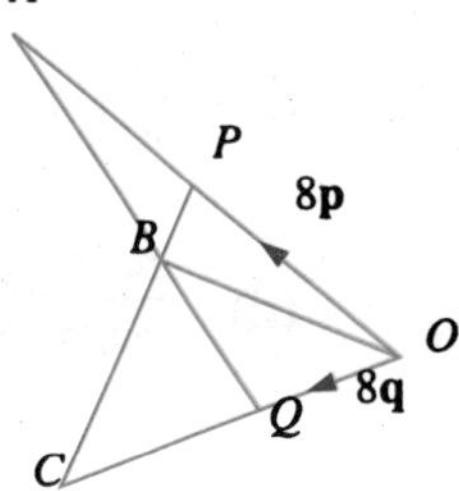

Fig. 3.68

17. In the diagram, $\overrightarrow{OA} = \mathbf{a}$, $\overrightarrow{OB} = \mathbf{b}$, $\overrightarrow{OP} = 2\mathbf{a}$, $OQ : QB = 2 : 1$, and M is the mid-point of AB.

(a) Express, as simply as possible, in terms of **a** and/or **b**,

(i) $\overrightarrow{OQ}$;

(ii) $\overrightarrow{PQ}$;

(iii) $\overrightarrow{OM}$;

(iv) $\overrightarrow{QM}$.

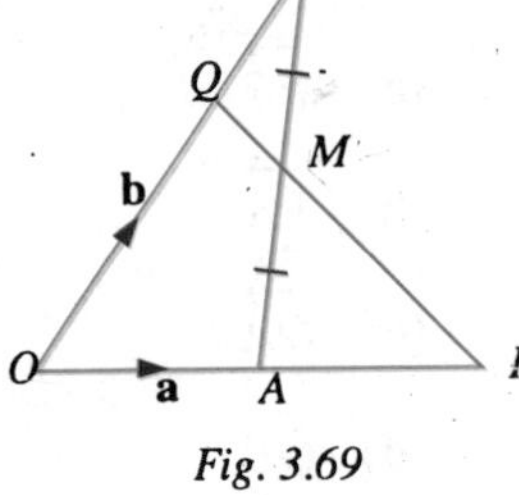

Fig. 3.69

(b) Find the value of $\frac{PM}{MQ}$.

18. $OABC$ is a parallelogram and ACT is a straight line. OC is produced to meet BT at R. $BT = 4BR$, $\overrightarrow{OA} = \mathbf{p}$, $\overrightarrow{OC} = \mathbf{q}$ and $\overrightarrow{TC} = 3(\mathbf{p} - \mathbf{q})$.

(a) Express, as simply as possible, in terms of **p** and **q**,

(i) $\overrightarrow{OT}$;

(ii) $\overrightarrow{AT}$;

(iii) $\overrightarrow{OB}$;

(iv) $\overrightarrow{BT}$;

(v) $\overrightarrow{TR}$.

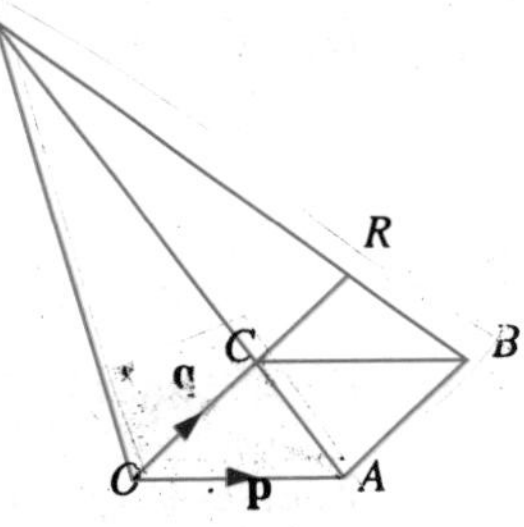

Fig. 3.70

(b) Show that $\overrightarrow{CR} = \frac{3}{4}\mathbf{q}$.

(c) Find the value of

(i) $\frac{CR}{OC}$;

(ii) $\frac{\text{area of } \Delta TCR}{\text{area of } \Delta TAB}$.

19. Relative to the origin O which is not shown in the diagram, P is the point (1, 11), Q is the point (2, 8), R is the point (–1, 7), S is the point (–2, 8) and T is the point (–4, 6). The lines PQ and SR produced intersect at U.

(a) Express the following as column vectors.

(i) $\overrightarrow{PQ}$

(ii) $\overrightarrow{SR}$

(iii) $\overrightarrow{RQ}$

(iv) $\overrightarrow{TQ}$

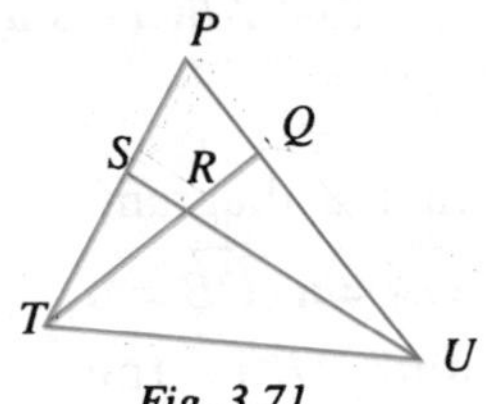

Fig. 3.71

(b) Find the numerical value of the ratio $\frac{RQ}{TQ}$.

1. A scalar has magnitude only but a vector has both **magnitude** and **direction**

2. Two vectors are equal when they have the same direction and magnitude.

3. The magnitude of a column vector $\mathbf{a} = \begin{pmatrix} x \\ y \end{pmatrix}$ is given by

$$|\mathbf{a}| = \sqrt{x^2 + y^2}.$$

4. The sum of two vectors, **a** and **b**, can be determined by using the Triangle Law or Parallelogram Law of Vector Addition.

5. The difference of two vectors, **a** and **b**, can be determined by using the Triangle Law of Vector Subtraction.

6. For any two column vectors $\mathbf{a} = \begin{pmatrix} p \\ q \end{pmatrix}$ and $\mathbf{b} = \begin{pmatrix} r \\ s \end{pmatrix}$,

$$\mathbf{a} + \mathbf{b} = \begin{pmatrix} p \\ q \end{pmatrix} + \begin{pmatrix} r \\ s \end{pmatrix} = \begin{pmatrix} p + r \\ q + s \end{pmatrix},$$

$$\mathbf{a} - \mathbf{b} = \begin{pmatrix} p \\ q \end{pmatrix} - \begin{pmatrix} r \\ s \end{pmatrix} = \begin{pmatrix} p - r \\ q - s \end{pmatrix}.$$

7. $\mathbf{b} = k\mathbf{a}$ is called the **scalar multiple** of **a** if $k \neq 0$ and $\mathbf{a} \neq \mathbf{0}$.
Then **a** and **b** are parallel vectors and $|\mathbf{b}| = |k|\,|\mathbf{a}|$.

8. The **position vector** of a point $P(x, y)$ is $\overrightarrow{OP} = \begin{pmatrix} x \\ y \end{pmatrix}$.

Given that $\mathbf{a} = \begin{pmatrix} x \\ 4 \end{pmatrix}$, $\mathbf{b} = \begin{pmatrix} 3 \\ y \end{pmatrix}$ *and* $3\mathbf{a} - 2\mathbf{b} = 4\begin{pmatrix} -1 \\ 3 \end{pmatrix}$, *find the values of x and y.*

$$3\mathbf{a} - 2\mathbf{b} = 4\begin{pmatrix} -1 \\ 3 \end{pmatrix}$$

$$3\begin{pmatrix} x \\ 4 \end{pmatrix} - 2\begin{pmatrix} 3 \\ y \end{pmatrix} = 4\begin{pmatrix} -1 \\ 3 \end{pmatrix}$$

$$\begin{pmatrix} 3x - 6 \\ 12 - 2y \end{pmatrix} = \begin{pmatrix} -4 \\ 12 \end{pmatrix}$$

$\therefore \quad 3x - 6 = -4 \quad$ and $\quad 12 - 2y = 12$

$x = \frac{2}{3} \quad$ and $y = 0$

In the diagram, $\overrightarrow{DX} = 2\overrightarrow{XB}$, $\overrightarrow{AD} = \mathbf{a}$, $\overrightarrow{BC} = 3\mathbf{a}$ *and* $\overrightarrow{BA} = \mathbf{b}$. *Find the following in terms of* **a** *and* **b**.

(a) $\overrightarrow{BD}$ *(b)* $\overrightarrow{XD}$ *(c)* $\overrightarrow{CD}$

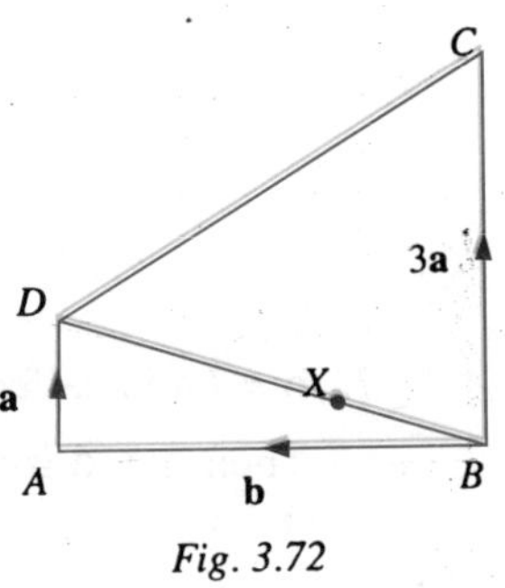

Fig. 3.72

(a) $\overrightarrow{BD} = \overrightarrow{BA} + \overrightarrow{AD}$

$= \mathbf{b} + \mathbf{a}$

$= \mathbf{a} + \mathbf{b}$

(b) $\overrightarrow{DX} = 2\overrightarrow{XB} \Rightarrow \frac{DX}{XB} = \frac{2}{1}$

$\therefore \quad \frac{XD}{BD} = \frac{2}{3}$ *(see Fig. 3.72(a))*

$\therefore \quad \overrightarrow{XD} = \frac{2}{3}\overrightarrow{BD}$

$\overrightarrow{XD} = \frac{2}{3}(\mathbf{a} + \mathbf{b})$

2 1
D X B
3

Fig. 3.72(a)

(c) $\overrightarrow{CD} = \overrightarrow{CB} + \overrightarrow{BD}$

$= -3\mathbf{a} + (\mathbf{a} + \mathbf{b})$

$= \mathbf{b} - 2\mathbf{a}$

Review Questions 3

1. The figure below shows vectors **a** and **b**. On a sheet of squared or graph paper, draw appropriate triangles to illustrate the following:

   (a) **a** + **b**,
   (b) 2(**a** + **b**),
   (c) **a** – **b**,
   (d) $\frac{2}{3}$**a** + 2**b**,
   (e) –(**a** + **b**),
   (f) **a** + 2**b**.

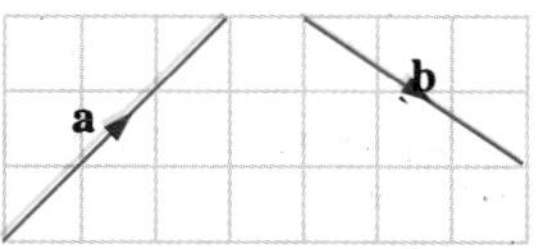

Fig. 3.73

Then express your answers as column vectors.

2. (a) Refer to Fig. 3.74 and write down the column vector representing the following.

   (i) $\overrightarrow{PQ}$
   (ii) $\overrightarrow{PR}$
   (iii) $\overrightarrow{RQ}$

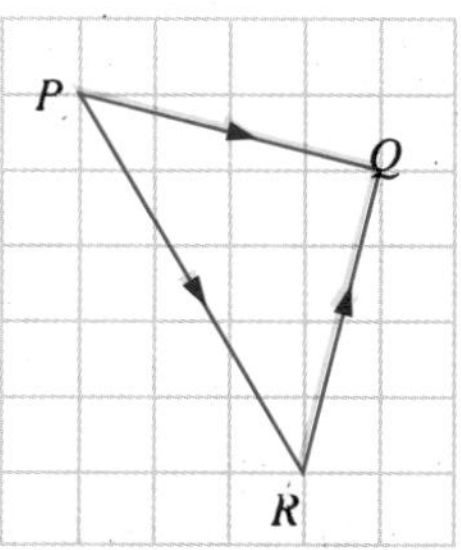

Fig. 3.74

   (b) If S is a point such that $PQRS$ is a square, write down $\overrightarrow{SQ}$ in column vector form.

   (c) Find the length of
   (i) a side of the square $PQRS$,
   (ii) the diagonal of the square $PQRS$.

3. Given that $\overrightarrow{OA} = \begin{pmatrix} 8 \\ a \end{pmatrix}$ and $\overrightarrow{OB} = \begin{pmatrix} a \\ 2 \end{pmatrix}$, where $a \neq 0$, find the possible values of a in each of the following cases.

   (a) $\overrightarrow{OA}$ and $\overrightarrow{OB}$ are parallel
   (b) $|\overrightarrow{OB}| = |\overrightarrow{AB}|$

4. It is given that $\overrightarrow{OA} = \begin{pmatrix} 1 \\ 2 \end{pmatrix}$, $\overrightarrow{OB} = \begin{pmatrix} 6 \\ 5 \end{pmatrix}$ and $\overrightarrow{OC} = \begin{pmatrix} 2 \\ 6 \end{pmatrix}$.

   (a) Express as a column vector and find the magnitude of each of the following.

   (i) $\overrightarrow{AB}$ (ii) $\overrightarrow{AC}$ (iii) $\overrightarrow{BC}$

   (b) Hence state the special property of $\triangle ABC$ and find its area.

5. Given that $\overrightarrow{AB} = \begin{pmatrix} a \\ b \end{pmatrix}$ and $|\overrightarrow{AB}| = 10$, find the value of a and of b where $b > 0$ such that $\overrightarrow{AB}$ is parallel to the vector $\begin{pmatrix} -3 \\ 4 \end{pmatrix}$.

6. Given three points A, B and C with position vectors $\overrightarrow{OA} = 2\mathbf{p} + \mathbf{q}$, $\overrightarrow{OB} = 2k\mathbf{p} + \mathbf{q}$ and $\overrightarrow{OC} = 12\mathbf{p} + 4\mathbf{q}$, where k is a constant, express the following in terms of **p**, **q** and/or k.

   (a) $\overrightarrow{AB}$ (b) $\overrightarrow{AC}$

7. In the figure, $\overrightarrow{OA} = 3\mathbf{a}$, $\overrightarrow{OC} = \mathbf{b}$ and $\overrightarrow{CB} = 3\mathbf{b}$. D is a point on AC such that $\frac{CD}{CA} = \frac{1}{3}$ and E is a point on AB such that $\frac{AE}{AB} = \frac{1}{3}$. Express the following in terms of **a** and **b**.

   (a) $\overrightarrow{AB}$
   (b) $\overrightarrow{AC}$
   (c) $\overrightarrow{OD}$
   (d) $\overrightarrow{OE}$

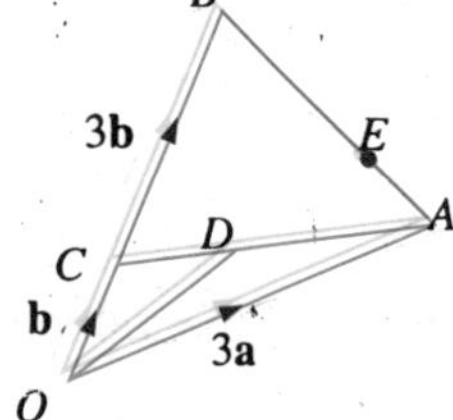

Fig. 3.75

8. In Fig. 3.76, $OABC$ is a parallelogram whose diagonals meet at D. M is the mid-point of BC. Given that $\overrightarrow{OA} = 5\mathbf{p} - \mathbf{q}$ and $\overrightarrow{OC} = \mathbf{p} + 3\mathbf{q}$, express the following in terms of **p** and **q**.

(a) $\overrightarrow{OD}$

(b) $\overrightarrow{AC}$

(c) $\overrightarrow{AM}$

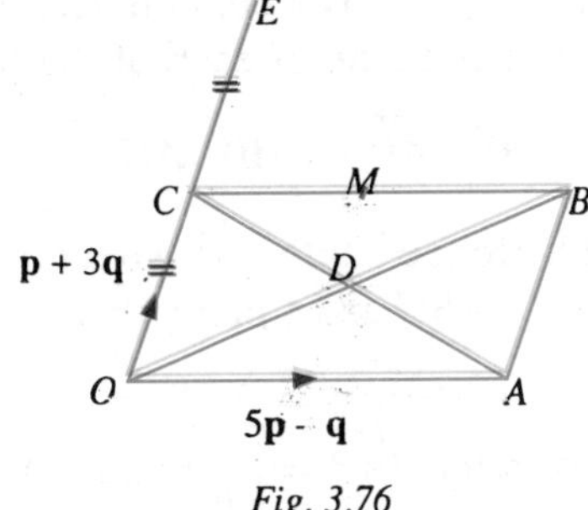

Fig. 3.76

(d) Express $\overrightarrow{AE}$ in terms of **p** and **q** if OC is produced to E such that $OC = CE$.

9. In Fig. 3.77, $ABCD$ is a parallelogram. The point E, on DC, is such that $DE = \frac{1}{3}DC$. The lines AD and BE, when produced, meet at F. Given that $\overrightarrow{AB} = \begin{pmatrix} 6 \\ 0 \end{pmatrix}$ and $\overrightarrow{AD} = \begin{pmatrix} 2 \\ 4 \end{pmatrix}$,

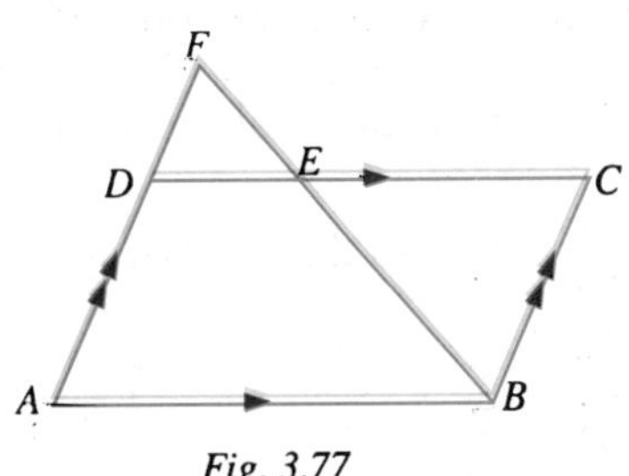

Fig. 3.77

(a) find the value of $|\overrightarrow{AB}|$,

(b) express each of the following as a column vector.

(i) $\overrightarrow{CB}$

(ii) $\overrightarrow{EC}$

(iii) $\overrightarrow{FE}$

10. In the diagram, $ABCDEFGH$ is a regular octagon where O is its centre, $\overrightarrow{AB} = \mathbf{p}$ and $\overrightarrow{AE} = \mathbf{q}$.

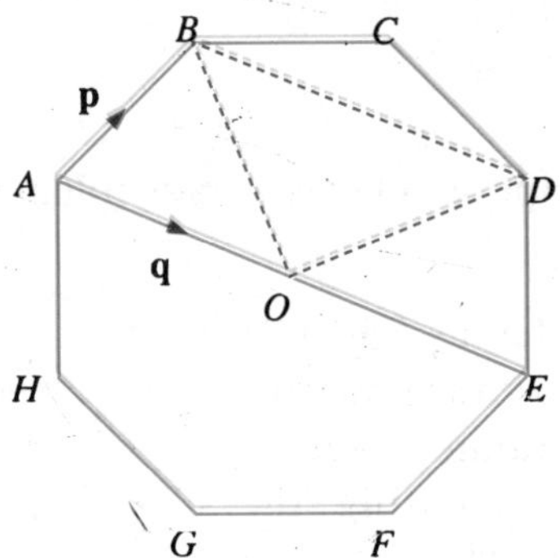

(a) Express, as simply as possible, in terms of **p** and/or **q**,

(i) $\overrightarrow{EF}$,

(ii) $\overrightarrow{BE}$.

(b) Given that $|\overrightarrow{AE}| = 2$ units, find the exact value of $|\overrightarrow{BD}|$.

(c) Hence express $\overrightarrow{BD}$, as simply as possible, in terms of **p** and/or **q**.

11. In the diagram, $\overrightarrow{OP} = \mathbf{p}$, $\overrightarrow{OQ} = \mathbf{q}$, $PS : SQ = 3 : 2$, $OQ : QT = 2 : 1$ and $OR : RP = 2 : 1$.

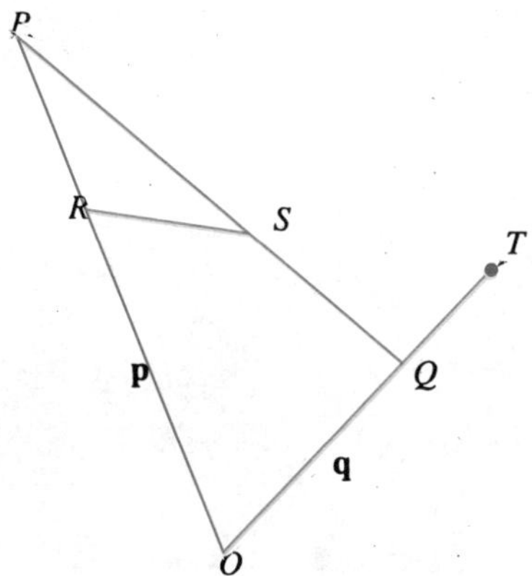

(a) Express, as simply as possible, in terms of **a** and/or **b**,

(i) $\overrightarrow{QP}$,

(ii) $\overrightarrow{QS}$,

(iii) $\overrightarrow{OS}$,

(iv) $\overrightarrow{ST}$.

(b) **(i)** Show that $\overrightarrow{RS} = k\overrightarrow{ST}$, where k is a constant.

(ii) Write down two facts about the points R, S and T.

12. In the diagram, $\overrightarrow{OP} = 2\mathbf{p}$ and $\overrightarrow{OQ} = \mathbf{q}$. $\overrightarrow{OP} = 2\overrightarrow{PR}$ and $\overrightarrow{OQ} = \overrightarrow{QS}$. T is the point on QP produced where $TQ = 3PQ$.

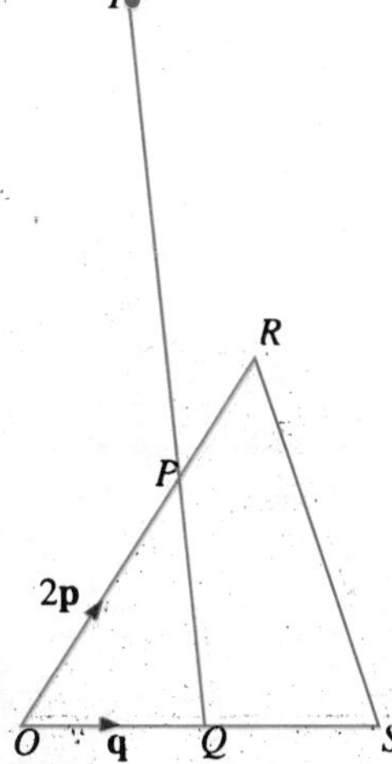

(a) Express the following vectors, as simply as possible, in terms of **p** and/or **q**.

(i) $\overrightarrow{QP}$,

(ii) $\overrightarrow{OR}$,

(iii) $\overrightarrow{SR}$,

(iv) $\overrightarrow{ST}$.

(b) Write down two facts about the points S, R and T.

(c) Find the value of $\dfrac{\text{Area of } \triangle OPQ}{\text{Area of } \triangle SPT}$.

In this chapter, you will learn how to

- ***calculate the standard deviation;***
- ***use the mean and standard deviation to compare two sets of data.***

CHAPTER

4

Standard Deviation and Mean

Introduction

If we are to classify this group of 13 year old secondary pupils according to their heights, then we will get a frequency distribution that is representative of all the pupils in the age group with a minority that are extremely tall or short, while the majority are of average height. Will the frequency distribution of their weights follow this pattern?

Mean (Revision)

In Book 2, we learnt to calculate the mean for a set of data.
For a set of n quantities $\{x_1, x_2, x_3, ..., x_n\}$,

$$\bar{x} = \frac{\Sigma x_i}{n}$$

For a frequency distribution,

$$\bar{x} = \frac{\Sigma fx}{\Sigma f}$$

where x is the mid-value of the class interval.

xample 1

The number of times that the students in a class fell ill last year is given in the table below.

	0	*1*	2	*3*
	30	*6*	2	2

Calculate the mean number of times that a student fell ill.

To find the mean, we use $\bar{x} = \frac{\Sigma fx}{\Sigma f}$.

The mean number of times that a student fell sick is $\frac{0 \times 30 + 1 \times 6 + 2 \times 2 + 3 \times 2}{30 + 6 + 2 + 2}$

$$= \frac{0 + 6 + 4 + 6}{40}$$

$$= 0.4$$

The table below shows the expenditure of the families in a housing estate.

	$0 < x \le 500$	$500 < x \le 1000$	$1000 < x \le 1500$	$1500 < x \le 2000$
	48	63	15	24

Calculate the mean expenditure of the families in the estate.

To calculate the mean of the distribution, we use $\bar{x} = \dfrac{\sum fx}{\sum f}$.

The mean expenditure of the families is $\dfrac{48 \times 250 + 63 \times 750 + 15 \times 1250 + 24 \times 1750}{48 + 63 + 15 + 24}$

$= \$800$

1. The number of goals scored by a soccer team in six matches are 2, 3, 0, 4, 1 and 3.
   (a) Calculate the mean number of goals.
   (b) Find the number of goals the team needs to score in its next match in order for its mean score to be 2 goals.

2. A die is tossed 30 times and the table below gives the results:

Number shown on the die	1	2	3	4	5	6
Frequency	3	6	8	a	2	5

   (a) Find the value of a.
   (b) Calculate the mean of the 30 tosses.

3. The table shows the number of books borrowed from a library by its members.

Number of books	1	2	3	4	5	6
Number of members	13	26	w	38	18	10

   If the mean number of books borrowed per member is 3.4, find w.

4. The table below shows the prices of an article sold in different stores.

Price ($)	$1 \leq x < 1.5$	$1.5 \leq x < 2$	$2 \leq x < 2.5$	$2.5 \leq x < 3$
Frequency	8	12	20	11

Find the mean price of the article.

5. The distribution table below shows the ages of 1107 members of a country club.

Age (as of last birthday)	20 – 29	30 – 39	40 – 49	50 – 59	60 – 69
Number of members	94	216	379	m	130

Calculate the mean age of the members.

6. The following histogram shows the frequency distribution of the speed of some cars on the ECP.

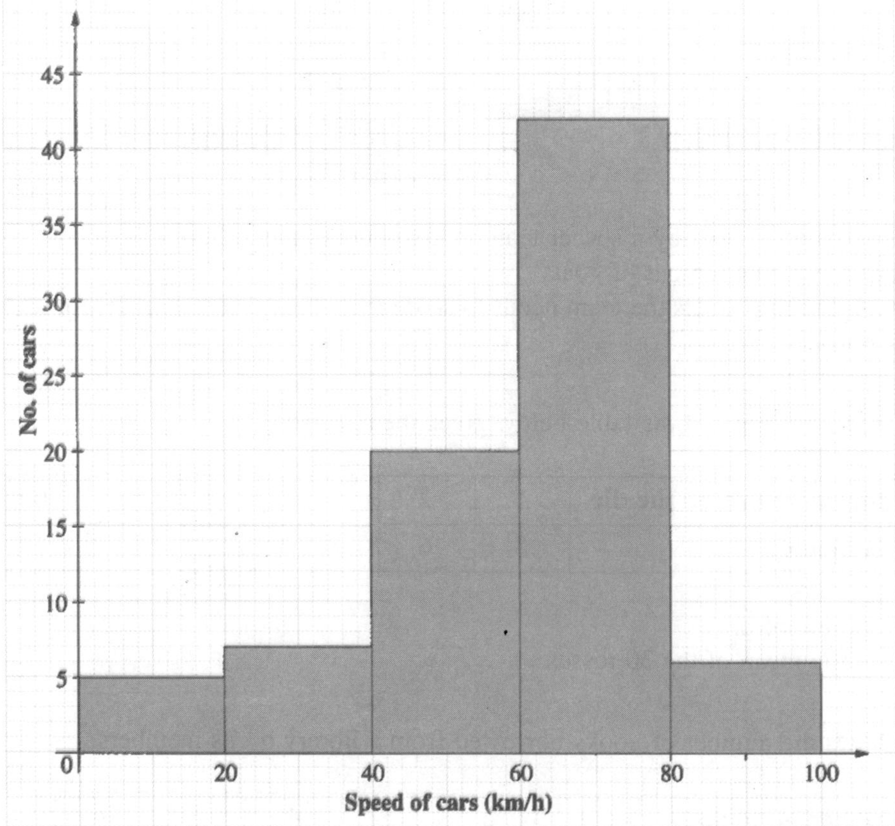

Calculate the mean speed of the cars.

Standard Deviation

Observe the two sets of data below.

Data Set A	Data Set B
3, 4, 5, 5, 6	1, 3, 4, 5, 10
Mean = 4.6	Mean = 4.6

Both sets of data have the same mean, but what do you notice about the spread of each set of data?

In Set A, the data are closed to the mean. In Set B, the data have varying differences from the mean and some of the data are far from the mean.

We use **standard deviation** to measure the spread of a set of data from its mean. Generally, the more widespread a set of data is, the higher the deviation. Standard deviation is useful when comparing the spread of two data sets that have approximately the same mean.

There are several notations that stand for standard deviation: S, SD or σ. We shall use S to represent standard deviation.

$$S = \sqrt{\frac{\Sigma(x - \bar{x})^2}{n}}$$

*You can find the standard deviation key on your calculator. It is represented by **S**, **SD** or **σ**.*

where n is the number of data in the set $\{x_1, x_2, x_3, \ldots, x_n\}$, and $\bar{x}$ is the mean of the data set.

$x - \bar{x}$ is the deviation of each data from the mean. For Set A,

$$\Sigma(x - \bar{x})^2 = (3 - 4.6)^2 + (4 - 4.6)^2 + (5 - 4.6)^2 + (5 - 4.6)^2 + (6 - 4.6)^2$$

$$= 5.2$$

$$\therefore \quad S = \sqrt{\frac{5.2}{5}} = 1.02 \quad \text{(correct to 3 sig. fig.)}$$

Calculate the standard deviation for Data Set B (correct to 3 sig. fig.).
Did you get 3.01?
Compare the standard deviation for the two sets of data.
What does the comparison tell you about the two sets of data?

xample 3

Calculate the mean and standard deviation of the two sets of marks below.

Set A: 4, 6, 6, 7, 8, 10, 11, 12
Set B: 0, 1, 1, 2, 3, 14, 17 and 25.

(a) Is it meaningful to compare the standard deviations of the data sets? Why?

(b) Compare and comment briefly on the two sets of marks.

$$\text{Mean of Set } A = \frac{4+6+6+7+8+10+11+12}{8}$$

$$= \frac{64}{8} = 8$$

$$\text{Mean of Set } B = \frac{0+1+1+2+3+14+17+25}{8}$$

$$= \frac{63}{8} = 7.88 \quad \text{(correct to 3 sig. fig.)}$$

(a) The two sets of data have approximately the same mean. Therefore, it is meaningful to compare the standard deviations of the two sets of marks.
Now we shall calculate the standard deviations of the two sets of data.

Set A:

4	−4	16
6	−2	4
6	−2	4
7	−1	1
8	0	0
10	2	4
11	3	9
12	4	16
		$\Sigma(x-\bar{x})^2 = 54$

$$S = \sqrt{\frac{54}{8}} = 2.60 \quad \text{(correct to 3 sig.fig.)}$$

Set *B*:

0	–7.88	62.09
1	–6.88	47.33
1	–6.88	47.33
2	–5.88	34.57
3	–4.88	23.81
14	6.12	37.45
17	9.12	83.17
25	17.12	293.1
		$\Sigma(x - \bar{x})^2 = 628.9$

$$S = \sqrt{\frac{628.9}{8}} = 8.87 \quad \text{(correct to 3 sig. fig.)}$$

(b) The two sets of marks have about the same values of mean, but very different values of standard deviation. Set *A*, with a smaller standard deviation, has a narrower spread of marks around the mean, i.e. most pupils have about 8 marks. However, Set *B*, with a higher standard deviation, has marks far away from the mean. The data is spreaded widely. This means that the pupils in Set B have extreme performances.

1. Why must we square $x - \bar{x}$ in the calculation of standard deviation?

2. Can we compare the mean and standard deviation of two data sets with different amounts of data, *n*?

We can also use the statistical functions of scientific calculators to find the mean and standard deviation directly.

Most scientific calculators in the market have statistical functions. Please refer to the instruction manual provided by your calculator on how to use the statistical functions to find the mean and standard deviation. The following steps are used use for certain models calculators.

1. Select **MODE** **1** for statistics.
2. Select **0** for single variable statistics.
3. Enter the data one at a time by keying in:

4	**DATA**
6	**DATA**
	DATA
7	**DATA**
8	**DATA**
10	**DATA**
11	**DATA**
12	**DATA**

To find the mean, press **RCL** and $\bar{x}$. Then the screen shows: $\bar{x} = 8$

To check the number of data entered, press **RCL** and n. Then the screen shows: $n = 8$

To find the standard deviation, press **RCL** and σx. Then the screen shows: $\sigma x = 2.598076211$

$\therefore$ the standard deviation of the above data is 2.60 (correct to 3 sig. fig.).

Use your calculator to find the mean and standard deviation of the data in set B. Do you get a mean of 7.875 and a standard deviation of 8.866192813?

When handling big sets of data, it is useful to include a frequency column in the calculation of standard deviation. Consider the set of 20 data below.

4, 5, 3, 2, 4, 0, 6, 4, 5, 6, 5, 5, 4, 1, 3, 2, 3, 4, 4, 6

We can include a frequency column when calculating the standard deviation. The formula for calculating the standard deviation is

$$S = \sqrt{\frac{\Sigma f(x - \bar{x})^2}{\Sigma f}}$$

where f is the frequency of the data x, and $\bar{x} = \dfrac{\Sigma f x}{\Sigma f}$.

x	Tally	Frequency (f)	fx	$x - \bar{x}$	$(x - \bar{x})^2$	$f(x - \bar{x})^2$
0	/	1	0	-3.8	14.44	14.44
1	/	1	1	-2.8	7.84	7.84
2	//	2	4	-1.8	3.24	6.48
3	///	3	9	-0.8	0.64	1.92
4	~~////~~ /	6	24	0.2	0.04	0.24
5	////	4	20	1.2	1.44	5.76
6	///	3	18	2.2	4.84	14.52
Sum		20	76			51.2

$$\bar{x} = \frac{\Sigma f x}{\Sigma f} = \frac{76}{20} = 3.8$$

$$S = \sqrt{\frac{51.2}{20}} = 1.6$$

Another formula for calculating standard deviation is

$$S = \sqrt{\frac{\Sigma f x^2}{\Sigma f} - \left(\frac{\Sigma f x}{\Sigma f}\right)^2}$$

For this formula, we tabulate the results as follows:

x	Frequency (f)	fx	fx^2
0	1	0	0
1	1	1	1
2	2	4	8
3	3	9	27
4	6	24	96
5	4	20	100
6	3	18	108
Sum	20	76	340

$$S = \sqrt{\frac{340}{20} - \left(\frac{76}{20}\right)^2} = 1.6$$

To calculate the standard deviation of the above group frequency distribution, the instruction for keying in the data are as shown below:

0 [DATA]

1 [DATA]

2 [DATA]

[DATA]

3 [(x, y)] 3 [DATA] [Equivalent to keying in 3 three times]

4 [(x, y)] 6 [DATA] [Equivalent to keying in 4 six times]

5 [(x, y)] 4 [DATA]

6 [(x, y)] 3 [DATA]

To find the mean, press [RCL] and [$\bar{x}$]. Then the screen shows: $\bar{x} = 3.8$

To check the number of data entered, press [RCL] and [n] Then the screen shows: $n = 20$

To find the standard deviation, press [RCL] and [σx]. Then the screen shows: $\sigma x = 1.6$

Example 4

A group of 100 Secondary 4 students in School A and School B were asked for the amount of time they spent watching television each week. The results were given below:

School A

Hours	*10 – 14*	*15 – 19*	*20 – 24*	*25 – 29*	*30 – 34*	*35 – 39*
Number of students	*3*	*12*	*19*	*36*	*22*	*8*

School B

Mean = 26.3
Standard Deviation = 5.12

(a) For School A, calculate the mean and standard deviation of the number of hours spent watching television by the 100 students.
(b) Compare, briefly, the results for the two schools.

Similar to the calculation of mean for grouped data, we use the mid-values of the class intervals in the calculation of standard deviation.

(a) **Method 1:** Use the formula $S = \sqrt{\dfrac{\Sigma f(x-\bar{x})^2}{\Sigma f}}$

Hours	Mid-value (x)	Frequency (f)	fx	$x - \bar{x}$	$(x-\bar{x})^2$	$f(x-\bar{x})^2$
10 – 14	12	3	36	–14.3	204.49	613.47
15 – 19	17	12	204	–9.3	86.49	1037.88
20 – 24	22	19	418	–4.3	18.49	351.31
25 – 29	27	36	972	0.7	0.49	17.64
30 – 34	32	22	704	5.7	32.49	714.78
35 – 39	37	8	296	10.7	114.49	915.92
Sum		100	2630			3651

$$\text{Mean} = \frac{\Sigma fx}{\Sigma f} = \frac{2630}{100} = 26.3 \text{ (correct to 3 sig. fig.)}$$

$$S = \sqrt{\frac{3651}{100}} = 6.04 \text{ (correct to 3 sig. fig.)}$$

Method 2: Use the formula $S = \sqrt{\frac{\Sigma fx^2}{\Sigma f} - \left(\frac{\Sigma fx}{\Sigma f}\right)^2}$

Hours	Mid-value (x)	Frequency (f)	fx	fx^2
10 – 14	12	3	36	432
15 – 19	17	12	204	3468
20 – 24	22	19	418	9196
25 – 29	27	36	972	26 244
30 – 34	32	22	704	22 528
35 – 39	37	8	296	10 952
Sum		100	2630	72 820

You may use your calculator to find the mean and standard deviation. With most calculators, you can find the keys: ***STAT, SD*** *(use* ***MODE****),* $\bar{x}$*,* σx*,* Σx *and* Σx^2*, to help in your calculation.*

We can use the statistical functions of a scientific calculator to find the value of Σfx^2, Σf and $\frac{\Sigma fx}{\Sigma f}$.

The data are keyed in using the following steps.

12 (x, y) 3 DATA

17 (x, y) 12 DATA

22 (x, y) 19 DATA

27 (x, y) 36 DATA

32 (x, y) 22 DATA

37 (x, y) 8 DATA

Press RCL and n to get $\Sigma f = 100$

Press RCL and Σx^2 to get $\Sigma fx^2 = 72\,820$

Press RCL and $\bar{x}$:o get $\bar{x} = 26.3$

Substituting these values into the fomula

$$S = \sqrt{\frac{72\,820}{100} - (26.3)^2} = 6.04 \text{ (correct to 3 sig. fig.)}$$

We can check our answer by pressing RCL and σx to get the standard deviation.

That is 6.042350536

(b) The students in both schools spent the same number of hours on average in watching television, but School A has a higher standard deviation. Hence it has a greater spread in the number of hours spent. i.e. some of them spent long hours watching TV while some of them spent very little time watching TV.

Ask 20 of your schoolmates, e.g. from Sec. 1 and 20 schoolmates from another level for the number of hours in a week spent on

(i) watching television,

(ii) doing homework

and record your findings.

(a) Construct grouped frequency tables for the sets of data obtained.

(b) Use computer software, eg. Excel to draw a histogram for each set of data.

(c) Using your histograms, create five questions and provide the solutions. Examples of questions: How many schoolmates watch between 5 to 10 hours of television a week? Which group of data has the highest frequency?

(d) Calculate the mean number of hours spent on

(i) watching television,

(ii) doing homework.

Hence comment briefly about the similarities and differences between the two levels.

(e) What recommendations, if any, do you have for your schoolmates?

1. Calculate the standard deviation of each set of data:

   (a) 3, 4, 5, 7, 8, 10, 12

   (b) 28, 25, 32, 20, 30, 19, 22, 24, 27, 23

   (c) 128, 135, 156, 123, 144, 130

   (d) 0, 1, 25, 14, 2, 16, 22, 4

2. A class of 80 pupils took a science test and their marks were grouped as shown below:

Marks	51 – 55	56 – 60	61 – 65	66 – 70	71 – 75	76 – 80
Number of pupils	4	12	20	24	16	4

   Calculate the mean mark and the standard deviation.

3. The table below shows the distribution of the mass of 60 snails in grams.

Mass (g)	0 – 9	10 – 19	20 – 29	30 – 39	40 – 49	50 – 59	60 – 69
Number of snails	1	2	10	18	20	6	3

   Find the mean mass and the standard deviation.

4. The weekly salary, in dollars, of 60 workers in a factory are shown in the table below:

Salary ($)	$100 < x \le 120$	$120 < x \le 140$	$140 < x \le 160$	$160 < x \le 180$	$180 < x \le 200$
Frequency	8	23	16	3	10

   Find the mean salary and the standard deviation.

5. The tables below show the mass of 100 students from School *X* and 100 students from School *Y*. (All masses are corrected to the nearest 5 kg.)

Mass of Students in School *X*

Mass (kg)	35	40	45	50	55	60
Number of students	5	36	28	22	7	2s

Mass of Students in School *Y*

Mass (kg)	30	35	40	45	50	55	60	65	70
Number of students	7	21	24	6	3	26	8	1	4

(a) Calculate the mean mass and standard deviation for the students in each school. Hence compare and comment briefly on the two sets of data.

(b) Find the mean and standard deviation of the combined set of all 200 students.

6. A survey was conducted to find out the number of hours in a day spent by pupils on the computer. The following table shows the results:

Number of hours	2	3	4	5	6	7	8
Number of pupils in Class A	2	3	6	11	10	7	1
Number of pupils in Class B	4	4	9	8	7	5	3

(a) Calculate the mean hour and standard deviation for each class.
(b) Which class spent less time on the computer?

7. The ages of 7 boys are 16, 21, 22, 18, 20, x and $2x$ years old. If the mean is 19, find the value of x and the standard deviation of the ages of the boys.

8. Alan scored x marks in a Mathematics quiz and his friends' scores were 5, 16, 6, 10 and 4. If the mean mark of these six students is 10, find the value of x and the standard deviation. How did Alan fare in this quiz among his friends?

9. Two trains, A and B, are scheduled to arrive at a station at a certain time. The time in seconds after the scheduled time for each of the 40 days was recorded and the results are as follows:

Time (s)	0.2	0.3	0.4	0.5	0.6	0.7	0.8	0.9
Number of days for Train A	3	2	5	12	10	6	1	1
Number of days for Train B	4	3	9	9	7	5	3	0

(a) Calculate the mean second and standard deviation for each train.
(b) Which train is more consistent in arriving late? Explain briefly.
(c) Which train is more punctual on the whole? Why?

10. Given that the six numbers 10, 6, 18, x, 15 and y have a mean of 9, find $x + y$. If the six numbers have a standard deviation of 6, find the value(s) of x and of y.

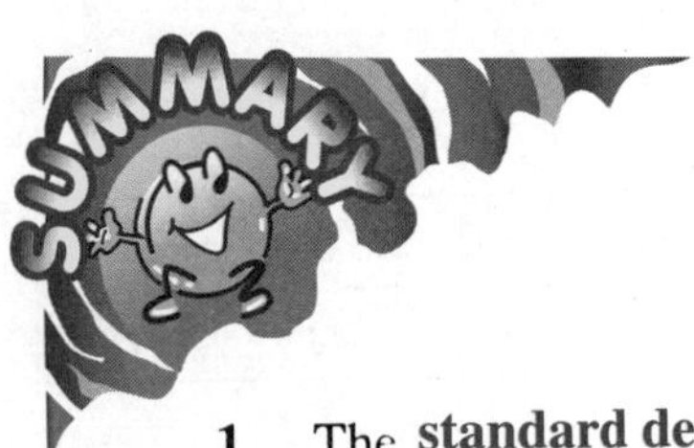

1. The **standard deviation** S measures the spread of a set of data from the mean.

2. For a set of n quantities, the standard deviation

$$S = \sqrt{\frac{\Sigma(x - \bar{x})^2}{n}}, \text{ where } \bar{x} \text{ is the mean .}$$

3. For a frequency distribution, the standard deviation

$$S = \sqrt{\frac{\Sigma f(x - \bar{x})^2}{\Sigma f}} \quad \text{or} \quad S = \sqrt{\frac{\Sigma f x^2}{\Sigma f} - \left(\frac{\Sigma f x}{\Sigma f}\right)^2}$$

Example 1

The following stem and leaf diagram represents the scores of a Science test taken by two groups of students.

Group A		Group B
Leaf	**Stem**	**Leaf**
8	1	2 3 3 0 0 0
9 9	2	
8 2 2	3	
9	4	
8 7 4	5	1 2
7 7 2	6	0 0 1 2 3 4 6 7
3 9 8	7	0 1 4 5 9
3 2 1 0	8	1 1 4 8
9 1	9	

(a) Convert the stem and leaf diagram to a histogram for each group of students, using the class intervals $10 < x \leq 20$, $20 < x \leq 30$, $30 < x \leq 40$ and so on.

(b) How would you judge which group performed better?

(c) Comment briefly on the performances of the two groups.

(a) Draw a frequency table as shown below.

Score	Frequency for Group A	Frequency for Group B
$10 < x \le 20$	1	6
$20 < x \le 30$	2	0
$30 < x \le 40$	3	0
$40 < x \le 50$	1	0
$50 < x \le 60$	3	2
$60 < x \le 70$	3	8
$70 < x \le 80$	3	5
$80 < x \le 90$	4	4
$90 < x \le 100$	2	0

Score of Group A Students

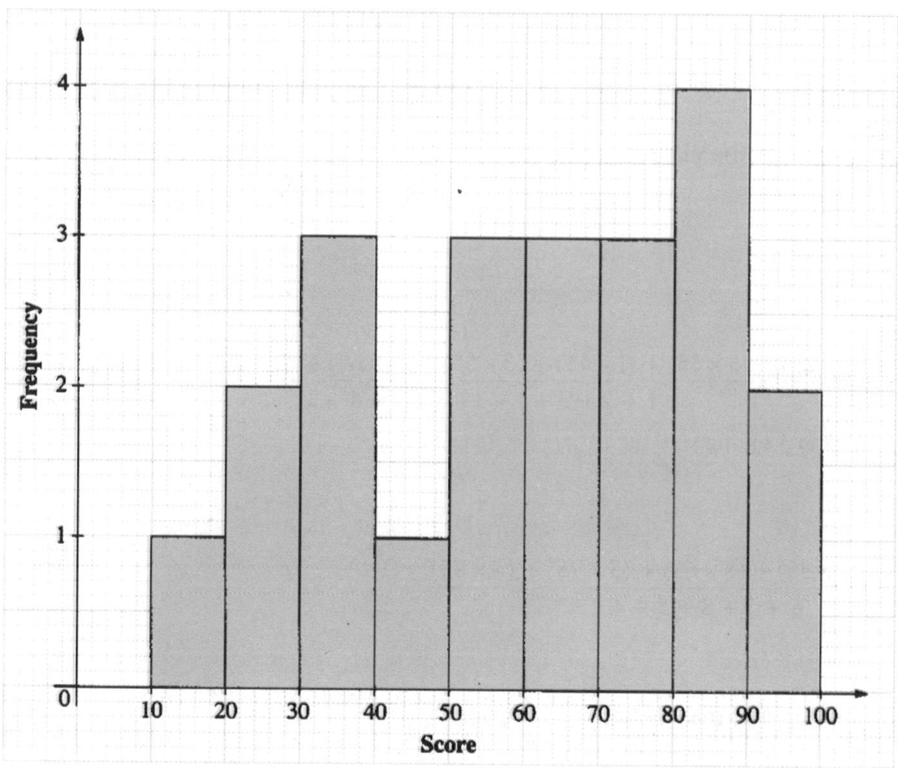

Score of Group B Students

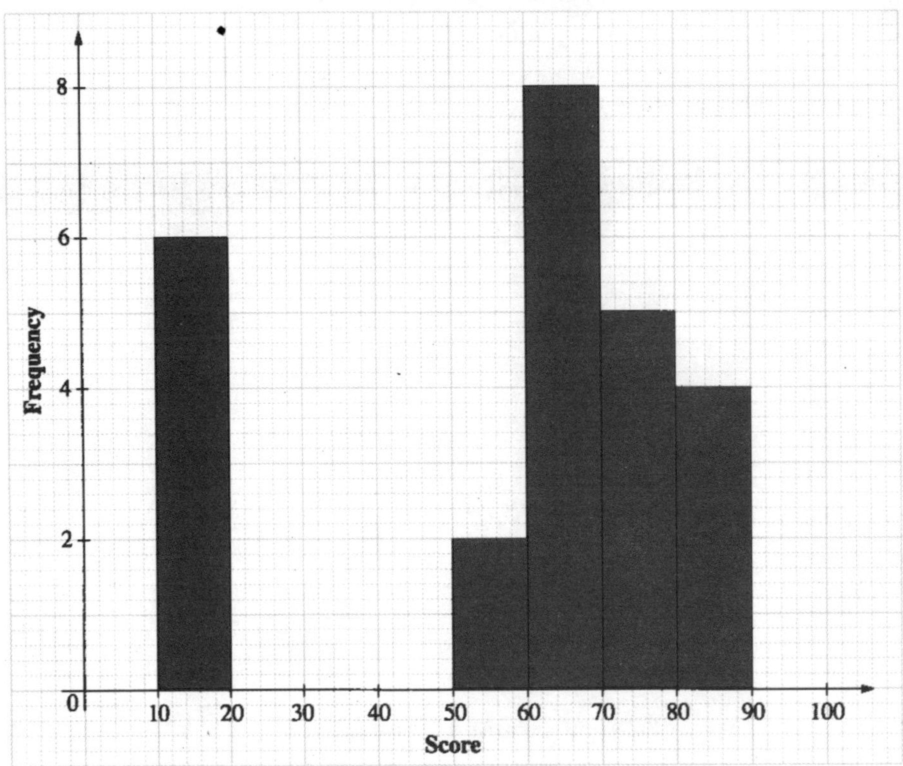

(b) We can compare the mean of the scores of each class. The class with the higher mean of scores performed better.
Using the mid-values of the class intervals,

for Group A,

$$\bar{x} = \frac{\Sigma fx}{\Sigma f}$$

$$= \frac{(1\times15)+(2\times25)+(3\times35)+(1\times45)+(3\times55)+(3\times65)+(3\times75)+(4\times85)+(2\times95)}{1+2+3+1+3+3+3+4+2}$$

≈ 60.5 (correct to 3 sig. fig.)

for Group B,

$$\bar{x} = \frac{(6\times15)+(2\times55)+(8\times65)+(5\times75)+(4\times85)}{6+2+8+5+4}$$

$= 57.4$

Therefore, Group A performed better.

(c) For Group A, the scores are more evenly spread in a wide range whereas for Group B, most scores fall in a narrower range of 60 to 90.

Using the statistical functions of a scientific calculator, try doing part (b) of Example 1 above.

Example 2

Dodo and Nana submitted 8 essays to their teacher in 3 months. The figures in the following table show the number of mistakes made in each essay by the two girls.

Essay No.	*1*	*2*	*3*	*4*	*5*	*6*	*7*	*8*	*Mean*	*Standard Deviation*
Dodo	21	43	x	8	34	24	12	2	20	12.7
Nana	6	9	15	26	10	14	21	3	y	7.18

(a) Find the value of x and of y.
(b) Who was more careless?
(c) Who was more consistent in making mistakes?

Give reasons for your answers.

(a) The mean of Dodo $= \dfrac{21 + 43 + x + 8 + 34 + 24 + 12 + 2}{8} = 20$

$$144 + x = 160$$

$$x = 16$$

The mean of Nana $= \dfrac{6 + 9 + 15 + 26 + 10 + 14 + 21 + 3}{8} = 13$

$\therefore \quad y = 13$

(b) Dodo was more careless because her mean number of mistakes made was higher than Nana's.

(c) Nana was more consistent in the number of mistakes made because her standard deviation was smaller than that of Dodo's i.e. the number of mistakes was not as widely spread as Dodo's.

1. The distribution of marks scored by students in a class is as follows:

Marks	2	3	4	5	6	7	8
Number of students	5	7	6	4	x	3	6

(a) If the mode is 6, write down an inequality in x.
(b) If the median is 5, write down the possible values of x.
(c) If the mean is 4.95, find the value of x.

2. The following dot diagram represents the number of booking calls received by a taxi company in a month.

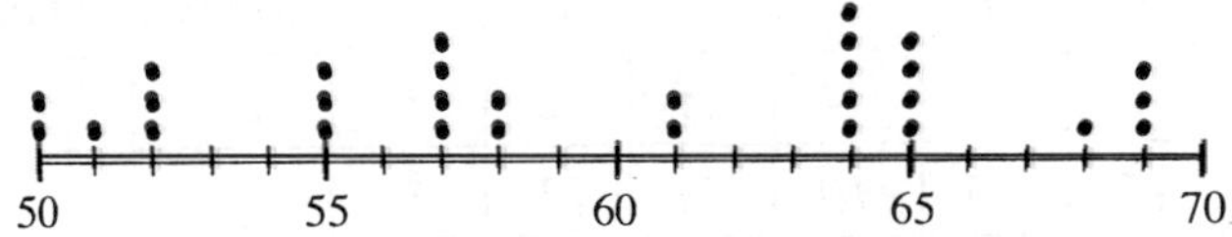

(a) Construct a frequency table and histogram for the above data, using the class intervals $50 \le x < 55$, $55 \le x < 60$, $60 \le x < 65$ and $65 \le x < 70$.
(b) Calculate the mean and standard deviation for the data.

3. The following dot diagrams represent the Pollutant Standards Index in two cities for 20 days.

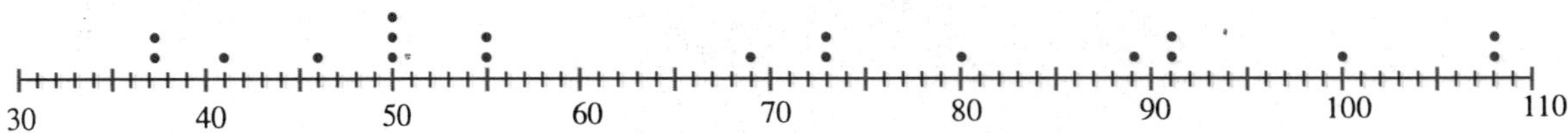

PSI in City *B*

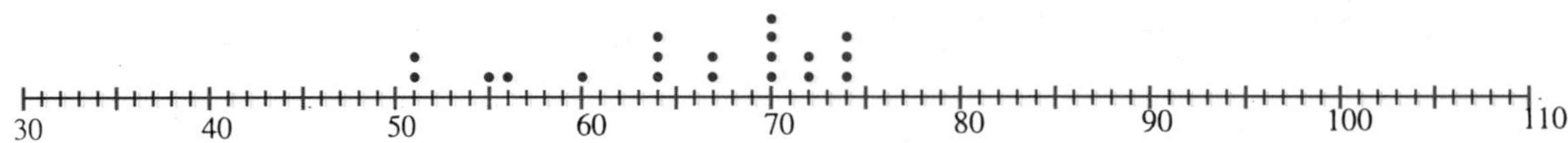

(a) Construct a frequency table for the PSI in each city, using the class intervals $30 < x \le 50$, $50 < x \le 70$, $70 < x \le 90$ and $90 < x \le 110$.
(b) Construct a pie chart for each frequency table.
(c) Calculate the mean and standard deviation for the PSI in each city.
(d) Compare and comment on the air qualities in the two cities.

4. Mrs Gibson reads bedtime story to her daughter, Katie, every night. The time taken for Katie to fall asleep on each night last week is as follows:

Day	Mon	Tue	Wed	Thu	Fri	Sat	Sun
Time taken to fall asleep (min)	23	15	8	13	28	6	15

(**a**) Find the mean and standard deviation for the time taken for Katie to fall asleep.

They went on a holiday in New Zealand for a week. The time taken for Katie to fall asleep on each night in the week is as follows:

Day	Mon	Tue	Wed	Thu	Fri	Sat	Sun
Time taken to fall asleep (min)	20	12	5	10	25	3	12

(**b**) Calculate the mean and standard deviation for the time taken for Katie to fall asleep during the holiday.

(**c**) Compare and comment on the answers in part (**a**) and part (**b**).

5. The speeds, in km/h, of 20 cars were measured at a check point on Monday and recorded below:

55 58 45 39 46 50 36 55 54 43
60 48 42 63 47 37 44 49 50 53

(**a**) (**i**) Copy and complete the frequency table.

Speed (km/h)	$35 \le x < 40$	$40 \le x < 45$	$45 \le x < 50$	$50 \le x < 55$	$55 \le x < 60$	$60 \le x < 65$
Number of cars	3		5			

(**ii**) Calculate the mean speed and standard deviation.

(**b**) The speeds, in km/h, of another group of 20 cars were measured at the same check point on Saturday and the mean and standard deviation are shown below:

Mean = 40.5	***Standard deviation*** = 6.28

Compare and comment briefly on the results of the two groups of cars on the two different days.

6. The students in two classes took the same test. Information relating to the results is shown in the table below.

Class X

Marks	1 – 4	5 – 8	9 – 12	13 – 16	17 – 20
Frequency	3	8	14	2	3

Class Y	
	***Mean** = 9.7*
	***Standard Deviation** = 3.1*

(a) For class X, calculate
(i) the mean mark,
(ii) the standard deviation.

(b) Compare and comment briefly on the results for the two classes.

7. The following table shows the life span, to the nearest hour, for 100 light bulbs from two factories:

		Number of light bulbs	
		Factory *ABC*	**Factory *XYZ***
Life Spans (h)	600 – 699	2	8
	700 – 799	9	10
	800 – 899	16	12
	900 – 999	21	16
	1000 – 1099	29	r
	1100 – 1199	18	18
	1200 – 1299	5	12
	Mean	p	989.5
	Standard Deviation	q	t

(a) Find the values of p, q, r and t.
(b) Compare and comment briefly on the life spans of the light bulbs produced by the two factories.

8. The following table shows the daily temperatures at two cities in Sahara Desert in 50 days:

Temperature (°C)		35 – 39	40 – 44	45 – 49	50 – 54	55 – 59	60 – 64
Number of days	**City *A***	1	4	12	23	7	3
	City *B*	2	14	16	10	5	3

(a) For each city, calculate
  (i) the mean temperature,
  (ii) the standard deviation.
(b) Which city is warmer on the whole? Give a brief reason.
(c) Which city is more consistent in temperature? Explain briefly why.

9. In a rifle range, Alvin and Bush fired 6 shots each at a target. The following table shows the distance, in millimeter, of each shot from the centre of the target.

	Distance from centre of target (mm)					
Alvin's shot	47	16	32	1	19	35
Bush's shot	20	9	16	43	13	4

(a) For each man, calculate
  (i) the mean distance from the centre of the target,
  (ii) the standard deviation.
(b) Who was more consistent in performance? Give a brief reason.
(c) Who was better in the shooting? Explain briefly why.

10. The waiting time, in minutes, for 60 patients at two hospitals are given as follows:

Hospital *EZY*

Time (min)	$20 < t \leq 22$	$22 < t \leq 24$	$24 < t \leq 26$	$26 < t \leq 28$	$28 < t \leq 30$
Number of patients	5	11	27	13	4

Hospital *SUSA*	***Mean* = 25**
	***Standard Deviation* = 3.2**

(a) For Hospital *EZY*, calculate
  (i) the mean waiting time,
  (ii) the standard deviation.
(b) Compare, briefly, the waiting time for the two hospitals.

In this chapter, you will learn how to

- ***recognise the features of cumulative frequency curves;***
- ***interpret and analyse cumulative frequency diagrams;***
- ***estimate the median, quartiles and percentiles from the cumulative frequency curves;***
- ***interpret and analyse box-and-wisker plots.***

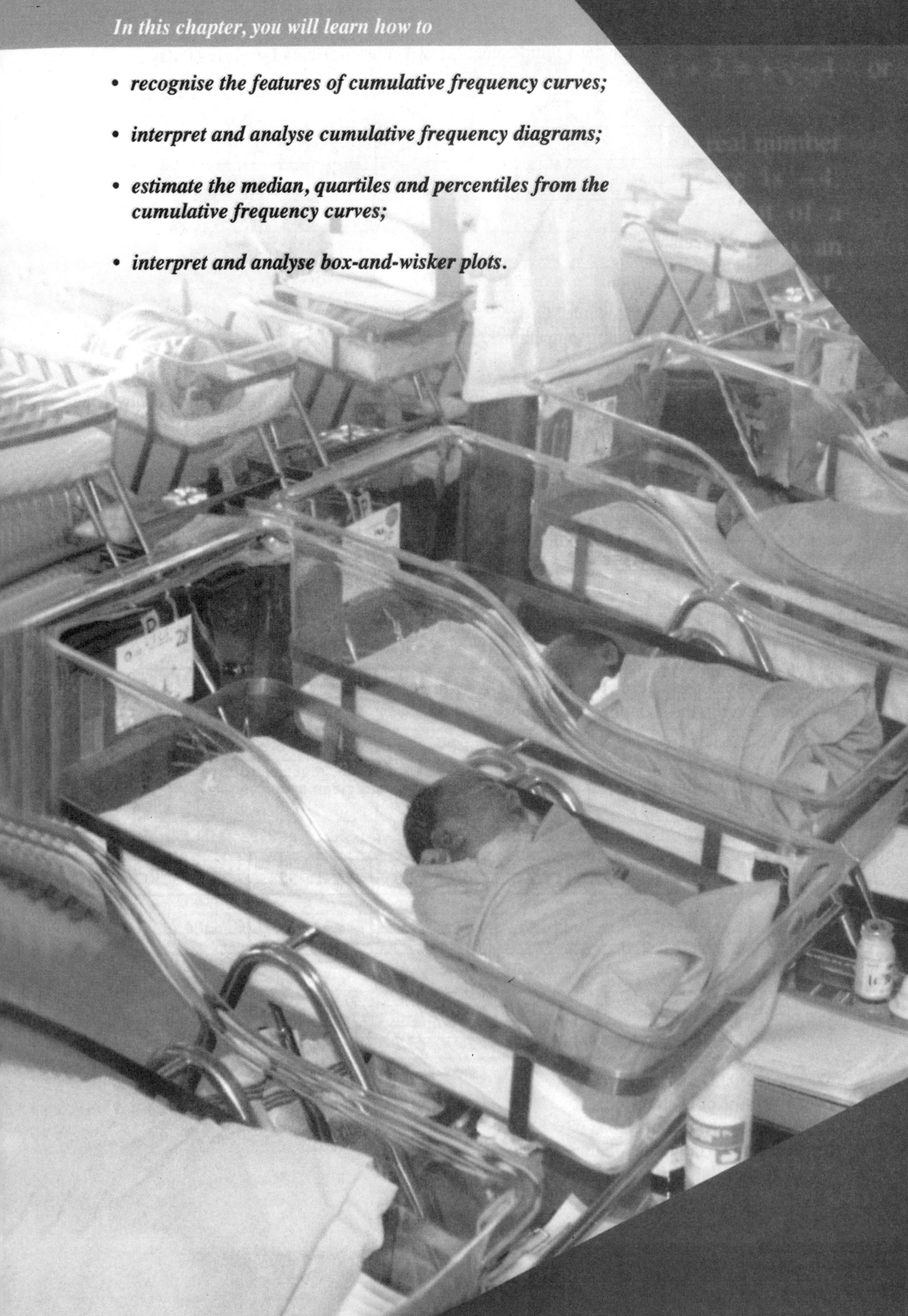

CHAPTER

5

Cumulative Frequency Distribution

Introduction

Do you know how many babies have been born in Singapore since 1983? Such figures are recorded by the Singapore Population Census Office. Each year, the number of babies that are born is added to the accumulated number of the previous years. In this way, the government is able to analyse the population growth.

Cumulative Frequency Table

So far, we have learnt different ways of presenting data. Another way of presenting a set of data is by using the **table of cumulative frequencies**.

A frequency table of the quiz scores of 38 students is shown below.

Score	0	1	2	3	4	5	6	7	8	9	10
Number of students (Frequency)	1	3	4	6	8	6	5	2	1	1	1

What is cumulative frequency?

Let's use the above data to illustrate this. From the above table, the cumulative number of students whose scores are less than or equal to 1 is $1 + 3 = 4$.

The cumulative number of students whose scores are less than or equal to 2 is $1 + 3 + 4 = 8$.

Similarly the cumulative number of students whose scores are less than or equal to 3 is $1 + 3 + 4 + 6 = 14$.

Therefore, to find the cumulative frequency for a particular score $\boldsymbol{a}$, we must add the frequencies of the scores $\leq \boldsymbol{a}$.

The following table shows the cumulative frequencies of the quiz scores.

Score	≤ 0	≤ 1	≤ 2	≤ 3	≤ 4	≤ 5	≤ 6	≤ 7	≤ 8	≤ 9	≤ 10
Cumulative frequency	1	4	8	14	22	28	33	35	36	37	38

Notice that the last cumulative frequency is the total number of students. From the cumulative frequency table, we can find information such as the number of students who get less than a certain score or the number of students who pass the quiz.

xample 1

The lengths of 40 insects of a certain species were measured correct to the nearest millimetre. The frequency distribution is given below:

Length (mm)	$25 < x \leq 30$	$30 < x \leq 35$	$35 < x \leq 40$	$40 < x \leq 45$	$45 < x \leq 50$	$50 < x \leq 55$	$55 < x \leq 60$
Frequency	*1*	*3*	*6*	*12*	*10*	*6*	*2*

Find the number of insects which are

(a) 50 mm or less in length;
(b) more than 45 mm in length;
(c) more than 35 mm but less than or equal to 50 mm in length.

(a) Number of insects that are 50 mm or less in length is

$$1 + 3 + 6 + 12 + 10 = 32$$

(b) Number of insects that are more than 45 mm in length is

$$10 + 6 + 2 = 18$$

(c) Number of insects that are more than 35 mm but less than or equal to 50 mm in length is

$$60 + 12 + 10 = 28$$

Cumulative Frequency Curve

For Example 1, let's draw the **Cumulative Frequency Curve** to find:

(i) the number of insects less than 44 mm long,
(ii) the percentage of insects of length 38 mm or more,
(iii) the value of l such that 75% of insects were less than l mm long.

First we construct a cumulative frequency table as shown below.

Length (mm)	Frequency	Length (mm)	Cumulative frequency
$25 < x \leq 30$	1	≤ 30	1
$30 < x \leq 35$	3	≤ 35	$1 + 3 = 4$
$35 < x \leq 40$	6	≤ 40	$4 + 6 = 10$
$40 < x \leq 45$	12	≤ 45	$10 + 12 = 22$
$45 < x \leq 50$	10	≤ 50	$22 + 10 = 32$
$50 < x \leq 55$	6	≤ 55	$32 + 6 + 38$
$55 < x \leq 60$	2	≤ 60	$38 + 2 = 40$

Then the cumulative frequency curve is drawn by plotting the cumulative frequencies. The points are joined by a smooth curve.

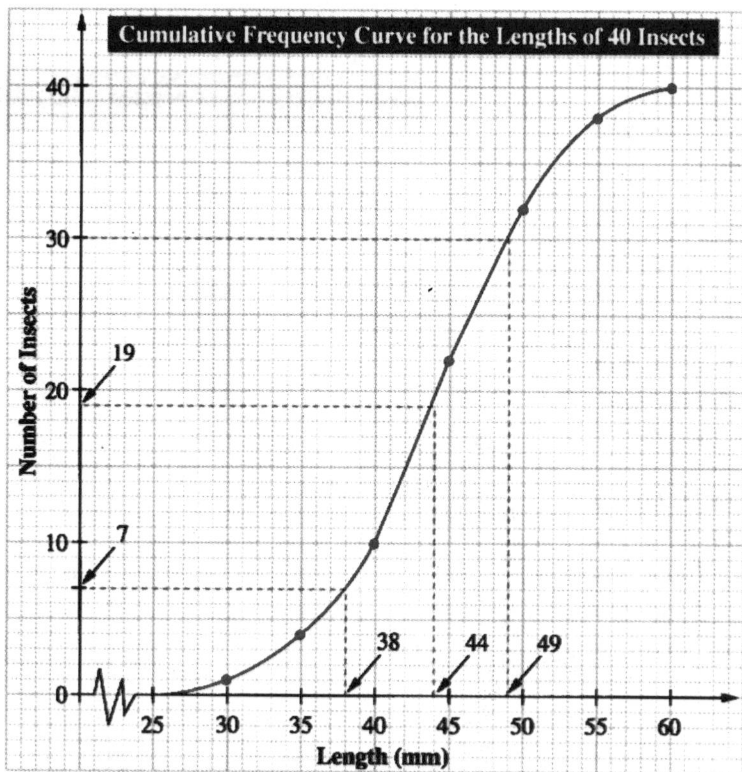

Fig. 5.1

Using the curve, we can answer the questions.

(i) Locate the point on the curve that has 44 as its x-coordinate and read the y value. The number of insects less than 44 mm long is 19.

(ii) Locate the point on the curve that has 38 as its x-coordinate and read the y value. 7 insects were less than 38 mm long.

$\therefore$ The number of insects 38 mm or more = 40 – 7 = 33.

The percentage of insects 37.5 mm or more is $\frac{33}{40} \times 100\% = 82.5\%$.

(iii) 75% of insects means $\frac{75}{100} \times 40 = 30$

$\therefore$ 30 insects were less than l mm long.

Locate the point on the curve that has 30 as its y-coordinate and read the x value.

$\therefore$ $l = 49$

xample 2

The cumulative frequency curve shows the distribution of the masses of 300 apples.

(a) Estimate from the curve

(i) the number of apples having masses 98 g or less,

(ii) the value of m given that 20% of the apples had masses more than m g.

(b) Taking class intervals $60 < x \leq 70$, $70 < x \leq 80$, $80 < x \leq 90$, $90 < x \leq 100$, $100 < x \leq 110$, construct a frequency distribution and draw a histogram.

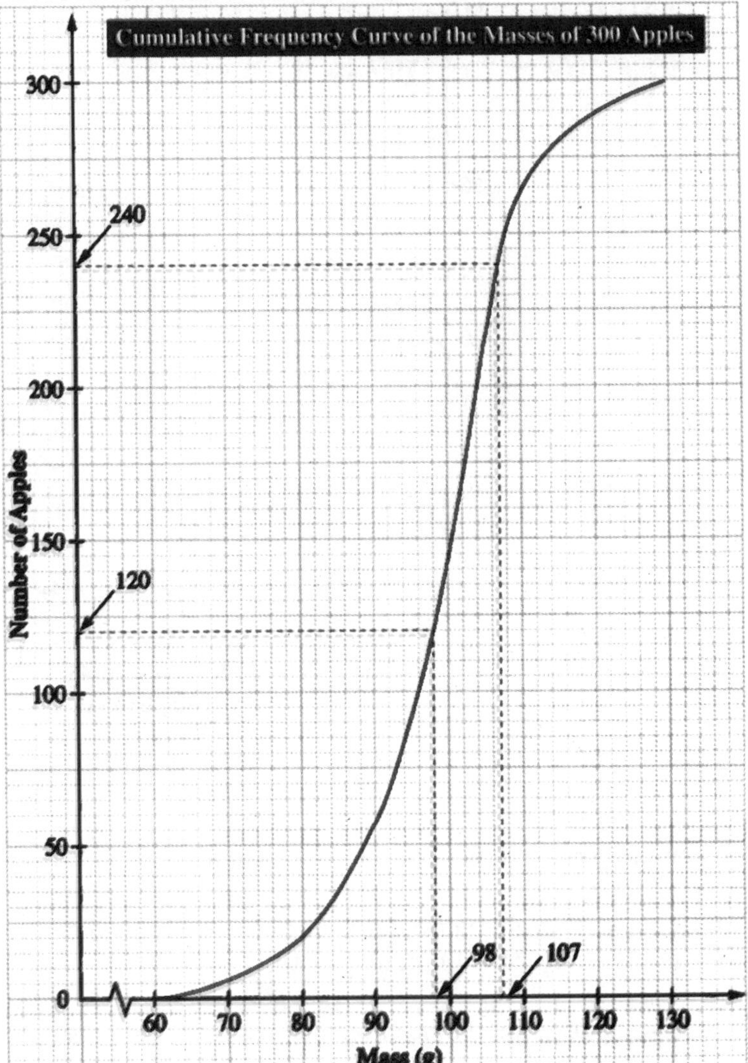

Fig. 5.2

(a) (i) From the curve, we estimate that 120 apples have masses 98 g or less.

(ii) 20% of 300

$= \frac{20}{100} \times 300 = 60$

$\therefore$ 60 apples have masses more than m g, i.e.
$300 - 60 = 240$ apples have masses m g or less.

From the curve, 240 apples have masses 107 g or less.

$\therefore$ $m = 107$.

(b) From the curve, we read the data to construct the frequency distribution table as shown below:

Mass (x g)	Cumulative frequency	Mass (x g)	Frequency
$x \leq 70$	8	$60 < x \leq 70$	8
$x \leq 80$	20	$70 < x \leq 80$	$20 - 8 = 12$
$x \leq 90$	56	$80 < x \leq 90$	$56 - 20 = 36$
$x \leq 100$	140	$90 < x \leq 100$	$140 - 56 = 84$
$x \leq 110$	262	$100 < x \leq 110$	$262 - 140 = 122$
$x \leq 120$	288	$110 < x \leq 120$	$288 - 262 = 26$
$x \leq 130$	300	$120 < x \leq 130$	$300 - 288 = 12$
			Total = 300

Figure 5.3 shows the histogram.

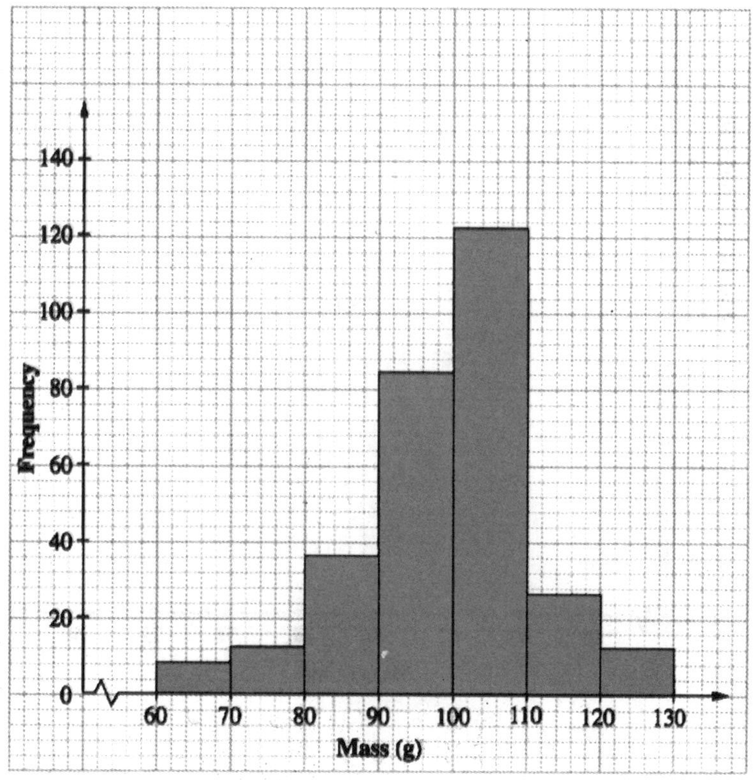

Fig. 5.3

1. The masses, in kg, of 50 students are measured. The cumulative frequency curve shows the mass, x kg, and the number of students whose masses are less than or equal to x kg. (As an example, 20 students have masses of 66.2 kg or less.)

Use the curve to estimate

(a) the number of students whose masses are less than or equal to 65 kg,

(b) the number of students whose masses are more than 68.6 kg,

(c) the percentage of the total number of students whose masses are more than 64.4 kg.

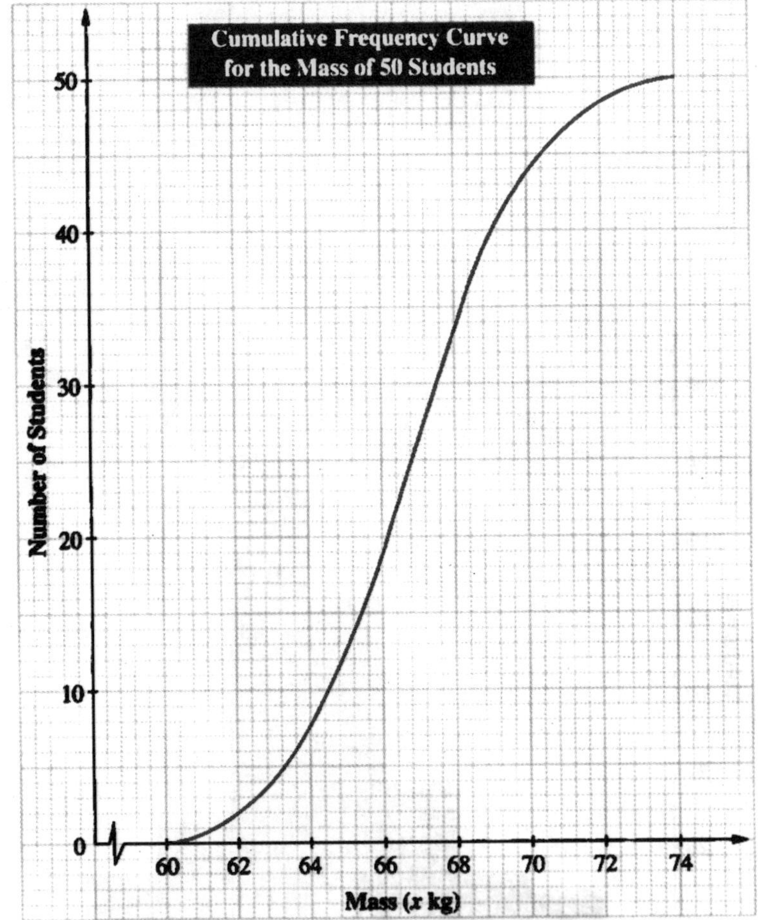

2. The results of a music examination taken by 160 pupils are shown in the cumulative frequency curve below:

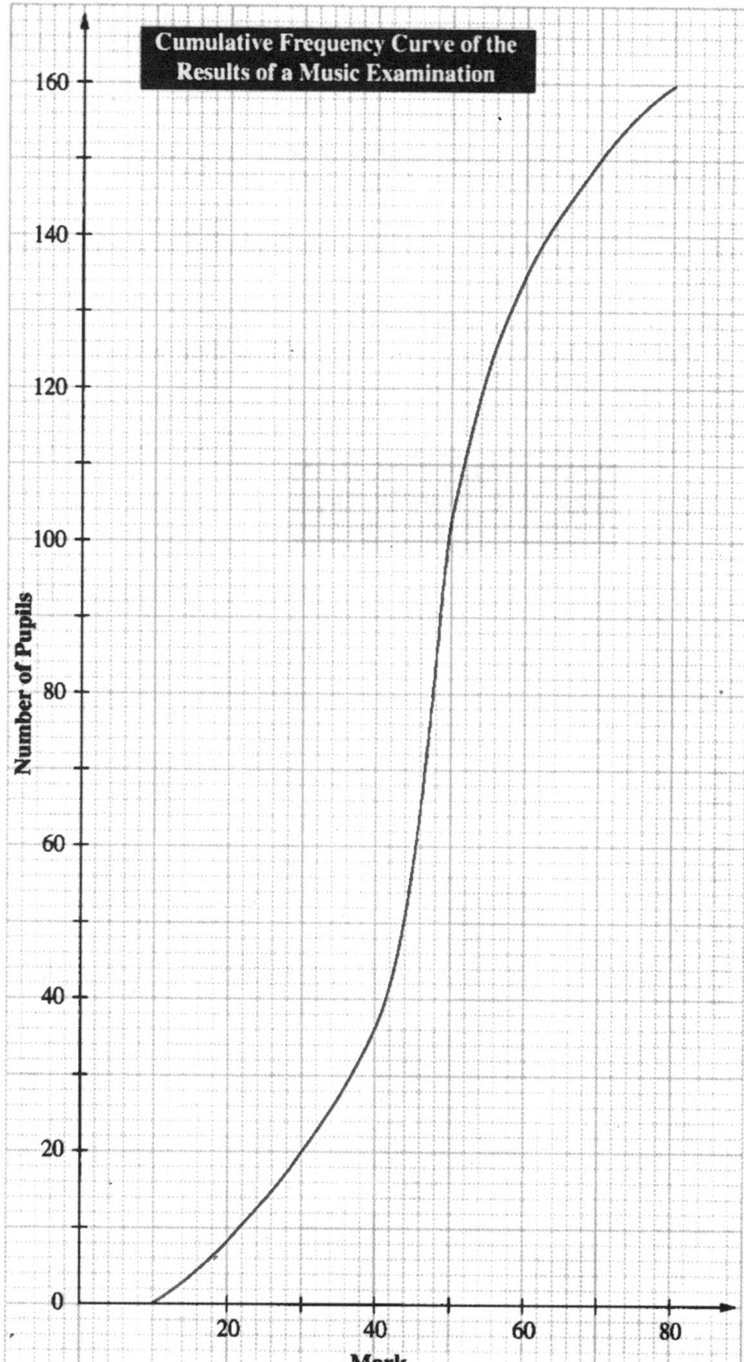

From the graph, estimate

(a) the number of pupils who scored less than 45 marks,

(b) the fraction of the total number of pupils who failed the music examination given that 34 is the lowest mark to pass the examination,

(c) the value of x if 22.5% of the pupils obtained at least x marks in the music examination.

3. The speed at which 100 motor vehicles passing a certain point in a busy street are recorded.

The cumulative frequency curve shows the speed, u km/h and the number of vehicles, that travelled at a speed less than u km/h. (As an example, 74 vehicles travelled at a speed less than 53 km/h.)

Use the curve to find

(a) the number of vehicles that travelled at a speed less than 34 km/h,

(b) the fraction of the total number of vehicles that travelled at a speed greater than or equal to 59 km/h,

(c) the value of v, if 40% of the vehicles have a speed less than v km/h.

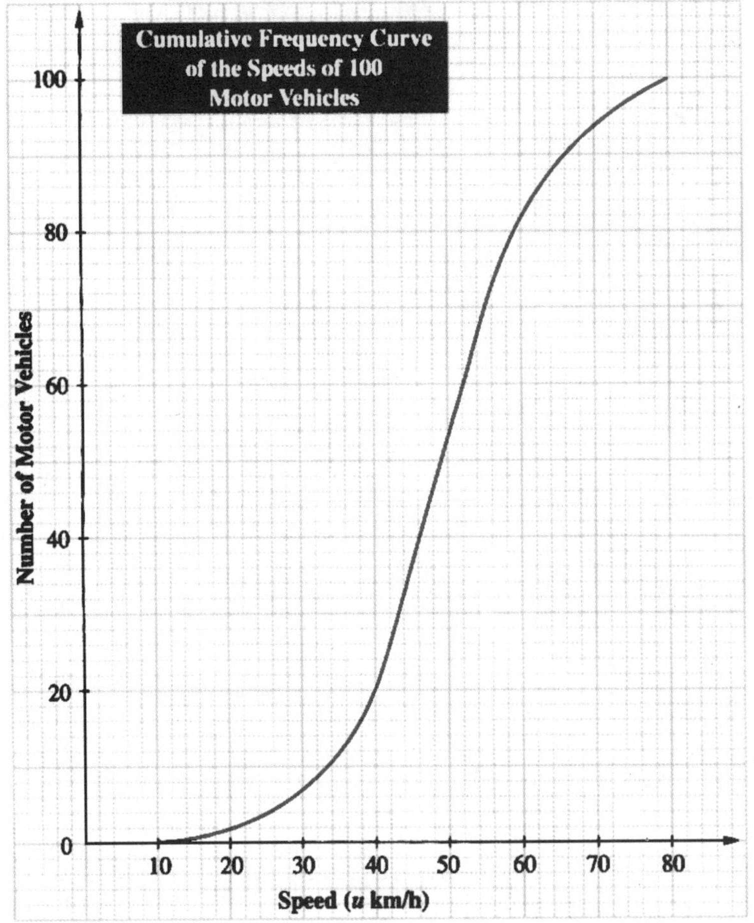

4. Fifty loaves of bread from a bakery are weighed. Their masses are distributed as shown in the cumulative frequency curve below:

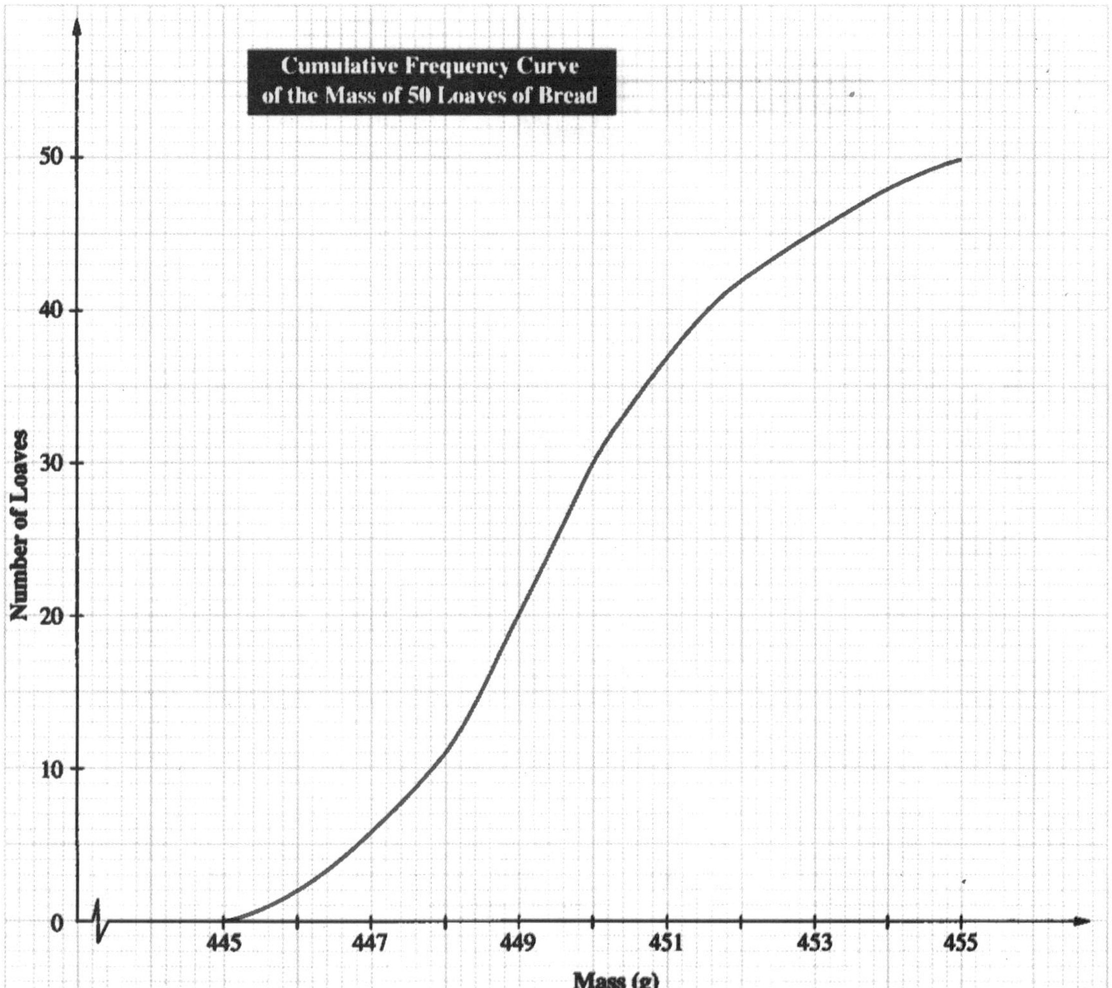

From the graph, estimate

(a) the number of loaves of bread whose masses are less than or equal to 450.4 g,

(b) the number of loaves rejected either because they are underweight or overweight, given that a loaf is underweight if its mass is 446.3 g or less and overweight if its mass is more than 453.7 g,

(c) the value of x if $\frac{3}{10}$ of the loaves weigh more than x g.

5. 500 earthworms were collected from a sample of Soil A and 500 earthworms from Soil B. Their lengths were recorded and the results are shown in the following diagram.

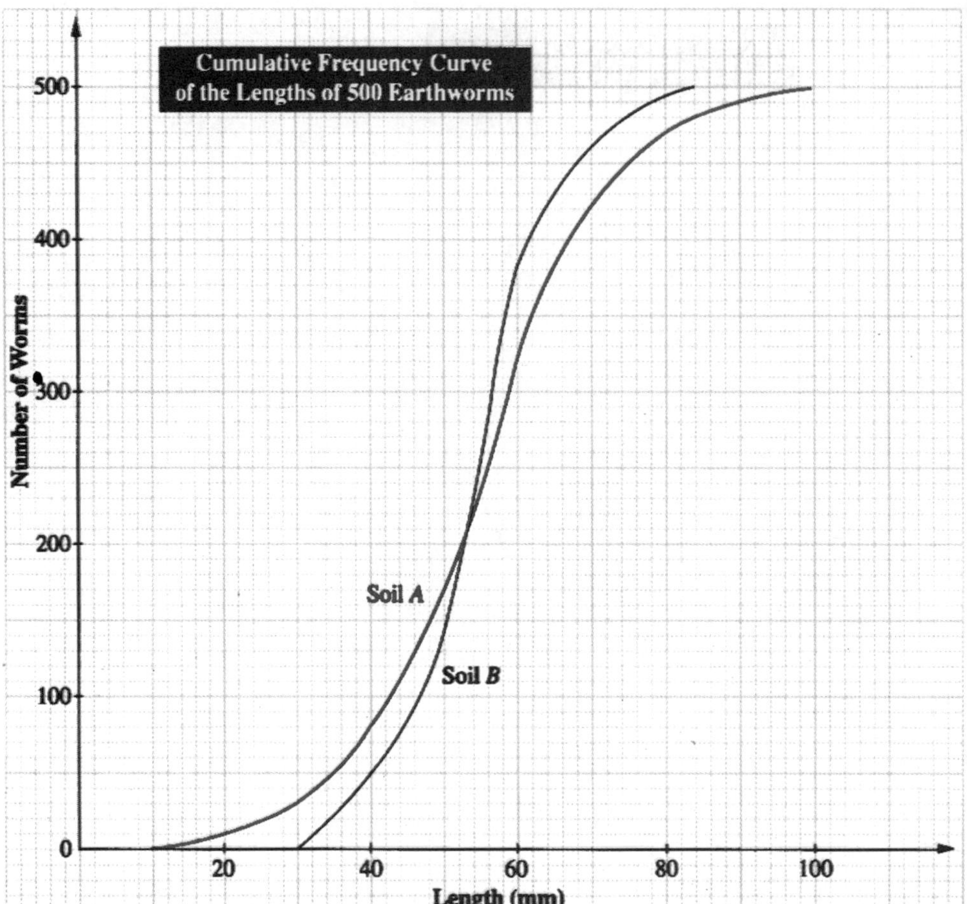

(a) Use your graph of Soil A and Soil B to estimate

(i) the number of earthworms whose lengths are less than or equal to 46 mm,

(ii) the percentage of earthworms whose lengths are greater than 76 mm,

(iii) the value of x if 18% of the earthworms are of length x mm or less.

(b) Which soil produced the longest earthworm among these 1000 earthworms?

(c) Earthworms which grew more than 60 mm are said to be satisfactory. From the graph, estimate the percentage of satisfactory earthworms of

(i) Soil A,

(ii) Soil B.

6. The amount of time spent by 750 pupils of a certain school to travel from home to school on a particular morning is shown in the curve.

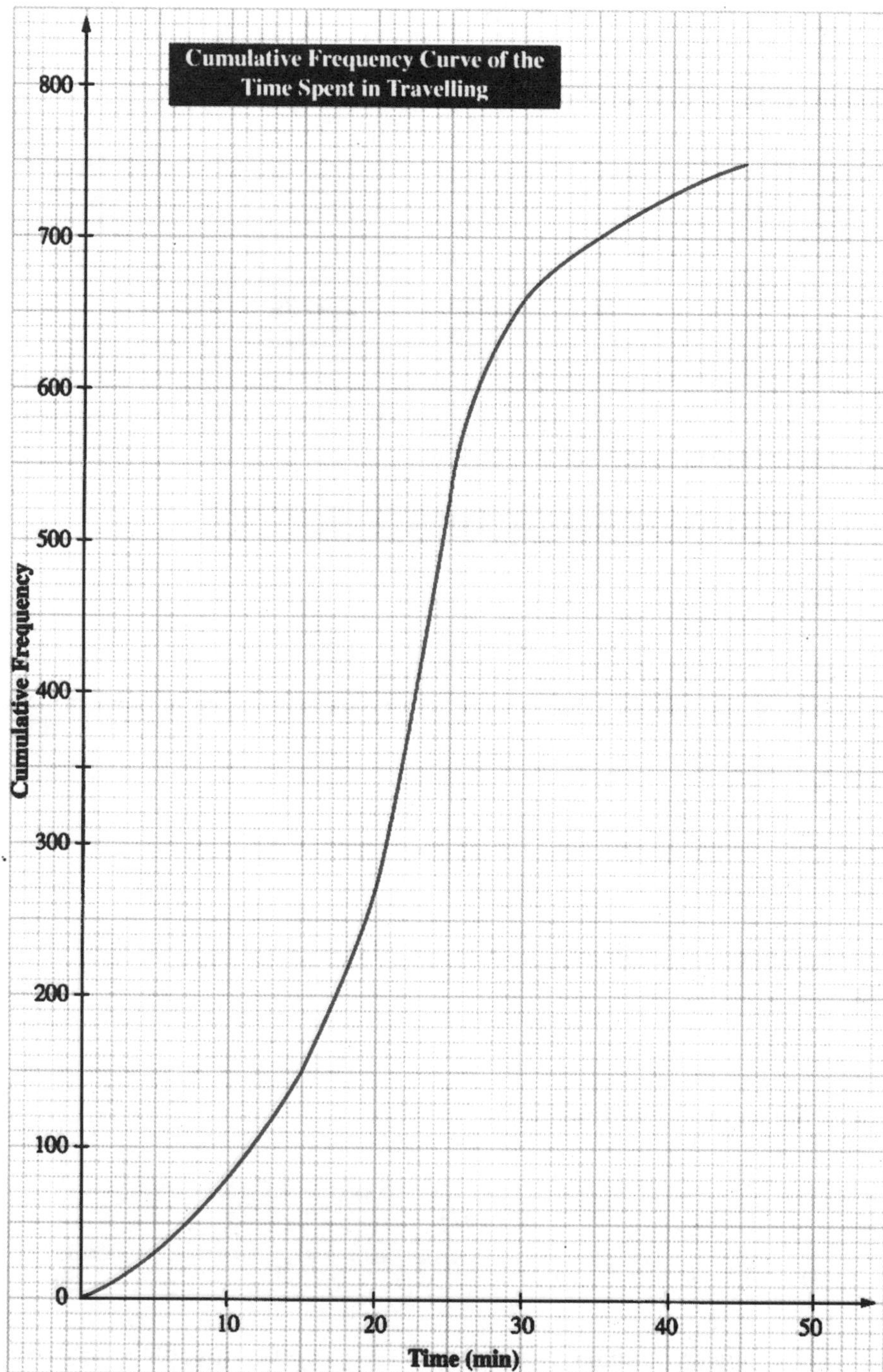

Use the graph to estimate

(a) the number of pupils who take less than 17.5 minutes to travel to school,

(b) the fraction of the 750 pupils who take at least 27 minutes to travel to school,

(c) the value of x given that 40% of the 750 pupils take at least x minutes to travel to school.

Median, Quartiles and Percentiles

Consider the following set of data which are arranged in ascending order,

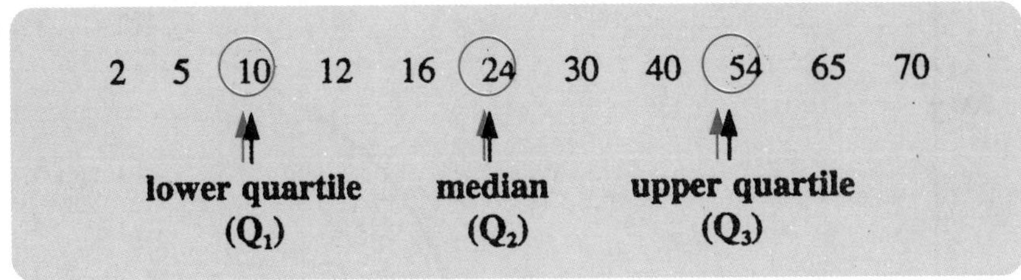

Notice that the number of data in this set is **odd**

(i) The **range** = the largest value – the smallest value
= 70 – 2
= 68

(ii) The **median** divides the set of data into equal halves.
Hence the median is the middle value when a set of data is arranged in order of increasing magnitude.
The median (Q_2) = 24

(ii) The **lower quartile** is the middle value of the lower half of the range,
i.e. $Q_1 = 10$.

(iv) The **upper quartile** is the middle value of the upper half of the range,
i.e. $Q_3 = 54$.

Now let us look at the set of numbers below:

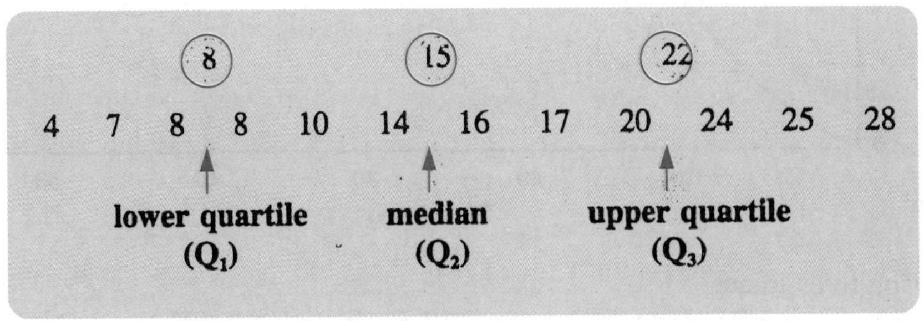

Notice that the number of data in the set is even

range $= 28 - 4 = 24$,

median, $Q_2 = \frac{14 + 16}{2} = 15$,

lower quartile, $Q_1 = \frac{8 + 8}{2} = 8$ and

upper quartile, $Q_3 = \frac{20 + 24}{2} = 22$.

Percentiles are values dividing a set of data into 100 equal parts.

For grouped data, the quartiles and percentiles of a frequency distribution can be estimated from the cumulative frequency curve. Let's look at Example 2 again.

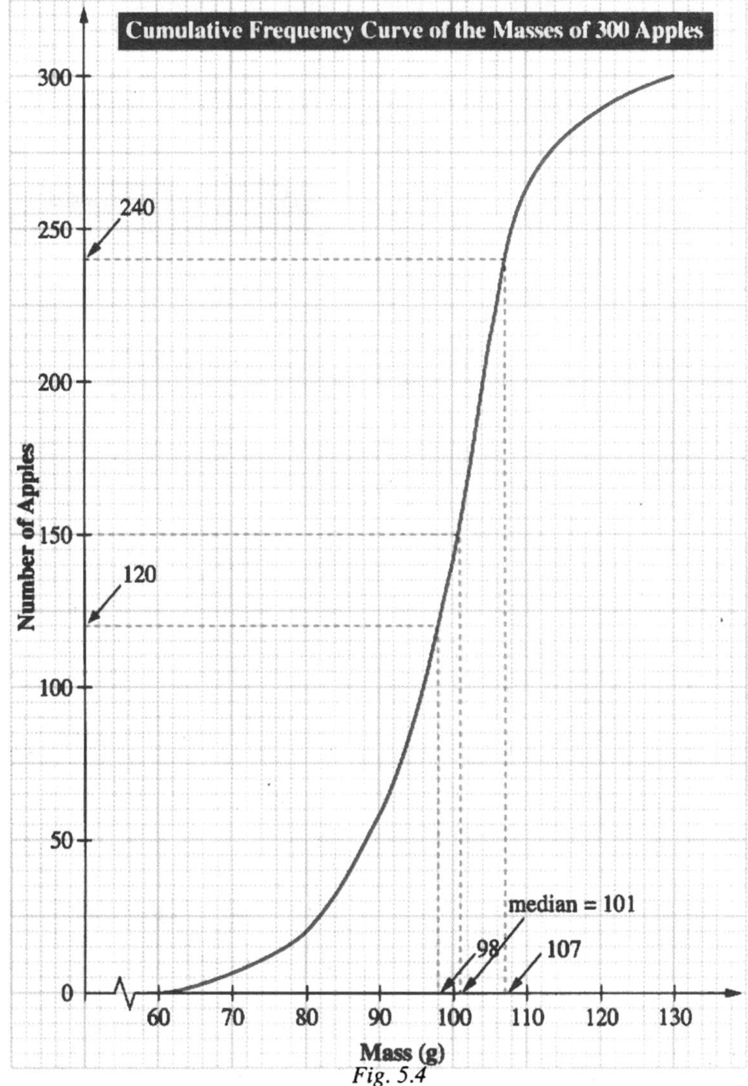

Fig. 5.4

120 apples have masses 98 g or less. 98 g is the $\frac{120}{300} \times 100\% = 40$th percentile.

Similarly, can you work out which percentile is 107 g?

Now we shall find the median of the distribution.

The median is the 50th percentile. $50\% \times 300 = \frac{1}{2} \times 300 = 150$

From the graph, the median mass is 101 g.

The lower quartile and upper quartile are the 25th percentile and 75th percentile respectively. Find out these two values for the frequency distribution above and compare your answers with your classmates.

example 3

The cumulative frequency curve shows the examination marks of 100 pupils.

(a) Find

(i) the median mark,

(ii) the upper quartile,

(iii) the lower quartile,

(iv) the range of the marks.

(b) Find the minimum mark required to gain a distinction if the top 5% of the pupils are awarded a distinction.

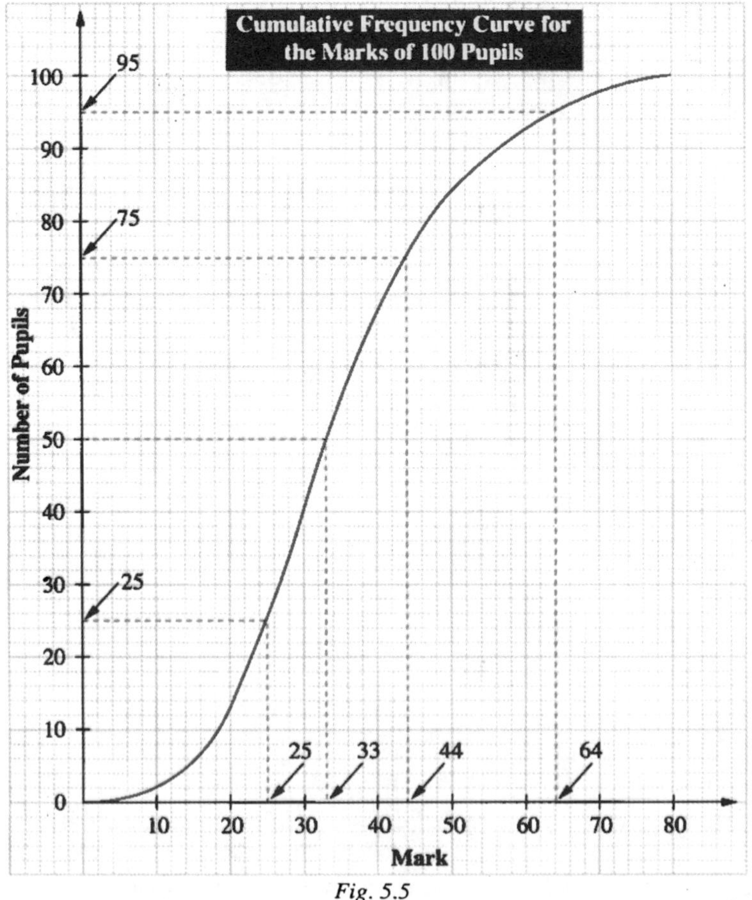

Fig. 5.5

(a) (i) 50% of the total frequency $= \frac{50}{100} \times 100 = 50$

From the curve, the median mark = 33.

(ii) 75% of the total frequency $= \frac{3}{4} \times 100 = 75$

From the curve, the upper quartile = 44.

(iii) 25% of the total frequency $= \frac{25}{100} \times 100 = 25$

From the curve, the lower quartile = 25.

(iv) The largest end point = 80
The smallest end point = 0
The range of marks = 80 – 0 = 80

(b) 95% of the total frequency $= \frac{95}{100} \times 100 = 95$

From the curve, 95% of the pupils obtained 64 marks or less.

$\therefore$ the minimum mark required for distinction = 65.

Interquartile Range

The interquartile range of a set of numbers is the *difference* between the upper quartile (Q_3) and the lower quartile (Q_1), i.e.

Interquartile range = **Upper quartile** Q_3 − **Lower quartile** Q_1

$$= Q_3 - Q_1$$

For Example 3, the interquartile range is given by 44 – 25 = 19 marks.

The **interquartile range** gives an indication of how the numbers in a set of data are spread about the median of the set. A **small interquartile range** indicates that the numbers cluster closely around the median while a *large interquartile range* indicates that the data are spread across a wide range of values.

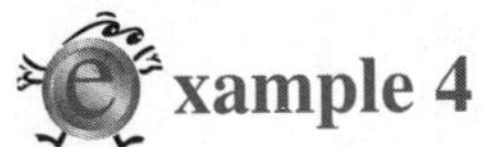

xample 4

The cumulative frequency curve represents the instantaneous speeds of 100 motor vehicles taken at a particular point on a busy street.

Find

(a) the median, the lower quartile and the upper quartile.

(b) the interquartile range.

(c) the range of the speed.

(d) the 10th and 90th percentiles.

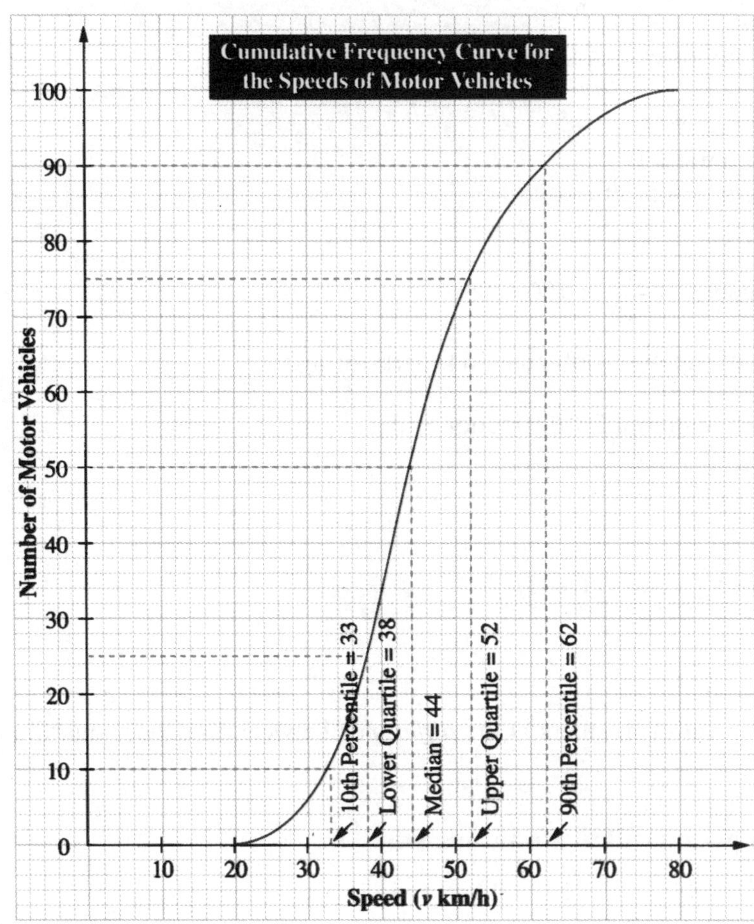

Fig. 5.6

There are 100 data. The median is at the 50th position. The lower quartile is at the 25th position, and the upper quartile is at the 75th position.

(a) From the graph,
the median speed = 44 km/h,
the lower quartile = 38 km/h,
the upper quartile = 52 km/h.

(b) The interquartile range = 52 – 38 = 14 km/h.

(c) The largest end point = 80
The smallest end point = 20
∴ the range of the speed = 80 – 20 = 60 km/h.

(d) 10% of the total frequency = $\frac{10}{100} \times 100 = 10$

From the graph, the 10th percentile = 33 km/h.

90% of the total frequency = $\frac{90}{100} \times 100 = 90$

From the graph, the 90th percentile = 62 km/h.

Mr William Goh, a P.E. teacher would like to know whether his Stay Healthy Programme has been effective in reducing the mass of overweight students. He measured the mass of 400 such students in 2006 and again, measured their mass in 2007.

He obtains two cumulative frequency curves, but does not know how to interpret them. Can you help him?

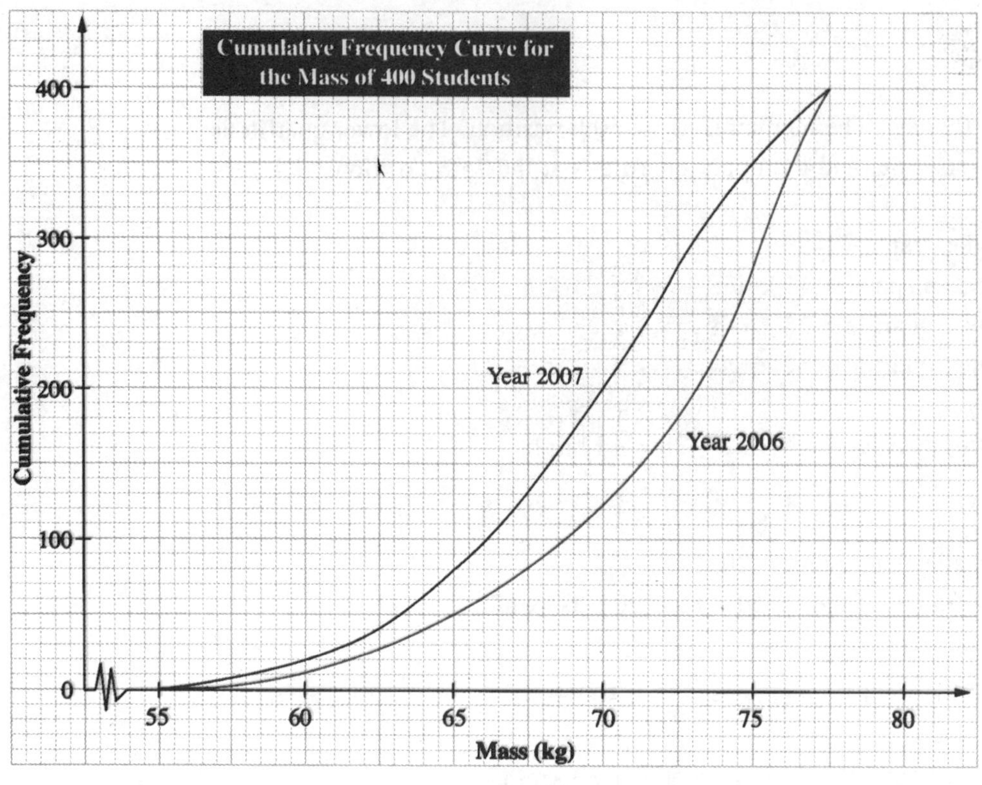

Fig. 5.7

First, record the information as follows:

	Year 2006	Year 2007
Mass of heaviest pupil (kg)		
Mass of lightest pupil (kg)		
The median mass (kg)		
The lower quartile (kg)		
The upper quartile (kg)		

Then answer the following questions:

(a) Calculate
   (i) the range of the mass,
   (ii) the interquartile range for the both years.

(b) Compare and comment on the mass of the students in the two years.

1. Find the range, lower quartile, median, upper quartile and interquartile range for the following set of data.
   (a) 7, 6, 4, 8, 2, 5, 10
   (b) 63, 80, 54, 70, 51, 72, 64, 66
   (c) 14, 18, 22, 10, 27, 32, 40, 16, 9
   (d) 138, 164, 250, 184, 102, 244, 168, 207, 98, 86
   (e) 10.4, 8.5, 13.1, 11.8, 6.7, 22.4, 4.9, 2.7, 15.1

2. The graph shows the cumulative frequency curve of the daily earnings of 50 employees in a company.

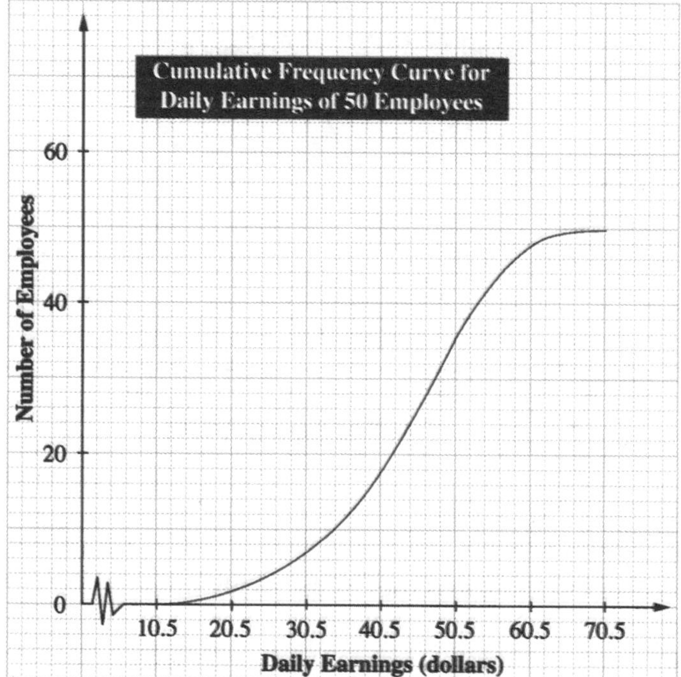

   (a) Use the graph to estimate
      (i) the median, the lower and upper quartiles,
      (ii) the interquartile range.

   (b) Find
      (i) the 20th percentile
      (ii) the 90th percentile
      of the daily earnings of the employees.

   (c) Estimate the percentage of the employees' earnings which are higher than $50.

3. The graph shows the cumulative frequency curves of the daily travelling expenses of 800 pupils in two schools, *A* and *B*.

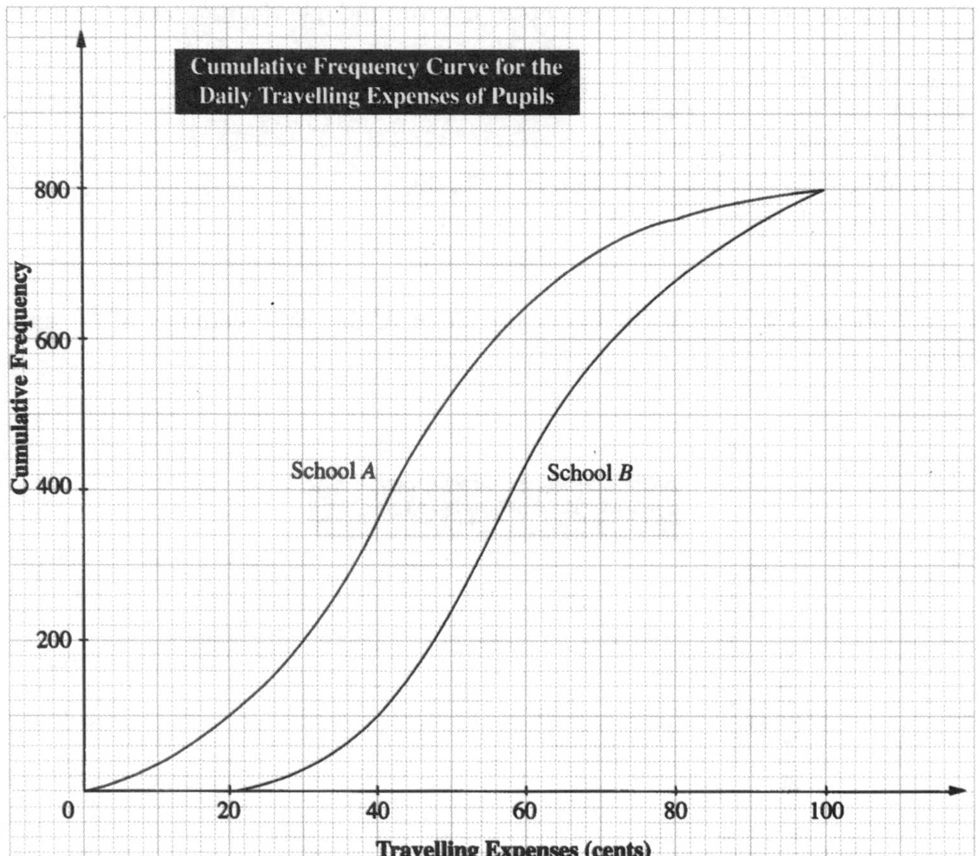

Use the graph to

(a) estimate the median travelling expenses of the pupils from
  (i) School *A*,
  (ii) School *B*;

(b) find the interquartile range of the travelling expenses of
  (i) School *A*,
  (ii) School *B*;

(c) find **(i)** the 30th percentile,
  (ii) the 80th percentile
  of the travelling expenses of the pupils of School *B*;

(d) state, with a reason, which school's pupils spent more on the daily travelling.

4. All the students from two classes, A and B, took the same general knowledge competition. The cumulative frequency curves show the results for the two classes.

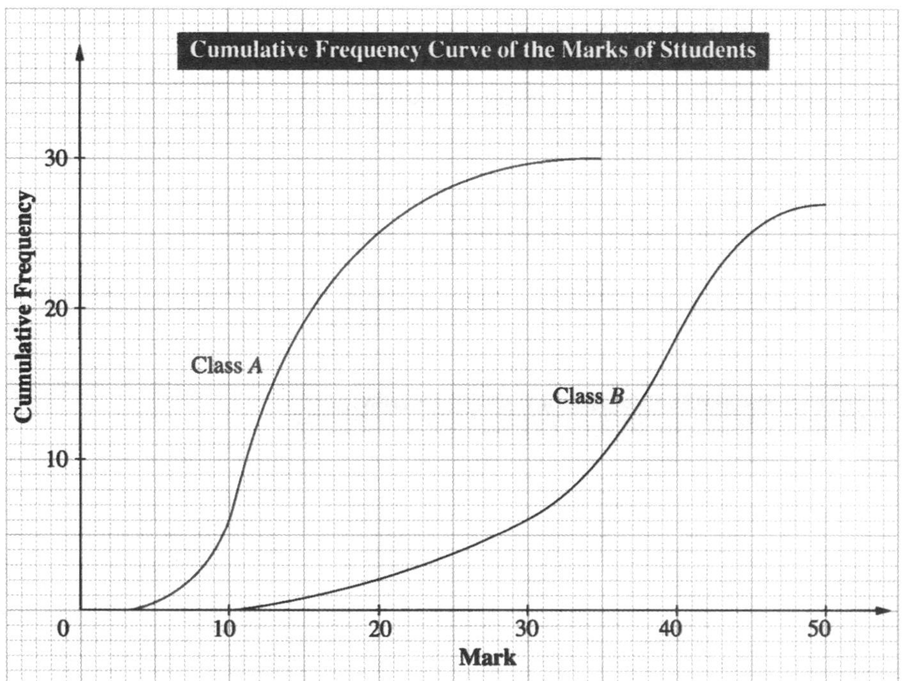

(a) Estimate the lower quartile, median and upper quartile in Class A.

(b) How many students are there in Class B?

(c) Find the interquartile range of Class B.

(d) Estimate the percentage of the students from Class B who received a gold award, if the mark for gold award is more than 40.

(e) Gauss said that Class B performed better in the competition than Class A. Do you agree? Give a reason for your answer.

5. The following are the PSI (Pollutant Standards Index) of two cities measured in 10 days.

City X

80	65	21	81	16
23	37	42	50	53

City Y

103	66	79	121	99
86	114	152	100	171

(a) For each city, find (i) the range,
(ii) the median, and
(iii) the interquartile range of the PSI.

(b) Which data set shows a greater spread?

(c) Comment briefly on the air quality of the two cities.

6. The following diagram is the cumulative frequency curve for the length of 600 leaves from a tree.

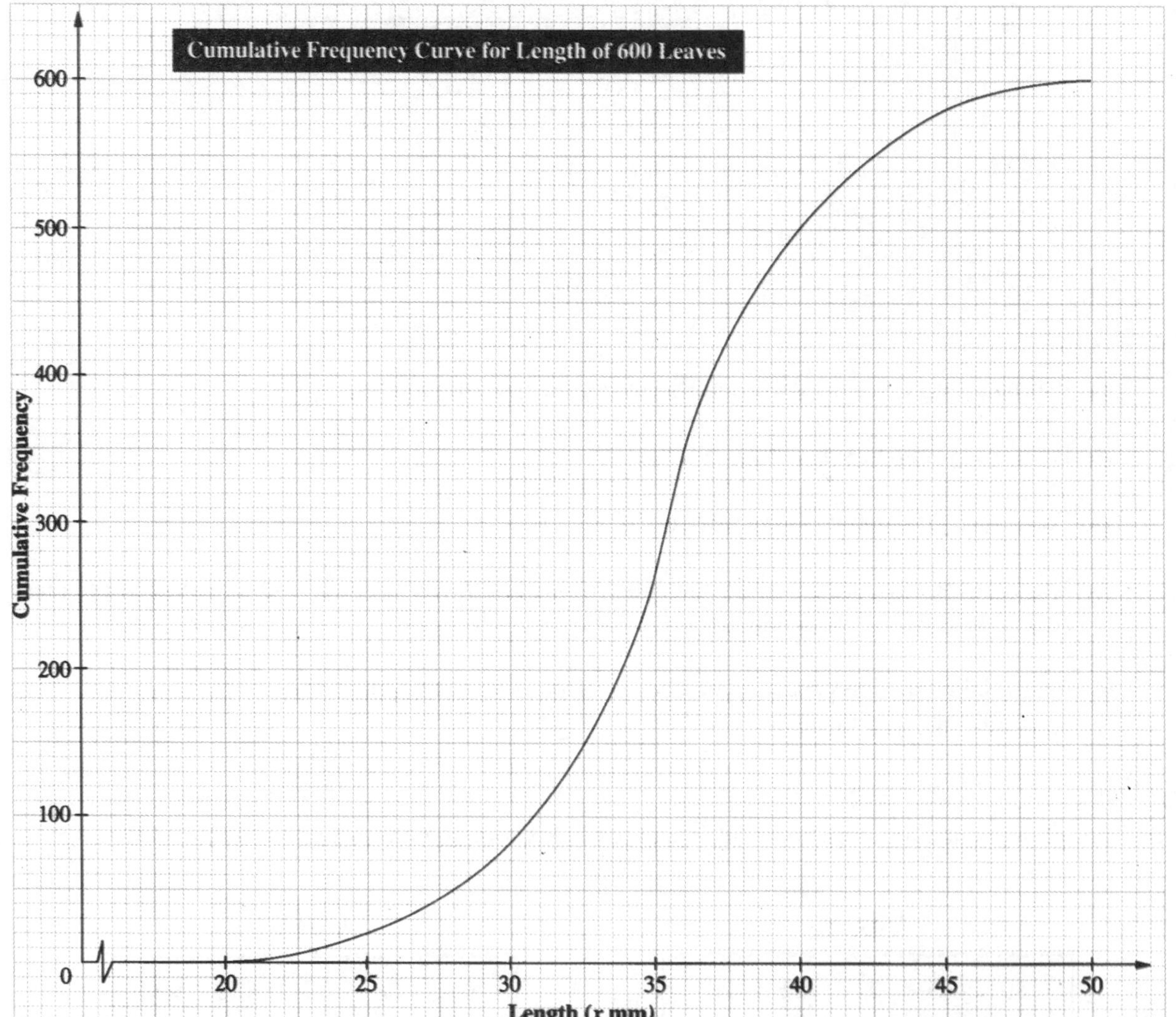

(a) Use the graph to find
    (i) the median length,
    (ii) the interquartile range.

(b) Given that 65% of the leaves are considered as healthy, use the graph to find the shortest length of the healthy leaves.

(c) Copy and complete the following frequency distribution table:

Length (x mm)	Number of Leaves
$20 < x \leq 25$	20
$25 < x \leq 30$	60
$30 < x \leq 35$	
$35 < x \leq 40$	
$40 < x \leq 45$	
$45 < x \leq 50$	

(d) Draw a histogram to represent the frequency distribution in (c).

Box-and-Whisker Plots

A box-and-whisker plot is a graph that shows the range of a set of data, together with the quartiles. Let us look at Example 4 again. In the example, the minimum speed is 20 km/h and the maximum speed is 80 km/h,

- the median speed is 44 km/h,
- the lower quartile is 38 km/h,
- the upper quartile is 52 km/h.

Now we present the above information on a **box-and-whisker plot**. To begin, we draw a horizontal line and choose a suitable scale (say 2 cm to 10 km/h). Then, we mark the **MIN** (the minimum speed), the **MAX** (the maximum speed), and the quartiles.

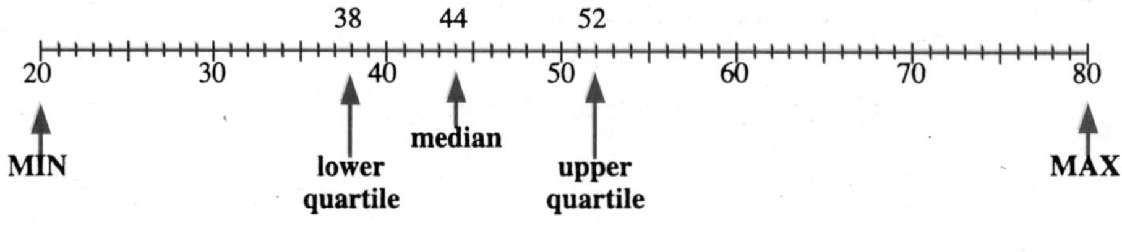

Fig. 5.8

Keeping only the 5 main values and the horizontal line (or the "whiskers"), draw a box with the left side at the lower quartile and the right side at the upper quartile and mark the median with a vertical line inside the box.

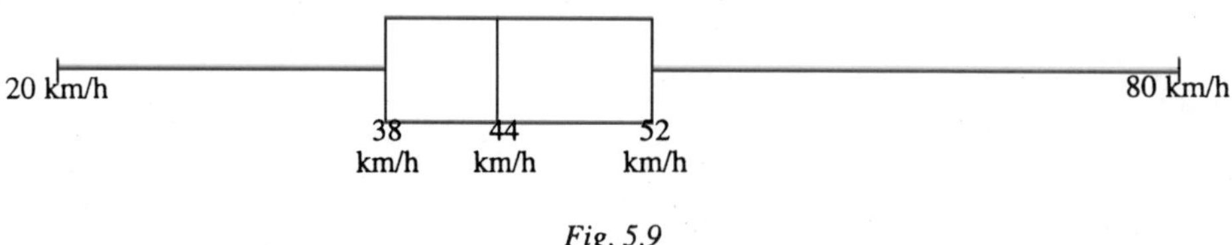

Fig. 5.9

This final figure is called the **box-and-whisker plot**

From the box-and-whisker plot, we can find the interquartile range easily, i.e. 52 – 38 = 14 km/h.

A box-and-whisker plot is a way of summarizing a set of data measured on an interval scale.

It does not show as much detail as in a stem and leaf diagram, a dot diagram or a histogram, but it is useful when large numbers of observations are involved and when two or more data sets are being compared. In general, the box-and-whisker plot is as shown below:

The box-and-whisker plots can be drawn either horizontally or vertically.

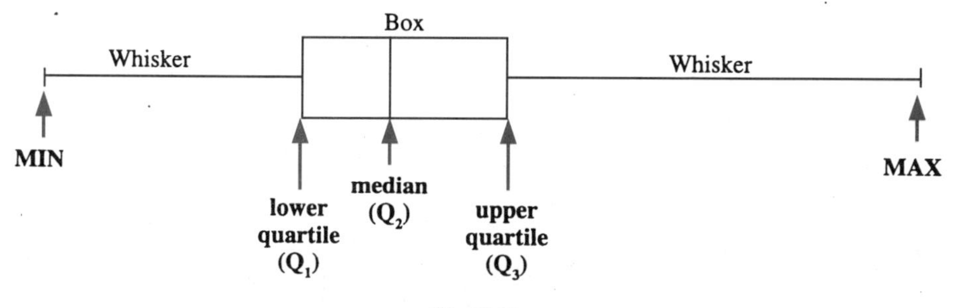

Fig. 5.10

Using computer software Excel, draw the box-and-whisker plot.

Step 1: Key in the data on an Excel worksheet as shown below:

Statistic	Group A	Group B	Group C
Q1	20	35	80
Min	10	20	10
Median	30	50	90
Max	80	120	110
Q3	60	70	100

Step 2: Highlight the whole table above. Go to **Insert, Chart, Line** and select the line diagram **with markers displayed at each data value**. Click **Next, Rows** (the default is **column**) and **Finish**.

Step 3: Go to **Chart, Chart Option** and **Gridlines**. Uncheck all the boxes to give a clear background. Do the same for the other data series.

Step 4: Right-click on one of the data series and select **Format Data Series**. Click the **Patterns** tab, **None** for **Line** and **OK**.

Step 5: Right-click on any of the data series, then go to **Format Data Series** click the **Options** tab, check the box for **High-Low lines** You will see the chart below:

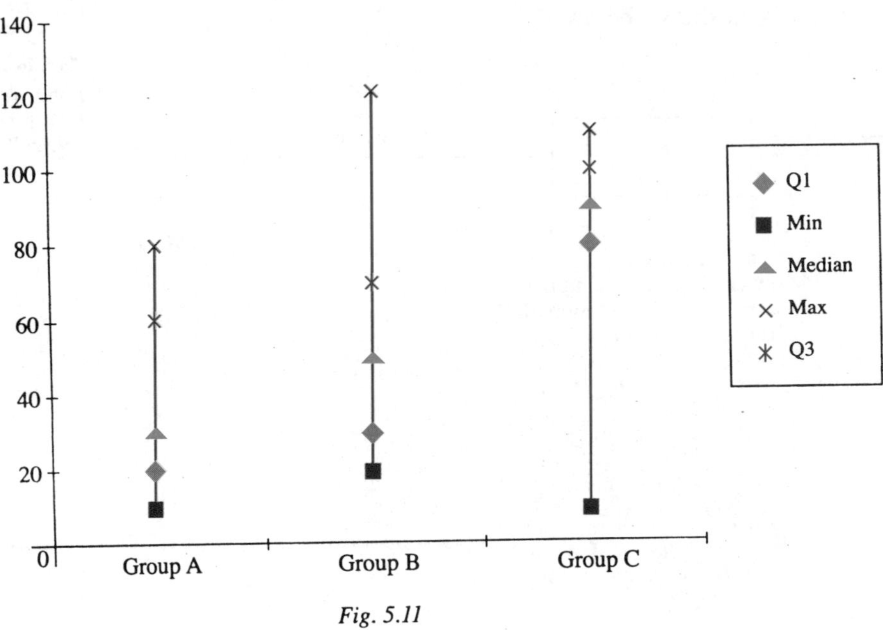

Fig. 5.11

Step 6: Check the box for**Up-Down bars** You will see the final box-and-whisker plots below:

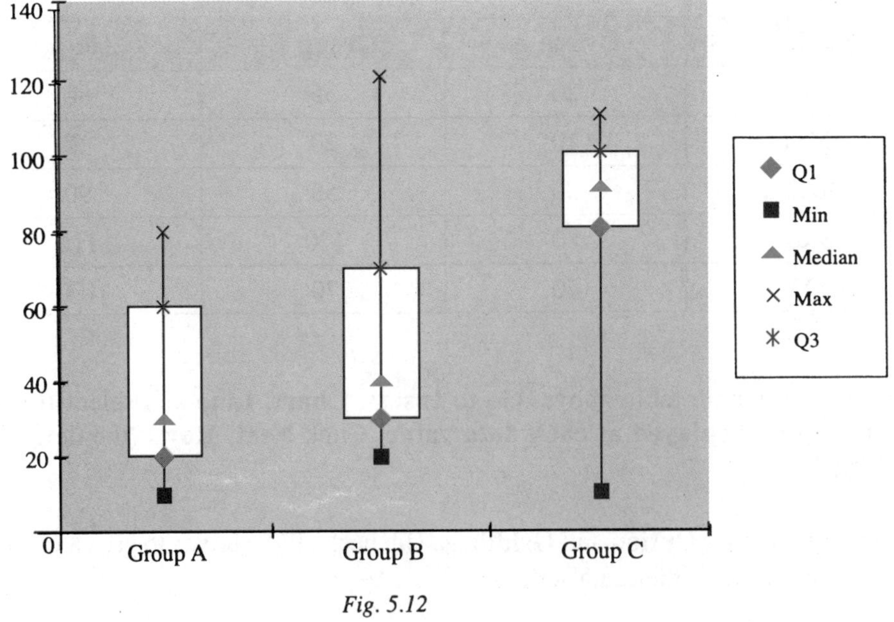

Fig. 5.12

Step 7: Compare and comment briefly on the 3 groups of data from the box-and-whisker plots.

Example 5

A class of pupils took an English test. The results are represented by a box-and-whisker plot as shown.

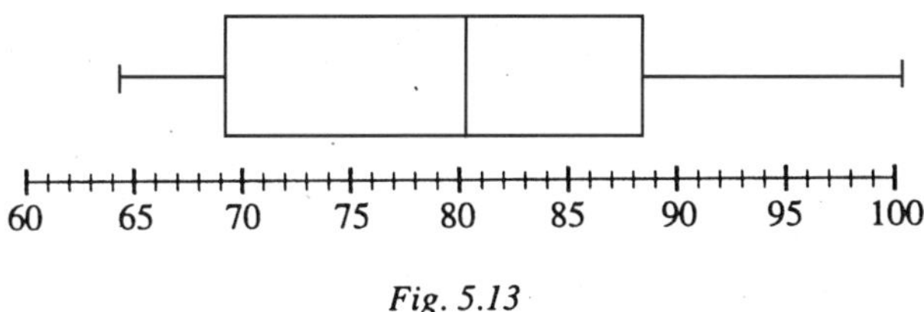

Fig. 5.13

(a) *State the median score.*
(b) *Find the range of the score of the class.*
(c) *Find the interquartile range of the score.*
(d) *Comment briefly on the distribution of the data given that the full score of the test is 100.*

(a)

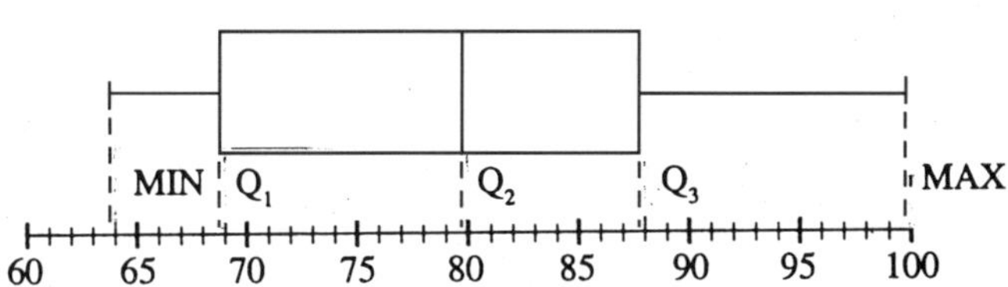

We read the data from the box-and-whisker plot by dropping perpendicular lines from the box to the horizontal scale.

$\therefore$ Median score $= Q_2 = 80$

(b) Range = MAX – MIN = 100 – 64 = 36

(c) Interquartile range $= Q_3 - Q_1$
$= 88 - 69$
$= 19$

(d) The high median score suggests that the class did well in the test and the wide interquatile range suggests that the scores are well spread.

xample 6

The following information gives the weekly expenditure on food for 80 households in Greenfield housing estate:

There are 5 households which have weekly expenditure no more than \$38.
- *No household spends more than \$100 on food.*
- *The median weekly expenditure on food is \$61.*
- *The lower quartile of the distribution is \$55.*
- *The interquartile range of the distribution is \$19.*

The cumulative frequency curve below shows the weekly expenditure on food for 80 households in Redwood housing estate:

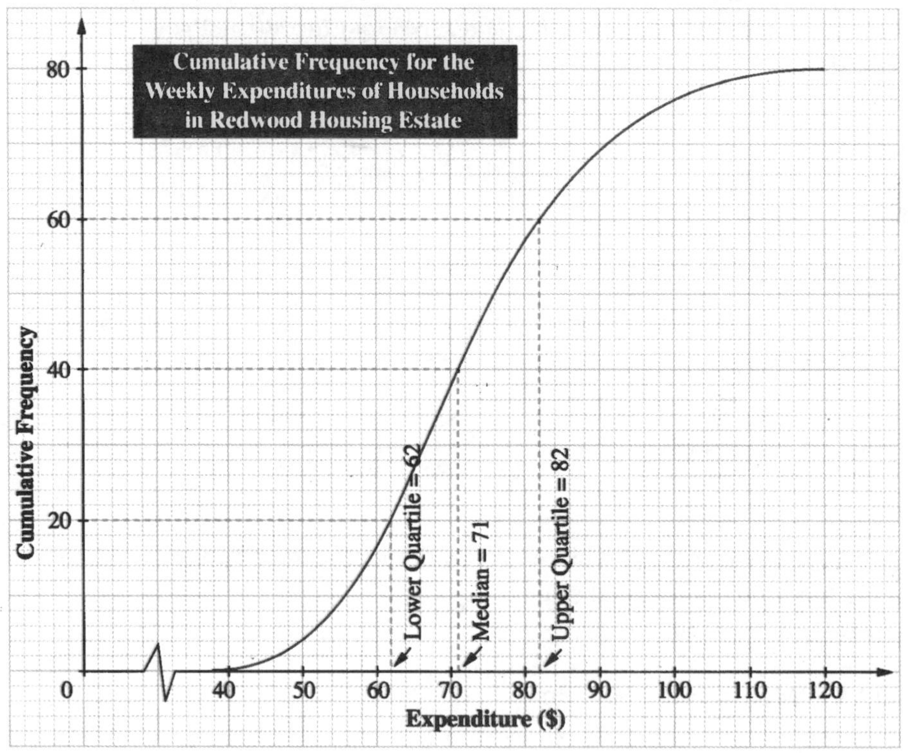

Fig. 5.14

(a) Calculate the upper quartile for Greenfield housing estate.
(b) Using the graph for households in Redwood housing estate, estimate the lower quartile, median and upper quartile, the minimum and maximum expenditure.
(c) Comment briefly on the weekly expenditure on food for the 80 households in the two housing estates.

(a) In Greenfield housing estate,
Interquartile range = Upper quartile – Lower quartile = 19

$\therefore$ Upper quartile = 19 + 55 = 74

(b) From the graph, we see that Lower quartile = 62, Median = 71, Upper quartile = 82, Minimum = 40 and Maximum = 120.

(c) Then we have the following table.

	Greenfield's expenditure	Redwood's expenditure (by reading the cumulative frequency curve)
MIN	\$38	\$40
Lower quartile	\$55	\$62
Median	\$61	\$71
Upper quartile	\$74	\$82
MAX	\$100	\$120

Using the data above, we can form the the box-and-whisker plots for the weekly expenditure on food for the two housing estates as shown below:

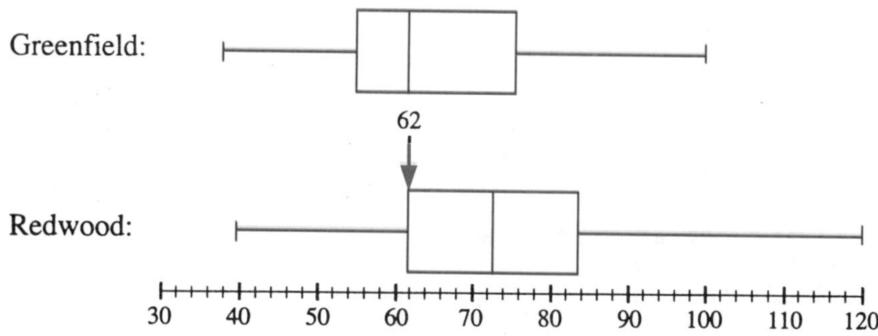

From the box-and-whisker plots, we can see that Redwood's highest and lowest expenditure are both higher than Greenfield's corresponding expenditures, and Redwood's median expenditure is higher than that of Greenfield's. Moreover, Redwood's interquartile range is larger than that of Greenfield's. Hence, residents in Redwood spend more on food than in Greenfield.

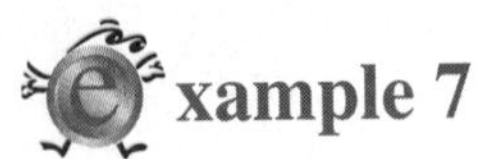

xample 7

In an agricultural experiment, the length of the ear of 124 barley from Country A were measured. The results obtained are is expressed in the following graph:

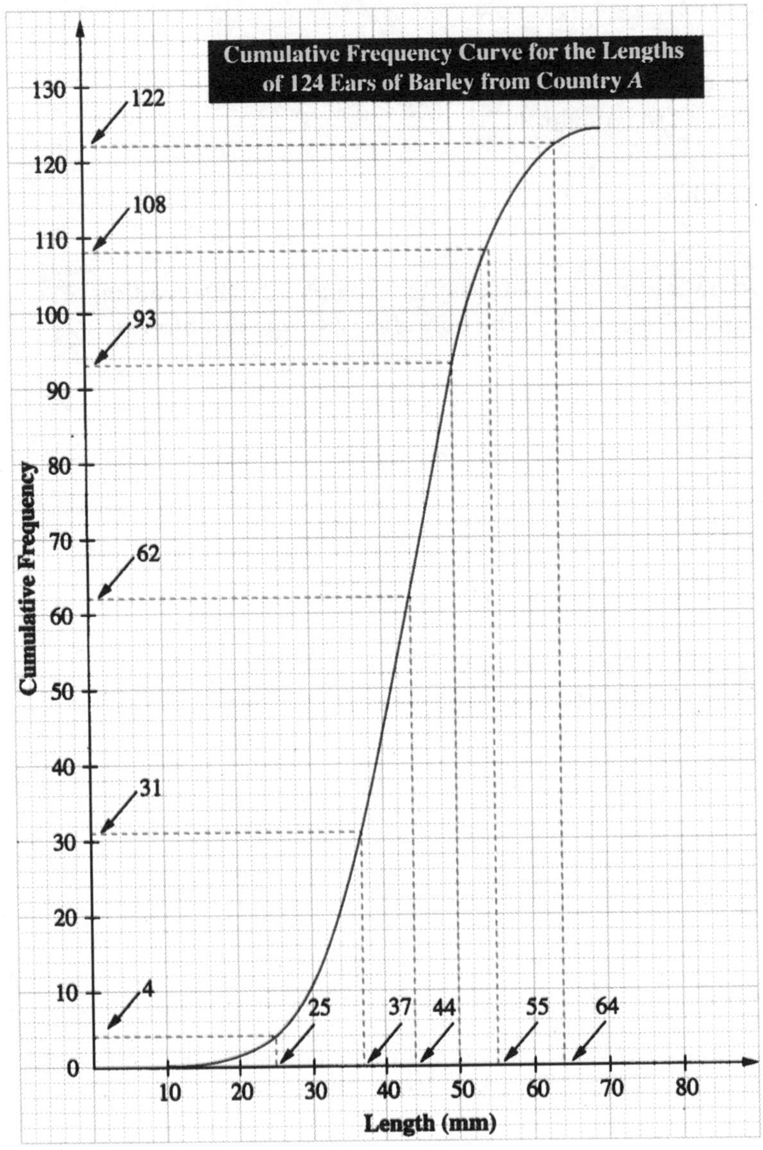

Fig.5.15

(a) *Use your graph to estimate the (i) median,*
(ii) interquartile range.

(b) *From the graph, find the number of ears of barley with lengths*
(i) greater than 55 mm,
(ii) either not greater than 25 mm or greater than 64 mm.

(c) It was discovered later that all the lengths were wrongly recorded such that 5 mm more should be added to all the lengths.
Find the correct value of (i) the median,
(ii) the interquartile range,
(iii) the minimum and maximum lengths,
(iv) the range.

(d) In the same experiment, the length of the ear of 124 barley from Country B were measured. The results are summarized by a box-and-whisker plot shown below.

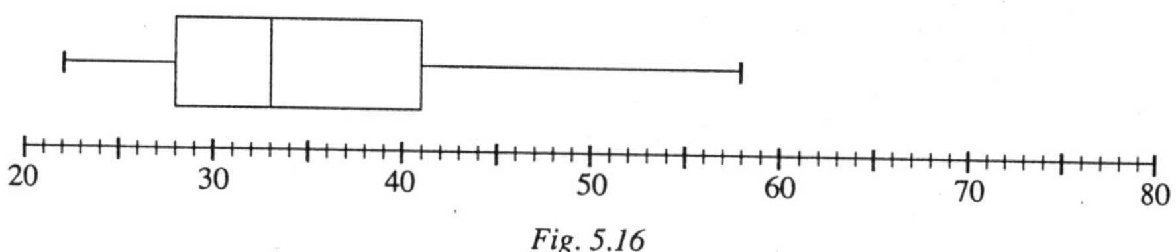

Fig. 5.16

(i) State the median and the interquartile range.
(ii) Write down the minimum and maximum lengths. Hence find the range.

(e) Compare the lengths obtained from the two countries in three different ways.

(f) Harry said that the barley did not grow well in Country B as compared to Country A. Do you agree? Give a reason for your answer.

(a) There are 124 data. The median is at the 62nd position. The lower quartile is at the 31st position, and the upper quartile is at the 93rd position.

From the cumulative frequency graph,
(i) the median = 44 mm
(ii) the lower quartile = 37 mm
the upper quartile = 50 mm

∴ the interquartile range = (50 – 37) mm = 13 mm.

(b) (i) Approximately 108 ears of barley have lengths 55 mm or less.

∴ the number of ears of barley with lengths greater than 55 mm is 124 – 108 = 16.

(ii) Number of ears of barley with lengths not greater than 25 mm = 4.

Numbers of ears of barley with lengths greater than 64 mm
= 124 – 122 = 2

∴ the number of ears of barley with lengths not greater than 25 mm or greater than 64 mm = 4 + 2 = 6.

The same adjustment was made to the lower and upper quartiles and so the interquartile range remained unchanged, i.e. no adjustment was needed to give the correct value of the interquartile range.

(c) Since all lengths should be 5 mm more, the correct value of

(i) the median = 44 + 5 = 49 mm,

(ii) the lower quartile = 37 + 5 = 42 mm,
the upper quartile = 50 + 5 = 55 mm,
and thus the interquartile range = 55 – 42 = 13 mm

(iii) MIN = 20 + 5 = 25 mm
MAX = 70 + 5 = 75 mm

(iv) range = 75 – 25 = 50 mm

(d) (i) From the box-and-whisker plot,
median = 33 mm
interquartile range = 41 – 28 = 13 mm

(ii) MIN = 22 mm, MAX = 58 mm
∴ range = 58 – 22 = 36 mm

(e) Barley from Country *A* has greater median length than Country *B* (49 mm for *A* and 33 mm for *B*).
The spread for both countries are the same.
Country *A* has a greater range than Country *B* (50 mm for *A* and 36 mm for *B*).

(f) I agree with Harry, because Country *B* produced barley that had lower median length than Country *A*.

Two murder suspects, A and B, were on trial. Four witnesses were questioned.

First witness answered: *I only know that A is innocent.*

Second witness said: *I only know that B is innocent.*

Third witness replied: *At least one of the first two witnesses is telling the truth.*

Fourth witness said: *I am positively sure that the third witness gave false evidence.*

After the investigation, it was confirmed that what the fourth witness said was true. Who was the murderer?

Do you think that the "box" must always lie in the middle of the "whisker"? What does it indicate if the "whisker" on the right hand side is longer than the "whisker" on the left hand side?

1. The following diagram shows the box-and-whisker plot for the daily temperature (°C) from 1 June to 30 June in a city.

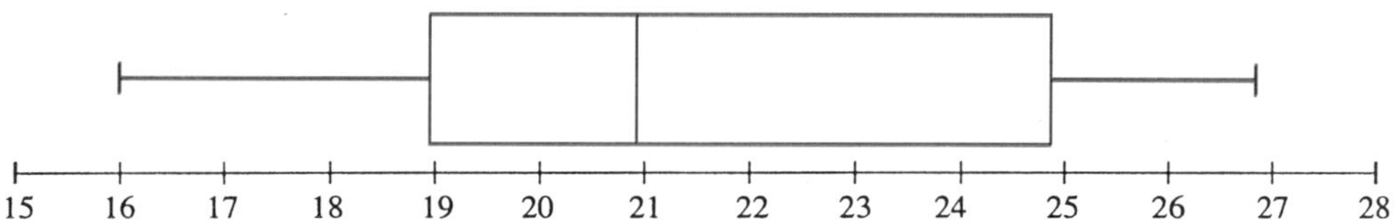

(a) State the lower quartile, median and upper quartile of the temperature.
(b) Find the range of the temperature in June.

2. The following diagram shows the box-and-whisker plot for the alcohol content in the blood of drivers who were given breathalyzer tests.

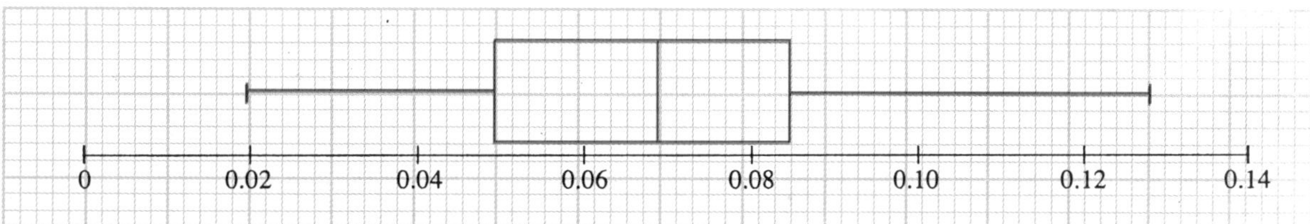

(a) State the lower quartile, median and upper quartile of the alcohol content of the drivers.
(b) Compare the spread of the alcohol content between the highest 25% and the lowest 25% of the drivers.

3. The height of basketball players (cm) in one NBA team as follows.

{158, 180, 185, 192, 192, 195, 195, 196, 198, 200, 205, 213}.

The data can be represented in the box-and-whisker plot below.

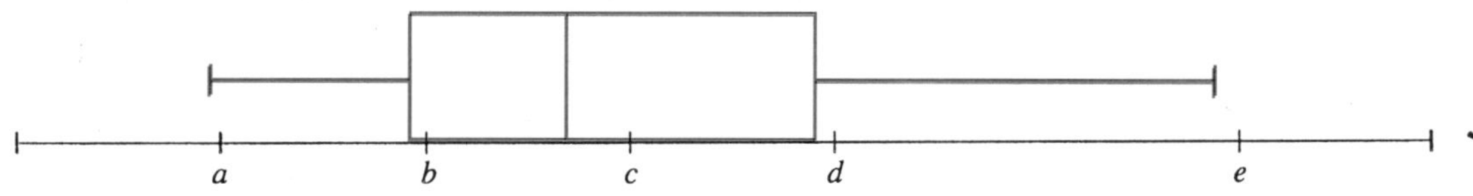

(a) Find the values of a, b, c, d and e.
(b) Calculate $d - b$. What does it represent?
(c) Calculate $e - a$. What does it represent?

4. The box-and-whisker plot shows the blood pressure level (in mm of mercury) for patients who have taken a certain drug.

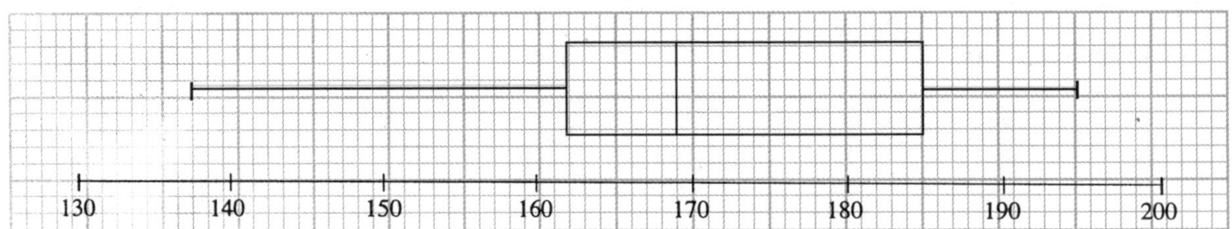

(a) State the median of the blood pressure levels of the patients.
(b) Find the interquartile range.
(c) The left whisker is longer than the right whisker in the above box-and-whisker plot. Explain what it means.

5. The following box-and-whisker plots show the masses (g) of 3 types of apples.

(a) Which type of apples has
 (i) the highest median,
 (ii) the lowest median?
(b) Which type of apples has a more uniformly-distributed mass?
(c) Which type of apples has a greater spread of mass?

Type *B*

Type *C*

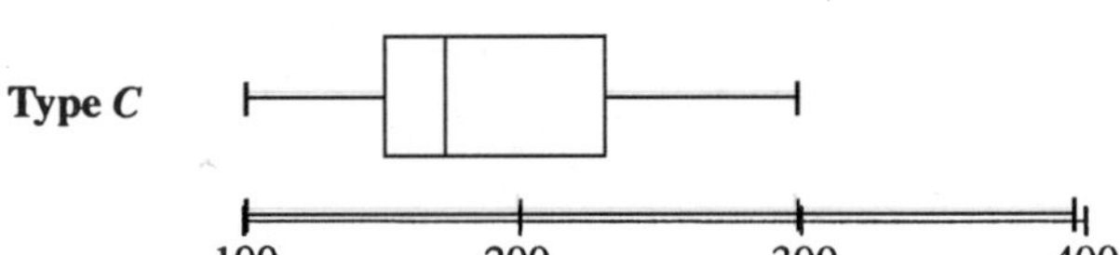

6. The box-and-whisker plot shows the masses (kg) of students from School *X* and School *Y* in Secondary 4.

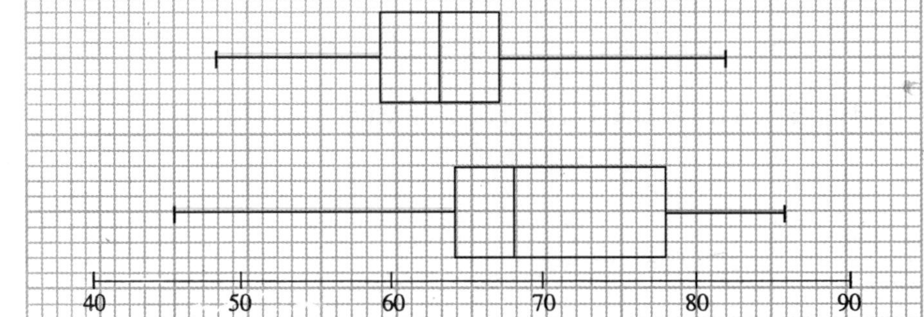

(a) For School *X* (i) state the median,
 (ii) find the interquartile range.
(b) Describe briefly the distribution of the mass of School *Y* students.
(c) Linda said the students from School *Y* are generally heavier than the students from School *X*. Do you agree? Give a reason for your answer.

7. The cumulative frequency curve below shows the distribution of the marks scored by 600 pupils in an examination in Euler High School:

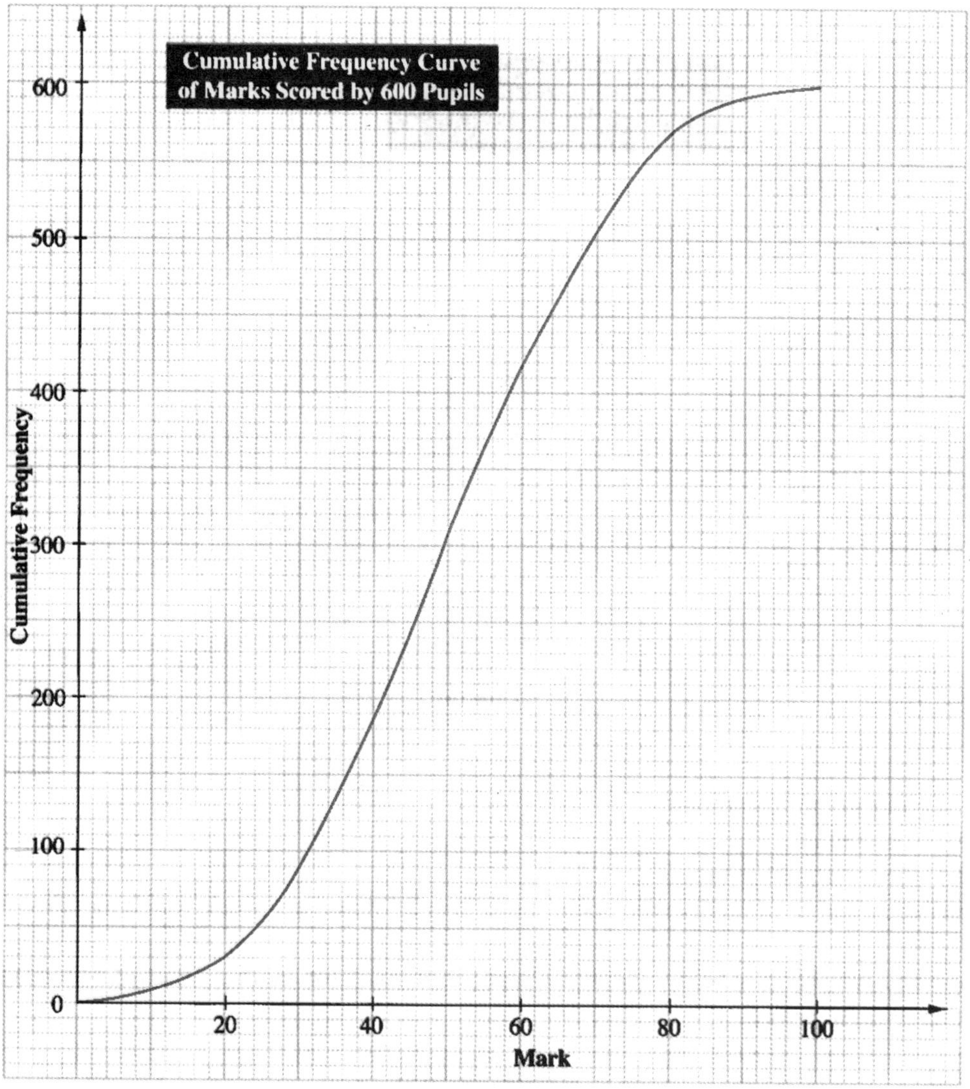

Cumulative Frequency Curve of Marks Scored by 600 Pupils

Cumulative Frequency

600

500

400

300

200

100

0

20 40 60 80 100

Mark

(a) Use your graph to estimate
 (i) the median mark,
 (ii) the pass mark such that 60% of the pupils will pass the examination.

(b) Indicate clearly the upper and lower quartiles on your graph and write down the interquartile range.

The box-and-whisker plot gives the information on the marks scored by 600 pupils in the same examination in Fermat High School:

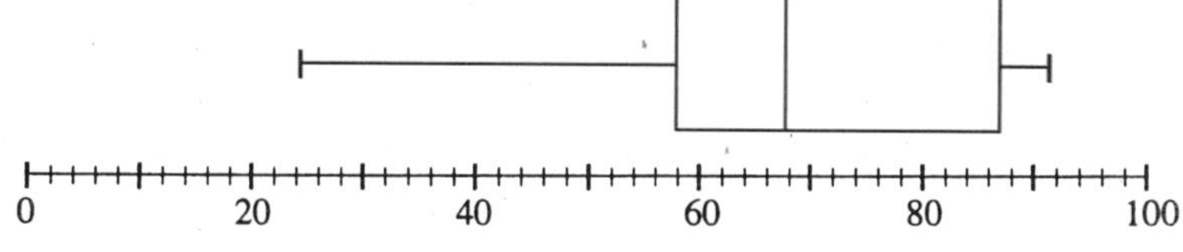

(c) Find the median mark and the interquattile range.
Hence, comment briefly on the performance of the pupils in the two schools.

8. 64 adults were asked to indicate the weekly number of hours they spent watching television. The cumulative frequency curve below shows the information obtained:

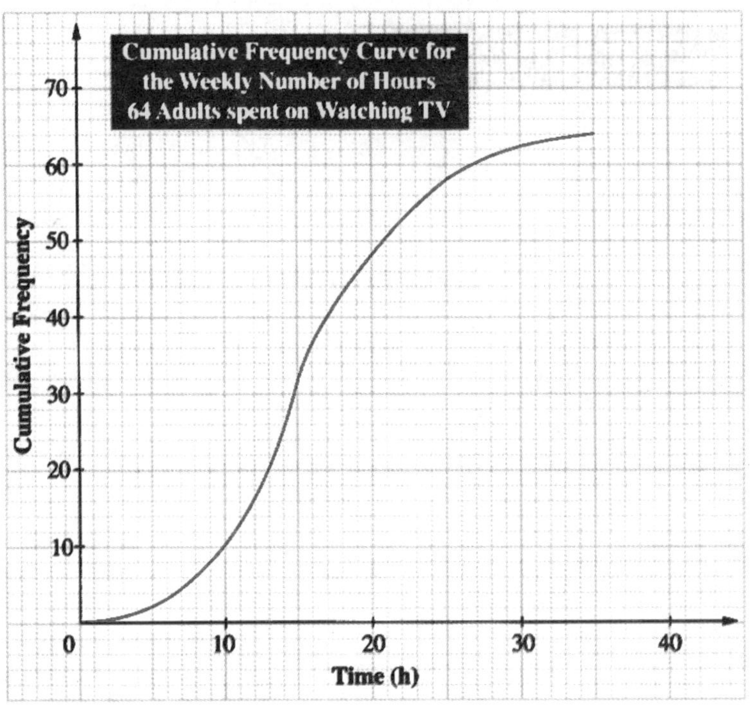

(a) Use your graph to estimate
 (i) the median,
 (ii) the interquartile range,
 (iii) the number of adults who spent more than 25 hours per week watching television.

The box-and-whisker plot below shows the number of hours for another group of 64 teenagers spent watching television weekly.

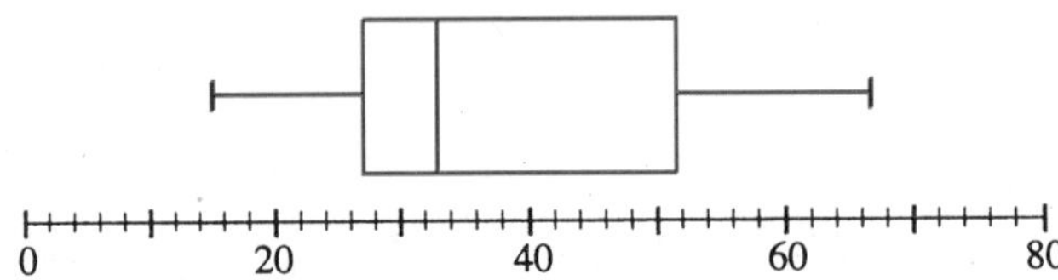

(b) Find (i) the median,
 (ii) the interquartile range.

(c) Compare and comment briefly on the time spent on watching television of the two groups of people.

9. The box-and-whisker plots show the age (years) distribution of 60 members of Club *ABC* and 60 members of Club *XYZ*.

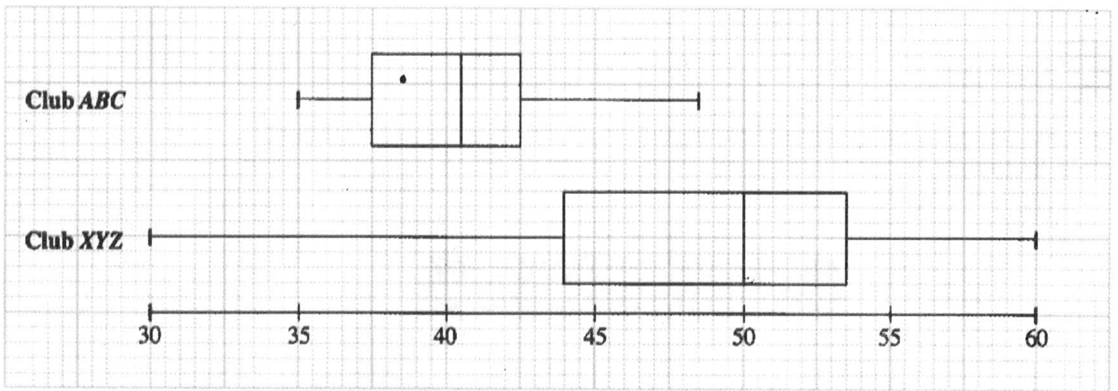

(a) For Club *ABC*, find **(i)** the median age, **(ii)** the interquartile range.
(b) For Club *XYZ*, find **(i)** the median age, **(ii)** the interquartile range.
(c) Which club shows a greater spread?
(d) Comment briefly on the age distribution of the members in Club *ABC* and Club *XYZ*.

1. The **cumulative frequency table** provides another way of representing a set of data. It can be obtained from the frequency table. The cumulative distribution can be displayed graphically by a **cumulative frequency curve**

2. A cumulative frequency curve can be used to estimate the median, quartiles and percentiles of a distribution. It can also be used to estimate information like how many pupils obtained less than a certain mark, how many people weigh less than a certain weight, and so on.

3. The interquartile range is the difference between the upper quartile and lower quartile.

4. A **box-and-whisker** plot illustrates the range, the median and the quartiles of a frequency distribution.

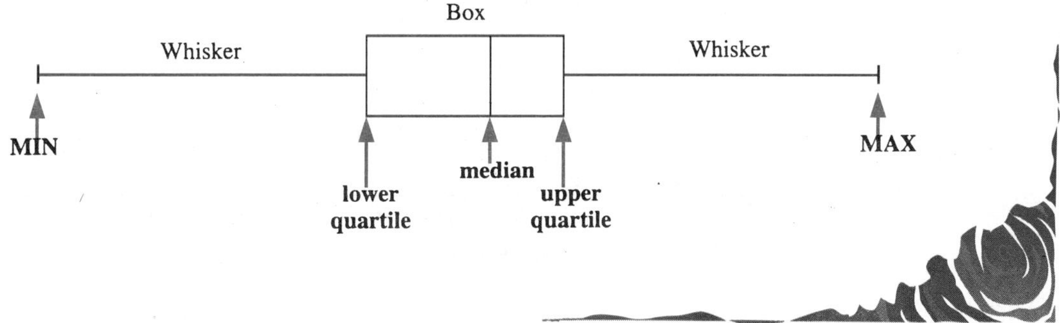

5

Example 1

The cumulative frequency curve below represents the distance of 16 students from a flagpole.

Cumulative Frequency Curve for the Distance of Students from a Flagpole

Cumulative Frequency

0, 1, 2, 3, 4, 5, 6, 7, 8, 9, 10, 11, 12, 13, 14, 15, 16

25%

50%

75%

x

y

x_1

x_3

10, 20, 30, 40, 50, 60, 70, 80, 90, 100, 110

Distance (cm)

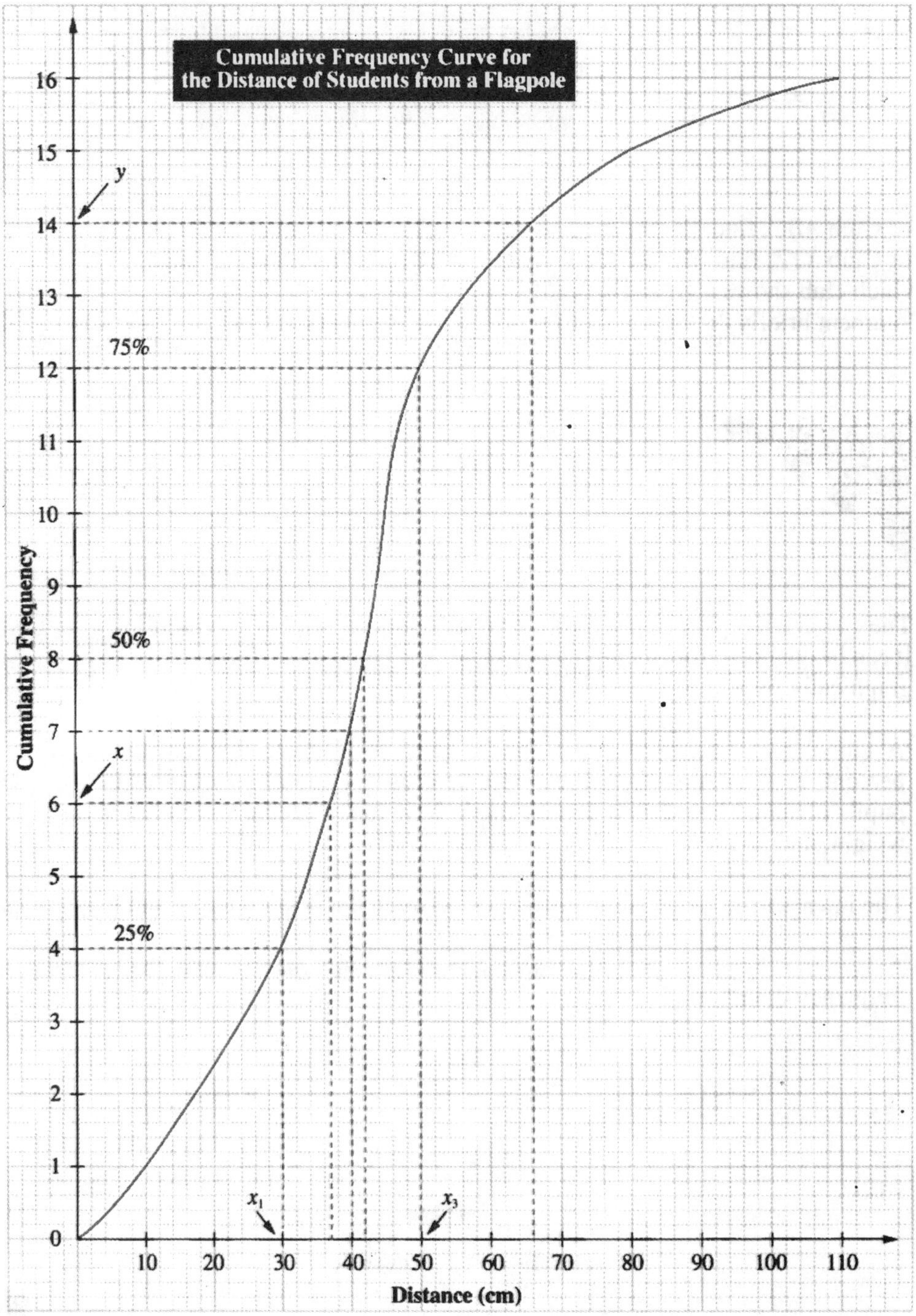

Fig. 5.17

(a) *Use the graph to find the value of x and of y in the cumulative frequency table below.*

Distance (cm)	Cumulative frequency
≤ 10	1
≤ 30	4
≤ 37	x
≤ 42	8
≤ 45	10
≤ 50	12
≤ 66	y
≤ 110	16

(b) *Find the percentile for distance less than 40 cm.*

(c) *A box-and-whisker plot is drawn to represent the quartiles of the above data. Find the values of x_1, x_2 and x_3.*

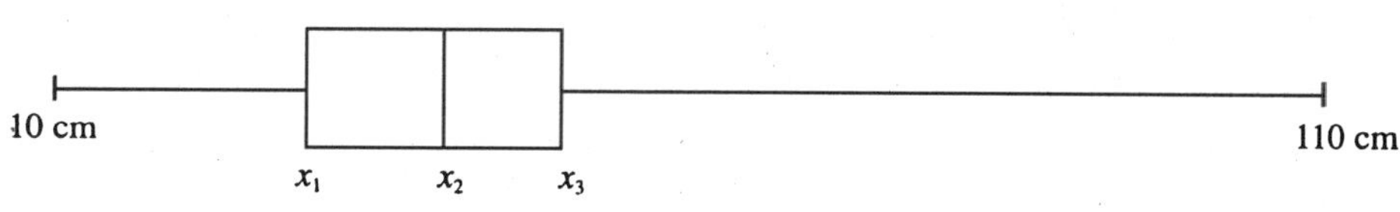

Fig. 5.18

(d) *Find the value of $x_3 - x_1$. What does it represent?*

(a) From the graph, $x = 6$, $y = 14$.

(b) 7 students are less than 40 cm from the flagpole.

$\therefore \quad \frac{7}{16} \times 100\% = 43.75$th percentile

(c) x_1 represents the lower quartile.

$\therefore \quad 25\%$ of the total frequency $= 16 \times \frac{25}{100} = 4$

From the curve, $x_1 = 30$ cm.

x_2 represents the median.

$\therefore \quad 50\%$ of the total frequency $= 16 \times \frac{50}{100} = 8$

From the curve, $x_2 = 42$ cm.

x_3 represents the upper quartile.

$\therefore \quad 75\%$ of the total frequency $= 16 \times \frac{75}{100} = 12$

From the curve, $x_3 = 50$ cm.

(d) $x_3 - x_1 = 50 - 30 = 20$ cm
This value represents the interquartile range.

1. The cumulative frequency curves show the distribution of marks scored by 500 cadets in a physical test from each of two schools, *A* and *B*.

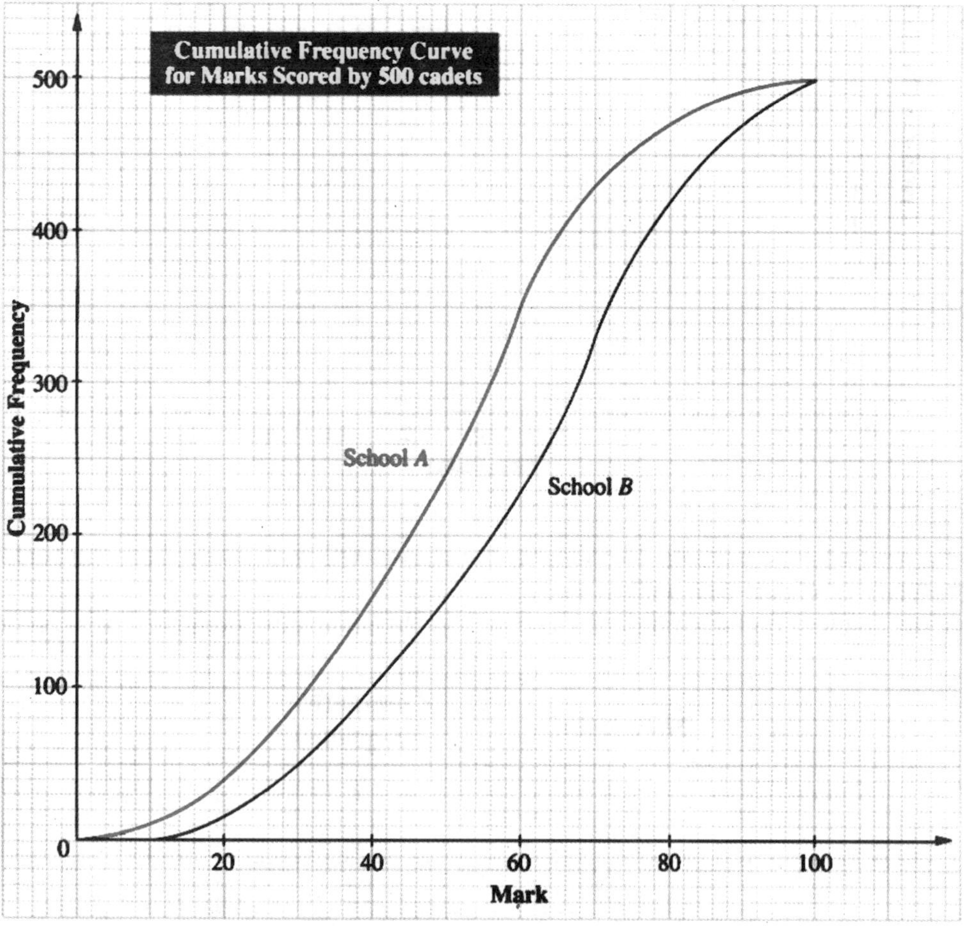

(a) For school *A*, estimate from the graph,
  (i) the median,
  (ii) the 70th percentile,
  (iii) the interquartile range,
  (iv) the number of cadets who scored less than 43 marks,
  (v) the pass mark given that 60% of the cadets passed the physical test.

(b) It is given that a distinction grade is equivalent to 70 marks and above. Find the percentage of cadets who scored distinction in each school.

(c) George commented that cadets from School *B* performed better in general. Do you agree? Give two reasons to support yourself.

2. The cumulative frequency curve below represents the waiting times (minutes) of 60 clients at a certain bank.

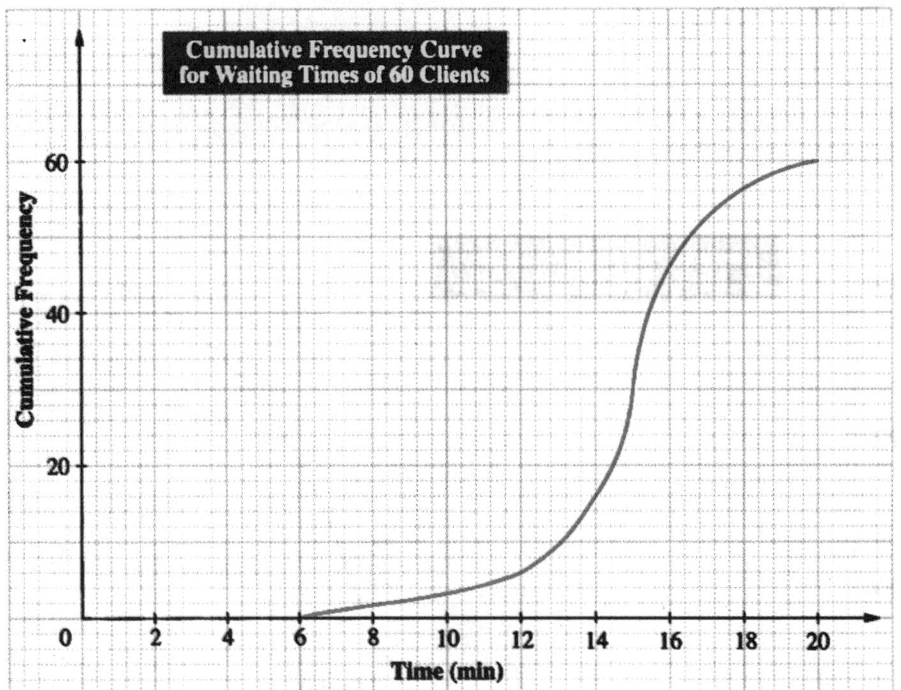

(a) If the waiting time exceeds 15 minutes, the clients will walk away from the bank. Find the percentage of clients who walked away.

(b) Use the graph to find the value of x and of y in the cumulative frequency table below.

Time (min)	Cumulative Frequency
≤ 8	1
≤ 12	x
≤ 14	15
≤ 15	30
≤ 16	45
≤ 18	y
≤ 20	60

(c) A box-and-whisker plot is drawn to represent the quartiles of the above data. Find the values of x_1, x_2 and x_3.

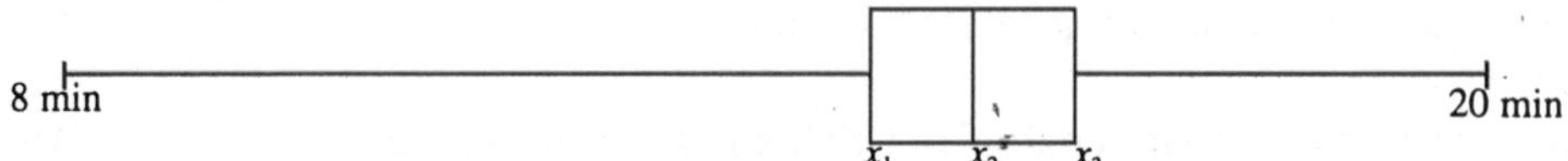

(d) Find the value of $x_3 - x_1$. What does it represent?

3. 80 pupils participated in a general knowledge quiz. The cumulative frequency curve below shows the marks scored. The maximum mark for the quiz was 50.

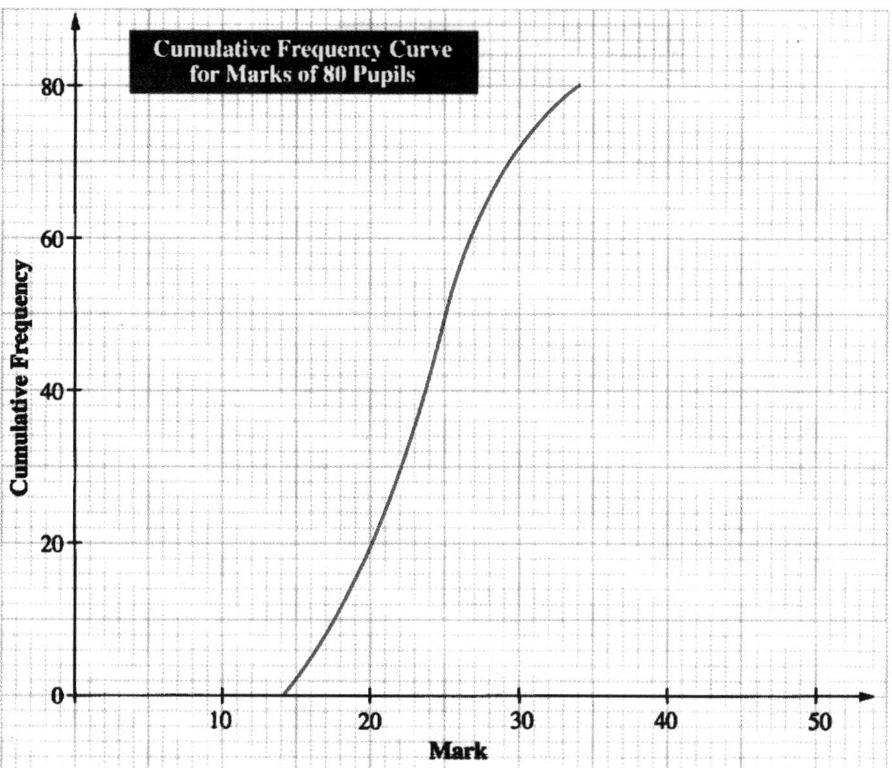

(a) Estimate from the graph,

(i) the median mark,

(ii) the upper quartile,

(iii) the interquartile range,

(iv) the number of participants who scored marks between 26 and 30 inclusive.

(b) Given that 35% of the pupils passed the quiz, use the graph to find the pass mark.

(c) The same 80 pupils took an IQ quiz. The box-and-whisker diagram below illustrates the marks obtained. The maximum mark was again 50.

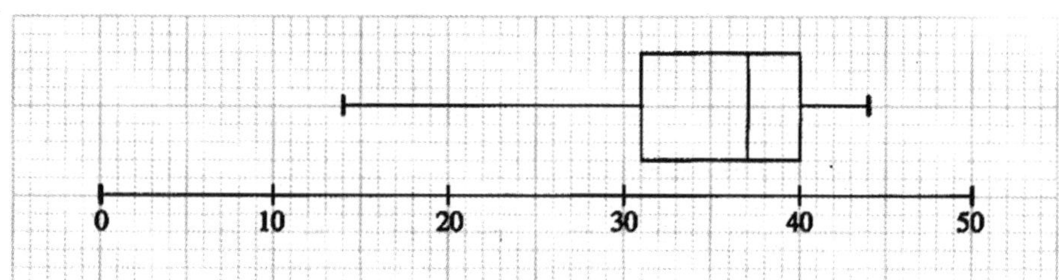

(i) Compare the marks gained for general knowledge quiz and IQ quiz in two different ways.

(ii) Garry said that the general knowledge quiz was easier than the IQ quiz. Do you agree? Give a reason for your answer.

4. The masses of 200 eggs from Rainbow Farm were measured and the results are illustrated in the cumulative frequency curve below:

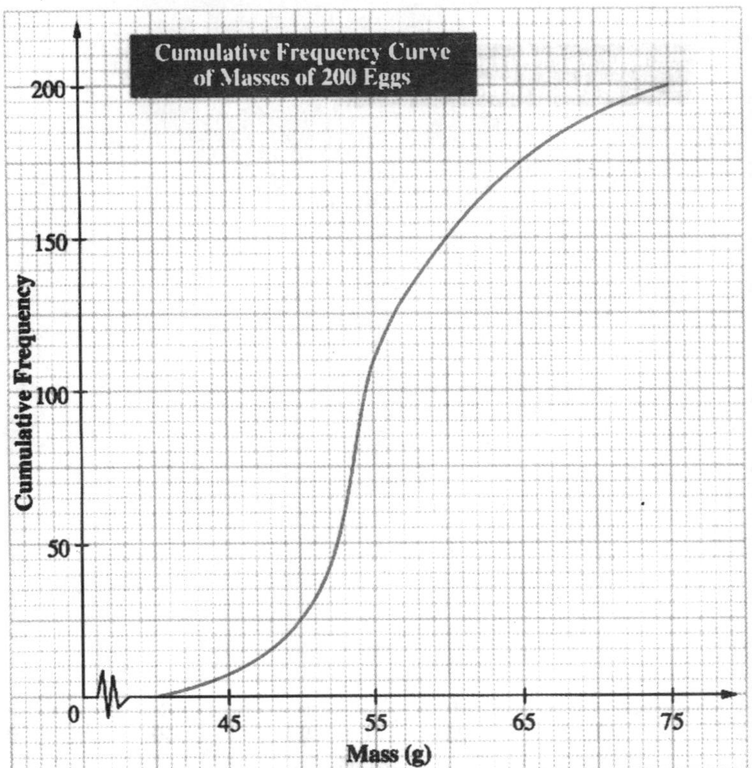

The eggs are graded according to their masses as follows:

Grade 1: $62 \text{ g} < x \leq 75 \text{ g}$
Grade 2: $51 \text{ g} < x \leq 62 \text{ g}$
Grade 3: $40 \text{ g} < x \leq 51 \text{ g}$

(a) Use your curve to estimate
(i) the median mass,
(ii) the interquartile range,
(iii) the percentage of eggs in each grade.

(b) The masses (g) of 200 eggs from Skyhi Farm were also measured and the results are shown in the box-and-whisker diagram below:

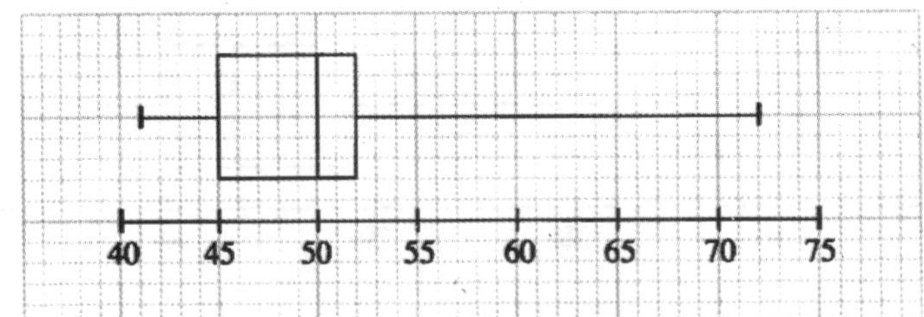

(i) State the median mass and the interquartile range.
(ii) Skyhi Farm produced 5% of Grade 1's eggs. Compare and comment briefly on the quality of the eggs from the two farms. Give two reasons to support your comment.

5. The following diagram is the cumulative frequency curve for the heights, in cm, of 56 plants grown under experimental conditions.

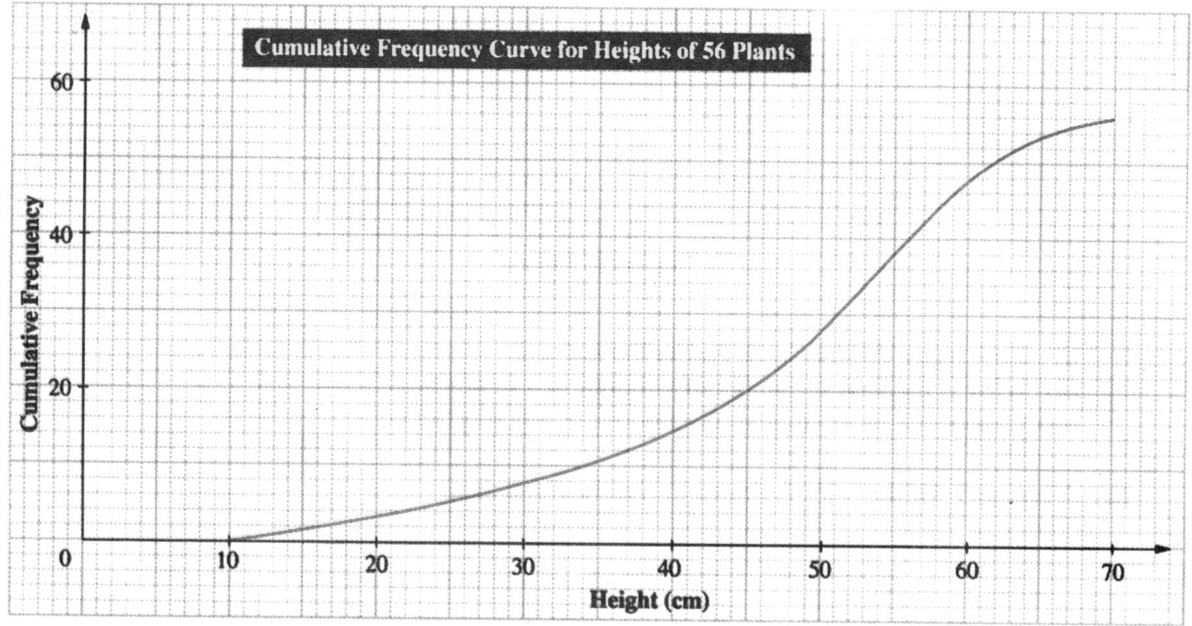

(a) Use your curve to estimate

(i) the median,

(ii) the upper quartile,

(iii) the lower quartile,

(iv) the number of plants having heights greater than 57 cm,

(v) the value of x if 37.5% of the 56 plants have a height of less than or equal to x cm.

(b) Given that 45% of the plants are considered unhealthy, use your graph to find the maximum height of the unhealthy plants.

(c) Copy and complete the following frequency distribution table:

Height (x cm)	Number of Plants
$10 < x \leq 20$	3
$20 < x \leq 30$	5
$30 < x \leq 40$	
$40 < x \leq 50$	
$50 < x \leq 60$	
$60 < x \leq 70$	

(d) Draw a histogram to represent the frequency distribution in (c).

6. (a) The dot diagram below shows the number of siblings that each child who took part in a survey, has

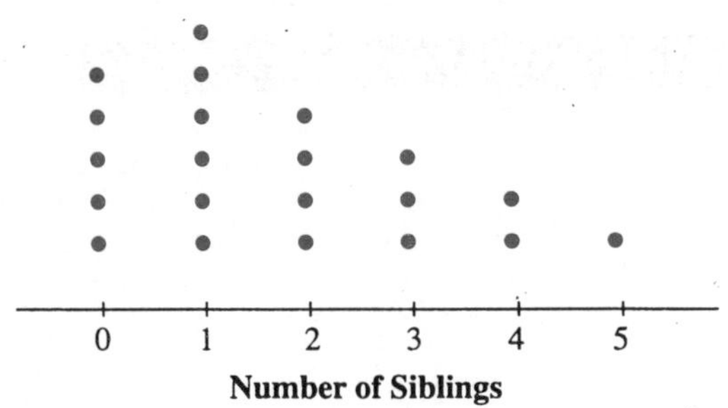

(i) How many children took part in the survey?
(ii) What is the largest number of children in a family?
(iii) What is the mean number of children in a family?

(b) A box-and-whisker plot is drawn to represent the data.

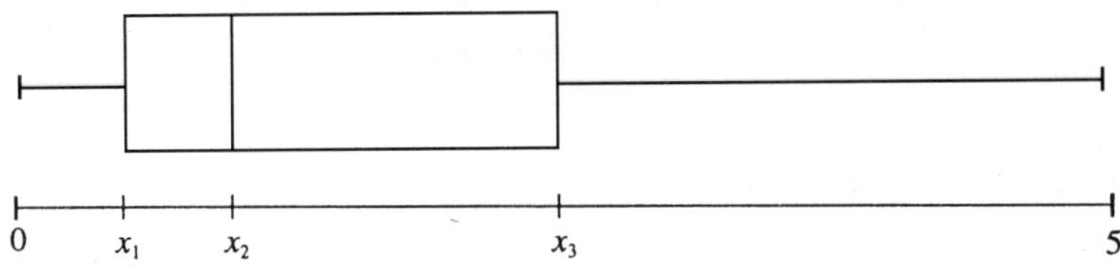

(i) Find the values of x_1, x_2 and x_3.
(ii) What does x_2 and x_3 each represent?
(iii) Find the interquartile range.

✱7. The following diagram shows the box-and-whisker plots for two sets of data, X and Y.

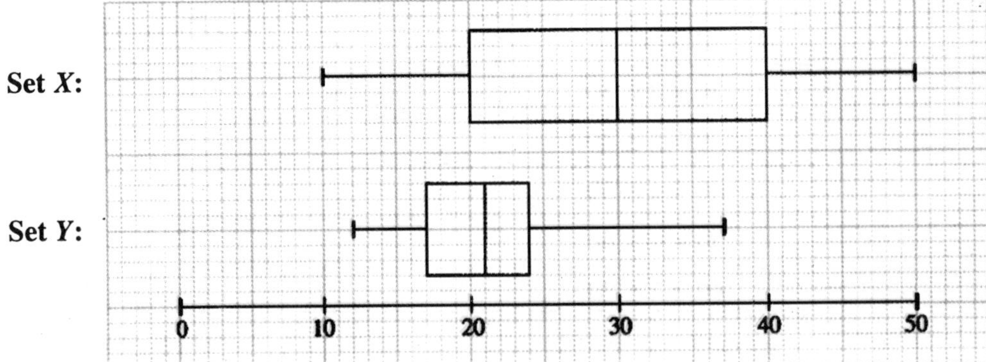

(a) For each set of data, find
  (i) the median,
  (ii) the range,
  (iii) the interquartile range.

(b) Which set of data has a more balanced spread?
(c) Which set of data has a greater spread?
(d) Which set of data has a lower median?
(e) Which one of the cumulative frequency curves below best represents Set X?

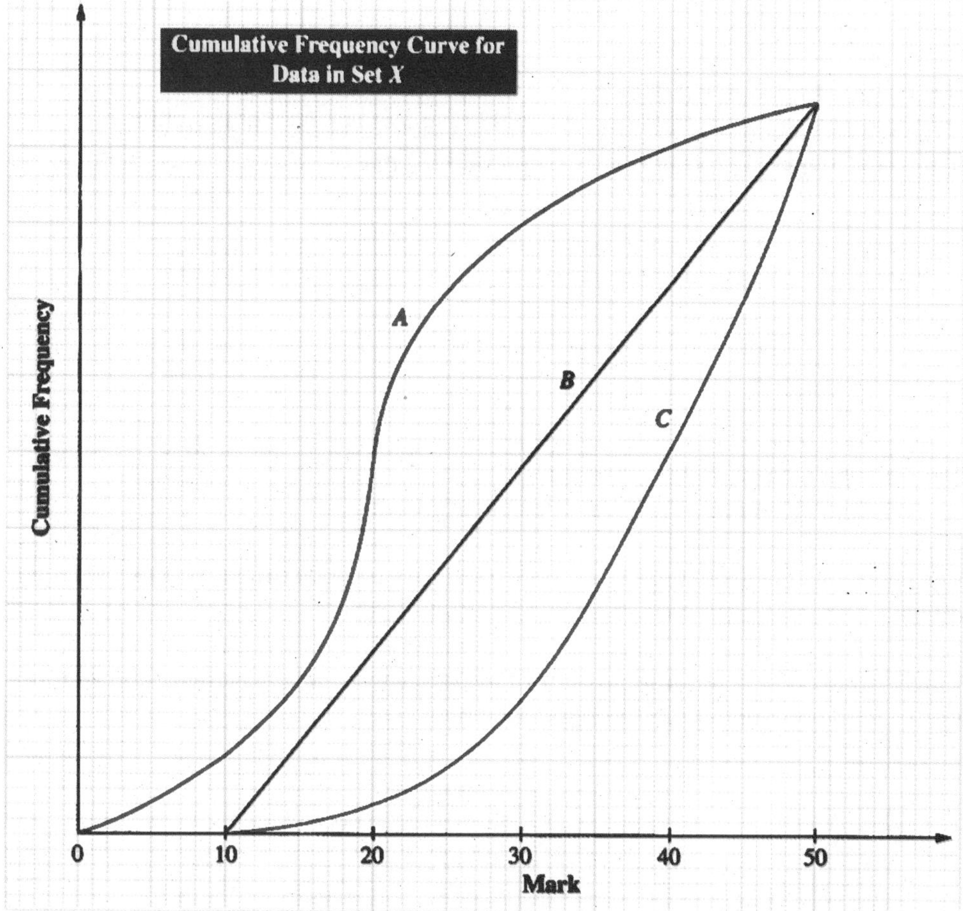

8. A group of children were weighed. The stem-and-leaf diagram shows the masses, in kg, of the children.

Stem (Whole Number)	Leaf (1st Decimal Place)									
30	2	3								
40	0	1	2	6	6	7	9	9		
50	3	3	3	4	6	6	8	8	9	9

(a) How many children were there?
(b) If the heaviest child was 50.9 kg, write down the mass of the lightest child.
(c) A box-and-whisker plot is drawn to represent the data.

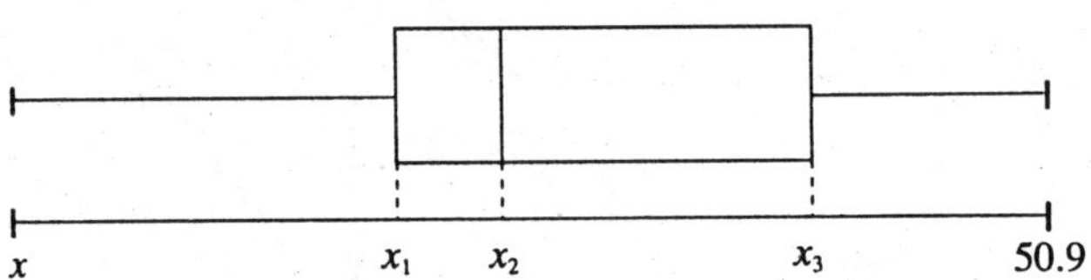

Find **(i)** the values of x, x_1, x_2 and x_3.
(ii) the value of $x_3 - x_1$. What does it represent?

(d) The children were encouraged to do more exercise to reduce their masses to less than or equal to 40.5 kg. Otherwise, they are considered as overweight.

Three months later, the same group of children were again weighed. The results (in kg) are shown in the box-and-whisker diagram below:

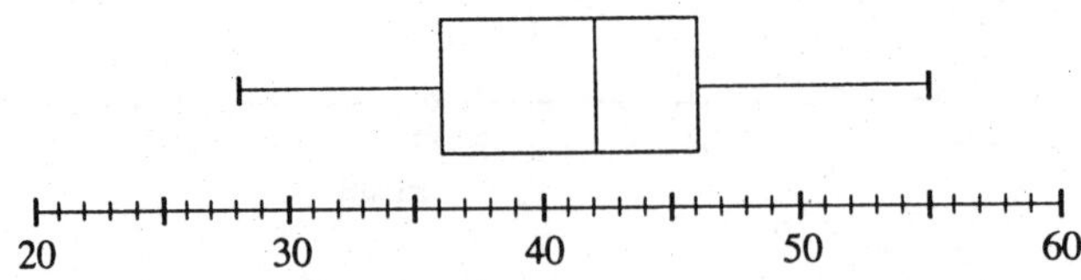

(i) What is the decrease in the upper quartile of the group of children after three months?
(ii) Which distribution has a smaller spread?
(iii) The masses of one child before and after the three months were 40.3 kg and 50.1 kg respectively. Can you say there is a mistake in the box-and-whisker diagram?

9. There are 160 students taking the same examination paper in each of two schools. The cumulative frequency curves show the marks scored by the students.

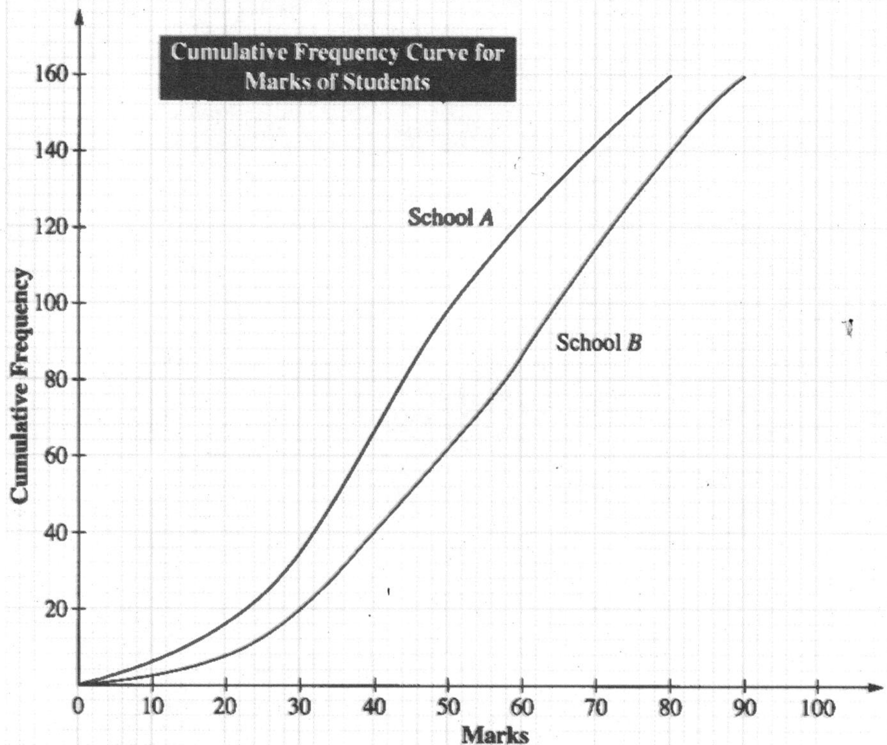

Use the curves to

(a) estimate the median mark of the students from school A.

(b) estimate the percentage of the students from school B who gained more than 80 marks.

(c) state, with a reason, which school achieved the better results.

Jane, Karen, Susan and Shirley were the first four competitors to complete a cross-country race. The following remarks were heard from 4 spectators:

(a) "Jane was first; Susan was second."
(b) "Shirley was third; Karen was fourth."
(c) "Susan was first; Jane was fourth."
(d) "Karen was first; Susan was third."

Give the order in which they finished the race if for each pair of clues in the remarks, only one is true.

In this chapter, you will learn how to

- *find the probability of simple combined events using possibility diagrams and tree diagrams;*
- *use addition and multiplication of probabilities;*
- *solve problems based on mutually exclusive events and independent events.*

CHAPTER

6

More on Probability

Introduction

As a promotional activity, each shopper in a particular shopping centre is given two golf balls. A shopper will win a prize if he/she gets a ball into one of the holes. A grand prize is given if a shopper gets both balls into the holes. What is the probability that this little girl and her mum will win a grand prize? We shall study some simple techniques to find the probability of an event happening in this chapter.

Revision

In Book 2, we learnt that in an experiment where there are n equally likely outcomes, and if m of these outcomes favour the occurrence of an event E, then the probability of the event E happening, written as P(E) is defined as

$$\mathbf{P}(E) = \frac{\textit{No. of outcomes favourable to the occurrence of E}}{\textit{Total number of equally likely outcomes}} = \frac{m}{n}$$

xample 1

A playing card is drawn at random from a standard pack of 52 playing cards. Find the probability of drawing

(a) the king of hearts, *(b) a red card,*
(c) a black queen, *(d) an ace.*

As the drawing of cards is at random, there are 52 equally likely possible outcomes.

(a) There is only 1 king of hearts in the pack.

$\therefore$ P(drawing the king of hearts) = $\frac{1}{52}$

(b) There are 26 red cards in the pack.

$\therefore$ P(drawing a red card) = $\frac{26}{52} = \frac{1}{2}$

(c) There are 2 black queens in the pack.

$\therefore$ P(drawing a black queen) = $\frac{2}{52} = \frac{1}{26}$

(d) There are 4 aces in the pack.

$\therefore$ P(drawing an ace) = $\frac{4}{52} = \frac{1}{13}$

Example 2

There are 22 white marbles, x red marbles and 2x + 8 blue marbles in a bag. One marble is selected at random from the bag. If the probability that the selected marble is red is equal to $\frac{1}{6}$, calculate the value of x. The selected marble is then put back into the bag and another marble is then selected, find the probability that the marble selected will be

(a) blue *(b) white* *(c) black*

Total number of marbles in the bag $= 22 + x + (2x + 8)$
$= 3x + 30$

P (selected marble is red) $= \dfrac{x}{3x+30} = \dfrac{1}{6}$

$\therefore$ $6x = 3x + 30$
$3x = 30$
$x = 10$
$2x + 8 = 28$ and $3x + 30 = 60$

(a) P (selected marble is blue) $= \dfrac{28}{60} = \dfrac{7}{15}$

(b) P (selected marble is white) $= \dfrac{22}{60} = \dfrac{11}{30}$

(c) There are no black marble in the bag.

$\therefore$ P (selected marble is black) $= 0$

JOURNAL WRITING

Try to write a story which involves at least three probabilities of events and each of these probabilities should have a specific value. Your story should tell us the reasons for the values of the probabilities.

1. A multiple choice question has 5 possible answers. If a student picks the answer at random, what is the probability that it is correct?

2. I throw an ordinary six-sided die. Write down, as a fraction, the probability that the number shown on the die is odd.

3. A bag contains 36 balls of which 6 are red and 30 are green. A ball is picked at random from the bag. What is the probability of picking a green ball?

4. Out of 50 light bulbs made by a certain company, 4 are faulty. If I buy one light bulb, what is the probability that it works?

5. A box of sweets contains 8 toffees, 12 liquorices and 4 chocolates. If a sweet is selected at random, what is the probability that it is a liquorice?

6. If a whole number from 1 to 20 inclusive is selected at random, what is the probability that the number selected will be a prime?

7. There are 54 marbles in a bag. Given that the probability of choosing a black marble is exactly $\frac{7}{9}$, calculate the number of marbles in the bag which are not black.

8. A box contains 18 pens, 6 of which are faulty. One pen is drawn from the box at random. What is the probability that the pen drawn is a faulty one? If the pen drawn is good and it is not replaced in the box, then a second pen is now drawn from the box. What is the probability that the second pen drawn will not be faulty?

9. The questions on an examination paper are numbered from 1 to 40 inclusive. A question is chosen at random. Write down, giving your answer as a fraction, the probability that the number of the question chosen will

   (a) contain more than one digit,
   (b) be a perfect square,
   (c) contain at least one figure 2,
   (d) not be divisible by 4 or 5.

10. A playing card is drawn at random from a pack of 52 playing cards. What is the probability of drawing

    (a) the king of spades,
    (b) the two or three of clubs,
    (c) a heart,
    (d) a black card,
    (e) a king, queen or jack,
    (f) the ace of spades or a king?

11. There are 30 multiple-choice questions in an examination paper. A question is chosen at random. Find the probability that the number of the question chosen

    (a) is a two-digit number,
    (b) is divisible by 4,
    (c) is a perfect square,
    (d) is greater than 25,
    (e) is greater than 8 but less than 16.

12. There are 38 twenty-cent coins, x ten-cent coins and $(2x - 15)$ fifty-cent coins in a box. A coin is selected at random and the probability that it is a fifty-cent coin is $\frac{1}{8}$. Find the value of x. Hence find the probability that the selected coin is a

    (a) twenty-cent coin,
    (b) ten-cent coin.

13. The alarm of Peter's digital clock rings at 06.03 every weekday. After a couple of hours, Peter looks at the alarm clock again. Find the probability that the number in

(a) column A is a '2',
(b) column B is a '2',
(c) column A is a '8',
(d) column B is more than '6'.

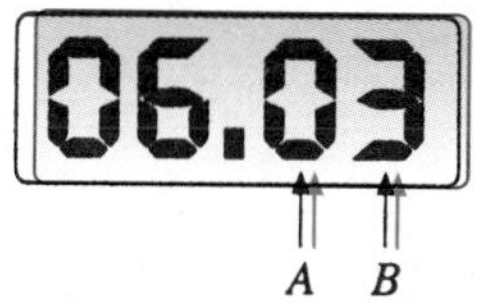

14. The time on Peter's digital clock reads 10.38. After x hours, where $1 < x < 25$, he looks at the clock again. Find the probability that the number in

(a) column P is less than 3,
(b) column Q is a '9',
(c) column P is a '5',
(d) column Q is less than 5.

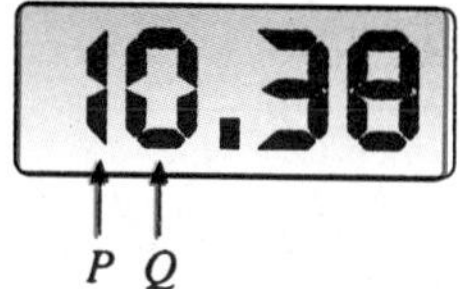

Possible Outcomes in the Sample Space

In Book 2, we learnt that listing all possible outcomes of an experiment in the sample space is a useful tool for solving problems in probabilities, we shall have a quick revision before looking at possibility or probability diagrams and tree diagrams.

xample 3

The numbers 2, 3, 5, 6 and 8 are written on five cards and these are placed on a table. Two of these cards are selected at random to form a two-digit number. List the sample space and hence find the probability that the number formed is

(a) odd, *(b) divisible by 7,*
(c) prime, *(d) greater than 54.*

Let S represent the sample space,
A be the set of odd numbers,
B be the set of numbers divisible by 7,
C be the set of prime numbers and
D be the set of numbers greater than 54.

We have

$S = \{23, 25, 26, 28, 32, 35, 36, 38, 52, 53, 56, 58, 62, 63, 65, 68, 82, 83, 85, 86\}$
$A = \{23, 25, 35, 53, 63, 65, 83, 85\}$
$B = \{28, 35, 56, 63\}$
$C = \{23, 53, 83\}$
$D = \{56, 58, 62, 63, 65, 68, 82, 83, 85, 86\}$

$\therefore \quad n(S) = 20, n(A) = 8, n(B) = 4, n(C) = 3$ and $n(D) = 10$.

(a) $P(A) = \dfrac{n(A)}{n(S)} = \dfrac{8}{20} = \dfrac{2}{5}$

(b) $P(B) = \dfrac{n(B)}{n(S)} = \dfrac{4}{20} = \dfrac{1}{5}$

(c) $P(C) = \dfrac{n(C)}{n(S)} = \dfrac{3}{20}$

(d) $P(D) = \dfrac{n(D)}{n(S)} = \dfrac{10}{20} = \dfrac{1}{2}$

Two fair coins are thrown at the same time. List the sample space of the event and hence find the probability of obtaining

(a) two heads in a throw,
(b) a head and a tail in a throw.

The possible outcomes of throwing two fair coins are $S = \{HH, HT, TH, TT\}$
As the coins are fair, each of the above 4 outcomes are equally likely to happen.

Let A = {obtaining 2 heads} = $\{HH\}$
B = {obtaining a head and a tail} = $\{HT, TH\}$

(a) P (obtaining 2 Hs) = $\dfrac{n(A)}{n(S)} = \dfrac{1}{4}$

(b) P (a head and a tail occurring) = $\dfrac{n(B)}{n(S)} = \dfrac{2}{4} = \dfrac{1}{2}$

xample 5

A fair coin and a fair die are thrown at the same time. List the sample space of the event S. Find the probability of obtaining

(a) a head and a prime number,
(b) a tail and a number that is divisible by 3.

The possible outcomes from throwing a coin and a die are

$H1, H2, H3, H4, H5, H6$
$T1, T2, T3, T4, T5, T6$

$\therefore \quad S = \{H1, H2, H3, H4, H5, H6, T1, T2, T3, T4, T5, T6\}$

If A denotes the event of obtaining a head and a prime number, then $A = \{H2, H3, H5\}$.

If B denotes the event of obtaining a tail and a number divisible by 3, then $B = \{T3, T6\}$.

(a) P (obtaining a head and a prime number) $= \dfrac{\text{n}(A)}{\text{n}(S)}$

$= \dfrac{3}{12} = \dfrac{1}{4}$

(b) P (obtaining a tail and a number divisible by 3) $= \dfrac{\text{n}(B)}{\text{n}(S)}$

$= \dfrac{2}{12} = \dfrac{1}{6}$

1. A two-digit number greater than 75 is written down at random. Write down the sample space. Hence find the probability that a number selected

   (a) is odd,
   (b) is divisible by 9,
   (c) contains the digit 8.

2. The numbers 1, 3, 7 and 8 are written on four cards. Two of these cards are picked at random to form a two-digit number. List the sample space. Hence find the probability that a number selected at random is

   (a) prime,
   (b) even,
   (c) a multiple of 5,
   (d) less than 75.

3. A fair coin is thrown and a card is picked from a suit of 13 diamonds of well-shuffled playing cards. List the sample space. Find the probability of getting

   (a) a head and a red card,
   (b) a tail and an ace,
   (c) a head and a picture card,
   (d) a tail and a card bearing a number that is divisible by 3,
   (e) a head and a queen of heart.

4. Three coins are tossed at the same time. List the sample space of the experiment. We define the following events:

   A: 2 heads and 1 tail appearing
   B: 3 tails appearing
   C: 1 head and 2 tails appearing
   Find the probability of each of the events A, B and C.

5. A bag P contains a red, a blue and a white marble while another bag Q contains a blue and a red marble. A marble is picked at random from both bag P and bag Q. List all the possible outcomes of the sample space. Hence find the probability that the two marbles selected are

   (a) of the same colour,
   (b) of the colours blue and red,
   (c) of different colours.

6. The three daughters-in-law of Mrs Tan are happily awaiting the arrival of their bundles of joy at the end of this year. Given that the babies are equally likely to be either a boy or a girl, list the sample space of the sexes of the three babies. Hence find the probability that Mrs Tan will have

   (a) 3 male grandchildren,
   (b) 2 male and 1 female grandchildren,
   (c) 1 male and 2 female grandchildren.

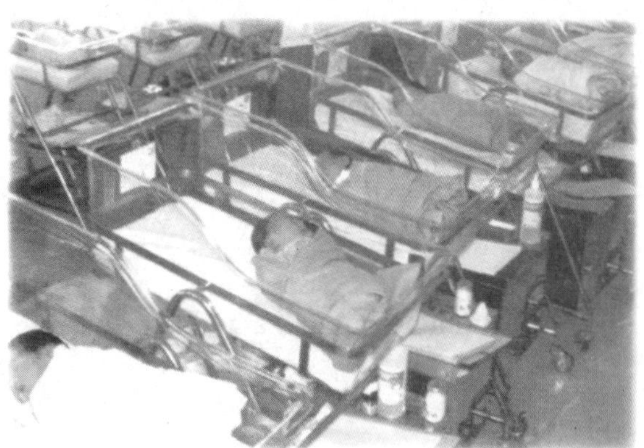

Simple Combined Events and Possibility Diagrams

Look at the two spinners below. Let's consider the case in which the pointer in each spinner is spun once.

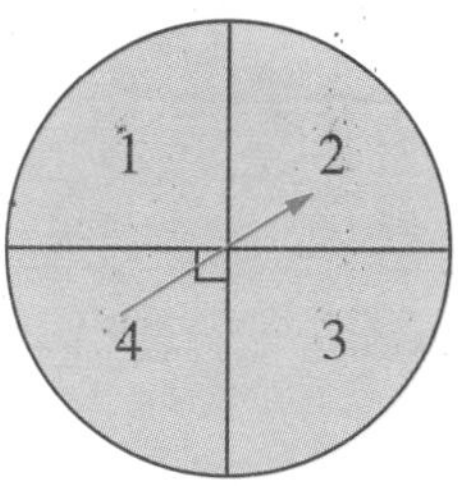

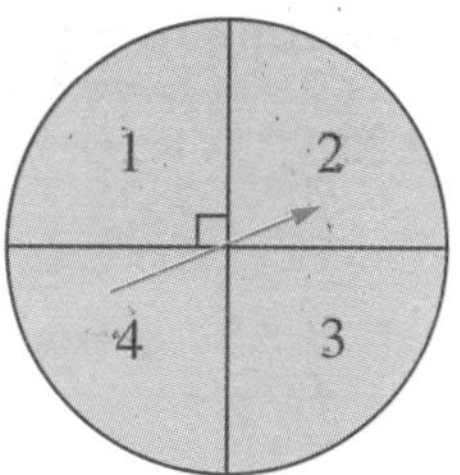

Fig. 6.1

Each spinner is divided into four equal sectors. Each spinner has a pointer which, when spun, is equally likely to come to rest in any one of the four sectors.

Find the probability that the pointers will stop at the same number.

To get the probability, we need to
- find S;
- find $n(S)$;
- find $n(B)$, where B is the event 'the pointers will stop at the same number'.

We can use two methods to find the possible outcomes.

Method 1

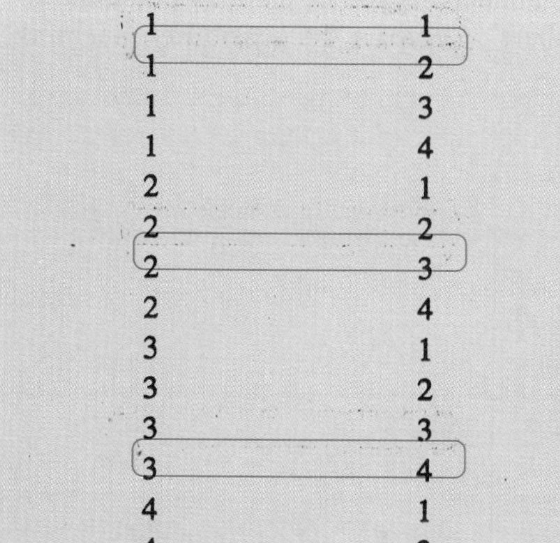

First Spinner	Second Spinner
1	1
1	2
1	3
1	4
2	1
2	2
2	3
2	4
3	1
3	2
3	3
3	4
4	1
4	2
4	3
4	4

Method 2

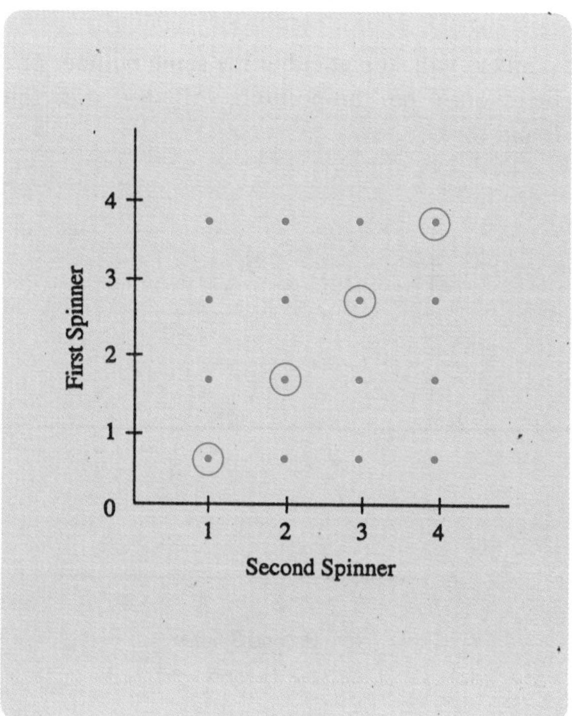

Fig. 6.2

In **Method 1**, we list all the possible outcomes. What are some disadvantages of this method? When is this method suitable?

In **Method 2**, we use a possibility diagram. What does each dot on the diagram represent?

From any of the above methods, we can get n(S) = 16 and n(B) = 4.

Probability of the event B occurring $= \frac{n(B)}{n(S)} = \frac{4}{16} = \frac{1}{4}$.

We can also write P(B) = 0.25.

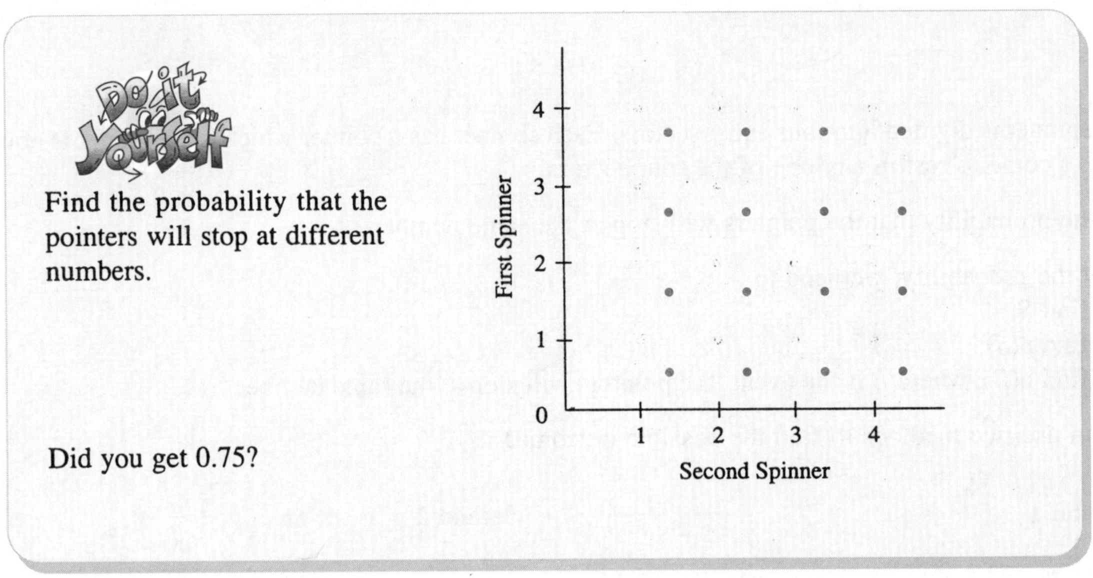

Find the probability that the pointers will stop at different numbers.

Did you get 0.75?

The pointers will stop at either the same number or different numbers. There are no other possibilities. Let the event C be 'the pointers will stop at different numbers'. Compare the possibility diagrams for B and for C.

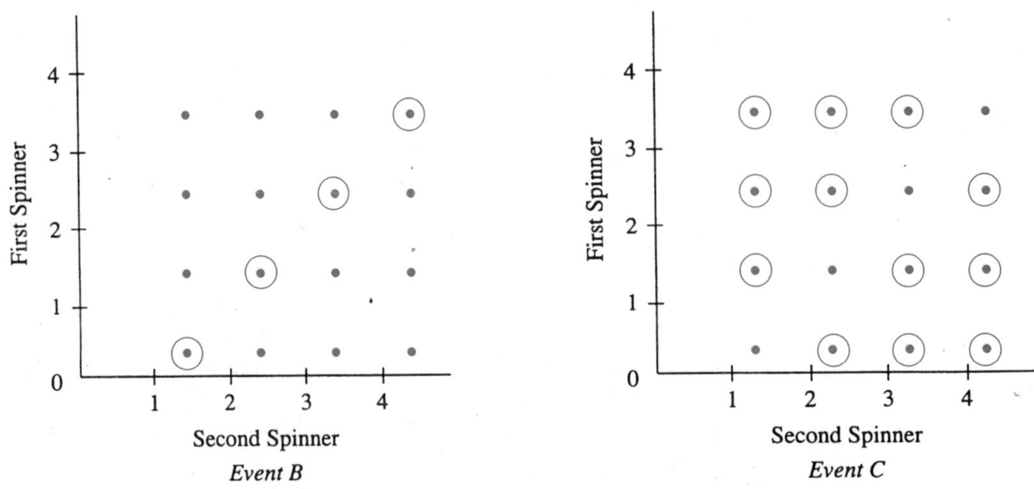

Fig. 6.3

Study the above diagrams. What do you observe?

The event C consists of all the outcomes in the sample space S that are not in B.

What do you think is the value of $P(B) + P(C)$?

$$P(B) + P(C) = 0.25 + 0.75 = 1$$

In general, we have

$P(\text{not } E) = 1 - P(E)$

where E is an event.

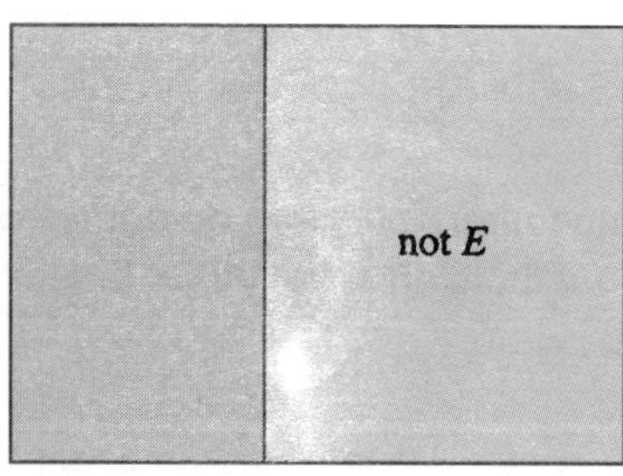

Fig. 6.4

(a) What is the probability that the first spinner shows the larger number?

Did you get $\frac{3}{8}$?

(b) What is the probability that

(i) both spinners show even numbers;

(ii) both spinners show odd numbers;

(iii) spinner 1 shows even number but spinner 2 shows odd number;

(iv) spinner 1 shows odd number but spinner 2 shows even number?

xample 6

Two dice are thrown together. Find the probability that the sum of the resulting numbers is

(a) odd,
(b) even,
(c) at least 7

Since many possible outcomes can occur, it is more efficient to show them on a possibility diagram. From the possibility diagram, n(S) = 36.

First die (columns); Second die (rows)

+	1	2	3	4	5	6
1	2	3	4	5	6	7
2	3	4	5	6	7	8
3	4	5	6	7	8	9
4	5	6	7	8	9	10
5	6	7	8	9	10	11
6	7	8	9	10	11	12

Fig. 6.5

(a) Let's define A as the event that "the sum is odd". Circle on the diagram the outcomes of A. Did you get 18 circles?

$$\therefore \quad P(A) = \frac{n(A)}{n(S)} = \frac{18}{36} = \frac{1}{2}$$

Do you think it is true that the chance of getting an odd sum is $\frac{1}{2}$?

(b) Let's define B as the event that "the sum is even". What do you think is the relationship between event A and event B?

The sum can only be odd or even.

$$\therefore \quad P(A) + P(B) = 1$$

$$P(B) = 1 - \frac{1}{2}$$

$$= \frac{1}{2}$$

Use the possibility diagram to confirm your answer.

(c) Let's define C as the event that "the sum is at least 7".
From the possibility diagram, n(C) = 21

$$\therefore \quad P(C) = \frac{n(C)}{n(S)} = \frac{21}{36} = \frac{7}{12}$$

Can you write down the probability that the sum is less than 7?

example 7

A circular card is divided into 3 equal sectors with scores of 1, 2 and 3. The card has a pointer pivoted at its centre. The pointer is spun twice.

Fig. 6.6

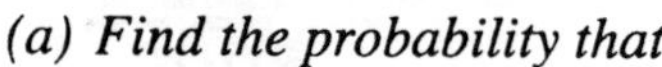

(a) Find the probability that
  (i) each score is 1,
  (ii) at least one of the scores is 3.

(b) In a game, a player spins the pointer twice. His final score is the larger of the two individual scores if they are different and their common value if they are the same. The possibility diagram in Fig. 6.7 shows his final score.
  (i) Copy and complete the possibility diagram.
  (ii) Using the diagram, find the probability that his final score is even.
  (iii) Using the same diagram, find the probability that his final score is a prime number.

	1	2	3
1	1		
2			
3			3

Fig. 6.7

Solution

(a) Let S denote the sample space.

From the possibility diagram,

$$n(S) = 9$$

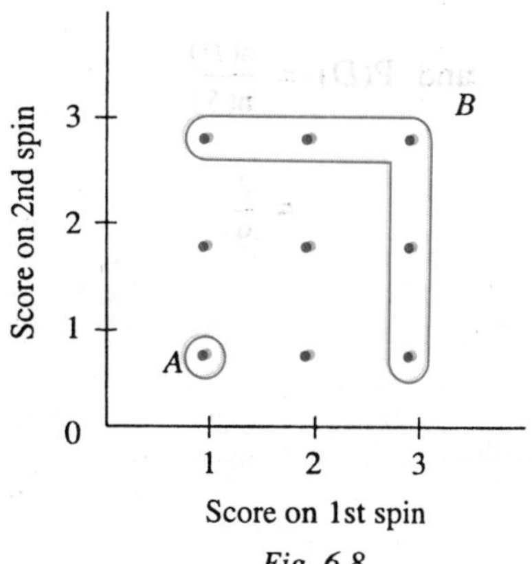

Fig. 6.8

(i) If A denotes the event that 'each score is 1', then $n(A) = 1$

and $P(A) = \dfrac{n(A)}{n(S)} = \dfrac{1}{9}$ *(See Fig. 6.8.)*

(ii) If B denotes the event that 'at least one of the scores is 3', then $n(B) = 5$

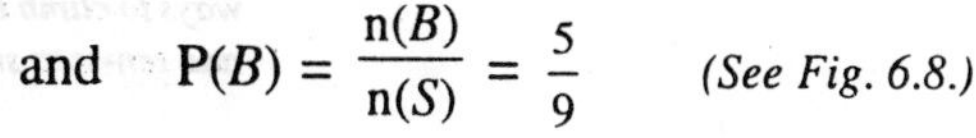

and $P(B) = \dfrac{n(B)}{n(S)} = \dfrac{5}{9}$ *(See Fig. 6.8.)*

(b) (i)

	1	2	3
1	1	2	3
2	2	2	3
3	3	3	3

Fig. 6.9

From the possibility diagram, n(S) = 9

(ii) Let C denote the event that 'his final score is even'.

Then n(C) = 3

and $P(C) = \frac{n(C)}{n(S)}$

$= \frac{3}{9} = \frac{1}{3}$

(iii) Let D denote the event that 'his final score is a prime number'.

Then n(D) = 8

and $P(D) = \frac{n(D)}{n(S)}$

$= \frac{8}{9}$

Consider a boy who can climb up the stairs in one step, or at most, two steps in one stride. For example, there is only one way to climb a one-step stair, two ways to climb a two-step stair and three ways to climb a three-step stairs.

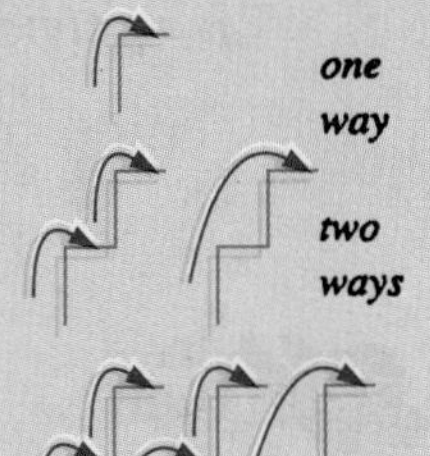

Find the number of ways to climb four-, five-, six- and seven-step stairs. Copy and complete the following table.

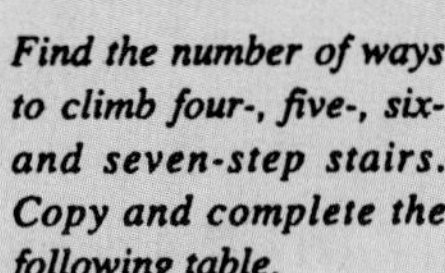

No. of steps	1	2	3	4	5	6	7
No. of ways	1	2	3				

Formulate a rule to help you find the number of ways to climb eight-, nine- and ten-step stairs.

Exercise 6c

1. A box contains three cards bearing the numbers 1, 2 and 3. A second box contains four cards bearing the numbers 2, 3, 4 and 5. A card is chosen at random from each box.
   - **(a)** Display all the possible outcomes of the experiment using a possibility diagram.
   - **(b)** With the help of the possibility diagram, calculate the probability that
     - **(i)** the cards bear the same number,
     - **(ii)** the numbers on the cards are different,
     - **(iii)** the larger of the two numbers on the cards is 3,
     - **(iv)** the sum of the two numbers on the cards is less than 7,
     - **(v)** the product of the two numbers on the cards is at least 8.

2. $X = \{4, 5, 6\}$ and $Y = \{7, 8, 9\}$. An element x is selected randomly from X and an element y is selected randomly from Y. The possibility diagrams in Fig. 6.10 display separately some of the values of $x + y$ and xy.

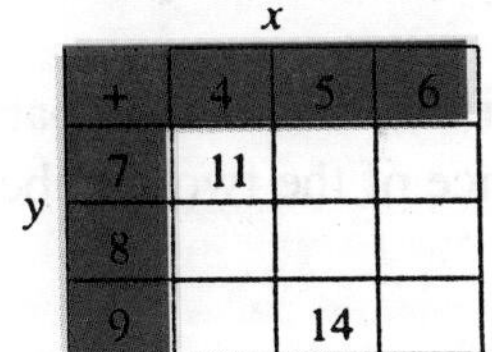

x (columns), y (rows)

+	4	5	6
7	11		
8			
9		14	

×	4	5	6
7			42
8		40	
9			

Fig. 6.10

   - **(a)** Copy and complete the possibility diagrams.
   - **(b)** Find the probability that the product xy is
     - **(i)** odd,
     - **(ii)** even,
     - **(iii)** at most 40.
   - **(c)** Find the probability that the sum $x + y$ is
     - **(i)** prime,
     - **(ii)** greater than 12,
     - **(iii)** at most 14.

3. Six cards numbered 0, 1, 2, 3, 4, and 5 are placed in a box and well-mixed. A card is drawn at random from the box and the number on the card is noted before it is replaced in the box. The cards in the box are thoroughly mixed again, a second card is drawn at random from the box and the number on it is noted. The sum of the two numbers is then obtained.
   - **(a)** Copy and complete Fig. 6.11, giving all the possible sums of the two numbers. Some of the possible sums are shown.

1st number (columns), 2nd number (rows)

	0	1	2	3	4	5
0						
1	1			4		
2						
3						
4		5				
5						

Fig. 6.11

   - **(b)** How many possible outcomes are there in the sample space of this experiment?
   - **(c)** What is the probability that the sum of the two numbers
     - **(i)** will be 7,
     - **(ii)** will be a prime number,
     - **(iii)** will not be a prime number,
     - **(iv)** will be even,
     - **(v)** will not be even?
   - **(d)** Which sum is more likely to occur, the sum of 7 or the sum of 8?

4. In an experiment, two spinners are constructed with spinning pointers as shown in Fig. 6.12. Both pointers are spun. Construct the sample space for this experiment.

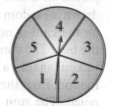

First Spinner Second Spinner

Fig. 6.12

(a) How many possible outcomes are there in the sample space? Use a possibility diagram to show all the possible outcomes.

(b) Find the probability that the pointers will stop
   (i) at numbers on the spinners whose sum is 6,
   (ii) at the same numbers on both spinners,
   (iii) at different numbers on the spinners,
   (iv) at two different prime numbers.

(c) What is the probability that the number on the first spinner will be less than the number on the second spinner?

5. In a game, the player throws a coin and a six-faced die simultaneously. If the coin shows a head, the player's score is the score on the die. If the coin shows a tail, then the player's score is twice the score on the die. Some of the player's possible scores are shown in the possibility diagram given in Fig. 6.13.

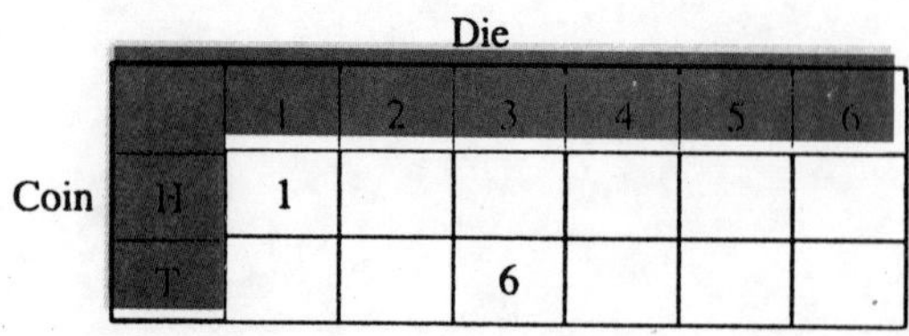

	Die					
Coin	1	2	3	4	5	6
H	1					
T			6			

Fig. 6.13

(a) Copy and complete the possibility diagram.

(b) Using the diagram, find the probability that the player's score is
   (i) odd,
   (ii) even,
   (iii) a prime number,
   (iv) less than or equal to 8,
   (v) a multiple of 3.

6. Two six-sided dice were thrown together and the difference of the resulting numbers on their faces was calculated. Some of the differences are shown in the possibility diagram given in Fig. 6.14.

2nd die \ 1st die	1	2	3	4	5	6
1	0					
2			1			4
3						
4						
5						
6		4				0

Fig. 6.14

(a) Copy and complete the possibility diagram.

(b) Using the diagram, find the probability that the difference of the two numbers is
   (i) 1,
   (ii) non-zero,
   (iii) odd,
   (iv) a prime number,
   (v) more than 2.

Simple Combined Events and Tree Diagrams

Toss two coins. Record the results. Repeat the experiment 20 times. Based on the results, what is the probability that both coins show head?

Let us check the conclusion using a possibility diagram.

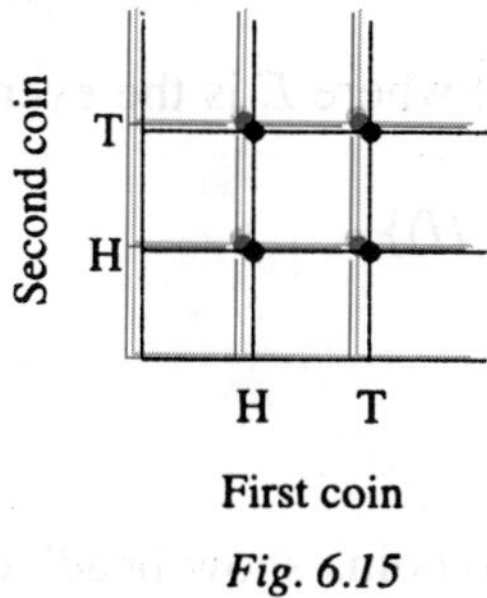

Fig. 6.15

Compare the probability that you obtained from the experiment and that calculated from the possibility diagram.

Another way of representing the possible outcomes is by using a **tree diagram**.

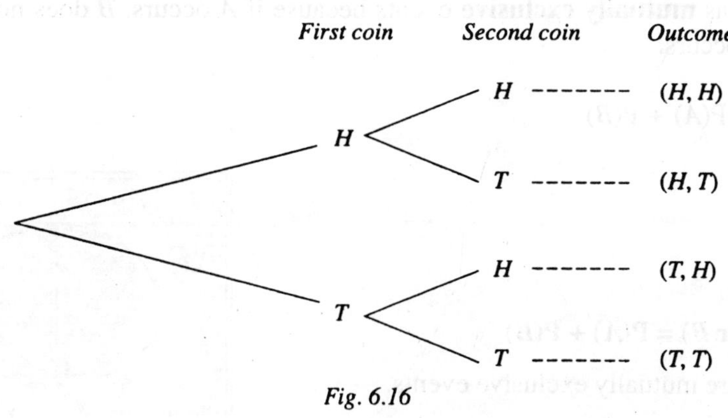

Fig. 6.16

Let's trace the path made to obtain the outcome (H, H) from left to right. For the first coin, there are two possible outcomes, H or T. We shall trace the path that goes upwards. For the second coin, H from the first coin branches out into H or T. Once more, we trace the path that goes upwards to reach the outcome (H, H).

The sample space S is $\{(H, H), (H, T), (T, H), (T, T)\}$.

Let A be the event that both coins show head.

$$P(A) = \frac{n(A)}{n(S)} = \frac{1}{4}$$

Compare the representation of outcomes using possibility diagram and that using tree diagram. When is it appropriate to use each method?

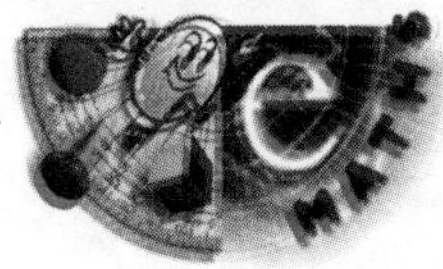

Addition of Probabilities and Mutually Exclusive Events

From the above activity, let's find P(E) where E is the event that "at least one coin shows head".

$$E = \{(H, H), (H, T), (T, H)\}$$

$$P(E) = \frac{n(E)}{n(S)} = \frac{3}{4}$$

We notice that E occurs if "exactly two coins show head" or "exactly one coin shows head". Let B be the event that "exactly one coin shows head".

Can the two events A and B occur at the same time?

After tossing the two coins, can you obtain exactly two heads and exactly one head simultaneously?

A and B are known as **mutually exclusive** events because if A occurs, B does not and vice versa. E occurs if A or B occurs.

In this case, $P(E) = P(A) + P(B)$

In general, we have

P(*A* or *B*) = P(*A*) + P(*B*)

where A and B are mutually exclusive events.

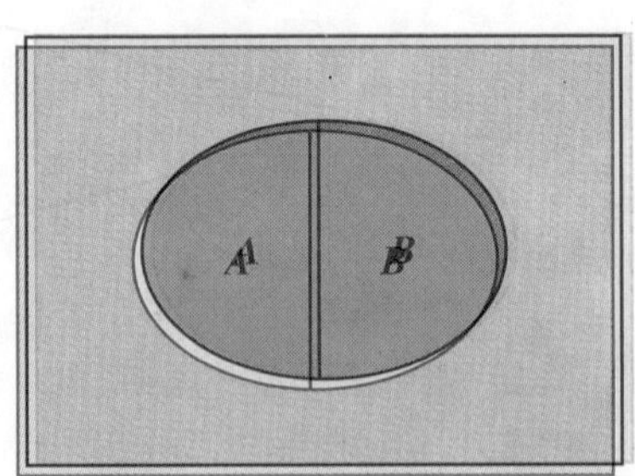

Fig. 6.17

Box A contains 4 pieces of paper numbered 1, 2, 3, 4. Box B contains 2 pieces of paper numbered 1, 2. One piece of paper is removed at random from each box. Draw a tree diagram to display all the possible outcomes of the experiment. Find the probability that

(a) at least one '1' is obtained,
(b) the sum of the two numbers is 3,
(c) the product of the two numbers is at least 4,
(d) the sum is equal to the product.

Solution

Box A	Box B	Outcome	Sum	Product
1	1	(1, 1)	2	1
	2	(1, 2)	3	2
2	1	(2, 1)	3	2
	2	(2, 2)	4	4
3	1	(3, 1)	4	3
	2	(3, 2)	5	6
4	1	(4, 1)	5	4
	2	(4, 2)	6	8

Fig. 6.18

From the diagram, n(S) = 8.

(a) Let A be the event that "at least one '1' is obtained".
$A = \{(1, 1), (1, 2), (2, 1), (3, 1), (4, 1)\}$

$\therefore \quad P(A) = \frac{5}{8}$

(b) Let B be the event that "the sum of the two numbers is 3".
From the 'sum' column, by counting, n(B) = 2

$\therefore \quad P(B) = \frac{2}{8} = \frac{1}{4}.$

(c) Let C be the event that "the product of the two numbers is at least 4".
From the 'product' column, by counting, n(C) = 4

$\therefore \quad P(C) = \frac{4}{8} = \frac{1}{2}$

(d) Let D be the event that "the sum is equal to the product".
From the 'sum' and 'product' columns, by comparing and counting,

$$n(D) = 1$$

$$\therefore \quad P(D) = \frac{1}{8}$$

Can you find the following probabilities?
(i) The sum of the two numbers is odd.
(ii) The product of the two numbers is exactly divisible by 4.
(iii) The product of the two numbers is not a prime.

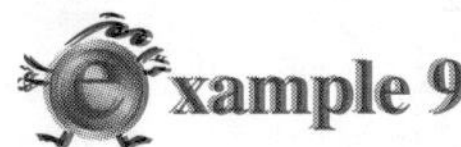

The probabilities of three teams, L, M and N, winning a football competition are $\frac{1}{4}$, $\frac{1}{8}$ and $\frac{1}{10}$ respectively. Assuming only one team can win, calculate the probability that

(a) either L or M wins,
(b) neither L nor N wins.

Since only one team can win, the events are mutually exclusive.

(a) $P(L \text{ or } M \text{ wins}) = P(L \text{ wins}) + P(M \text{ wins}) = \frac{1}{4} + \frac{1}{8} = \frac{3}{8}$

(b) $P(L \text{ or } N \text{ wins}) = P(L \text{ wins}) + P(N \text{ wins}) = \frac{1}{4} + \frac{1}{10} = \frac{7}{20}$

$P(\text{neither } L \text{ nor } N \text{ wins}) = 1 - P(L \text{ or } N \text{ wins}) = 1 - \frac{7}{20} = \frac{13}{20}$

Example 10

A card is drawn at random from an ordinary pack of 52 playing cards. Find the probability that the card is
(a) an ace or king,
(b) a heart or a diamond,
(c) neither a king nor a queen.

We define the following events:

A: the card drawn is an ace.
H: the card drawn is a heart.
D: the card drawn is a diamond.
K: the card drawn is a king.
Q: the card drawn is a queen.

(a) $P(A) = \frac{4}{52} = \frac{1}{13}$ and $P(K) = \frac{4}{52} = \frac{1}{13}$

Now, the events A and K are mutually exclusive since they cannot happen at the same time, i.e. a card cannot be both an ace and a king.

$$\therefore \quad P(A \text{ or } K) = P(A) + P(K)$$
$$= \frac{1}{13} + \frac{1}{13} = \frac{2}{13}$$

(b) $P(H) = \frac{13}{52} = \frac{1}{4}$ and $P(D) = \frac{13}{52} = \frac{1}{4}$

The events H and D are mutually exclusive.

$$\therefore \quad P(H \text{ or } D) = P(H) + P(D)$$
$$= \frac{1}{4} + \frac{1}{4} = \frac{1}{2}$$

(c) $P(K \text{ or } Q) = P(K) + P(Q) = \frac{1}{13} + \frac{1}{13} = \frac{2}{13}$

$$\therefore \quad P(\text{neither } K \text{ nor } Q) = 1 - P(K \text{ or } Q)$$
$$= 1 - \frac{2}{13} = \frac{11}{13}$$

1. A spinner as shown in Fig. 6.19 and a coin are used in a game. The spinner is spun once and the coin is tossed once. Draw a tree diagram to list all possible outcomes. With the help of the tree diagram, calculate the probability of getting

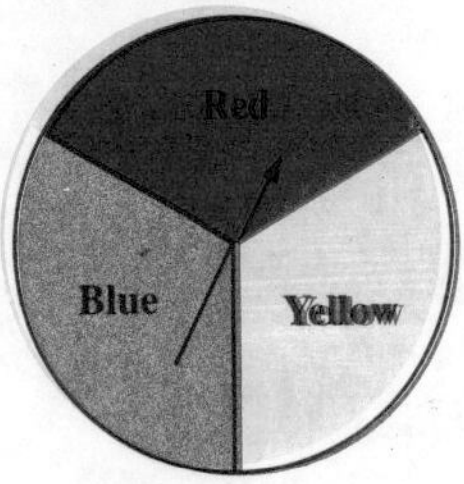

Fig. 6.19

   (a) red on the spinner and tail on the coin,
   (b) blue or yellow on the spinner and head on the coin.

2. A bag contains 4 cards numbered 1, 3, 5, 7. A second bag contains 3 cards numbered 1, 2, 7. One card is drawn at random from each bag.
   (a) Draw a tree diagram for the experiment.
   (b) With the help of your tree diagram, calculate the probability that the two numbers obtained
      (i) have the same value,
      (ii) are both odd,
      (iii) are both prime,
      (iv) have a sum greater than 4,
      (v) have a sum that is even,
      (vi) have a product that is prime,
      (vii) have a product that is greater than 20,
      (viii) have a product that is divisible by 7.

3. Fig. 6.20 shows two cards, each with a pointer pivoted at its centre. The first card is divided into 4 equal sectors scoring 1, 2, 4 and 5. The second card is divided into 4 equal sectors scoring 0, 1, 3 and 5. In a game, the pointers are spun.

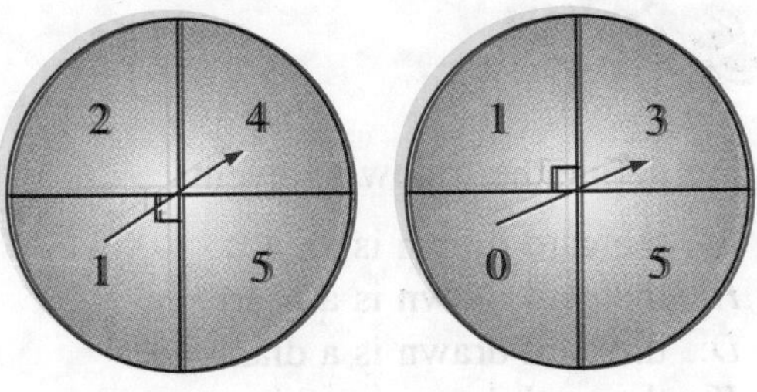

Fig. 6.20

   Using a tree diagram, find the probability that
   (a) the score on each card is the same,
   (b) the score on each card is prime,
   (c) the sum of the scores is odd,
   (d) the sum of the scores is divisible by 5,
   (e) the sum of the scores is 6 or less,
   (f) the product of the scores is not zero,
   (g) the product of the scores is greater than 11.

4. A die in the form of a tetrahedron (solid regular triangular pyramid) has the numbers 1, 2, 3 and 4 printed on its four faces.
   (a) When the die is thrown what is the probability that
      (i) it will land with the face printed 4 down,
      (ii) it will land so that the sum of the three upper faces is an odd number.
   (b) If the die and a coin are thrown together, list all possible outcomes of the experiment using a tree diagram.

5. Eleven cards numbered 11, 12, 13, 14, ... 21 are placed in a box. A card is removed at random from the box. Find the probability that the number on the card is

(a) even,
(b) prime,
(c) either even or prime,
(d) divisible by 3,
(e) either even or divisible by 3,
(f) odd,
(g) divisible by 4,
(h) either odd or divisible by 4.

6. A bag contains 7 red, 5 green and 3 blue counters. A counter is selected at random from the bag. Find the probability of selecting

(a) a red counter,
(b) a green counter,
(c) either a red or a green counter,
(d) neither a red nor a green counter.

7. The letters of the word '*MUTUALLY*' and the word '*EXCLUSIVE*' are written on individual cards and the cards are put into a box. A card is picked at random. What is the probability of picking

(a) the letter '*U*',
(b) the letter '*E*',
(c) the letter '*U*' or '*E*',
(d) a consonant,
(e) the letter '*U*' or a consonant,
(f) the letter '*U*' or '*E*' or '*L*'?

8. A coin is tossed three times. Display all the possible outcomes of the experiment using a tree diagram.
From your tree diagram, find the probability of obtaining

(a) three heads,
(b) exactly two heads,
(c) at least two heads.

9. The probability of a football team winning any match is $\frac{7}{10}$ and the probability of losing any match is $\frac{2}{15}$.

(a) What is the probability that the team wins or loses a particular match?
(b) What is the probability that the team neither wins nor loses a match?

★10. When a golfer plays any hole, the probabilities that he will take 4, 5 or 6 strokes are $\frac{1}{14}$, $\frac{2}{7}$ and $\frac{3}{7}$ respectively. He never takes less than 4 strokes. Calculate the probability that in playing a hole, he will take

(a) 4 or 5 strokes,
(b) 4, 5 or 6 strokes,
(c) more than 6 strokes.

★11. In a basketball tournament, three of the participating teams, Panda, Spaceship and Rocket have the probabilities $\frac{4}{15}$, $\frac{1}{10}$ and $\frac{1}{5}$ respectively, of winning the tournament. Find the probability that

(a) Panda or Rocket will win the tournament,
(b) Panda, Spaceship or Rocket will win the tournament,
(c) neither Panda nor Rocket will win the tournament,
(d) none of these three teams will win the tournament.

Multiplication of Probabilities and Independent Events

Put 2 red balls and 4 blue balls in a bag. Pick a ball at random and place it back in the bag. Mix the balls well and pick a ball randomly again.

Repeat this process of picking two balls with replacement for 20 times. Based on the results, what is the probability that both balls are red?

In the above Exploration, we replace the first ball that has been picked before the second ball is picked. Therefore, whether the first ball picked is red or blue has no effect on the probability of whether the second ball picked is red or blue. In this case, picking the two balls with replacement is called **independent events**.

Let *A* be the event that "two red balls are drawn".

From Fig. 6.21, $P(A) = \frac{4}{36} = \frac{1}{9}$.

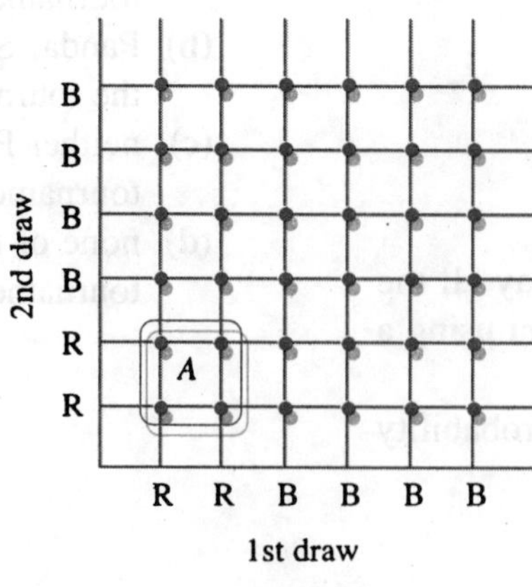

Fig. 6.21

We can also construct a probability tree as shown in Fig. 6.22 to solve the problem.

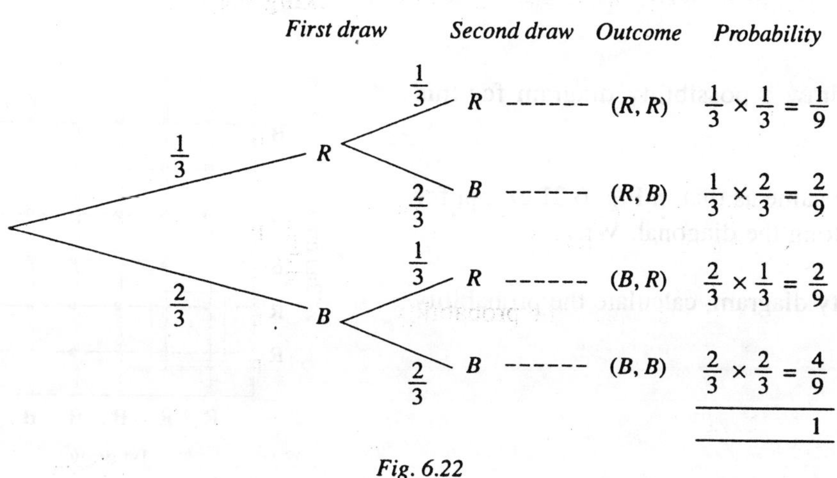

Fig. 6.22

To obtain P(*A*) from the probability tree (outcome *R*, *R*), we **multiply** the probabilities along the 'branch' leading to (*R*, *R*).

$$P(A) = \frac{1}{3} \times \frac{1}{3} = \frac{1}{9}$$

Why do we multiply in this case? To draw two red balls, a red ball taken in the first draw and a red ball taken in the second draw must occur. Thus we multiply the probabilities of the two events that must occur for event *A* to occur.

Compare the probability that is obtained from the experiment, the possibility diagram and the probability tree.

Let's do the previous activity again, but this time, after picking the first ball randomly, do not replace the ball before picking the second ball.

Record 20 sets of results for this process of picking two balls without replacement. Is the probability that both balls are red different from that in the previous experiment?

In the above Exploration, the second ball is picked without replacement of the first ball. The colour of the first ball affects the probability of whether the secound ball is red or blue. In this case, the event of picking the second ball is dependent on the event of picking the first ball without replacement.

How would you draw a possibility diagram for this experiment?

The diagram is the same as that in Fig. 6.21 except for the missing dots along the diagonal. Why?

From the possibility diagram, calculate the probability of event *A*.

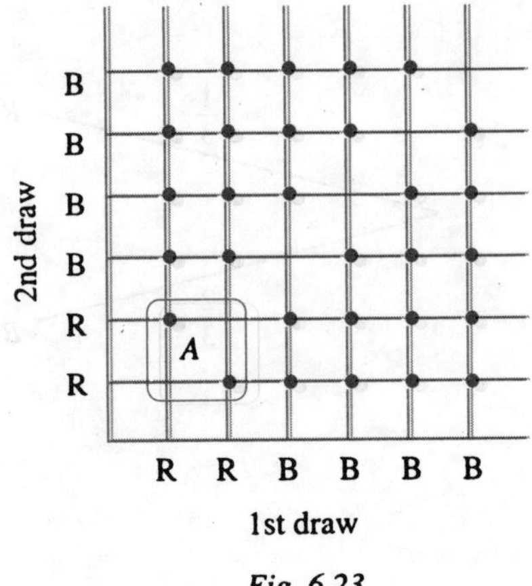

Fig. 6.23

If a ball is picked from the bag and not replaced, what is the number of balls in the bag just before the second ball is picked? Notice that in the probability tree of Fig. 6.24, the probabilities for the outcomes of the second draw have been adjusted to $\frac{1}{5}$, $\frac{4}{5}$ and $\frac{2}{5}$, $\frac{3}{5}$ respectively. The numerator value depends on whether the first ball drawn is red or blue. Why?

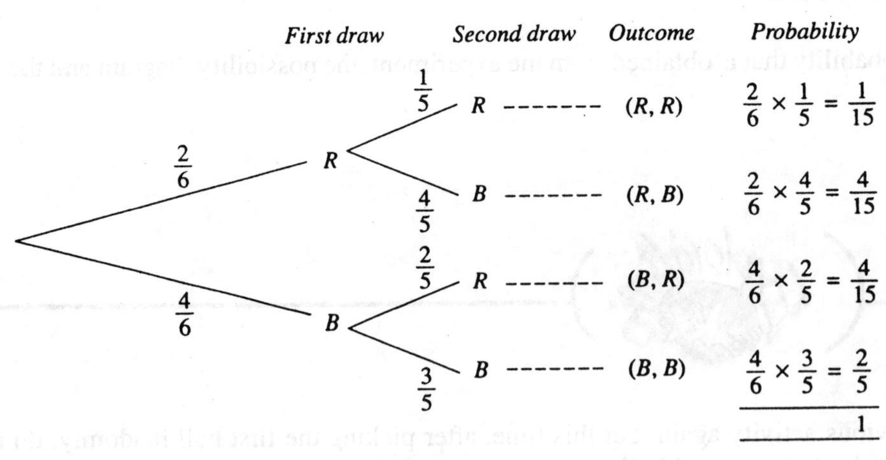

Fig. 6.24

From Fig. 6.24, by multiplying probabilities along appropriate 'branches',

$$P(A) = \frac{2}{6} \times \frac{1}{5} = \frac{1}{15}$$

Example 11

A box contains some sweets, identical except for the colours. One quarter of the sweets are green and two thirds are red. The remainder of the sweets are yellow.

(a) A sweet is taken at random from the box.

(i) Explain why the probability of picking a yellow sweet is $\frac{1}{12}$.

(ii) Find the probability of obtaining a sweet that is not green.

(b) The sweet that is picked in part (a) is put back into the box and another one is taken at random from the box. Using a probability tree, calculate the probability that

(a) both sweets picked are red,
(b) one sweet picked is yellow and the other is red,
(c) at least one sweet taken is red,
(d) neither sweets taken is green.

Toss a coin 5, 10, 15, 20, 30, 50, 80, 100 times. You may work with a partner so that your partner can help in recording the number of times heads and tails turn up for each set of tosses. Enter your results in the table where m denotes the number of heads, l the number of tails, n the number of tosses.

5			
10			
15			
20			
30			
50			
80			
100			

Complete the table by

(a) calculating the values of $p = \frac{m}{n}$, giving your answers in decimals correct to 2 decimal places.

(b) On a sheet of graph paper plot the points with coordinates given by (n, p). Add to your graph the horizontal line p = 0.5. What do you notice about the points plotted in relation to this line as n increases?

(a) (i) Since $1 - \frac{1}{4} - \frac{2}{3} = \frac{1}{12}$ of the sweets in the box is yellow, the probability of picking a yellow sweet at random from the box is $\frac{1}{12}$.

(ii) P(sweet picked is not green) = 1 – P (sweet picked is green)

$$= 1 - \frac{1}{4} = \frac{3}{4}$$

(b) (i) The probability tree is as shown in Fig. 6.25.

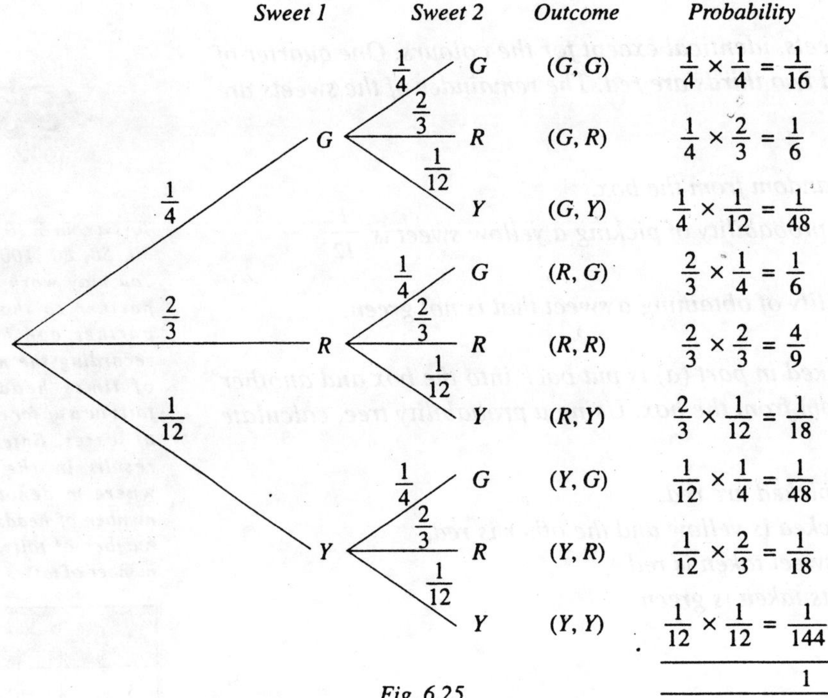

Fig. 6.25

(ii) Define the following events:
A: both sweets picked are red
B: one sweet picked is yellow and the other is red
C: at least one sweet picked is red
D: neither sweets picked is green

Using the probability tree:

(a) $P(A) = P[(R, R)] = \frac{4}{9}$

(b) $P(B) = P[(R, Y) \text{ or } (Y, R)]$

$= \frac{1}{18} + \frac{1}{18} = \frac{1}{9}$

(c) $P(C) = P(A \text{ or } B \text{ or } [(R, G) \text{ or } (G, R)]$

$= \frac{4}{9} + \frac{1}{9} + \left(\frac{1}{6} + \frac{1}{6}\right) = \frac{8}{9}$

(d) $P(D) = P[A \text{ or } B \text{ or } (Y, Y)]$

$= \frac{4}{9} + \frac{1}{9} + \frac{1}{144} = \frac{9}{16}$

Alternatively, using the answer to (a)(ii),
$P(D) = P(\text{both sweets are not green})$

$= \frac{3}{4} \times \frac{3}{4} = \frac{9}{16}$

(c) By combining the results for the set of 100 tosses for the whole class, i.e. using the values of m corresponding to n = 100 for the whole class, calculate the value

$$\frac{\text{total number of heads}}{\text{total number of tosses}},$$

giving your answer correct to 2 decimal places.

(d) What conclusion can you draw concerning this experimental probability of obtaining a head when a coin is tossed once?

Example 12

Twelve pupils in a group study either Chemistry or History but not both. 7 of them study Chemistry and 5 study History.

(a) A pupil is selected at random from the group. Write down the probability that the pupil studies Chemistry.

(b) If two pupils are chosen at random from the group on another occasion, find the probability that
(i) they both study History,
(ii) they study the same subject,
(iii) the first pupil studies Chemistry and the second pupil studies History,
(iv) they study different subjects.

(a) P(the selected pupil studies Chemistry) $= \frac{7}{12}$

(b) Choosing two pupils from the group can be done by first selecting one pupil followed by selecting another pupil from the remaining pupils. This is a case of selection without replacement.
The probability tree for the selection is as shown in Fig. 6.26.
C denotes 'a pupil studies Chemistry'.
H denotes 'a pupil studies History'.

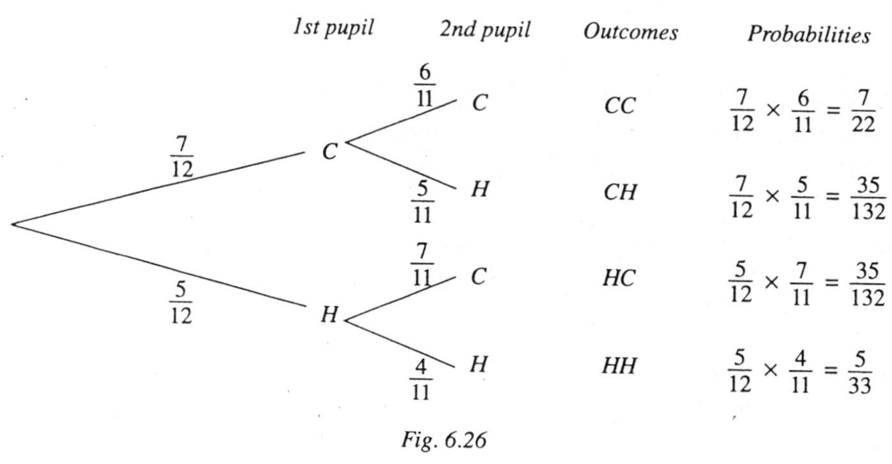

Fig. 6.26

Note: Check that $\frac{7}{22} + \frac{35}{132} + \frac{35}{132} + \frac{5}{33} = \frac{132}{132} = 1$.

From the probability tree,

(i) P(they study History) = P(HH)

$$= \frac{5}{33}$$

(ii) P(they study the same subject) = P(CC or HH) $= \frac{7}{22} + \frac{5}{33}$

$$= \frac{31}{66}$$

(iii) P(1st pupil studies Chemistry and 2nd pupil studies History) = P(CH)

$$= \frac{35}{132}$$

(iv) P(they study different subjects) = P(CH or HC)

$$= \frac{35}{132} + \frac{35}{132} = \frac{35}{66}$$

Alternatively,
P(they study different subjects) = 1 – P(they study the same subject)

$$= 1 - \frac{31}{66} = \frac{35}{66}$$

Example 13

Bag X contains 10 balls of which 3 are red and 7 are blue. Bag Y contains 10 balls of which 4 are red and 6 are blue. One ball is drawn at random from Bag X and placed in Bag Y.

After thoroughly mixing, a ball is taken from Bag Y and placed in Bag X. With the help of a probability tree, calculate the probability that

(i) a red ball is drawn from Bag X and a blue ball is drawn from Bag Y,
(ii) two balls of different colours are drawn,
(iii) the ball drawn from Bag Y is red,
(iv) Bag X still contains exactly 3 red balls after the two draws.

Fig. 6.27 shows the probability tree.

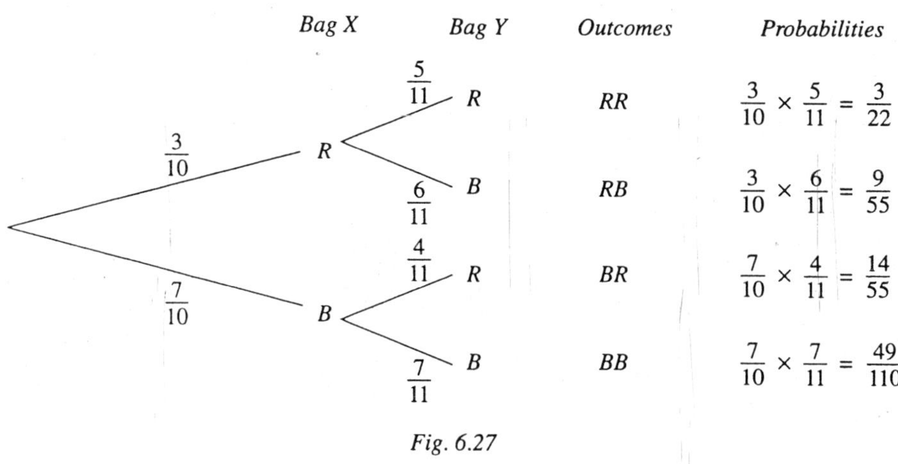

Fig. 6.27

Note that the number of balls in Bag Y is 11 after the ball drawn from Bag X is placed in it. The number of red and blue balls in Bag Y then depends on the result of the draw from Bag X.

Note: Check that $\dfrac{3}{22} + \dfrac{9}{55} + \dfrac{14}{55} + \dfrac{49}{110} = 1$

From the probability tree,

(a) P(a red ball from Bag X and a blue ball from Bag Y) = P(RB) = $\dfrac{9}{55}$

(b) P(two balls of different colours) = P(RB or BR)

$$= \frac{9}{55} + \frac{14}{55} = \frac{23}{55}$$

(c) P(ball from Bag Y is red) = P(RR or BR)

$$= \frac{3}{22} + \frac{14}{55} = \frac{43}{110}$$

(d) In order that Bag X still contains exactly 3 red balls, the balls drawn from Bag X and Bag Y must be of the same colour.

$\therefore$ P(Bag X still contains exactly 3 red balls) = P(RR or BB)

$$= \frac{3}{22} + \frac{49}{110} = \frac{32}{55}$$

1. Peter has two bags each containing 5 black marbles and 4 red marbles. He takes one marble at random from each bag.
   (a) Copy and complete the probability tree in Fig. 6.28.
   (b) Calculate the probability that he takes
      (i) a red marble from the first bag and a black marble from the second bag,
      (ii) two marbles having different colours,
      (iii) a black marble from the second bag.

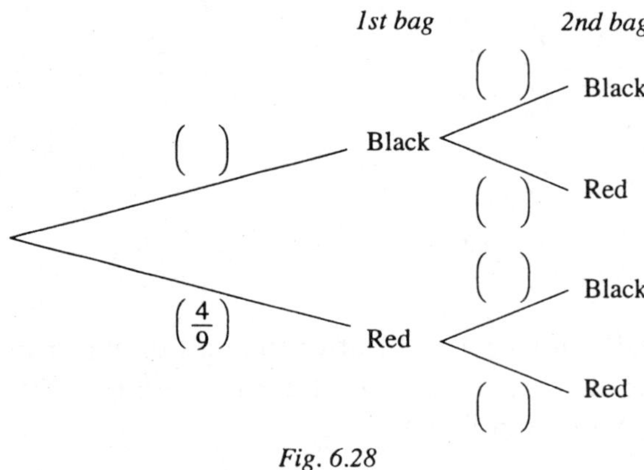

Fig. 6.28

2. A bag contains 6 red balls and 4 yellow balls. A ball is chosen at random and then put back into the bag. The process is carried out twice.
   (a) Copy and complete the probability tree shown in Fig. 6.29.
   (b) Find the probability of taking out
      (i) two red balls,
      (ii) one ball of each colour.

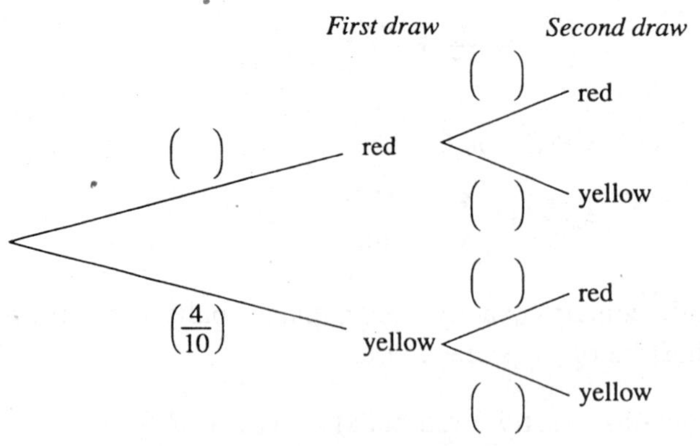

Fig. 6.29

3. Fig. 6.30 shows two discs each of which is divided into four equal sectors. Each disc has a pointer which, when spun, is equally likely to come to rest in any of the four equal sectors.
In a game, the player spins each pointer once. His score is the sum of the numbers shown by the pointers.

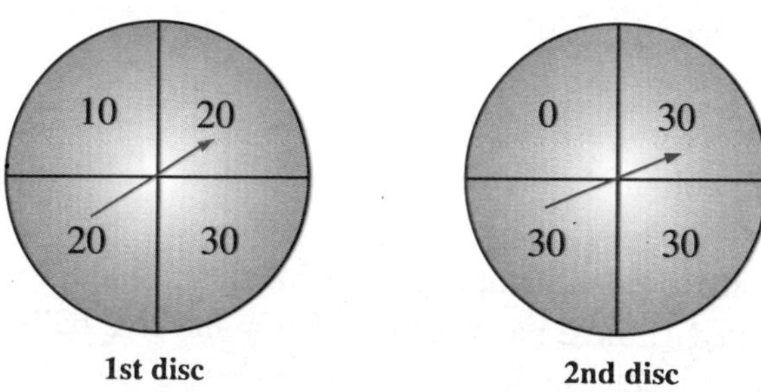

Fig. 6.30

(a) Copy and complete the probability tree in Fig. 6.31.

(b) With the help of the diagram, calculate the probability that
(i) the first score is less than or equal to the second score,
(ii) the second score is zero.

(c) If the player's score is between 10 and 50 but excluding 10 and 50, he receives \$2. If his score is more than 40, he receives \$5. Otherwise, he receives nothing. What is the probability that he receives
(i) \$2,
(ii) \$5,
(iii) \$2 or \$5,
(iv) nothing.

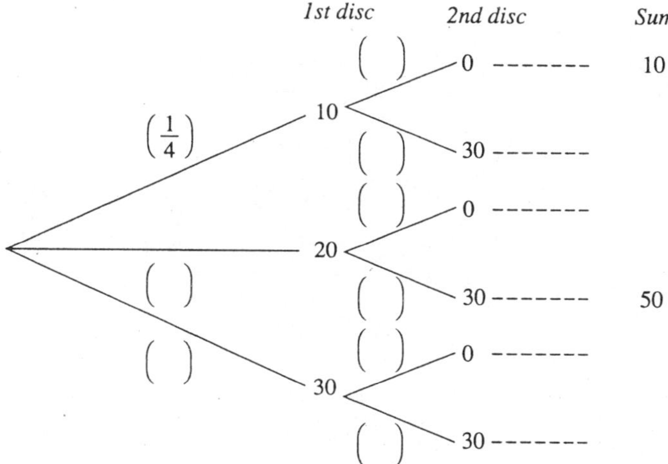

Fig. 6.31

4. (a) Box A contains 12 balls, 6 of which are blue, 2 are red and the remaining are yellow. Box B contains 10 balls, 4 of which are blue and the remaining are red. One ball is removed at random from each box.

Find the probability that

(i) the ball from Box A is red and the ball from Box B is blue,

(ii) one red ball and one blue ball are removed,

(iii) the ball removed from Box B is blue,

(iv) balls of the same colour are removed,

(v) balls of different colours are removed.

(b) In Box A, three balls are labelled 2, four balls are labelled 3 and five balls are labelled 5. In Box B, two balls are labelled 1, three balls are labelled 4 and five balls are labelled 6. One ball is selected at random from each box.

Copy and complete the probability tree in Fig. 6.32.

(c) With the help of the probability tree, calculate the probability of obtaining

(i) a sum which is a prime number,

(ii) a sum which is less than 6,

(iii) a product which is divisible by 3 and greater than 12,

(iv) a product which is less than or equal to 5.

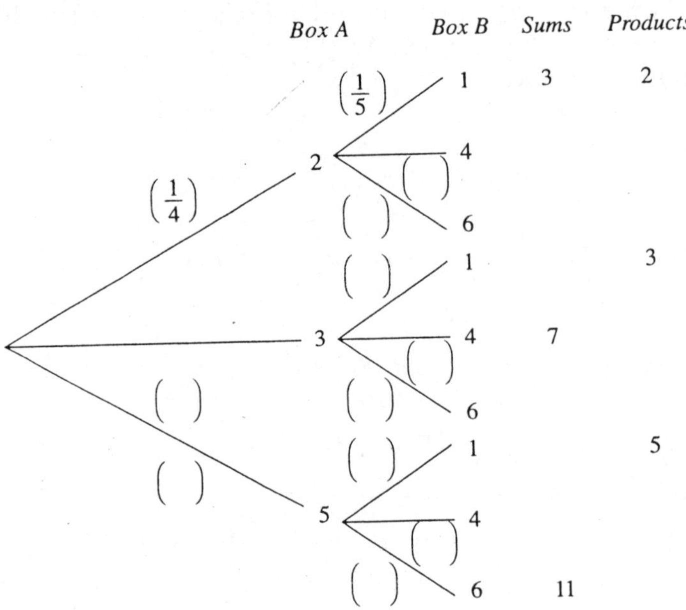

Fig. 6.32

5. A red die has the number 1 on one face, the number 2 on two faces and the number 3 on three faces. Two green dice each has the number 6 on one face and the number 5 on five faces. The three dice are thrown together.

(a) Copy and complete Fig. 6.33 by adding probabilities to the 'branches'.

(b) Using the probability tree, calculate the probability of obtaining

(i) 2 on the red die, 5 on the first green die and 6 on the second green die,

(ii) 3 on the red die and 6 on each of the two green dice,

(iii) exactly 2 sixes,

(iv) a sum of 12,

(v) a sum which is divisible by 3.

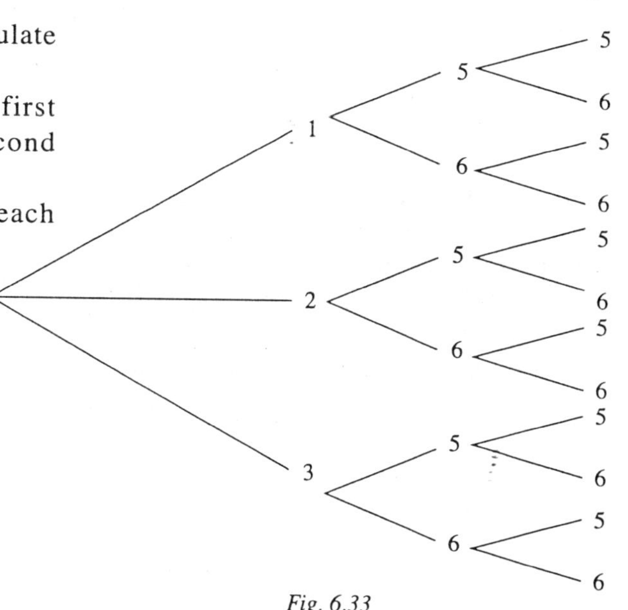

Fig. 6.33

6. In a group of 8 boys, 3 are left-handed. The remaining 5 boys are right-handed. If a boy is chosen at random from the group, state the probability that the boy chosen is left-handed.

(a) A second boy is then chosen at random from the remaining 7 boys. Given that the first boy chosen is left-handed, state the probability that the second boy chosen is also left-handed.
On another occasion, two boys are chosen at random from the same group of eight boys.

(b) Copy and complete the probability tree in Fig. 6.34.

(c) From your probability tree in **(b)**, find the probability that

(i) both boys are left-handed,

(ii) both are right-handed,

(iii) only one boy is left-handed.

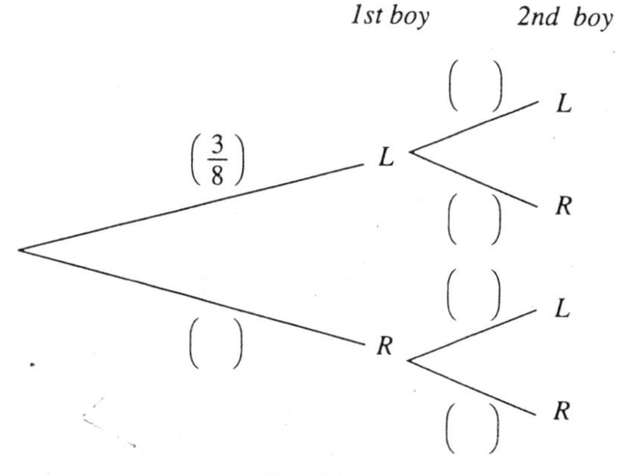

Fig. 6.34

7. A bag contains 5 blue, 3 red and 2 yellow balls.
   (a) A ball is chosen at random from the bag. Find the probability that the ball is not red.

   (b) Two balls are chosen at random from the bag. Draw a probability tree to show the possible outcomes and use it to find the probability that
   (i) both balls are blue,
   (ii) both balls are black,
   (iii) one ball is red and the other yellow,
   (iv) only one ball is red.

8. A woman goes to the hairdresser once a week. The probability that she has a perm is $\frac{4}{9}$. Find the probability that

   (a) she will not have a perm in a particular week,

   (b) she will have a perm in each of two particular consecutive weeks,

   (c) she will have a perm in just one of two particular consecutive weeks.

9. A bag contains 20 potatoes, 4 of which are rotten. Another bag contains 12 potatoes, 3 of which are rotten.

   (a) If one potato is selected at random from the first bag, what is the probability that it is rotten?

   (b) If one potato is selected at random from the second bag, what is the probability that it is good?

   (c) If one potato is selected from each bag, what is the probability that
   (i) the potato from the first bag is good and the potato from the second bag is rotten,
   (ii) one potato is good and the other potato is rotten,
   (iii) either both potatoes are good or both are rotten,
   (iv) there is at least one good potato?

10. A bag contains 6 green and 4 blue cards.

    (a) A card is drawn at random. Find the probability that it is green.

    (b) The card drawn is returned to the bag and after mixing the cards thoroughly, Jane takes two cards at random from the bag, one after the other. Using a probability tree, or otherwise, calculate the probability that she has taken out
    (i) two green cards,
    (ii) one card of each colour,
    (iii) at least one blue card.

11. A class has 30 girls and 15 boys. Two representatives are to be selected at random from the class. What is the probability that

    (a) the first representative selected is a girl,
    (b) the first representative selected is a boy and the second one is a girl,
    (c) 1 boy and 1 girl are selected as representatives?

12. In a drawer there are 16 pairs of socks, 8 black, 6 white and 2 grey.

    (a) If two pairs of socks are taken out of the drawer, find the probability that
    (i) both pairs are black,
    (ii) one pair is black and the other is white,
    (iii) the two pairs are of the same colour.

    (b) If a third pair of socks is drawn out, calculate the probability that all 3 pairs are black.

13. A box contains 15 components. This box was dropped in transit and five components became defective, but not visibly.

(a) If 2 components are selected at random without replacement from the box, what is the probability that
   (i) both are good,
   (ii) only one is good?

(b) If the components are taken at random from the box and tested until a good one is obtained, what is the probability that the first good component obtained is the
   (i) 2nd component tested,
   (ii) 3rd component tested?

14. Ten cards are marked with the letters $P, R, O, P, O, R, T, I, O$ and N respectively. These cards are placed in a box. Two cards are drawn at random without replacement. Calculate the probability that

(a) the first card bears the letter O,
(b) the two cards bear the letters P and O in that order,
(c) the two cards bear the letters P and O in any order,
(d) the two cards bear the same letter.

15. Five balls numbered 1, 2, 5, 8 and 9 are put in a bag.

(a) One ball is selected at random from the bag. Write down the probability that it is a ball numbered 8.

(b) On another occasion, two balls are selected at random from the bag.
Find the probability that
   (i) the number of each ball is even,
   (ii) the sum of the numbers on the balls is more than 10,
   (iii) the number on each ball is not prime,
   (iv) only one ball bears an odd number.

16. Six cards are marked with the letters F, O, L, L, O and W respectively.

(a) One card is chosen at random. State the probability that it is the card bearing the letter L or O.

(b) The cards are put face down on the table and their positions are randomly mixed. The cards are turned over one at a time. In each of the following cases, find the probability that
   (i) the first two cards turned over will each have the letter O marked on them,
   (ii) the second card turned over will have the letter F marked on it,
   (iii) the first three cards turned over are in the order L, O and W.

17. (a) My dog Ben is given 11 biscuits for his breakfast. 7 of them are black, 3 are red and 1 is yellow.
   (i) He eats one of them. Assuming that he is equally fond of each sort of biscuit, what is the probability that the biscuit he eats is red?
   (ii) He then eats a second biscuit. What is the probability that the first biscuit is red and the second is black?

(b) On another day he is again given 7 black biscuits, 3 red biscuits and 1 yellow biscuit. He eats only 2 of them. What is the probability that one is yellow and the other is black?

1. The probability of an event E occurring is given by $P(E) = \frac{n(E)}{n(S)}$, where $n(E)$ and $n(S)$ represent the number of outcomes in E and the total number of possible outcomes in S.

2. For any event E,

$$P(\text{not } E) = 1 - P(E).$$

3. **Possibility diagrams** and **tree diagrams** are useful in solving probability problems. The diagrams are used to list all possible outcomes of an experiment.

4. **Addition of Probabilities:**
   Two **mutually exclusive** events A and B cannot occur together. The probability that either A occurs **or** B occurs is given by

$$P(A \text{ or } B) = P(A) + P(B).$$

5. **Multiplication of Probabilities:**
   A **probability tree**, a tree diagram with appropriate probabilities displayed on the 'branches', can be used to find the probability that event A and event B occur together written P(A and B). Each main 'branch' of the probability tree leads to an outcome representing 'A and B'. Probability of an outcome and hence P(A and B) is obtained by **multiplying** the probabilities displayed along the 'branches' leading to that outcome.

6. Two events are **independent events** if the outcome of one event does not affect the probability of the outcome of the other event.

Bag A contains four cards bearing the numbers 2, 3, 4 and 5. Bag B contains six cards bearing the numbers 4, 5, 6, 7, 8 and 9. A card is drawn at random from each bag.

(a) *Display all the possible outcomes of the event using a possibility diagram.*
(b) *With the help of the possibility diagram, find the probability that*
  (i) *the two cards bear the same number,*
  (ii) *the larger of the two numbers on the cards is 5,*
  (iii) *the sum of the two numbers on the cards is equal to 10,*
  (iv) *the product of the two numbers on the cards is less than 15.*

(a)

Bag *B*

Bag A	4	5	6	7	8	9
2	2, 4	2, 5	2, 6	2, 7	2, 8	2, 9
3	3, 4	3, 5	3, 6	3, 7	3, 8	3, 9
4	4, 4	4, 5	4, 6	4, 7	4, 8	4, 9
5	5, 4	5, 5	5, 6	5, 7	5, 8	5, 9

(b) There is a total of 24 equally possible outcomes.

(i) There are two occurrences with the two cards bearing the same number.

$\therefore$ P(two cards bearing the same number) $= \frac{2}{24} = \frac{1}{12}$

(ii) The larger of the two numbers on the cards is 5 are (5, 4), (2, 5), (3, 5) and (4, 5).

$\therefore$ P(the larger of the two numbers on the cards is 5) $= \frac{4}{24} = \frac{1}{6}$

(iii) There are 4 occurrences where the sum of the numbers on the cards is 10.

$\therefore$ P(sum of the two numbers on the cards is 10) $= \frac{4}{24} = \frac{1}{6}$

(iv) The occurrences where the product of the two numbers on the cards is less than 15 are (2, 4), (3, 4), (2, 5), (2, 6) and (2, 7).

$\therefore$ P(the product of the two numbers is less than 15) $= \frac{5}{24}$

6

1. Two balanced dice are thrown together. Find the probability that they will show
   (a) the same number,
   (b) two even numbers,
   (c) two odd numbers,
   (d) one odd and one even number.

2. A man throws a die and a coin. Find the probability that he will get
   (a) the number 3 followed by a head,
   (b) an even number followed by a tail.

3. In an experiment, a card is drawn from a pack of playing cards and a coin is tossed. Find the probability of obtaining
   (a) a card which is a king and a 'head' on the coin,
   (b) the ace of diamonds and a 'tail' on the coin.

4. In an experiment consisting of throwing a die followed by drawing a card from a pack of playing cards, find the probability of obtaining
   (a) an odd number on the die and a card which is an ace,
   (b) a six on the die and a picture card,
   (c) a six on the die and a club.

5. On any day, the probability that I will miss my bus is $\frac{1}{7}$. Find the probability that
   (a) I will catch my bus on a particular day,
   (b) I will miss my bus on two particular consecutive days,
   (c) I will miss my bus on just one of two particular consecutive days,
   (d) I will catch my bus on three particular consecutive days.

6. Peter has five pairs of socks, one black, one green, one blue and two white. He has three pairs of shoes, one brown, one white and one black. He selects a pair of socks and a pair of shoes at random. Find the probability that Peter has selected
   (a) a pair of socks which is not green,
   (b) a pair of white socks and a pair of black shoes,
   (c) a pair of socks and a pair of shoes of the same colour.

7. In a class of 30 pupils, 20 are boys and 10 are girls. Of the 10 girls, 6 travel to school by bus and 4 travel by car.
   (a) If two pupils are selected at random, calculate the probability that
      (i) one is a girl and one is a boy,
      (ii) no girls are selected.
   (b) If two of the 10 girls are selected at random, calculate the probability that
      (i) both travel to school by bus,
      (ii) both travel to school by different means of transportation,
      (iii) at least one travels to school by bus.

∗8. A bowl of sweets contains 2 fruit gums, 3 mints and 5 toffees. Three sweets are to be chosen at random and without replacement, from the bowl.
   Calculate the probability that
   (a) the first sweet chosen will be a mint,
   (b) the first two sweets chosen will be different,
   (c) the three sweets chosen will be the same,
   (d) of the three sweets chosen, the first two will be the same and the third a toffee,
   (e) a fruit gum, a mint and a toffee, in that order, will be chosen.

∗9. A garden has three flower beds. The first bed has 20 daffodils and 20 tulips, the second has 30 daffodils and 10 tulips and the third has 10 daffodils and 20 tulips.

A flower bed is to be chosen by throwing a die which has its six faces numbered 1, 1, 1, 2, 2, 3. If the die shows a '1', the first flower bed is chosen, if it shows a '2' the second flower bed is chosen and so on. A flower is then to be picked at random from the chosen bed.

(a) Copy and complete the probability tree in Fig. 6.36.

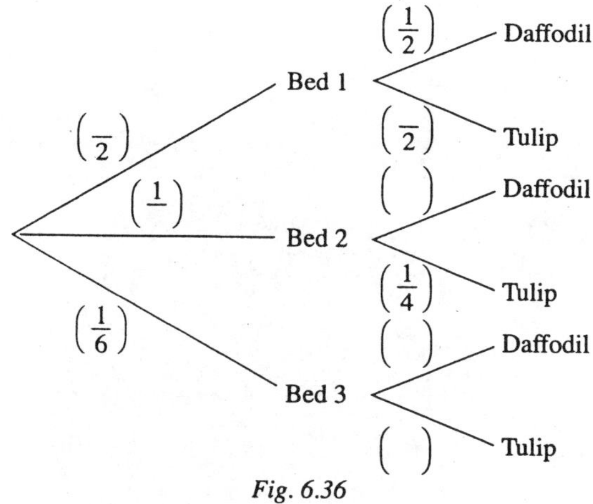

Fig. 6.36

(b) Calculate the probability of picking a daffodil.

★**10.** A fair die is made from a regular eight-faced solid by numbering the faces from 1 to 8. The die is thrown twice. Draw a possibility diagram to represent the possible outcomes in the sample space. With the help of your possibility diagram, find the probability of obtaining

(a) the first score less than 5,

(b) the same score for each throw,

(c) the first score less than the second score,

(d) a total score of 8.

11. A regular octahedron which has its eight faces numbered 1, 1, 1, 1, 1, 2, 2 and 3 is to be used as a die.

(a) If the die is thrown once, write down the probability that the score on the die is

(i) 1,

(ii) a prime number.

(b) If two such octahedral dice are thrown together, find the probability that

(i) each die shows a score of 2,

(ii) the sum of the two scores is 6,

(iii) the sum of the two scores is 4,

(iv) the two scores are not equal,

(v) when the two scores are multiplied together, the result is an even number.

12. I have to find two light bulbs from a collection of 12, all but 3 of which are working. If I test each one in turn, what is the probability that I would find two working bulbs

(a) among the first three bulbs tested,

(b) when three bulbs have been tested, but not before?

13. Two cards, one yellow on both sides and the other yellow on one side and green on the other, are placed in a box. One card is chosen at random from the box and placed on the table. Given that the upper side of the card on the table is yellow, find the probability that the underside is also yellow.

14. A point in the plane with coordinates (x, y), where x and y are integers having numerical values less than or equal to four, i.e., $|x| \leqslant 4$ and $|y| \leqslant 4$, is chosen at random. What is the probability that the distance of the point from the origin is at most two units?

15. Three fair dice are thrown. What is the probability of obtaining three consecutive numbers in any order?

16. A bag contains 7 green and 5 blue marbles. 6 marbles are drawn at random in succession from the bag without replacement. What is the probability that the colours appear alternately?

17. A number of identical purses are such that 2 purses each contains 50¢, 9 purses each contains 20¢ and 14 purses each contains 5¢. Calculate the probability that 3 purses, selected simultaneously, will together contain exactly 60¢.

CHAPTER

7

Revision

Introduction

"Practice Makes Perfect" goes the saying. It is applicable for people learning games or art and also many other learning subjects. What do you think?

This chapter will provide you with many opportunities to perfect your mathematical skills.

Arithmetic 1: Numbers, Percentages, Time

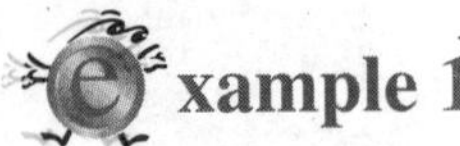

xample 1

(a) When the petrol tank of a car is full, the weight of the petrol is $29\frac{1}{4}$ kg. Given that 1 cm^3 of petrol weighs 0.78 g, calculate the volume of the tank in litres.

(b) When a discount of 15% of the marked price of an air-cleaner is given, the air-cleaner is sold for \$323. Find the discount.

(a) The weight of the petrol is $29\frac{1}{4}$ kg = 29 250 g.

$\therefore$ the volume of the tank = $\frac{29\,250}{0.78}$ = 37 500 cm^3 = 37.5 litres.

(b) \$323 is 85% of the marked price.

$\therefore$ the discount = $\frac{15}{85} \times \$323 = \$57$.

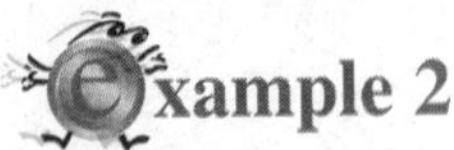

xample 2

A night train left Tanjong Pagar railway station at 21 46 on Tuesday and arrived at Kuala Lumpur railway station at 07 22 on Wednesday morning.

(a) Calculate the total time taken for the journey.

(b) The train made a stop at Gemas station at exactly mid-way from 21 46 to 07 22. Find the exact time the train stopped at Gemas.

(a) Total time taken = (24 00 – 21 46) + 07 22
= 02 14 + 07 22
= 9 h 36 min.

$$\begin{array}{r} \overset{2\,3}{\cancel{2\,4}}\;\overset{6\,0}{\cancel{0\,0}} \\ -\;2\;1\;4\;6 \\ \hline 2\;1\;4 \\ +\quad 7\;2\;2 \\ \hline 2\,\big)\,9\;3\;6 \\ 4\;4\;8 \end{array} \qquad \begin{array}{r} 0\;7\;2\;2 \\ -\;0\;4\;4\;8 \\ \hline 0\;2\;3\;4 \end{array}$$

(b) $\frac{1}{2}$ of 9 h 36 min = 4 h 48 min
Time the train stopped at Gemas = 07 22 – 04 48
= 02 34

i.e. at 2.34 am on Wednesday.

Exercise 7a

1. The volume of metal in a piece of metal pipe is calculated to be 0.034 56 m^3. Express this volume
   (a) correct to 2 decimal places,
   (b) correct to 3 significant figures,
   (c) in standard form.

2. The average yield of a certain variety of wheat from seven plots of experimental land was 4.034 7 kg. Express this weight
   (a) correct to 2 significant figures,
   (b) correct to 2 decimal places.

3. Express 74 cm^3 in m^3, giving your answer
   (a) as a decimal,
   (b) in standard form.

4. (a) A bus leaves a terminal at 11.15 a.m. It arrives at the next terminal at 2.08 p.m. How many minutes does the journey take?
   (b) The last bus for the day leaves the terminal at 23 45. If the journey to the next terminal takes 1 hour 23 minutes, find the time of arrival of the bus at the next terminal.

5. If $a = 7.8 \times 10^5$ and $b = 3.9 \times 10^3$, find the value of each of the following, giving your answer in standard form.
   (a) $2a - b$
   (b) $3a + 12b$
   (c) $a \div b$
   (d) $4ab$
   (e) $4ab^2$
   (f) $4b \div a$

6. Estimate $\frac{11.9 \times 0.598}{23.6}$, giving your answer correct to one significant figure.

7. The diameter of the sun is 1 387 570 km. Express 1 387 570 in standard form, correct to 2 significant figures.

8. Evaluate each of the following, giving your answer correct to 2 decimal places.
   (a) $25 \div 13$
   (b) 3.14×3.47
   (c) $7.58 \div 0.12$

9. Given that $a = 1.37 \times 10^{-10}$, $b = 2.53 \times 10^{-9}$ and $c = 9.43 \times 10^{-8}$, evaluate each of the following, giving your answer in the standard form.
   (a) $8a + 3b + 5c$
   (b) $4c - 3b + 17a$

10. In 1997, the total trade in Singapore was \$382 218 million. In 1998 the total trade dropped to \$353 627 million due to the Asian economic crisis.
    (a) Express 382 218 million in standard form giving your answer correct to 3 significant figures.
    (b) Calculate the percentage drop in trade in 1998 as compared with 1997 figures, giving your answer correct to 2 decimal places.
    (c) Given that the total gross domestic product in 1997 was \$141 262 million, how many times larger was the total trade figure as compared with the gross domestic product? Give your answer correct to 4 significant figures.

11. In a sale, prices are reduced by 22.5%. The price of a wrist blood pressure monitor in the sale is \$170.50. Find its normal price.

12. In a sale, all prices are reduced by 20%. Calculate the original price of an article whose sale price is \$68.

13. A man bought 20 books for \$100, 15 of which were sold for \$7 each and the rest for \$4 each. What was his profit?

14. An article was sold at a loss of 12% on its cost. If the cost price had been \$350, what would the selling price have been?

15. There are 600 boys and 400 girls in a school. One day, 2% of the pupils were absent. If 1% of the boys were absent, how many girls were present?

16. Thirty-eight members from the youth club of Greenview Community Centre plan a day-trip to the zoo. The cost of hiring the bus is \$62.50. The zoo tickets cost \$3.20 each but one extra ticket is given free for every eight tickets bought.
   (a) How many zoo tickets will have to be paid to enable the 38 members to enter the zoo?
   (b) Calculate the total cost of the day-trip.

17. 240 boys and 180 girls sat for an examination. If 65% of the boys and 60% of the girls passed, what percentage of the total number of candidates passed?

18. In 2005, the price of a handphone was \$480. In the year 2006, the price of the same handphone was reduced by 15%. Find its new price in 2006.
   The price of \$480 was actually a decrease of 25% over the price in 2004. Calculate the initial price in 2004.

19. The price of coffee has increased by 25%. What percentage of coffee consumption is to be decreased, so that there would be no increase in the expenditure for a household?

20. In 1999, there were 1080 Singaporeans infected with the Aids virus, 150 more than in 1998. Of these, 11 were babies who caught the virus from their mothers, 126 were women and 88 of these women were married. Calculate
   (a) the percentage increase in the number of Aids cases from 1998 to 1999,
   (b) the percentage of male Aids carriers in the 1080 Singaporeans,
   (c) the percentage of women Aids carriers who were married.

21. The lowest temperatures recorded at the South Pole and in Singapore were –89.2°C and 19.4°C respectively.
   (a) Find the difference in the temperatures recorded.
   (b) On the day the Singapore expedition team arrived at the South Pole, the temperature was mid-way between the two extreme temperatures. Find this temperature.

22. The Primary Production Department (PPD) in Singapore aims to increase the local fish production from the 1999 level of 3000 to 40 000 tonnes per year in its 10-year plan. This represents an increase from 3% to 32% of total consumption. Calculate the total fish consumption in 1999 and 2009.

23. **(a)** Express 525 as the product of prime factors.
   (b) Given that the LCM of 15, x and 35 is 525. Find two possible values of x between 15 and 35.
   (c) If $525k$ is a perfect square, find the smallest possible integer value of k.

24. The length of a rectangle is increased by 20% and its width is decreased by 20%. Find the percentage change, if any, in its area.

25. A man bought an article for \$360. At what price must he mark the article so that he can allow a discount of 10% of the marked price and still make a profit of 10% on the cost price?

26. A man's petrol bill for 2006 was \$3000. In 2007, the price of petrol was increased by 20% and his petrol consumption increased by 15%. Find his petrol bill for 2007.

Arithmetic 2: Rate, Ratio, Proportion, Speed and Map Problems

Example 1

A car travelled for 4 hours at 75 km/h. It then travelled anothe 280 km at 80 km/h. Calculate

(a) the distance travelled in the first part of the journey,
(b) the time taken for the second part of the journey,
(c) the average speed of the car for the whole journey.

(a) The distance travelled = speed × time = 75 × 4 = 300 km.

(b) The time taken = distance ÷ speed = $\frac{280}{80} = 3\frac{1}{2}$ hours.

(c) The total distance travelled = 300 + 280 = 580 km

The total time taken = $4 + 3\frac{1}{2} = 7\frac{1}{2}$ hours

$\therefore$ the average speed of the car = $\dfrac{\text{Total distance travelled}}{\text{Total time taken}}$

$= 580 \div 7\frac{1}{2}$

$= 77.3$ km/h (correct to 3 sig. fig.)

Example 2

Given that y is directly proportional to x^3 and that y = 24 when x = 2. Express y in terms of x and

(i) find the value of y when x = 5,

(ii) find the value of x when $y = 10\frac{1}{8}$.

y is directly proportional to x^3 i.e. $y = kx^3$ where k is a constant.

When $y = 24$, $x = 2$

$$24 = k(2^3)$$
$$k = 3$$
$$\therefore \quad y = 3x^3$$

(i) When $x = 5$

$$y = 3(5^3)$$
$$= 3(125)$$
$$= 375$$

(ii) When $y = 10\frac{1}{8}$,

$$10\frac{1}{8} = 3x^3$$
$$x^3 = 10\frac{1}{8} \div 3 = \frac{27}{8}$$
$$\therefore \quad x = \sqrt[3]{\frac{27}{8}} = 1\frac{1}{2}$$

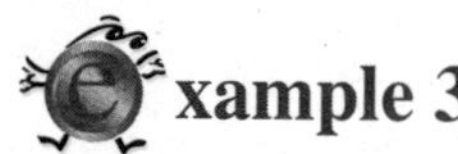

Example 3

(a) A map is drawn to a scale of 1 : 20 000

(i) Calculate the actual distance, in kilometres, between two towns which are represented on the map by points 15.5 cm apart.

(ii) On the map, a lake has an area of 150 cm². Calculate, in square kilometres, the actual area of the lake.

(b) A sum of money is divided among three men, A, B and C, in the ratio 9 : 5 : 3. If B has \$12 more than C, calculate how much A has.

(a) (i) 1 cm on the map represents 20 000 cm or 200 m or $\frac{1}{5}$ km on the ground.

$\therefore$ 15.5 cm on the map represents $\left(15.5 \times \frac{1}{5}\right)$ km or 3.1 km between the two towns.

(ii) 1 cm on the map represents $\frac{1}{5}$ km on the ground.

$\therefore$ 1 cm² represents $\left(\frac{1}{5}\right)^2$ or $\frac{1}{25}$ km² on the ground.

$\therefore$ the actual area of the lake $= \left(150 \times \frac{1}{25}\right)$ km² $= 6$ km²

(b) If $A : B : C = 9 : 5 : 3$, then B has 2 shares more than C and this is equivalent to \$12.

$\therefore$ 1 share is equivalent to \$6.

Thus, A has $9 \times 6 = \$54$.

1. 2 litres of paint containing 10% of turpentine are mixed with 5 litres of paint containing 8% of turpentine. 1 litre of turpentine is then added to the mixture. Find the percentage of turpentine in the final mixture.

2. The cost of manufacturing radio sets comprises the cost of materials and the cost of labour in the ratio 5 : 7. If the cost of materials increases by 20% and the cost of labour decreases by 4%, find the resulting percentage change in the cost of manufacturing radio sets.

3. John can do a piece of work in 8 days and Peter can do the same piece of work in 6 days. They work together on it for two days and then Peter stops working altogether. How long will it take for John to complete the remaining part of the work by himself?

4. Meiling can complete a piece of work in 12 days and Suling can complete it in 18 days. Find the number of days in which both, working together, will take to complete the work.

5. A man walks 9 km at 6 km/h and then jogs 18 km at 12 km/h. Find his average speed for the whole journey.

6. Forty-eight workers can build a hut in 60 hours. How many workers are needed if the hut is to be built in 32 hours?

7. The ratio of the number of boys to the number of girls in a school is 7 : 5. If the student population is 1200, find the number of boys and girls in the school.

8. If 4 men can make 80 chairs in 12 days, how long will 24 men take to make 300 chairs?

9. A, B and C share \$180 in such a way that A has $2\frac{1}{2}$ times as much as B, and B has 4 times as much as C. How much money would each of them receive?

10. (a) Given that y is directly proportional to x^3 and that $y = 10$ when $x = 1$, find the value of y when $x = 3$.
    (b) Given that y is directly proportional to $\sqrt{x}$ and that $y = 5$ when $x = 4$, find the value of y when $x = 9$.
    (c) Given that y is directly proportional to $x^{\frac{2}{3}}$ and that $y = 14$ when $x = 8$, express y in terms of x and find the value of y when $x = 27$.

11. Given that y is inversely proportional to x^2 and that $y = 2$ when $x = 3$, find the value of y when $x = 2$.

12. Given that y varies inversely as z^3 and that $y = 7$ when $z = 1$, find the value of y when $z = 2$ and express y in terms of z.

13. If y varies inversely as x^2, copy and complete the table below and express y in terms of x.

y	16		4
x	1	3	

14. Given that y is inversely proportional to $(x + 7)$ and that $y = 2$ when $x = 3$, find the value of y when $x = 1$ and the value of x when $y = 5$.

15. Given that y is directly proportional to $(x + 1)^2$ and that the difference between the value of y when $x = 2$ and $x = 5$ is 32, express y in terms of x and find the value of y when $x = 3$.

16. A map is drawn to a scale of 1 : 40 000.

(a) Two towns are 25 cm apart on the map. Calculate the actual distance of the two towns in km.

(b) A forest reserve has an area of 8 km^2. Calculate, in cm^2, the area of the forest reserve on the map.

17. On a map whose scale is 1 : 50 000, the distance between two places A and B is 8 cm and the area of the lake L is 28 cm^2. Calculate

(a) the actual distance between A and B, giving your answer in kilometres,

(b) the actual area of the lake L, giving your answer in square kilometres.

18. A model lorry is made on a scale of 1 : 20.

(a) If the model lorry is 24 cm long, how long is the real lorry?

(b) If the area of the load platform of the lorry is 10 m^2, find the area of the load platform of the model lorry in cm^2.

(c) If the fuel tank of the model lorry is 30 cm^3, find the volume of the fuel that the tank of the real lorry can hold, giving your answer in litres.

19. On a map whose scale is 1 cm to 4 km, the distance between two places A and B is 6 cm and the area of forest F is 40 cm^2.

(a) Calculate the actual distance of AB in metres.

(b) On another map whose scale is 1 : n, the area of the forest F is 0.4 cm^2. Calculate n.

20. A cyclist rode from P to Q for 2 hours at an average speed of x km/h and then for $1\frac{1}{2}$ hours at $(x - 3)$ km/h.

(a) Find, in terms of x, an expression for the distance of PQ.
After he had rested for half an hour at Q, he rode back from Q to P for 3 hours at the speed of $(x + 1)$ km/h.

(b) Find in terms of x, an expression for the distance QP.

(c) Form an equation in x and find the distance of PQ.

(d) Find the average speed for the two way journey.

21. A car travels a distance of 30 km at an average speed of 40 km/h and then travels for 40 minutes at an average speed of 60 km/h. Find

(a) the total distance travelled,

(b) the average speed for the whole journey.

22. (a) A cyclist has to cover a journey of 117 km in $6\frac{1}{2}$ hours. After $2\frac{3}{4}$ hours, he finds that he has travelled 57 km. Find the decrease in speed he has to make in order to arrive at his destination on time.

(b) A man drove for 2 hours at a speed of 36 km/h, 1 hour at 60 km/h and $1\frac{1}{2}$ hours at 50 km/h. Find his average speed for the whole journey.

23. The Defence Ministry (Mindef) started the construction of an ammunition storage complex deep underground in a disused quarry in Mandai in 1999. The project will help to save more than 300 ha of land for other valuable uses in Singapore where land is scarce. If 1 square metre of land is valued at \$2580, calculate the cost of a land of area 300 ha (1 ha = 10 000 m^2).

24. Given that y is directly proportional to the square of $(x + 1)$, and that $y = 9$ when $x = 1$,

(a) express y in terms of x,

(b) find the value of y when $x = 3$.

25. A radar station transmits a signal which travels at 298 000 km per second. This signal, when reflected from an aircraft, returns to the transmitter at the same speed.

(a) Write down the speed at which the signal is transmitted, giving your answer in standard form.

(b) Find the difference in time between the signals received by reflection from two aircrafts if one is $372\frac{1}{2}$ metres farther away from the station than the other.

Arithmetic 3: Simple and Compound Interest, Money Exchange, Financial Transactions

xample 1

A bank exchanged American dollars (US$) for Singapore dollars (S$) at a rate of US$1 to S$1.62 in March 2006.

(a) Calculate, in S$, the amount received in exchange for US$104.
(b) Calculate, in US$, correct to the nearest cent, the amount received in exchange for S$110.

(a) US$1 is equivalent to S$1.62.
Thus, US$104 is equivalent to $1.62 \times 104 =$ S$168.48

(b) S$1 is equivalent to US$$\frac{1}{1.62}$.

Thus, S$110 is equivalent to $\frac{1}{1.62} \times 110 =$ US$67.90 (correct to the nearest cent)

xample 2

A firm hires out vans.
A van can be hired for $40 per day plus an insurance coverage of $15 per van for a period of less than a week. If the total distance travelled during the total period of hire is 150 km or less, no extra charge is made. However, every extra kilometre travelled in excess of 150 km is charged at 10¢ per extra kilometre.

(a) A van was hired for 4 days and travelled 400 km in this time. Calculate the total hire charge.
(b) A man who hired a van for 2 days was charged $108. Calculate the total distance he travelled.

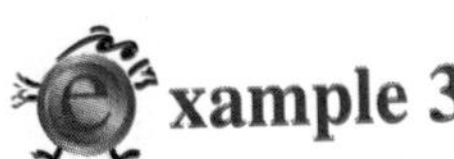

(a) Total hire charge $= \$(4 \times 40 + 15 + (400 - 150) \times \frac{10}{100})$

$= \$200$

(b) Let x be the number of km travelled.

$108 = 2 \times 40 + 15 + (x - 150) \times \frac{10}{100}$

$\therefore \quad 108 = 95 + 0.1x - 15$

$0.1x = 28$

$\therefore \quad x = 280$

Example 3

(a) When a local bank increases its rate of interest from 5% to 5.5% per annum, a man finds that he has to pay an extra \$2370 on simple interest in 3 years. Find the amount of money the man borrowed from the bank.

(b) A man deposited \$2000 into a bank that paid compound interest of 3.28% compounded half yearly. He continued depositing \$2000 into the bank every six months. Calculate the amount of money he had after he made his fifth deposit of \$2000, giving your answer correct to the nearest cent.

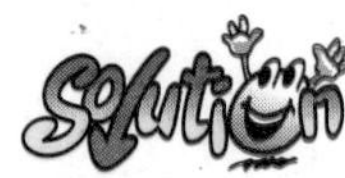

(a) We have $I = \frac{PRT}{100}$

Now $I = \$2370$, $R = 0.5\%$ and $T = 3$

$2370 = \frac{P \times 0.5 \times 3}{100}$

$P = \frac{2370 \times 100}{1.5} = \$158\ 000$

(b) As interest is compounded half yearly, we can take the rate of interest to be $\frac{1}{2}(3.28\%)$ i.e. 1.64%.

The first \$2000 will be compounded to $2000 \times \left(1 + \frac{1.64}{100}\right)^4 = \$2134.46$

The second \$2000 will be compounded to $2000 \times \left(1 + \frac{1.64}{100}\right)^3 = \$2100.02$

The third \$2000 will be compounded to $2000 \times \left(1 + \frac{1.64}{100}\right)^2 = \$2066.14$

The fourth \$2000 will be compounded to $2000 \times \left(1 + \frac{1.64}{100}\right)^1 = \$2032.80$

The fifth \$2000 has yet to earn any interest.

$\therefore$ The total amount the man had after his fifth deposit

$= \$2134.46 + \$2100.02 + \$2066.14 + \$2032.80 + \$2000 = \$10\ 333.42$

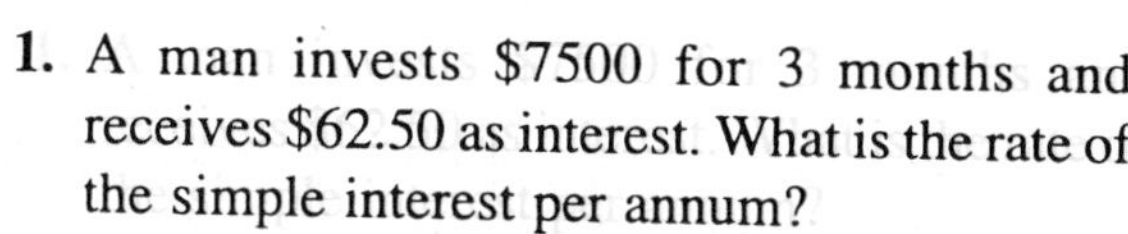

1. A man invests \$7500 for 3 months and receives \$62.50 as interest. What is the rate of the simple interest per annum?

2. A Singaporean obtained US\$2500 at a rate of S\$1.70 to US\$1. He spent US\$1850 and exchanged the remaining US dollars for Singapore dollars at a rate of S\$1.68 to US\$1. How many equivalent Singapore dollars had he used up?

3. A man bought a car for \$33 000. He made the first payment of \$12 000 and borrowed the rest from a bank at 10% per annum simple interest. At the end of the first year, he repaid a certain sum to the bank after which he still owned the bank \$9000. Calculate the sum he repaid.

4. Carol deposits \$800 in a bank that offers interest of 3% per annum. If the money and its interest are not withdrawn but allowed to compound annually, how much will she have at the end of 3 years? (Give your answer correct to the nearest cent.)

5. A shopkeeper bought a batch of goods. He fixed the price at 30% above his cost price. He managed to sell half of the stock at this price, one quarter of the stock at a discount of 20% on the marked price and the remainder at a discount of 40% on the marked price. Find his percentage profit on the batch of goods.

6. Mr Ong invests \$25 000 in a fixed deposit that pays an interest of 3% per annum. If Mr Ong reinvests the interest, how much money will he get if he withdraws his money after 3 years. Give your answer correct to the nearest 50 cents.

7. The table below shows the amount of monthly educational subsidies given to a student in a country. The amount of subsidy given varies with the student's age.

Age (years)	10	11	12	13	14	15
Subsidy (\$)	250	260	280	310	350	400

The amount of subsidy given increases on each birthday of a student. The increase on a student's 11th birthday was \$10, the increase on his 12th birthday was \$20, the increase on his 13th birthday was \$30 and so on.

(a) What was the increase on his 15th birthday?
(b) The increases follow a pattern. Using this pattern, find the increase on his
   (i) 16th birthday,
   (ii) 18th birthday.
(c) Calculate the amount of monthly subsidy given to a student on his
   (i) 16th birthday,
   (ii) 18th birthday.
(d) How old is a student when the amount of educational subsidy given is \$800?
(e) Will the amount of educational subsidy given to a student be exactly \$1000 per month? Explain your answer.
(f) In a school of 200 students, 15% are 14 years old, 35% are 15 years old, 20% are 16 years old and the rest are 17 years old. Calculate the amount of subsidy given to this school in a month.

8. A householder paid the Singapore Power (SP) 21.02 cents for every unit of electricity he used and \$1.98 for every cubic metre of water. If the water consumption exceeded 40 m^3 per month, the rate was \$2.13 per cubic metre for any additional amount of water used.

Calculate his utility bill for a month in which he used

(a) 425 units of electricity and 46 m^3 of water,
(b) 450 units of electricity and 18 m^3 of water.

SP then revised the rate so that a unit of electricity now costs 19.86 cents and one cubic metre of water costs \$2.07 if the number of cubic metres of water used was less than 30. For any additional amount of water used, the rate was \$2.32 per cubic metre. Calculate the utility bill at the new rate for the month in which he used 425 units of electricity and 48 m^3 of water.

9. In the gravel-pump mining method for tin, the alluvial ore extracted contains 1.2% tin, 0.04% zinc and 0.002% tungsten. Given that 5000 tonnes of alluvial ore are extracted each week and that the mine operates only 50 weeks in each year, calculate, in tonnes per year,

(a) the mass of alluvial ore extracted,
(b) the mass of each mineral present in the extracted ore.

As the gravel-pump mining method is not very efficient, only 80% of the three minerals present can be recovered and used.

(c) Calculate, in tonnes, the mass of each mineral that can be recovered.

The three minerals are used in making an alloy. The masses of tin, zinc and tungsten used are in the ratio 241 : 8 : 1.

If 25 000 articles are made for each tonne of tungsten used, calculate

(d) the number of articles made in a year if all the tungsten recovered is used,
(e) the mass of tin and of zinc recovered there are not used.

10. In January 1995, Mr Abdul Rahman exchanged RM50 000 for Singapore dollars at a rate of RM10 to S$6.20. He placed this money in a financial institution which paid a simple interest of 4% per annum for a period of 3 years. In January 1998, he withdrew all the money and exchanged the Singapore dollars for Malaysian ringgits at a rate of RM10 to S$4.45.

Calculate

(a) the sum in Singapore dollars that he received for the RM50 000 in 1995,

(b) the amount of money at the end of the 3-year period,

(c) the amount of Malaysian ringgits that he got in 1998,

(d) the percentage gain or loss that he got out of this investment.

11. In a small workshop, twenty-four workers and two supervisors are employed. Each worker receives $324 for a working week of 45 hours and each supervisor is paid $410 per week.

As a result of installing new machinery, it is possible to run the workshop with one supervisor and to reduce the number of workers by a quarter. The supervisor is given a raise of 15%. The workers now work a 40-hour week but receive $1.20 an hour more than before. Find the reduction in the total weekly wages for the workshop and express it as a percentage of the original cost.

12. (a) The cost of making an article is $7.

(i) Calculate the cost of making 32 such articles.

(ii) The cost of making an article is divided between materials, wages and overheads in the ratio 3 : 5 : 6. Calculate the cost of materials used in making each article.

(iii) A person is paid $1.80 for making an article. Calculate the amount he earns in one hour when he makes 4 articles in 12 minutes.

(iv) The articles are sold at a profit of 20% on cost. Calculate the selling price of each article.

(b) In 2006, the cost of making an article increased and was divided between materials, wages and overheads in the ratio 1 : 4 : 5. An article was sold for $9.20, with a profit of 15%. Calculate the cost of making an article.

In 2007, the cost of materials increased by 25%, wages doubled, and overheads remained the same.

Calculate the total percentage increase in cost.

13. The Central Provident Fund (CPF) is a social security savings plan for Singaporeans and permanent residents. The table below gives the contribution rate in 1999 for the various age groups.

Age Group y (years)	Employer's Contribution (% of salary)	Employee's Contribution (% of salary)	Total Contribution (% of salary)	Credited to Ordinary Account	Credited to Medisave Account
$y < 35$	10	20	30	24	6
$35 \leq y < 45$	10	20	30	23	7
$45 \leq y < 55$	10	20	30	22	8
$55 \leq y < 60$	4	12.5	16.5	8.5	8
$60 \leq y < 65$	2	7.5	9.5	1.5	8
$y \geq 65$	2	5	7	0	7

(a) Mr Lim is 28 years old and he works as a supervisor in a factory, earning a monthly income of $1650.

(i) Calculate his take-home pay after CPF is deducted.

(ii) How much will be credited into his ordinary account per month?

(b) Madam Alinah is 47 years old and she works as a marketing executive, earning $2380 per month. Calculate the amount that will be credited into her Medisave account from January 1999 to March 2000.

(c) Mr Rajakumar is 56 years old and he works as a lawyer, earning $8500 per month. Calculate the amount credited into his ordinary account for the whole of 1999, assuming that he also gets 5-month bonus at the end of the year.

(d) Mr Ismail is a retired teacher re-employed by the government to teach Malay in a secondary school. He is 61 years old and earns $4300 per month. Calculate his total contribution to his CPF account for the period from January 1999 to August 1999.

(e) Mr Wong is a 67 year-old retiree working in a fast food outlet, earning $780 per month. Calculate his take-home pay and the amount credited into his Medisave account per month.

(f) A trading company has a staff strength of 67 consisting of 43 employees aged 55 years old and below, 9 employees aged between 55 and 60 years old, 6 employees aged between 60 and 65 years old and the remaining staff are over 65 years old. Calculate the total monthly CPF contribution that the company must contribute for all the 67 employees. Assume that each employee earns an average of $2500 per month.

Algebra 1: Simplification, Substitution, Expansion and Factorization

Example 1

Peter is x years old. He is 6 years younger than his twin sisters, Jane and Jennifer.

(a) Write down Jane's age, in terms of x.
(b) Find, as simply as possible, the mean age of the three children, giving your answer in terms of x.

(a) Jane is $(x + 6)$ years old.

(b) The mean age of the three children $= \frac{1}{3}[x + 2(x + 6)]$

$$= \frac{1}{3}(3x + 12)$$

$$= (x + 4) \text{ years old}$$

Example 2

(a) Simplify

(i) $4(3x - 2) - 3(2x - 7)$;
(ii) $6 - [(3x - 7) - (7x - 3)]$;
(iii) $(2x - 3)^2 - 4x(x - 5)$.

(b) Given that $a = -2$, $b = 5$ *and* $c = -1$, *find the value of each of the following.*

(i) $2a + b$
(ii) $a^2 + 2bc$
(iii) $(a + b - c)^2$

(a) (i) $4(3x - 2) - 3(2x - 7) = 12x - 8 - 6x + 21$
$= 6x + 13$

(ii) $6 - [(3x - 7) - (7x - 3)] = 6 - [3x - 7 - 7x + 3]$
$= 6 - (-4x - 4)$
$= 6 + 4x + 4$
$= 4x + 10$

(iii) $(2x - 3)^2 - 4x(x - 5) = (2x)^2 - 2(2x)(3) + (3)^2 - 4x^2 + 20x$
$= 4x^2 - 12x + 9 - 4x^2 + 20x$
$= 8x + 9$

(b) (i) $2a + b = 2(-2) + 5$
$= -4 + 5$
$= 1$

(ii) $a^2 + 2bc = (-2)^2 + 2(5)(-1)$
$= 4 - 10$
$= -6$

(iii) $(a + b - c)^2 = [-2 + 5 - (-1)]^2$
$= (-2 + 5 + 1)^2$
$= 4^2$
$= 16$

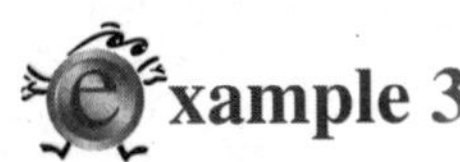

Factorise each of the following completely.

(a) $4x - 12y$

(b) $12x^2 - 20x - 8$

(c) $5x^2 - 20y^2$

(d) $3xy + 2y - 12x - 8$

(a) $4x - 12y = 4(x - 3y)$

(b) $12x^2 - 20x - 8 = 4(3x^2 - 5x - 2)$
$= 4(3x + 1)(x - 2)$

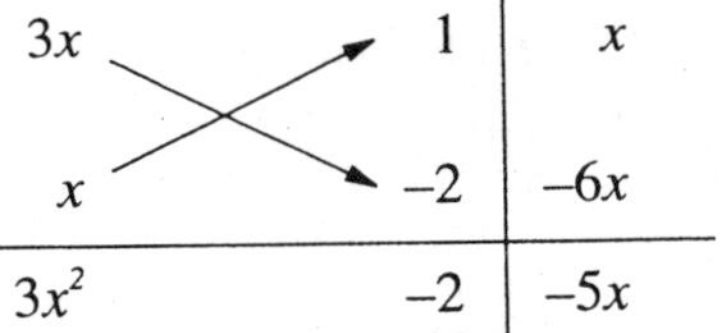

(c) $5x^2 - 20y^2 = 5(x^2 - 4y^2)$
$= 5[x^2 - (2y)^2]$
$= 5(x + 2y)(x - 2y)$

(d) $3xy + 2y - 12x - 8 = y(3x + 2) - 4(3x + 2)$
$= (3x + 2)(y - 4)$

Example 4

(a) Solve the following equations:

(i) $5x - 4 = x + 12$

(ii) $2(5x + 1) = 32$

(iii) $3(x - 1) = 5(4 - 7x)$

(b) Solve the simultaneous equations $5x + 3y = 4$, $2y - 3x = 9$.

(a) (i)
$$\begin{aligned} 5x - 4 &= x + 12 \\ 5x - x &= 12 + 4 \\ 4x &= 16 \\ \therefore \quad x &= 4 \end{aligned}$$

(ii)
$$\begin{aligned} 2(5x + 1) &= 32 \\ 5x + 1 &= 16 \\ 5x &= 15 \\ \therefore \quad x &= 3 \end{aligned}$$

(iii)
$$\begin{aligned} 3(x - 1) &= 5(4 - 7x) \\ 3x - 3 &= 20 - 35x \\ 3x + 35x &= 20 + 3 \\ 38x &= 23 \\ \therefore \quad x &= \frac{23}{38} \end{aligned}$$

(b) $5x + 3y = 4$ ———————— (1)

$2y - 3x = 9$ ———————— (2)

From (2): $2y = 3x + 9$, i.e. $y = \dfrac{3x + 9}{2}$ ———————— (3)

Substitute (3) into (1):
$$\begin{aligned} 5x + 3\left(\frac{3x + 9}{2}\right) &= 4 \\ 5x + 4\frac{1}{2}x + 13\frac{1}{2} &= 4 \\ 9\frac{1}{2}x &= -9\frac{1}{2} \\ x &= -1 \end{aligned}$$

Substitute $x = -1$ into (3): $y = \dfrac{3(-1) + 9}{2} = 3$

Therefore $x = -1$, $y = 3$ is the solution.

1. Devi is x years old and Shanti is twice as old as Devi.
   (a) Find the sum of the ages of Devi and Shanti in
      (i) two years' time,
      (ii) k years' time.
   (b) How old will Shanti be when Devi is $2x$ years old?
   (c) How old will Devi be when Shanti is $6x$ years old?

2. The cost of unleaded petrol is $\$x$ per litre while the cost of leaded petrol is 10 cents more per litre.
   (a) Find the cost of buying
      (i) 5 litres,
      (ii) k litres of unleaded petrol.
   (b) Find the cost of buying
      (i) 8 litres,
      (ii) h litres of leaded petrol.
   (c) Find the total cost of buying y litres of unleaded petrol and z litres of leaded petrol.

3. A cyclist can travel at an average speed of v km/h. How long would he take to travel a distance of
   (a) 10 km, (b) x km, (c) y m?
   (Give your answer in hours.)

4. A swimming pool can be filled by a large pipe operating alone in x hours. If the pool is to be filled by a small pipe alone, it will take 6 hours longer than the large pipe filling it alone. Write an expression for the part of the pool that
   (a) the large pipe can fill in one hour,
   (b) the small pipe can fill in four hours,
   (c) both pipes can fill together in one hour.

5. Simplify each of the following:
   (a) $3(2x - 1) - 4(x - 7)$
   (b) $5(3x + 4) - 2(7x - 4)$
   (c) $6(2x - 3) + 5(3 - 7x)$
   (d) $14 - 3(5 - 4x) + 6x$
   (e) $7(2a + 3) - 4(3 - a)$
   (f) $9(5k - 6) + 4(7 - 13k)$
   (g) $5 - 3(c + a) - 6(3a - 2c)$
   (h) $15p - 3(p - q) + 4(q - 3p)$
   (i) $(x + 2y)^2 - 4x(x + y)$
   (j) $(a + 2b)^2 - (a - 2b)^2$

6. Simplify each of the following below by removing the brackets.
   (a) $2[3a - 2(3a - 1) + 4(a + 1)]$
   (b) $x - (x - y) - [x - y - z - 2(y + z)]$
   (c) $8(x - y) - [x - y - 3(y - z - x)]$
   (d) $-5(a + b) - [3(a - b) - 2(3b - c)]$
   (e) $2b - [5a - 2(4b - 3a)]$
   (f) $2x - (3y - 5z) - [2x - (5y + z) - (2z - 7y)]$
   (g) $a(2b - c) - c(a + 3b) + 5a(c - a)$
   (h) $2a(5b - 2c) - [2(a - b + c) - b(a - c)]$
   (i) $2b(c - a) - [3c(a - b) - 3a(b + c)]$
   (j) $3(a - c) - \{5(2a - 3b) - [5a - 7(a - b)]\}$

7. Given that $a = 2$, $b = -3$, and $c = -1$, find the value of each of the following:
   (a) $2a + 3b - c$
   (b) $a^2 - c^2$
   (c) $(a + b)(2a - c)$

8. Solve the following equations:
   (a) $3(5 - 3x) = 25$
   (b) $3(2x - 3) - 2(5x + 4) = 5$
   (c) $\frac{1}{2}x + 3 = \frac{3}{4}x$
   (d) $\frac{3x + 5}{6} = \frac{2x + 7}{7}$
   (e) $\frac{1}{x + 3} - \frac{7}{2x - 5} = 0$
   (f) $\frac{2x + 3}{5} + \frac{1 - x}{3} = 0$
   (g) $7 - 3x = 2(5x - 1)$
   (h) $2(5y - 7) - 2(3y - 1) = 8$

(i) $5(3x - 7) - 8 = 2(7x + 1)$
(j) $9(2x - 4) = 8 - 2(x - 7)$
(k) $\frac{3}{x + 7} = \frac{5}{3x + 4}$
(l) $\frac{2x + 17}{3} - \frac{7x - 4}{5} = 0$

9. Solve the following pairs of simultaneous equations.

(a) $x + 2y = 8$, $3x + 2y = 12$
(b) $2x - 3y = 7$, $x + 3y = -1$
(c) $x + y = \frac{5}{6}$, $x - y = \frac{1}{6}$
(d) $5x + 3y = 2$, $2y - 5x = -7$
(e) $3a - 2b = 1$, $5a + 3b = -11$
(f) $a + 2b = 3$, $3a + 4b = 11$
(g) $2p + 3q = 0$, $4p - 5q = 22$
(h) $3p - 4q - 24 = 0$, $5p - 6q - 38 = 0$

10. Factorise the following expressions completely.

(a) $8x^2 + 16x$
(b) $10x^2 - 9(x^2 + 16)$
(c) $x^2 - 4xy + 4y^2$
(d) $3x^3y - 9xy^2$
(e) $25 - 64k^2$
(f) $(3x + 4y)^2 - 9z^2$
(g) $(a - b)^2 - (x - y)^2$
(h) $x^2 - 14x - 51$
(i) $2a^2 + 3a - 2$
(j) $3a^2 + 7a - 6$
(k) $4k^2 + k - 14$
(l) $5x^2 + 11x + 2$
(m) $6a^2 - 31a + 35$
(n) $7a^2 + 69a - 10$

11. Factorise the following expressions completely.

(a) $x^2 + 3y + xy + 3x$
(b) $ab - bc - ac + c^2$
(c) $ax - ab + kx - kb$
(d) $3x + cx + 3c + c^2$
(e) $ax - kx - ah + kh$
(f) $5ax + ay + 5bx + by$
(g) $3xy + 2y - 12x - 8$
(h) $20ac - 4ad - 15kc + 3kd$
(i) $6a^2 + 3ab - 8ka - 4kb$
(j) $2a^4 - a^3 + 4a - 2$

12. The cost of two cups of coffee and three bowls of noodles is \$6.80 while the cost of five cups of coffee and seven bowls of noodles is \$16.10. Find the cost of a cup of coffee and that of a bowl of noodles.

13. Solve the following simultaneous equations:

(a) $\frac{1}{2}y + 2x = 36$, $\frac{1}{2}x - \frac{1}{4}y + 3 = 0$
(b) $3x + 5y = 4$, $5x = 16 + y$
(c) $3x - 4y = 73$, $5x + y = 22$
(d) $3x - 2y = 3$, $4x - 5y + 10 = 0$
(e) $x + 2y = 2$, $2x - 3y = 7\frac{1}{2}$
(f) $x + 3y = 5$, $4x + 13y = 3$
(g) $\frac{1}{4}x + \frac{3}{5}y = -4$, $\frac{1}{5}x + \frac{1}{4}y = -\frac{9}{10}$
(h) $x = 3 + 4y$, $y = 2 + 3x$

14. If x books cost \$$y$ and z cents, find the cost of one book in cents. Also write down an expression for the number of books that could be bought for \$$k$.

15. (a) Solve the simultaneous equations $8x - 3y = 21$, $5x + 2y = 17$.

(b) Explain briefly why the following pair of simultaneous equations has no solutions.
$8x - 3y = 21$, $24x - 9y = 17$

16. Given that $x = 2$, $y = -4$ and $z = 3$, find the values of

(a) $(x + y + z)^2 + (x - y - z)^2$,
(b) $(3x - 4y)(z - 2y)$,
(c) $\sqrt{y + z^2 + x^2 + y^2}$,
(d) $\frac{x}{y} - z^2$,
(e) $(x + y^3) \div (y^2 - z^2)$.

17. If $5 : 7 = (x - y) : (x + 2y)$, find the value of $\frac{4x}{5y}$.

Algebra 2: Algebraic Manipulation and Indices

Make a the subject of each of the following formula.

(a) $3x - 5a = 2y$
(b) $5x - 3a = 7ax + k$
(c) $y^2 - a^2 = 2xy$

(a) $3x - 5a = 2y \Rightarrow 5a = 3x - 2y$

$\therefore \quad a = \dfrac{3x - 2y}{5}$

(b) $5x - 3a = 7ax + k \Rightarrow 5x - k = 7ax + 3a$

$\therefore \quad a(7x + 3) = 5x - k \Rightarrow a = \dfrac{5x - k}{7x + 3}$

(c) $y^2 - a^2 = 2xy \Rightarrow a^2 = y^2 - 2xy$ and $a = \pm\sqrt{y^2 - 2xy}$

Solve the following equations.

(a) $(7 - 2x)(4 + 3x) = 0$ *(b)* $6x^2 - 19x + 15 = 0$

(a) $(7 - 2x)(4 + 3x) = 0$
$7 - 2x = 0$ or $4 + 3x = 0$
$\therefore \quad x = 3\frac{1}{2}$ or $x = -1\frac{1}{3}$

(b) $6x^2 - 19x + 15 = 0$
$(2x - 3)(3x - 5) = 0$
$(2x - 3) = 0$ or $(3x - 5) = 0$
$\therefore \quad x = 1\frac{1}{2}$ or $x = 1\frac{2}{3}$

Example 3

(a) *Simplify* (i) $3a^2 \times 4a^5$, (ii) $8x^{2\frac{1}{2}} \div 2x^{\frac{1}{2}}$.

(b) *Evaluate* (i) $8^{-\frac{2}{3}}$, (ii) $\left(\frac{2}{3}\right)^{-2}$,

(iii) $3^0 + 4^{\frac{1}{2}} \times 4^{1\frac{1}{2}}$.

(c) *If* $3^{14} \div 9^2 = 3^x$, *find the value of* x.

Solution

(a) (i) $3a^2 \times 4a^5 = (3 \times 4)a^{2+5}$
$= 12a^7$

(ii) $8x^{2\frac{1}{2}} \div 2x^{\frac{1}{2}} = (8 \div 2)x^{2\frac{1}{2} - \frac{1}{2}}$
$= 4x^2$

(b) (i) $8^{-\frac{2}{3}} = \dfrac{1}{8^{\frac{2}{3}}}$
$= \dfrac{1}{(\sqrt[3]{8})^2}$
$= \dfrac{1}{2^2}$
$= \dfrac{1}{4}$

Alternatively, $8^{-\frac{2}{3}} = \left(2^3\right)^{-\frac{2}{3}}$
$= 2^{-2}$
$= \dfrac{1}{2^2}$
$= \dfrac{1}{4}$

(ii) $\left(\frac{2}{3}\right)^{-2} = \dfrac{1}{\left(\frac{2}{3}\right)^2}$
$= \dfrac{1}{\frac{4}{9}}$
$= \dfrac{9}{4}$
$= 2\dfrac{1}{4}$

(iii) $3^0 + 4^{\frac{1}{2}} \times 4^{1\frac{1}{2}} = 1 + 4^{\frac{1}{2} + 1\frac{1}{2}}$
$= 1 + 4^2$
$= 1 + 16$
$= 17$

(c) $3^{14} \div 9^2 = 3^{14} \div (3^2)^2$
$= 3^{14} \div 3^4$
$= 3^{14-4}$
$= 3^{10}$

i.e. $3^{10} = 3^x$

$\therefore \quad x = 10$

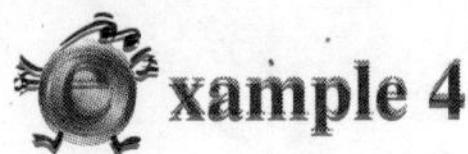

Express each of the following as a fraction in its lowest terms.

(a) $\frac{2-7x}{3} - \frac{3x-1}{5}$

(b) $\frac{4}{5} + \frac{a-3}{4a}$

(c) $\frac{a}{a-5} - \frac{2}{a+1}$

(d) $\frac{5}{x-3} - \frac{2x-3}{x^2-x-6} - \frac{4}{x+2}$

(a) $$\frac{2-7x}{3} - \frac{3x-1}{5} = \frac{5(2-7x)-3(3x-1)}{3\times 5}$$
$$= \frac{10-35x-9x+3}{15}$$
$$= \frac{13-44x}{15}$$

(b) $$\frac{4}{5} + \frac{a-3}{4a} = \frac{4(4a)+5(a-3)}{5(4a)}$$
$$= \frac{16a+5a-15}{20a}$$
$$= \frac{21a-15}{20a}$$

(c) $$\frac{a}{a-5} - \frac{2}{a+1} = \frac{a(a+1)-2(a-5)}{(a-5)(a+1)}$$
$$= \frac{a^2+a-2a+10}{(a-5)(a+1)}$$
$$= \frac{a^2-a+10}{(a-5)(a+1)}$$

(d) $$\frac{5}{x-3} - \frac{2x-3}{x^2-x-6} - \frac{4}{x+2} = \frac{5}{x-3} - \frac{2x-3}{(x-3)(x+2)} - \frac{4}{x+2}$$
$$= \frac{5(x+2)-(2x-3)-4(x-3)}{(x-3)(x+2)}$$
$$= \frac{5x+10-2x+3-4x+12}{(x-3)(x+2)}$$
$$= \frac{-x+25}{(x-3)(x+2)}$$

1. Simplify each of the following.

(a) $3x^5 \times 7x^2$ (b) $2x^{\frac{1}{2}} \times 3x^{\frac{1}{3}}$

(c) $(2x^2)^3 \times (x^{\frac{1}{2}})^3$ (d) $8x^8 \div 2x^4$

(e) $9x^5 \div 3x^{\frac{1}{2}}$ (f) $(2x^7)^3 \div (4x^2)$

(g) $(7x^0)^4 \div 49x^2$ (h) $(5x)^0 \div 8x^{-4}$

(i) $3x^{-2} \times 7x^5$ (j) $x^{\frac{2}{3}}y^{\frac{3}{4}} \div x^{\frac{1}{3}}y^{\frac{1}{2}}$

(k) $(x^{\frac{1}{3}}y^2)^3 \div (x^{\frac{1}{3}}y^{\frac{3}{4}})^2$

(l) $(2x^3y^{\frac{1}{2}})^3 \div 4x^2y^{\frac{1}{2}}$

2. Find the value of each of the following without using a calculator.

(a) 3^{-2} (b) $4^{1.5}$

(c) $64^{-\frac{2}{3}}$ (d) $9^{-2.5}$

(e) $\frac{1}{5^0}$ (f) $625^{\frac{3}{4}}$

(g) $\left(\frac{3}{4}\right)^{-3}$ (h) $8^{-\frac{4}{3}}$

(i) $\frac{1}{27^{-\frac{2}{3}}}$ (j) $\frac{1}{36^{\frac{3}{2}}}$

(k) $\frac{2}{8^{-\frac{1}{3}}}$ (l) $\frac{5}{2^5}$

(m) $\frac{26}{2^{-4}}$ (n) $\frac{9}{4^0}$

(o) $27^{\frac{2}{3}} \times \left(\frac{1}{8}\right)^{\frac{1}{3}}$ (p) $\frac{2^0 - 2^{-1}}{4 - 3(4)^{-1}}$

(q) $\frac{8^2 + (4)^3}{7^0 - 3^{-1}}$ (r) $\frac{3^{-2} - 5 \times 2^0}{6^{-1} + 2 \div 4^{-1}}$

3. (a) Given that $(2^{42} - 2^{43})(2^1 - 2^2) = 2^{2x}$, find the value of x.

(b) Given that $3 \times 9^{k+1} = 27$, find the value of k.

(c) Show that $3^{n+2} - 3^n$ is divisible by 2^3 for all whole numbers n.

4. Express each of the following as a fraction in its simplest form.

(a) $\frac{x}{2} + \frac{5x}{7}$ (b) $\frac{x-2}{3} - \frac{2x-5}{4}$

(c) $\frac{x+7}{5} + \frac{3-x}{4}$ (d) $\frac{3}{4} + \frac{x-3}{2x}$

(e) $3 - \frac{x-2}{2x-3}$ (f) $\frac{2a}{5a-1} + \frac{2}{5}$

(g) $\frac{2}{x-1} + \frac{3}{x+2}$ (h) $\frac{5}{x+1} - \frac{3}{2x-1}$

(i) $\frac{4}{3a-1} - \frac{3}{2a-3}$ (j) $\frac{a}{1-2a} + \frac{3}{4+a}$

(k) $\frac{x}{x+1} - \frac{5}{x-2}$ (l) $\frac{3x}{x-3} + \frac{2}{x+4}$

(m) $\frac{5p}{p-3} - \frac{4}{p+1}$ (n) $\frac{1}{2a-3} + \frac{a}{a+1}$

(o) $\frac{2}{x-y} - \frac{3}{x}$ (p) $\frac{5x}{2x-y} + \frac{y}{3x-y}$

5. Solve the following equations.

(a) $(x-5)(x+14) = 0$

(b) $(x-12)(x+13) = 0$

(c) $(12-3x)(14-2x) = 0$

(d) $(7-3x)(23-2x) = 0$

(e) $x^2 + 4x - 21 = 0$

(f) $x^2 - 8x + 15 = 0$

(g) $x^2 - 19x + 48 = 0$

(h) $x^2 - 32x + 175 = 0$

(i) $7 - 8x + x^2 = 0$

(j) $9x + x^2 + 20 = 0$

(k) $2x^2 - 9x + 4 = 0$

(l) $3x^2 - 10x + 3 = 0$

(m) $4x^2 + 7x - 2 = 0$

(n) $5x^2 + 26x + 5 = 0$

(o) $6x^2 - 17x + 12 = 0$

(p) $9x^2 - 17x - 2 = 0$

6. Evaluate (a) $\left(\frac{3}{4}\right)^{-2}$ and

(b) $16^{-\frac{3}{4}} + \left(\frac{1}{27}\right)^{\frac{2}{3}}$

7. Solve the following equations.

(a) $5^x - 25^{3x-1} = 0$

(b) $3^{2x} - 27^{x+1} = 0$

(c) $16^{3x+1} = 32^{1-x}$

8. Solve the following equations:

(a) $25^{x-4} = 0.2$

(b) $\sqrt{3} \times \sqrt[x]{9} = \frac{1}{27}$

(c) $49^{x-1} \div \sqrt{7} = \frac{1}{343}$

(d) $9^{x+4} = 2^6 \div 4^3$

(e) $(3x-4)^3 - \frac{1}{8} = 0$

(f) $25^{x+3} \div 125^{x-4} = 0.04$

9. Make the letter in the brackets the subject of the formula below.

(a) $ax^2 + bx + c = 0$ (b)

(b) $t = \frac{\pi}{4}\sqrt{\frac{2l}{g}}$ (l)

(c) $\frac{1}{a} + \frac{b}{2} + \frac{3}{c} = k$ (c)

(d) $\sqrt{4x^2 - 5k} = 2x + 3$ (x)

(e) $v^2 = u^2 + 2as$ (u)

(f) $x = \sqrt[3]{\frac{a}{b-a}}$ (a)

10. Simplify each of the following:

(a) $\frac{1}{1-x} + \frac{2}{1+x} + \frac{2x}{x^2-1}$

(b) $\frac{3}{x+2} - \frac{x-5}{x^2-4} + \frac{1}{x-2}$

(c) $\frac{1}{2x-3} - \frac{2}{x+2} - \frac{2x-x^2}{2x^2+x-6}$

(d) $\frac{5}{x-2} - \frac{3x+x^2}{x^2-x-2} + \frac{x}{x+1}$

11. Given that $y = \sqrt{2x - a}$,

(a) find the value of y when $x = 4$ and $a = -1$,

(b) express x in terms of a and y.

12. Given that $y^2 = 2k(x + 1)$,

(a) find the two possible values of y when $k = \frac{1}{16}$ and $x = 3$,

(b) express k in terms of x and y.

13. Given that $y + 2 = \frac{3y + k}{a}$, express y in terms of a and k.

14. Given that $x = 2t - 1$ and $y = \frac{2}{3}t + 2$,

(a) express $3x - y + 2$ in terms of t,

(b) find the value of t, x and y when $3x - y + 2 = 0$.

15. Given that $a = 3x + 7$ and $b = 2x - 5$,

(a) express $2a + 3b + 1$ in terms of x,

(b) find the value of x, a and b when $2a + 3b + 1 = 3$.

16. Given that $a = 3t - 1$ and $b = 2t^2 + 3$,

(a) find the value of a and of b when $t = -4$,

(b) express $2a + 3b + 7$ in terms of t.

17. Given that $y = \frac{1-x}{1+x}$,

(a) find the value of y when $x = -4$, giving your answer as a fraction in its lowest terms,

(b) express x in terms of y.

18. Given that $\frac{3a + b}{2a - b} = \frac{2}{5}$, express a in terms of b.

19. Given that $\frac{3}{a} = \frac{2}{b} + \frac{1}{c}$, express b in terms of a and c.

Algebra 3: Inequalities

Example 1

Find the integer values of x for which $x - 3 \leqslant 7$ and $4x - 5 > 22$.

$x - 3 \leqslant 7$
$\therefore \quad x \leqslant 7 + 3$
i.e. $x \leqslant 10$

$4x - 5 > 22$
$\therefore \quad 4x > 22 + 5$
i.e. $4x > 27$
$x > \frac{27}{4}$
i.e. $x > 6\frac{3}{4}$

The integer values satisfying $x \leqslant 10$ and $x > 6\frac{3}{4}$ are 7, 8, 9 and 10.

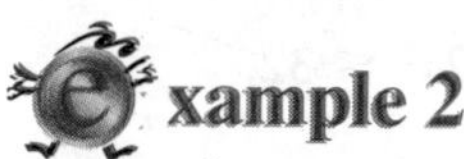

Example 2

Given that x and y are integers such that $-8 \leqslant x \leqslant 4$ and $-2 \leqslant y \leqslant 3$.
Calculate

(a) the greatest value of $x - y$,

(b) the least value of $2x + y^2$,

(c) the greatest value of xy,

(d) the least value of $\frac{x}{y}$.

(a) the greatest value of $x - y = 4 - (-2) = 6$

(b) the least value of $2x + y^2 = 2(-8) + 0^2 = -16$

(c) the greatest value of $xy = (-8) \times (-2) = 16$

(d) the least value of $\frac{x}{y} = \frac{-8}{1} = -8$

1. Given that $-2 \leqslant x \leqslant 7$, write down
   (a) the largest integer value of x,
   (b) the smallest integer value of x,
   (c) the largest prime number in the given range.

2. List the integer value of x for which $-5 < 12 - 3x < -1$.

3. List the integer value of a for which $2a + 1 < 14 \leqslant 5a - 2$.

4. List the possible values of (x, y) for which x and y are positive integers such that $x + y = 3$.

5. Given that $1 \leqslant x \leqslant 5$ and $-1 \leqslant y \leqslant 7$, find
   (a) the greatest possible value of $2x - y$,
   (b) the least possible value of $2xy$,
   (c) the greatest possible value of $\frac{y}{x}$.

6. Solve the following inequalities:
   (a) $9x - 7 \leqslant 12$
   (b) $7 - 2x > 2$
   (c) $3 + 5x \geqslant 32$
   (d) $3x - 4 \geqslant \frac{1}{3}x - 2$

7. Find the odd integer values of x for which $x - 5 \leqslant 7$ and $3x - 2 \geqslant 11$.

8. It is given that $-1 \leqslant x \leqslant 6$, $2 \leqslant y \leqslant 13$ and $0.1 \leqslant z \leqslant 2$. Calculate
   (a) the smallest possible value of $x + y + z$,
   (b) the largest possible value of $y - 2x^2$,
   (c) the largest possible value of $\frac{x}{z}$,
   (d) the least possible value of $x^2 - \frac{y}{z}$.

9. The sides of a rectangle are given as x cm and y cm where $8.5 \leqslant x \leqslant 9.5$ and $5.5 \leqslant y \leqslant 6.5$. Calculate
   (a) the smallest possible value of the perimeter of the rectangle,
   (b) the largest possible value of the area of the rectangle.

10. Find the integer values of x for which $12 < 3x - 1 < 27$.

11. Find the integer values of x which satisfy all the conditions below.
    $3x + 15 \geqslant 0$, $x \neq -4$, $x < -1$

12. (a) Find the smallest prime number x such that $5x - 1 > 58$.
    (b) Find the largest integer k for which $4k - 3 < 24$.
    (c) Solve the inequality $2x^2 \leqslant 32$.

13. Given that $-5 \leqslant 4x + 1 \leqslant 2x + 9$ and $-6 \leqslant 2y - 2 \leqslant 8$, find
    (a) the greatest value of $x - y$,
    (b) the smallest value of $(x + y)(x - y)$.

14. A woman buys x oranges at 50 cents each and $(2x + 1)$ pineapples at \$1.20 each. If she wishes to spend not more than \$25 on these produce,
    (a) form an inequality in x and
    (b) find the largest number of x.

15. Given that $3 \leqslant x \leqslant 5$ and $-1 \leqslant y \leqslant 3$, find the smallest value of
    (a) $\frac{1}{x} + y$,
    (b) $\frac{y^2}{x} + xy$

Algebra 4: Quadratic Equations

xample 1

The figure shows the lengths of the sides of a right-angled triangle ABC. Given that BC = (x + 1) cm, AB = (x + 2) cm and AC = (2x + 2) cm, form an equation in x. Solve this equation for values of x correct to 2 decimal places. Hence or otherwise, find the perimeter and area of △ABC.

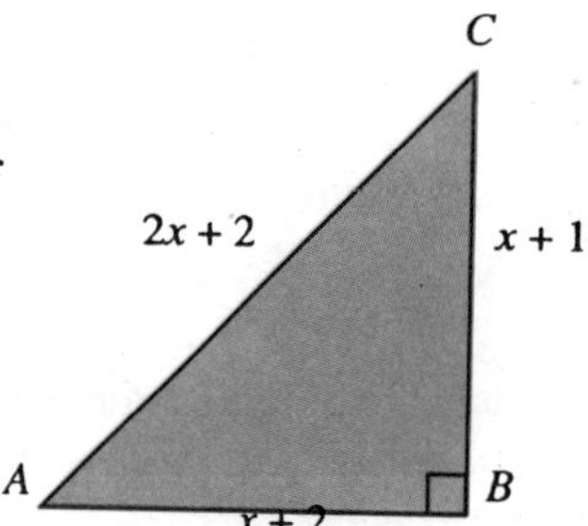

$$(x+1)^2 + (x+2)^2 = (2x+2)^2$$

$$x^2 + 2x + 1 + x^2 + 4x + 4 = 4x^2 + 8x + 4$$

$$2x^2 + 2x - 1 = 0$$

$$x = \frac{-b \pm \sqrt{b^2 - 4ac}}{2a}$$

$$= \frac{-2 \pm \sqrt{2^2 - 4(2)(-1)}}{2(2)}$$

$$= \frac{-2 \pm \sqrt{12}}{4}$$

$$= 0.37 \quad \text{or} \quad -1.37 \quad \text{(correct to 2 decimal places)}$$

$$\therefore \quad x = 0.37 \text{ (since } BC > 0)$$

Hence $AB = 2.37$ cm, $BC = 1.37$ cm and $AC = 2.74$ cm.

The perimeter of $\triangle ABC = 2.37 + 1.37 + 2.74 = 6.48$ cm.

The area of $\triangle ABC = \frac{1}{2}(1.37)(2.37) = 1.62 \text{ cm}^2$.

Example 2

A man walked a distance of 25 km from P to Q, at an average speed of v km/h. Write down an expression for the time, in hours, he took for the journey from P to Q.

He returned by the same route but his average speed was 2 km/h less. Write down an expression for the time, in hours, he took for the journey from Q to P.

Given that the difference between these two times was 35 minutes, form an equation in v and show that it reduces to $7v^2 - 14v - 600 = 0$.

Solve the above equation correct to 2 decimal places. Hence find the time taken for the man to walk from Q to P, giving your answer correct to the nearest minute.

Time taken for the journey from P to $Q = \dfrac{25}{v}$ h

Time taken for the journey form Q to $P = \dfrac{25}{v - 2}$ h

We have $\dfrac{25}{v - 2} - \dfrac{25}{v} = \dfrac{35}{60}$

$$\frac{25v - 25(v - 2)}{v(v - 2)} = \frac{7}{12}$$

$$7v(v - 2) = 12(25v - 25v + 50)$$

$$\therefore \quad 7v^2 - 14v - 600 = 0$$

$$v = \frac{-(-14) \pm \sqrt{(14)^2 - 4(7)(-600)}}{2(7)}$$

$$= 10.31 \text{ or } -8.31 \quad \text{(Not applicable)}$$

$\therefore$ The average speed the man walked from Q to P was $(10.31 - 2)$ km/h, i.e 8.31 km/h and the time taken was $\dfrac{25}{8.31}$ h $= 3.008$ h
$= 3$ h 1 min

Note: Make sure the units are the same.

1. Solve the following equations, giving your answers correct to 2 decimal places where necessary.

   (a) $2x - 7 = \frac{2}{x}$

   (b) $x + 2 = \frac{3}{5 - 3x}$

   (c) $4x - 7 = \frac{2}{x - 1}$

   (d) $3x - 2 = \frac{1}{x - 1}$

   (e) $x + 2 = \frac{4}{4 - 3x}$

   (f) $\frac{x}{x + 1} = \frac{4}{3x + 2}$

2. The diagonal of a rectangle exceeds its length by 4 cm and its width by 6.4 cm. Find the length of the diagonal.

3. If the side of a cube is increased by 2 cm, its volume will be increased by 54 cm^3. Find the original length of the cube.

4. The length of a page of a book is 3.4 cm more than the width and the area is 125 cm^2. If the width is x cm, form an equation in x and hence, find the length in centimetres, giving your answer correct to 2 decimal places.

5. A stone is thrown down from a high building, and the formula $d = 7t + 5t^2$ gives the distance, d m, that it has fallen after t seconds. How long does it take to reach a distance of 100 m?

6. The area of a rectangular picture is 156 cm^2 and the width is 2.4 cm less than the length. Find the perimeter of the picture, giving your answer correct to 2 decimal places.

7. A man swims at a speed of 50 m/min in still water, swims 100 m *against* the current and 100 m *with* the current. If the difference between the two times is 3 min 45 s, find the speed of the current.

8. Two trains A and B travel between two stations 80 km apart. If train A travels at an average speed of 5 km/h faster than train B and completes the journey 20 minutes earlier, find the average speeds of the two trains.

9. Two numbers differ by 5 and the sum of their reciprocals is $\frac{13}{36}$. Find the numbers.

10. The numerator of a fraction is 2 less than the denominator. When both numerator and denominator are increased by 3, the fraction is increased by $\frac{3}{20}$. Find the original fraction.

11. A motorist makes a journey of 380 km from Singapore to Kuala Lumpur, at an average speed of x km/h. Write down an expression for the number of hours taken for the journey. On his return journey from Kuala Lumpur to Singapore, his average speed for the journey is reduced by 5 km/h due to heavy traffic along the stretch of road from Ayer Hitam to Kulai. Write down an expression for the number of hours taken for the journey.

    If the return journey takes 25 minutes longer, form an equation in x and solve it. Hence, find the average speed for each journey.

12. A water tank is filled by two pipes in 48 minutes. If the larger pipe alone can fill it in 40 minutes less time than the smaller pipe, find the time it takes for the smaller pipe to fill the tank alone.

13. A curve has equation $x^2 + y^2 + 8x - 16y + 15 = 0$. Find the coordinates of the points where the curve cuts

(a) the x-axis,

(b) the y-axis.

14. In the diagram, the circle with centre B has radius 1 cm. The semicircle with centre A and the semi-circle with centre C are identical and each has radius r cm. O is the centre of the larger semicircle.

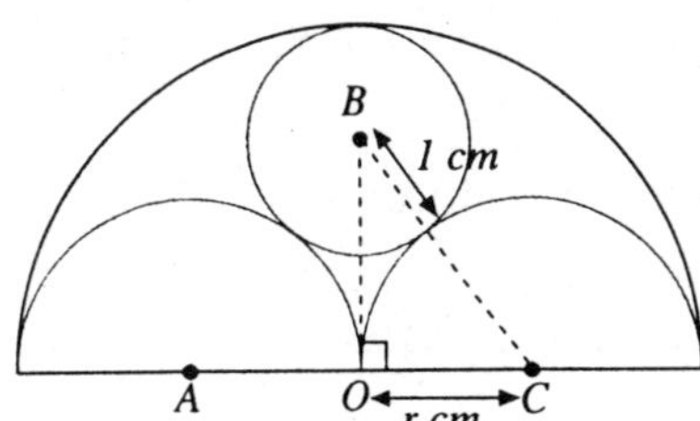

(a) Write an expression for BO in terms of r.

(b) Using Pythagoras' theorem, form an equation in r and show that it reduces to $2r^2 - 3r = 0$.

(c) Solve the equation to find the radius of the larger semicircle.

15. A book publisher produced a book at a selling price of \$5.80 per copy. The publisher agreed to pay the author 8% of the selling price of the first 2000 copies sold, 10% of the selling price of the next 2000 copies and 12% of the selling price of the remaining copies sold.

(a) If 6435 copies were sold, calculate the amount the author received.

(b) If the production cost together with the author's royalties amounted to \$28 400, calculate correct to 3 significant figures, the percentage profit made by the publisher.

(c) The publisher exports the book to a Malaysian distributor at RM7.20 per copy.
For the export sales, the publisher pays the author a flat rate of 5% of the sales receipt. If the publisher exports 2840 books to Malaysia, calculate the amount in Singapore dollars that

(i) the publisher will receive if the exchange rate is RM100 = S\$62.80

(ii) the author will receive if the exchange rate is S\$100 = RM158.

16. A night train leaves Singapore for Segamat and returns to Singapore.

(a) If the train leaves Singapore at 22 30 and arrives at Segamat at 04 15 the next morning, find the time taken for the journey.

(b) The fare for an adult ticket from Segamat to Singapore is RM22.40 and the child fare is RM12.60. On a certain journey, there are 250 adult and 80 child passengers. Calculate the total amount of fares collected in RM. Given that the exchange rate is S\$100 = RM228.50, calculate the total amount of fares collected for the above trip in S\$, giving your answer correct to the nearest 10 cents.

(c) The distance between Singapore and Segamat is 200 km.

(i) If the train travels from Singapore to Segamat at an average speed of x km/h, write down an expression for the time taken, in hours, for the journey.

(ii) On the return trip from Segamat to Singapore, the train increases its speed by 5 km/h. Write down an expression for the time taken.

(iii) If the difference in time between the two journeys is 1 hour 15 minutes, form an equation in x and show that it reduces to $x^2 + 5x - 800 = 0$.

(iv) Solve the equation $x^2 + 5x - 800 = 0$ and hence, find the speed of the train from Segamat to Singapore.

Measuration (2-Dimensional Problems)

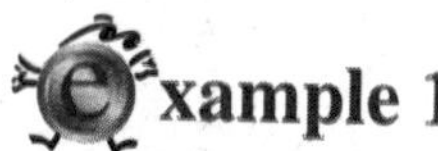

Example 1

The figure shows a circular pattern of radius 21 cm, O is the centre of the circle. AD, BC and PQ are diameters of the circle. $A\hat{O}P = 60°$ and $B\hat{O}Q = 30°$.

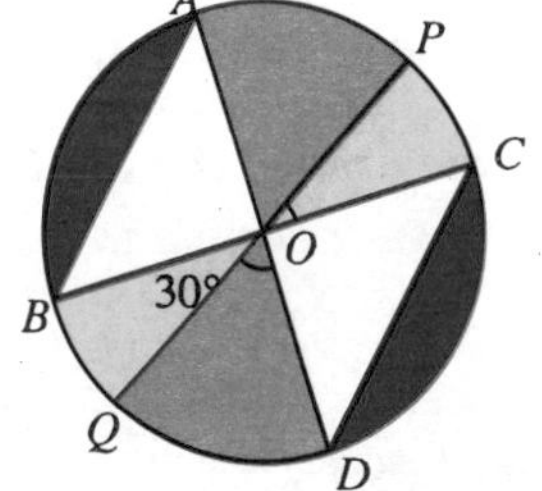

(a) Calculate
- *(i) the length of the arc of a blue sector,*
- *(ii) the area of a blue sector,*
- *(iii) the area of a red segment.*

(b) Given that the circular pattern is the top face of a cake of thickness 4 cm, calculate the volume of a yellow slice.
(Take π to be 3.142)

(a) (i) Length of arc of a blue sector = $\frac{60°}{360°} \times 2 \times 3.142 \times 21 = 21.994$ cm

(ii) Area of blue sector = $\frac{60°}{360°} \times 3.142 \times 21^2 = 230.937$ cm^2

(iii) $A\hat{O}B = 180° - 60° - 30° = 90°$

Area of sector $AOB = \frac{90°}{360°} \times 3.142 \times 21^2 = 346.4055$ cm^2

Area of $\triangle AOB = \frac{1}{2} \times 21 \times 21 = 220.5$ cm^2

$\therefore$ Area of a red segment = $346.4055 - 220.5 = 125.9055$ cm^2

(b) Area of a yellow sector = $\frac{30°}{360°} \times 3.142 \times 21^2 = 115.4685$ cm^2

$\therefore$ the volume of a yellow slice = $115.4685 \times 4 = 461.874$ cm^3

Example 2

In the diagram, OPQ is a sector of a circle with centre O and radius 10 cm. Given that the arc PQ = 8 cm and OR = 15 cm, find

(a) the angle POQ in radian,

(b) the length of PR, giving your answer correct to 2 decimal places,

(c) the area of the shaded region PQR, giving your answer correct to 3 significant figures.

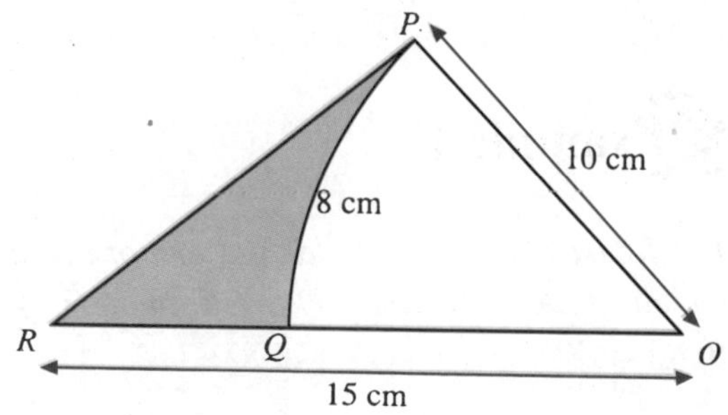

(a) $P\hat{O}Q = \frac{s}{r} = \frac{8 \text{ cm}}{10 \text{ cm}} = 0.8$ radian

(b) $PR = \sqrt{10^2 + 15^2 - 2\,(10)\,(15)\cos 0.8}$

$= 10.77$ cm (correct to 2 decimal places)

(c) Area of shaded region = area of $\triangle ABC$ – area of sector POQ

$= \frac{1}{2}(10)(15)\sin 0.8 - \frac{1}{2}(10)^2(0.8)$

$= 13.8 \text{ cm}^2$ (correct to 3 sig. fig.)

1. In the figure, the area of the shaded sector POQ is $\frac{3}{20}$ of the area of the whole circle.

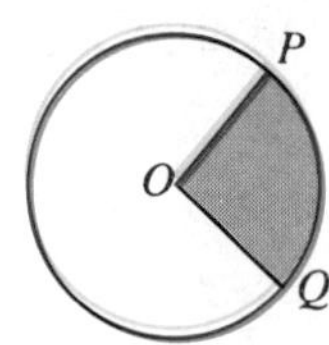

(a) Calculate $P\hat{O}Q$.

(b) Given that the area of the circle is 616 cm², calculate the

(i) radius of the circle,

(ii) area of the shaded sector POQ.

2. (a) The radius of the chain wheel of a bicycle is 7 cm. Given that the portion of chain in contact with the wheel is of length 11 cm, calculate the angle subtended at the centre of the wheel by this portion of chain.

(b) The figure below shows a sector of a circle of radius 14 cm. Find its perimeter and area.

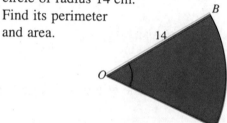

3. The square $ABCD$ is inscribed in the circle of radius 8 cm. Calculate the following to the nearest cm², taking π to be 3.142:
   (a) The area of the circle.
   (b) The area of the shaded portion.

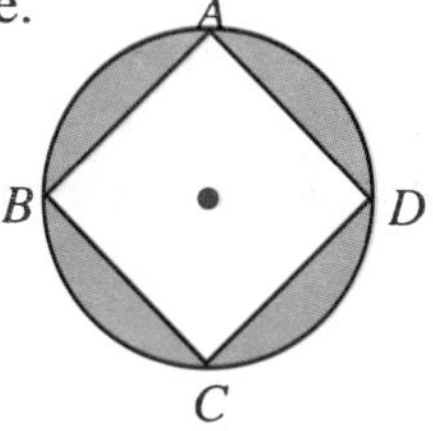

4. The diagram shows the top face of a concrete logo of a firm. It consists of a quadrant $OABC$ with a blue segment ABC and a red sector OAD of a circle of radius 64 cm. The red sector has an angle of 120° at the centre of the circle.

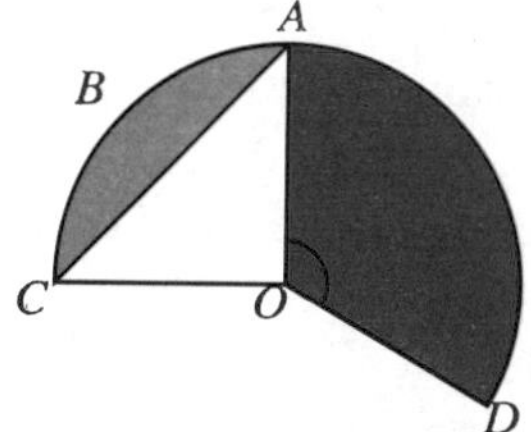

   (a) Calculate
      (i) the length of the arc of the red sector,
      (ii) the area of the red sector,
      (iii) the area of the blue segment.
   (b) Given that the logo has a uniform thickness of 5 cm, find the volume of concrete used. (Take π to be 3.142.)

5. The length of the minor arc and the length of the major arc of a circle are 7π cm and 15π cm respectively. Find, taking $\pi = 3.142$,
   (a) the radius of the circle,
   (b) the area (shaded region) enclosed by the minor arc and the radii.

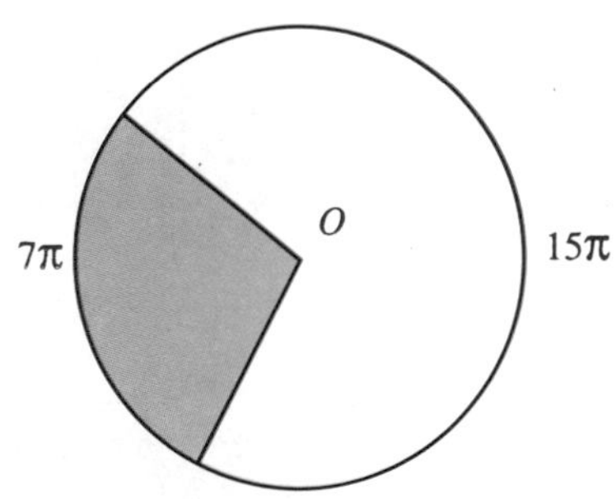

6. In the diagram, OPQ is a sector of a circle with centre O and radius 5 cm. Given that $P\hat{O}Q = 50°$, calculate
   (a) the perimeter of the sector;
   (b) the area of the sector;
   (c) the area of $\triangle OPQ$. (Take π to be 3.142.)

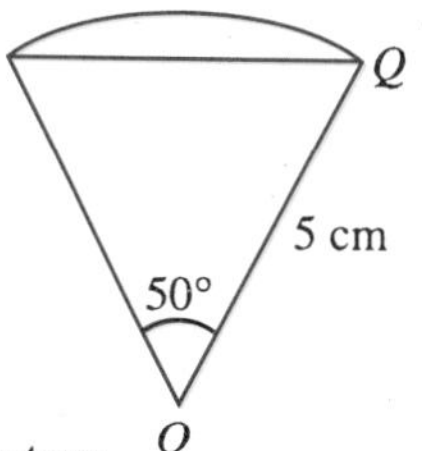

7. The bull's eye, **X**, and the shaded outer ring, **R**, of a target are formed by two concentric circles of radius 3 cm and 9 cm.
   (a) Express, in terms of π, the area of **X**.
   (b) Find the numerical value of the ratio $\frac{\text{area of } R}{\text{area of } X}$.

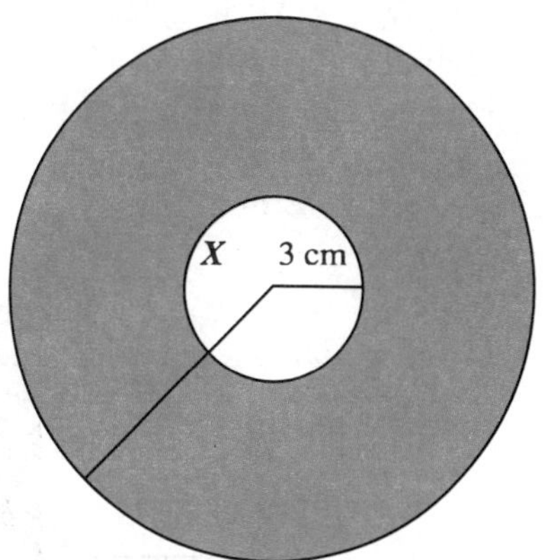

8. In the diagram below, POQ is the sector of a circle, with centre O and radius 7 cm. Given that $R\hat{P}O = 60°$, $P\hat{O}Q = 120°$ and $P\hat{O}R = 90°$, calculate
   (a) OR;
   (b) PR;
   (c) the area of sector POQ.

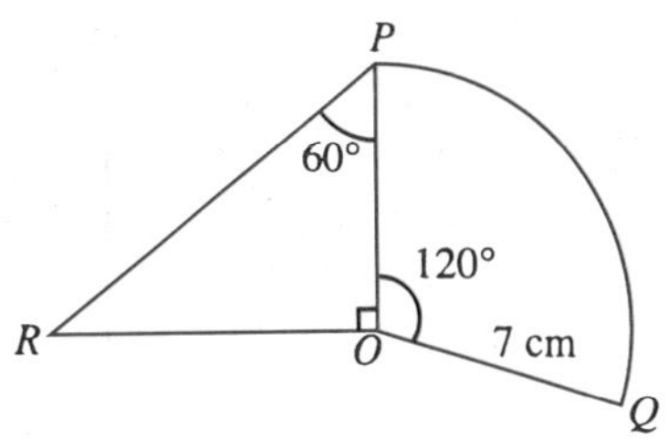

9. The windscreen wiper of a car sweeps through an angle of 120°. The shaded region in the given diagram represents the area of the windscreen swept by the wiper. Given that $OQ = PQ = 7$ cm, find the area of the windscreen that has been swept. (Take π to be 3.142.)

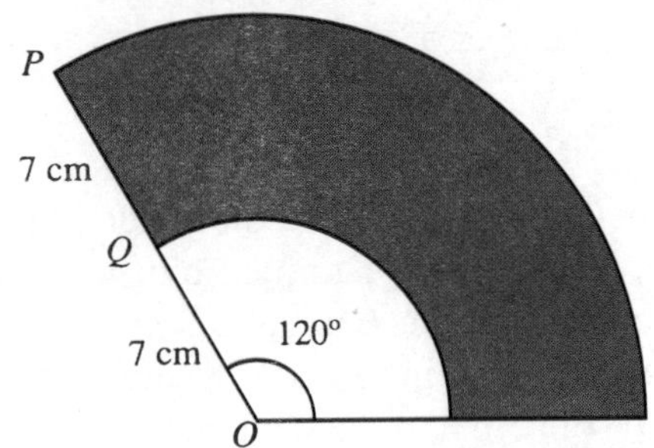

10. In the diagram, OAB is a sector of a circle centre O and radius 8.5 cm, K is a point on OA such that $KA = 3$ cm and the length of the arc $AB = 7$ cm. Calculate
 (a) the angle AOB in radian;
 (b) the length of BK;
 (c) the area of the shaded region.

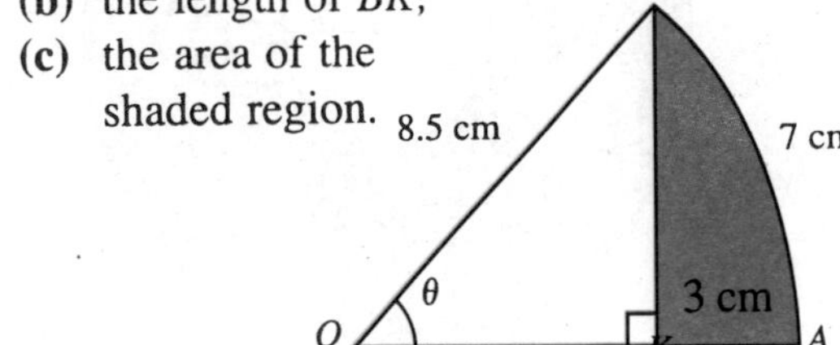

11. The figure shows the sector OAB with centre at O. The shaded crescent is obtained by drawing a semicircle ACB of diameter AB. Given that $OA = 1.8$ cm and angle $AOB = 2.2$ radians, calculate, correct to 3 significant figures,
 (a) the perimeter and
 (b) the area of the shaded crescent.

A
1.8 cm
O
2.2 rad
C
B

12. The diagram shows a framework made from a length of wire bent into the shape of a sector of a circle of radius r and angle θ radians.
 (a) Express in terms of r and θ,
  (i) the length of the wire,
  (ii) the area, A, of the sector.
 (b) It is given that the length of the wire is 3 metres, find the area A in terms of r and hence, find the value of θ when $A = 0.45$ m^2.

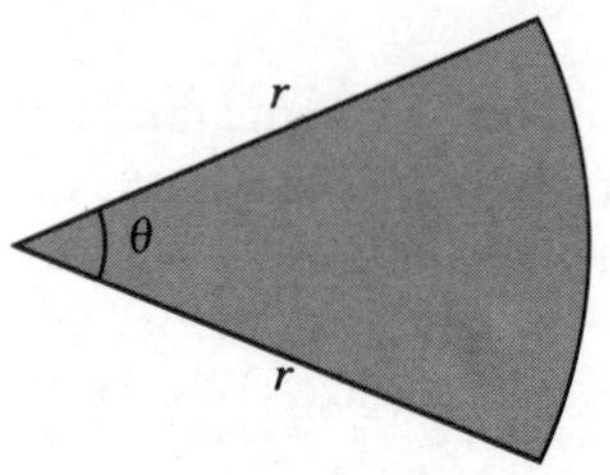

13. The diagram shows an arc PQ of a circle, centre O, radius 12 cm and an arc RS of a circle, centre O, radius 15 cm. The angle POQ is 1.2 radians.
 Calculate
 (a) the length of the perimeter of the region B,
 (b) the difference between the areas of the regions A and B.

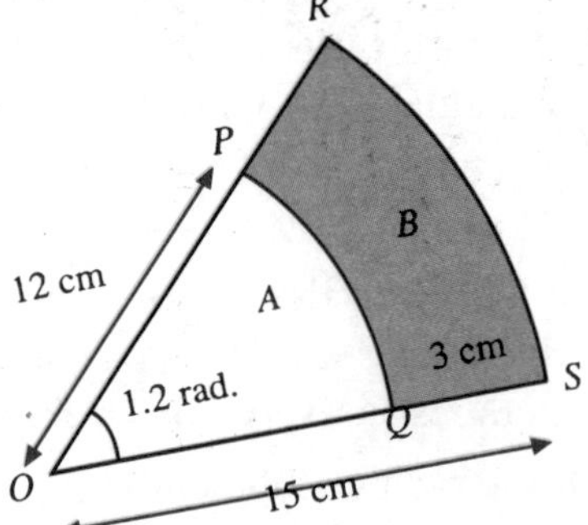

Mensuration (3-Dimensional Problems)

Example 1

A solid is cylindrical with hemispherical ends as shown in the figure. The height of the cylinder is 56 cm and the area of its base is 1386 cm²^{2}.

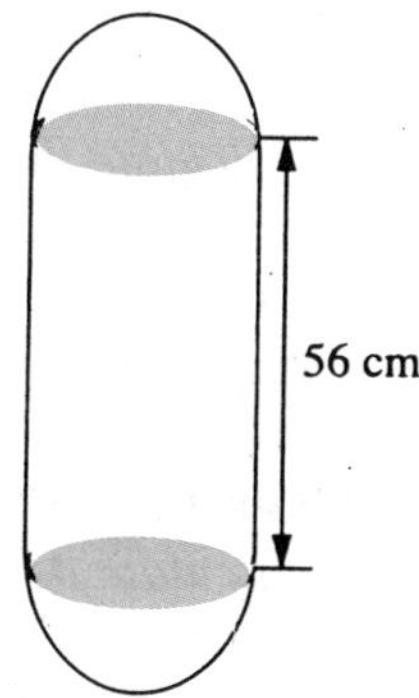

(a) Calculate the volume of the cylinder.
(b) Calculate the radius of the base of the cylinder.
(c) Calculate the volume of the solid.
(d) Given that the solid is made from material of density 0.05 g/cm^3, calculate its mass.
(e) Calculate the total surface area of the solid.
(f) Given that the solid is melted down and made into a cone having a base radius of 28 cm, calculate the height of the cone.
(Take π to be 3.142 and corect all your answers to the nearest whole number.)

(a) Volume of the cylinder = area of base × height = $1386 \times 56 = 77\,616$ cm^3

(b) Let r be the radius of the base of the cylinder.
Area of base = πr^2

i.e. $\pi r^2 = 1386$

$$r^2 = \frac{1386}{3.142}$$

$$\therefore \quad r = \sqrt{\frac{1386}{3.142}} \approx 21 \text{ cm}$$

(c) Volume of the two hemispheres = volume of a sphere = $\frac{4}{3} \times 3.142 \times 21^3 \approx 38\,797$ cm^3
∴ the volume of the solid = $77\,616 + 38\,797 = 116\,413$ cm^3

(d) The mass of the solid = $116\,413 \times 0.05 \approx 5821$ g

(e) The curved surface area of the cylinder = $2 \times 3.142 \times 21 \times 56 \approx 7390$ cm^2
The surface area of a sphere of radius 21 cm = $4 \times 3.142 \times 21^2 \approx 5542$ cm^2
∴ the total surface area of the solid = $7390 + 5542 = 12\,932$ cm^2

(f) Let h be the height of the cone.

Volume of the cone = $\frac{1}{3} \times \pi \times (28)^2 \times h$

i.e. $\frac{1}{3} \times 3.142 \times 28^2 \times h = 116\,413$

$$h = \frac{116\,413 \times 3}{3.142 \times 28^2} \approx 142 \text{ cm}$$

Example 2

A model consists of a solid cuboid attached to a solid pyramid as shown in the diagram. The height of the cuboid is 24 cm and the area of its base is 96 cm^2.

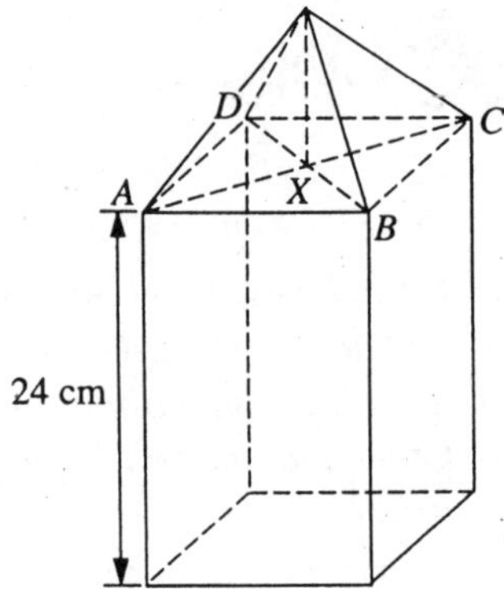

(a) Calculate the volume of the cuboid.

(b) Given that the volume of the pyramid is 144 cm^3, calculate the height of the pyramid.

(c) Given that the model is made from material of density 0.5 g/cm^3, calculate its mass.

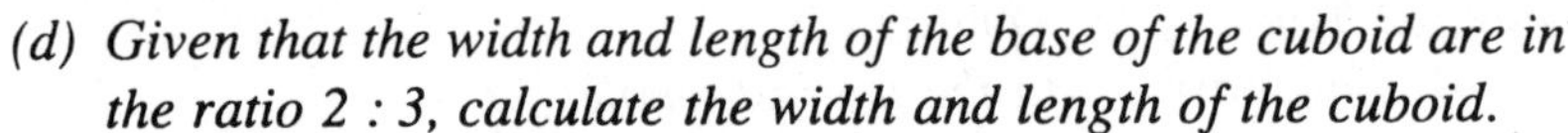

(d) Given that the width and length of the base of the cuboid are in the ratio 2 : 3, calculate the width and length of the cuboid.

(a) The volume of the cuboid = base area × height = 96 × 24 = 2304 cm^3

(b) The volume of the pyramid = $\frac{1}{3}$ × base area × height

i.e. $\frac{1}{3} \times 96 \times \text{height} = 144$

$\therefore$ height = $\frac{144 \times 3}{96}$ = 4.5 cm

(c) The volume of model = volume of the cuboid + volume of the pyramid
= 2304 + 144
= 2448 cm^3

The mass of the model = 2448 × 0.5 = 1224 g

(d) Let the width of the base = $2x$
$\therefore$ the length of the base = $3x$

Area of the base = $2x \times 3x = 6x^2$
i.e. $6x^2 = 96$
$x^2 = 16$
$\therefore$ $x = 4$ ($x = -4$ not applicable here)

$\therefore$ the width of the base = 8 cm and the length of the base = 12 cm.

1. **(a)** Find the volume of a pyramid with height 5 cm and square base of sides 2 cm each.
   (b) If the volume of sphere of radius r is $\frac{4\pi r^3}{3}$, find the volume of another sphere of radius $\frac{r}{4}$.

2. A hollow sphere is made of metal 1.5 cm thick and has an external diameter of 22 cm. Calculate the volume of metal used to make the hollow sphere. If the metal weighs 10.7 g/cm^3, calculate the mass of the sphere. (Take $\pi = 3.142$)

3. A right pyramid has a square base of sides 4 cm each and height 8 cm. Calculate
   (a) its volume,
   (b) $\angle VAN$.

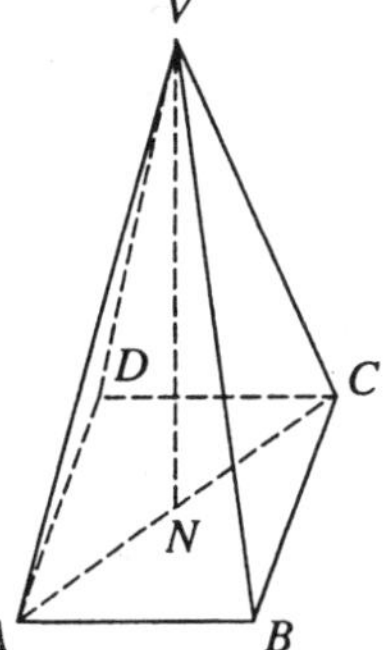

4. A quarter of a sphere of radius 7 cm is removed, with the remaining figure as shown in the diagram below. Taking $\pi = 3.142$, find the total surface area of the figure.

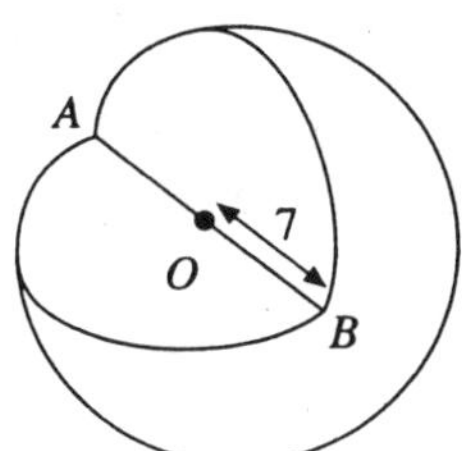

5. **(a)** A solid cylinder with base diameter of 14 cm, has a height of 20 cm. It is made of iron and has a mass of 7 g per cm^3. Find
   (i) the area of its curved surface;
   (ii) its mass.
   (b) The lower part of a toy is a hemisphere of radius 3.5 cm and its upper part is a cone of the same radius and a height of 10 cm. Find its volume.
   (c) A conical monument is 16 m high and has a base diameter of 24 m. How many litres of paint will be required to paint the monument if 1 litre of paint is needed for an area of 100 m^2?

6. The diagram represents a prism in which each cross-section of the prism is a sector of a circle of radius 7 cm, with angle at centre equal to 45°. Two cross-sections are *OAB* and *PQR* where *A*, *B*, *Q*, *R* lie on the curved surface of the prism. The cross-sections *OAB* and *PQR* are horizontal and 8 cm apart. The vertical planes *OAQP* and *OBRP* are rectangular.

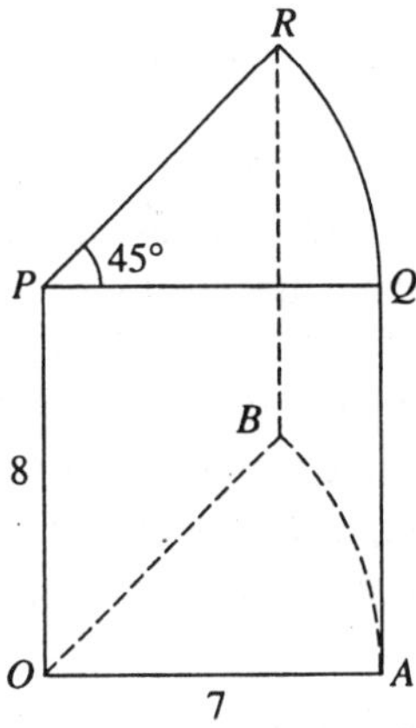

Calculate, taking $\pi = 3.142$,
(a) the length of the arc *AB*,
(b) the area of sector *PQR*,
(c) the volume of the prism,
(d) the total surface area of the prism.

7. Calculate the volume of each of the following figures

(a) (b)

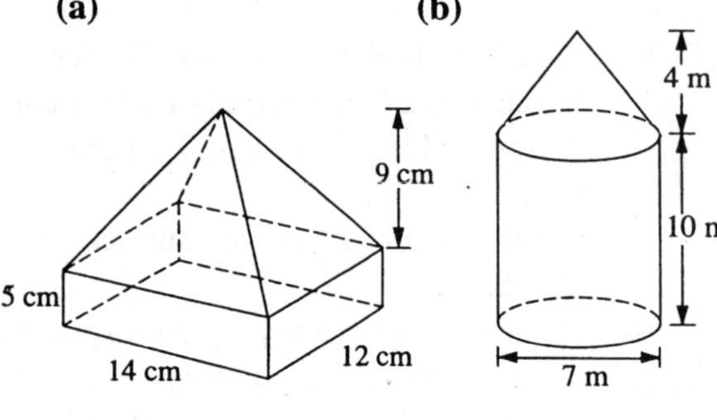

(c) (d)

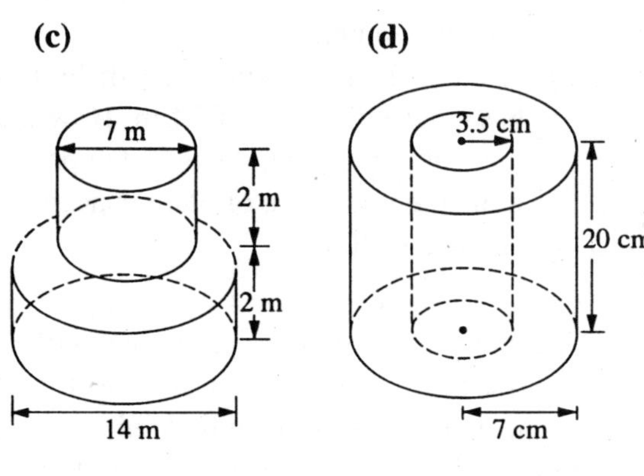

8. A solid metal cylinder A has a volume of 176 cm^3.

(a) Calculate the volume of another cylinder B which has the same height as the cylinder A but a base radius three times that of A.

(b) Given that the cylinder A is melted and made into a cone of height 3.5 cm, calculate the radius of the base of the cone.

(c) Given that the cylinder B is melted and made into a pyramid with the area of its base equal to 528 cm^2, calculate the height of the pyramid.

9. The diagram below shows a container made of metal sheets and closed at both ends. Both the base $PQVU$ and the top $SRWT$ are horizontal and rectangular. Each of the vertical sides $PQRS$ and $UVWT$ is a trapezium. The two sloping ends $SPUT$ and $RQVW$ are rectangular and are inclined at the same angle to the horizontal. $SR = TW = 2$ m, $PQ = UV = 1.5$ m, $ST = RW = PU = QV = 1.2$ m and the perpendicular height of $SRWT$ above the base is 1.2 m.

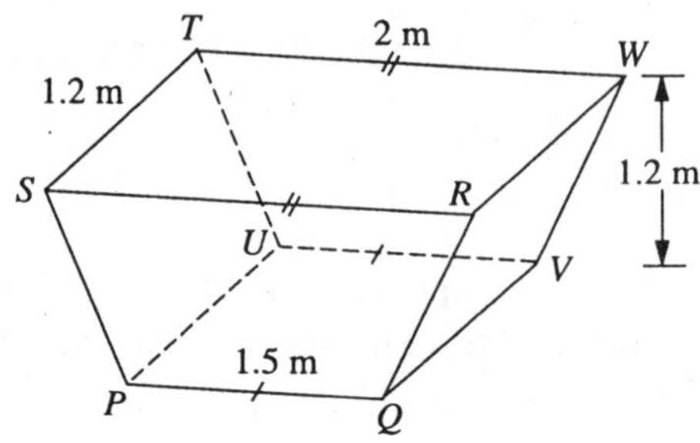

(a) Calculate

(i) the cross-sectional area $PQRS$,

(ii) the mass of the container in kg, correct to 1 decimal place, given that the metal sheet weighs 30 kg per square metre.

(b) The container is completely filled with paint. Find the volume of paint in the container in m^3.

(c) The paint is sold in cylindrical tins of radius 4.3 cm and volume 500 cm^3. Taking π to be 3.142, calculate the height of one of these tins.

(d) Assuming that each tin is completely filled and that no paint is wasted, how many tins can be filled from the paint in the container?

(e) A shopkeeper buys 70 tins of paint for \$112 and marks each tin at the price which gives him a 27.5% profit. In addition, a customer has to pay 3% GST (goods and services tax) which is charged on the marked price. Calculate, to the nearest cent, the total amount the customer must pay for a tin of paint.

10. 80 spheres, each of radius 35 mm are packed in a rectangular wooden box, 8 to a layer, as shown in the diagram. Calculate

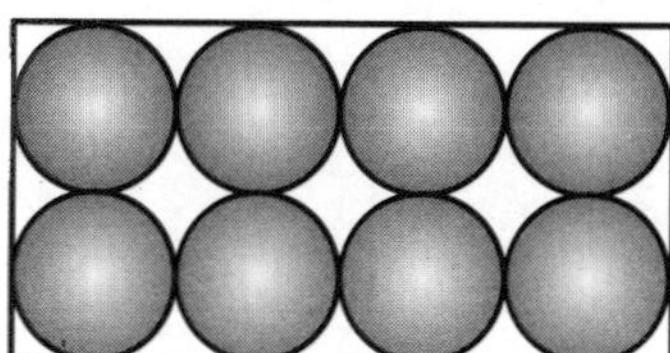

(a) the volume of the smallest box required in cm^3,

(b) the percentage of the total volume of the box filled by the spheres.

When unpacked, each sphere is coated with paint 0.002 mm thick.

(c) How many boxes of spheres can be painted with 1 litre of paint?

11. In the figure, the rocket model consists of three parts. Parts A and C can be joined together to form a right circular cone. Part B is a right cylinder. Find,

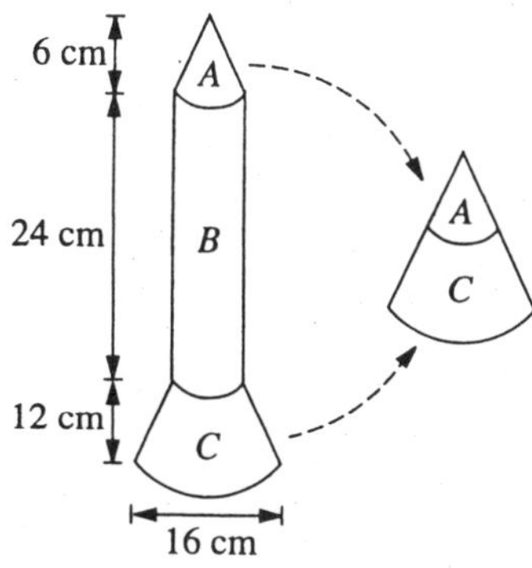

(a) the volume of the rocket model,

(b) the total curved surface area of the rocket model.

(Take $\pi = 3.142$.)

12. The diagram shows a container which consists of a cylinder with a cone attached to one end and a hemisphere attached to the other end.

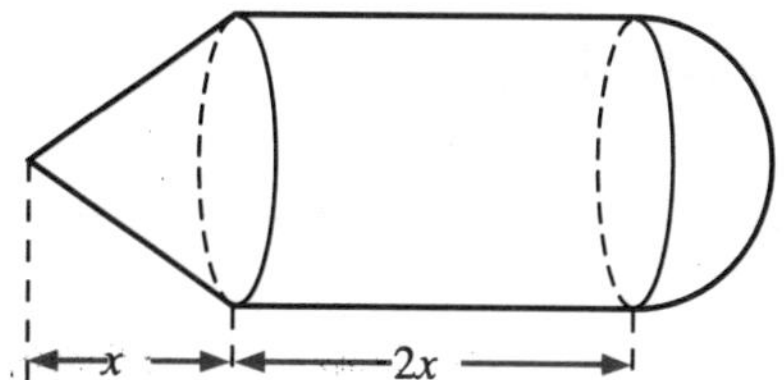

(a) Given that the height of the cone is x cm while the length of the cylinder is $2x$ cm, find the ratio of $\frac{\text{volume of cone}}{\text{volume of cylinder}}$.

(b) If the volume of the cylinder is 485 cm^3 and its height is 12 cm, find the radius of the cylinder.

(c) Find the curved surface area of the cone.

(d) The exterior of the container is to be painted with a coat of paint with a thickness of 0.3 mm, find the volume of paint needed to paint such a container.

13. Rain water collected in a rectangular container, with a base measuring 5 m by 8 m, reached a height of 4.5 cm. All the water was then allowed to run into a cylindrical tank of internal diameter 2.4 m.

(a) Calculate the depth of water in the cylindrical tank.

(b) Part of the water in the cylindrical tank was used to completely fill 5 hemispherical containers of internal radius 26 cm. Find the drop in the water level in the cylindrical tank.

(c) The remaining water in the cylindrical tank was allowed to drain through a valve at a rate of 2.5 litres per minute. Calculate the time needed to drain all the remaining water from the cylindrical tank. Give your answer correct to the nearest minute.

Coordinate Geometry

Example 1

The coordinates of $\triangle ABC$ are $A(-2, 1)$, $B(4, 4)$ and $C(6, 1)$.

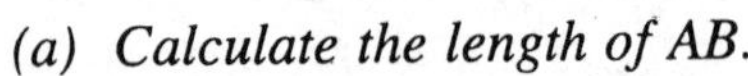

(a) *Calculate the length of AB.*
(b) *Find the equation of AB.*
(c) *Given that AC is the axis of symmetry of the quadrilateral ABCD, find the coordinates of D.*

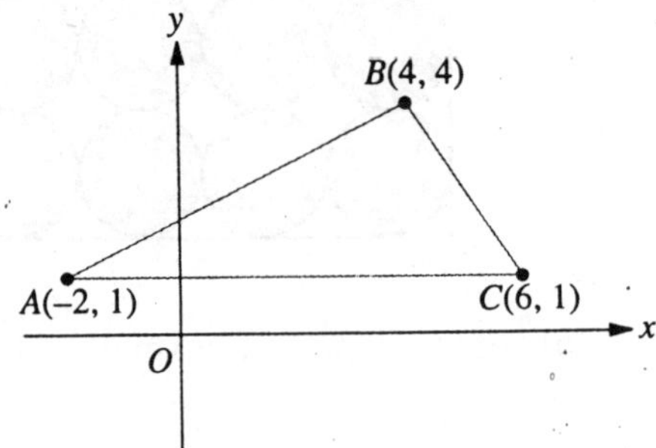

(a) $AB = \sqrt{[4 - (-2)]^2 + (4 - 1)^2}$

$= \sqrt{6^2 + 3^2}$

$= \sqrt{45}$

$= 6.71$ units.

(b) Gradient of $AB = \dfrac{4 - 1}{4 - (-2)}$

$= \dfrac{1}{2}$

$\therefore$ equation of AB is $y = \frac{1}{2}x + c$.

Since $(4, 4)$ lies on AB, $4 = \frac{1}{2}(4) + c$, i.e. $c = 2$

$\therefore$ equation of AB is $y = \frac{1}{2}x + 2$.

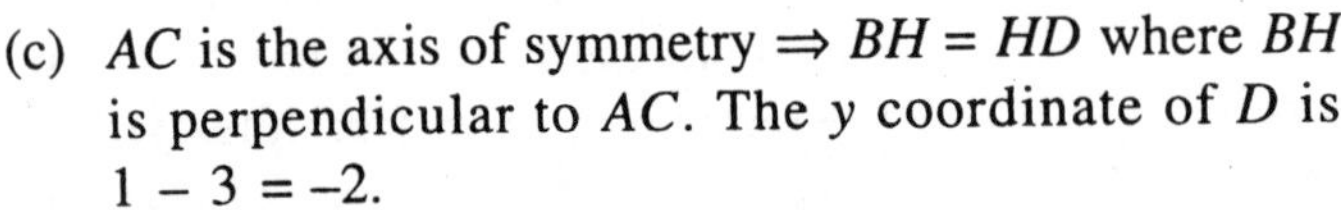

(c) AC is the axis of symmetry $\Rightarrow BH = HD$ where BH is perpendicular to AC. The y coordinate of D is $1 - 3 = -2$.

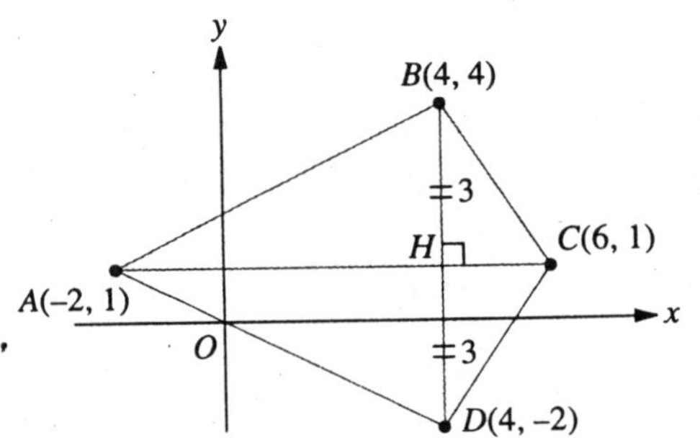

$\therefore$ point D is $(4, -2)$

Example 2

The coordinates of A, B, P and Q are A (5, 0), B (0, h), P (k, 0) and Q (0, 11). Given that OB = AP and the length of AB = 13 units, calculate

(a) the value of h and of k,
(b) the length of PQ,
(c) the length of OR where OR is perpendicular to PQ.

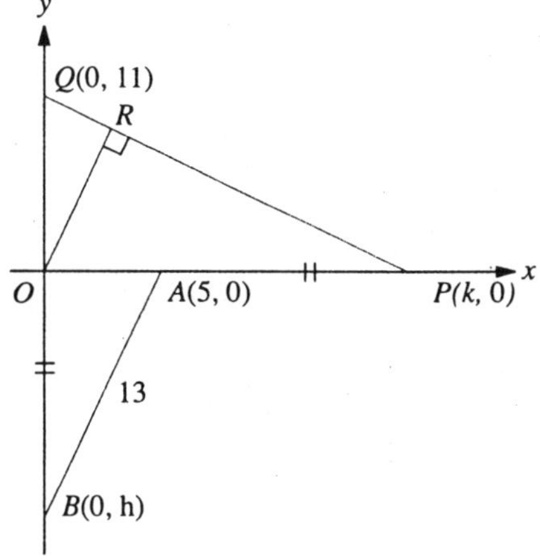

(a) We have $5^2 + h^2 = 13^2$

$\therefore \quad h = \sqrt{13^2 - 5^2} = 12$

and $k = 5 + 12 = 17$

(b) $PQ = \sqrt{11^2 + 17^2} = 20.25$ units

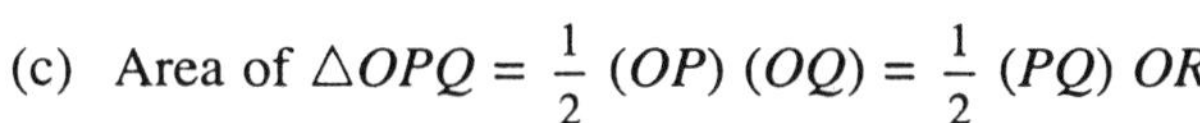

(c) Area of $\triangle OPQ = \frac{1}{2}(OP)(OQ) = \frac{1}{2}(PQ)\,OR$

$\therefore \quad \frac{1}{2} \times 17 \times 11 = \frac{1}{2}(20.25)\,OR$

$\therefore \quad OR = \dfrac{17 \times 11}{20.25} = 9.24$ units

Exercise 7j

1. **(a)** Find the gradient of the straight line passing through the points (1, 2) and (9, 10).
   (b) Find the equation of the straight line passing through the point (2, 3) and having a gradient of 5.

2. Given that the gradient of the line joining $(5, k)$ and $(4, -3)$ is 2, find k. Find the equation of the straight line having a gradient of $-\frac{1}{2}$ and passing through the point $(1, -5)$.

3. The straight line $3x + 4y = 24$ cuts the axes at the points P and Q. Calculate the length of PQ.

4. The line $2x + 3y = 18$ intersects the x-axis at P and the y-axis at Q.
   (a) Find the coordinates of P and Q.
   (b) Find the length of PQ.
   (c) Find the equation of the straight line which passes through $(4\frac{1}{2}, 3)$ and has a gradient of 3.

5. The line $\frac{x}{4} + \frac{y}{6} = 1$ cuts the x-axis at H and the y-axis at K. Find the length of HK.

6. **(a)** If the straight line $3y = k - 2x$ passes through $(-1, -5)$, find k.
   (b) If the gradient of the straight line $(2k - 1)y + (k + 1)x = 3$ is equal to the gradient of the line $y = 3x - 7$, find the value of k.
   (c) Find the equation of the line joining the points $A(1, 5)$ and $B(7, 2)$.

7. The equation of the line $3x + 4y = 35$ cuts the x- and y-axes at A and B.

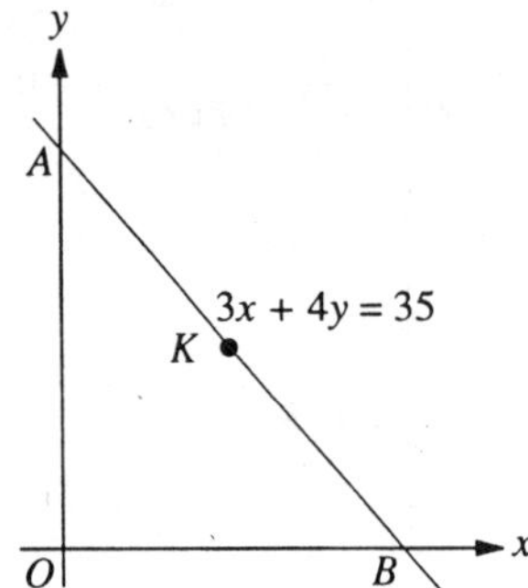

   (a) Write down the gradient of AB.
   (b) A point K lies on the line and is equidistant from the x- and y-axes. Find the coordinates of K.

8. The figure shows a line segment AB where A is the point $(0, 4)$ and B is the point $(3, 0)$.
   (a) Find the equation of the line AB.
   (b) If the line AB is reflected in the y-axis, find the equation of the image of the line.

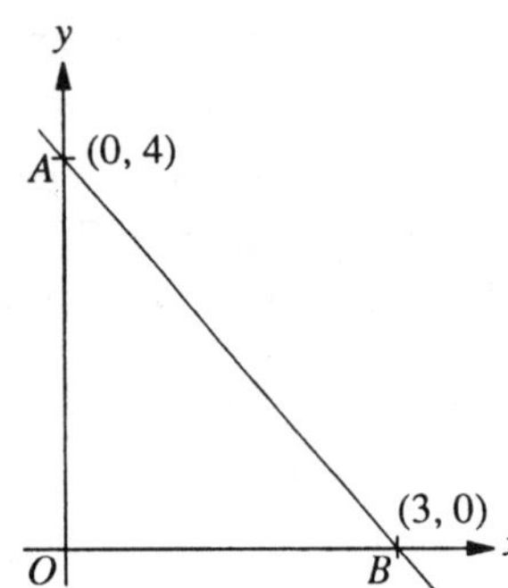

9. Find the equation of the line having a gradient $-1\frac{1}{2}$ and passing through the point of intersection of the lines $5x + 3y = 2$ and $x - y = 6$.

10. The coordinates of P, Q and R are $P(2, -5)$, $Q(3, -2)$ and $R(5, k)$ respectively.
   (a) If P, Q and R lie on a straight line, find the value of k.
   (b) With this value of k, find the length of PR.
   (c) Find the equation of the line passing through the point Q and having a gradient of $\frac{2}{3}$.

11. Find the equation of the line joining the point $(3, 7)$ to the point of intersection of the lines $x + y = 4$ and $x - y + 3 = 0$.

12. The vertices of a triangle ABC are $A(-3, 7)$, $B(11, 3)$ and $C(2, -2)$, show that $\triangle ABC$ is an isosceles right-angled triangle.

13. In the figure, $A(0, -3)$, $B(4, -2)$ and $C(2, 6)$ are the vertices of $\triangle ABC$.
   (a) Calculate the length of each of the sides, AB, BC and AC, and hence, show that $\triangle ABC$ is a right-angled triangle.
   (b) Find the area of $\triangle ABC$.
   (c) Calculate the length of the perpendicular from B to AC.
   (d) If a circle is to be drawn so that it will pass through points A, B and C, find the radius of this circle.

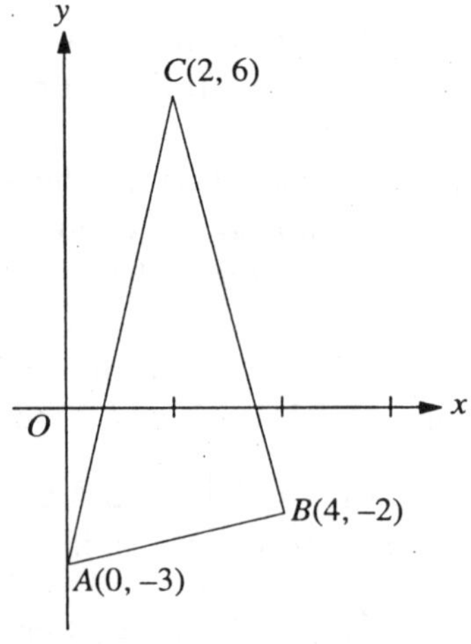

14. Given that the coordinates of the points A, B and C are $(1, -4)$, $(-3, 2)$ and $(7, 9)$ respectively, find the equation of the line passing through A and having the same gradient as BC.

15. In the figure, it is given that the equation of the line $ABCD$ is $2y = 3x - 14$, the coordinates of B and D are $(2, h)$ and $(k, 8)$.

(a) Find the values of h and k.

(b) Find the equation of CP, given that the gradient of OB is equal to the gradient PC.

(c) Calculate the area of $\triangle OCP$.

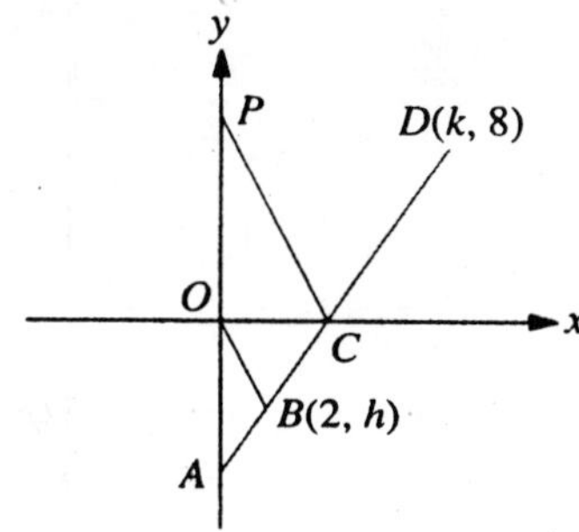

16. In the diagram, OAB is a straight line such that $OB = 3OA$ and the coordinates of A are $(-4, 3)$. Calculate

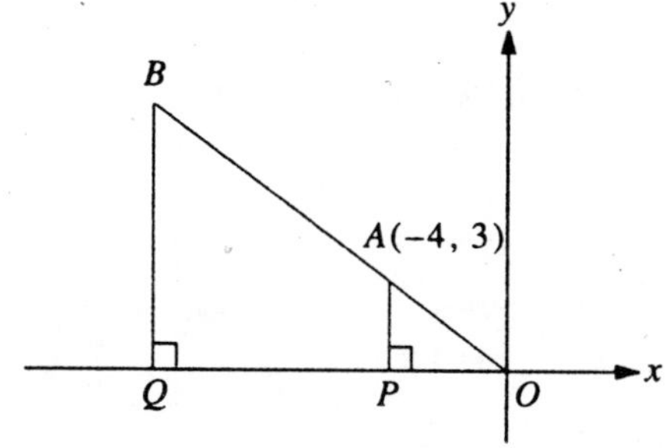

(a) the length of OB,

(b) the coordinates of B,

(c) the area of $ABQP$,

(d) the length of AQ.

17. In the diagram, OA and BC have the same gradient and the coordinates of the points A, P and C are $A(4, 6)$, $P(10, -4)$ and $C(15, t)$. Calculate

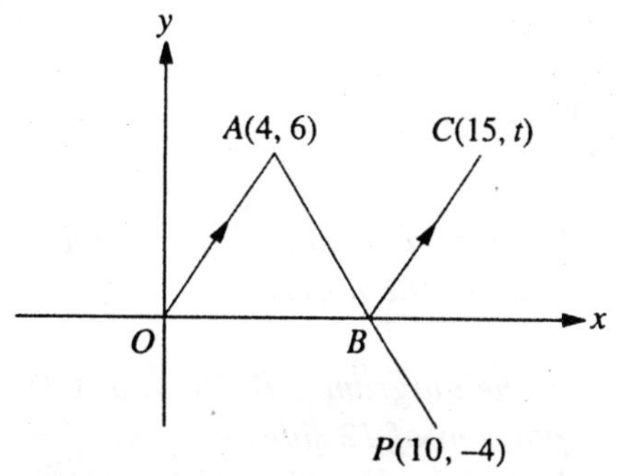

(a) the coordinates of B,

(b) the equation of BC,

(c) the value of t,

(d) the area of $\triangle OAB$.

18. In the diagram, A is the point $(15, 0)$, $OA = OP$, $OB = BQ$ and AB has a length of 17 units. Calculate

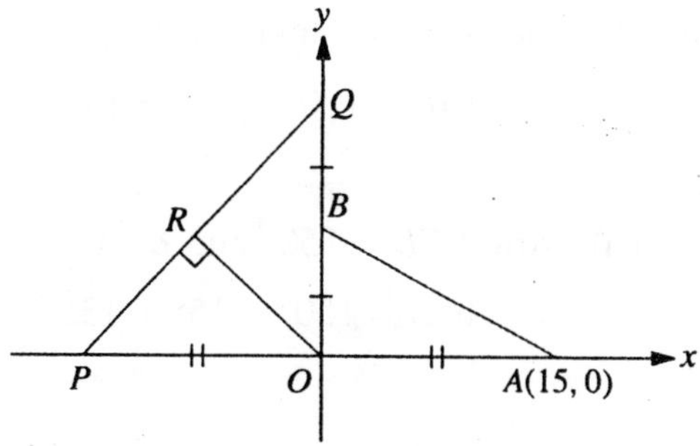

(a) the coordinates of B, Q and P,

(b) the equation of the line joining PQ,

(c) the length of PQ,

(d) the length of OR where OR is perpendicular to PQ.

Geometry 1: Geometrical Properties of Angles and Angle Properties of Polygons

(a) *Each interior angle of a regular polygon is 168°. Find the number of sides of the polygon.*

(b) *In the diagram, AB, BC and CD are three adjacent sides of a regular polygon of 12 sides.*
Calculate the value of (i) $A\hat{B}C$,
(ii) $A\hat{C}D$.

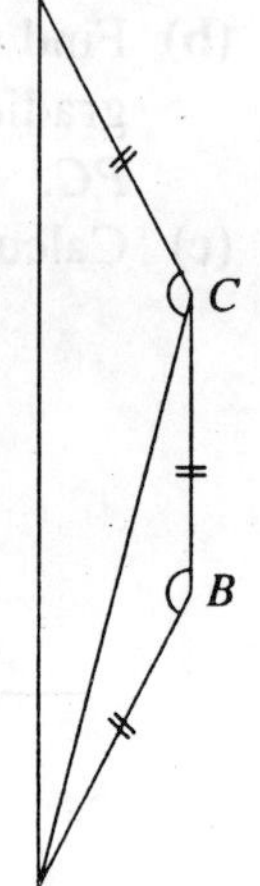

Solution

(a) Each exterior angle = 180° − 168° = 12°

$\therefore$ number of sides of the polygon = $\dfrac{360^\circ}{12^\circ} = 30$

(b) (i) Each exterior angle of the polygon = $\dfrac{360^\circ}{12} = 30^\circ$

$\therefore$ $A\hat{B}C = 180^\circ - 30^\circ = 150^\circ$

(ii) Now $B\hat{C}D = 150^\circ$ and $B\hat{C}A = \dfrac{180^\circ - 150^\circ}{2} = 15^\circ$ ($\triangle ABC$ is isosceles)

$\therefore$ $A\hat{C}D = 150^\circ - 15^\circ = 135^\circ$.

In the diagram, the line PAHD is parallel to QBC, AB = BC, $P\hat{A}B = 122^\circ$, $A\hat{C}D = 90^\circ$ and BH is the angle bisector of $A\hat{B}C$. Calculate

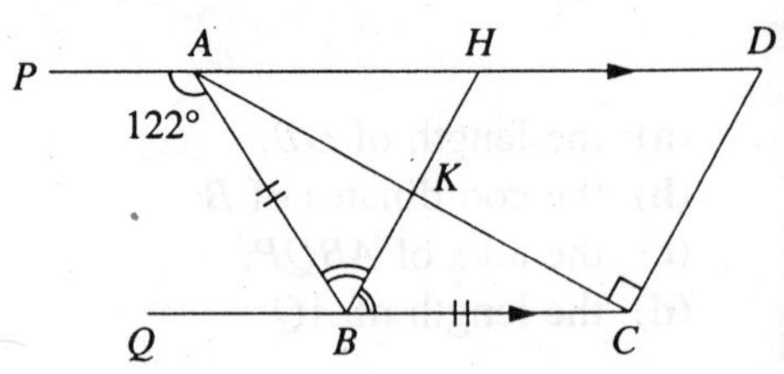

(a) $A\hat{B}H$,
(b) $B\hat{K}C$,
(c) $A\hat{D}C$.

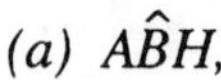

(a) $A\hat{B}C = 122°$ (alt ∡, $PD//QC$)

$A\hat{B}H = \frac{122°}{2} = 61°$

(b) $B\hat{C}A = \frac{180° - 122°}{2}$ (base ∡ of isoceles △)

$= 29°$

$\therefore \quad B\hat{K}C = 180° - 29° - 61° = 90°$ (∡ sum of a △)

(c) $A\hat{D}C + 90° + A\hat{C}B = 180°$ (interior ∡, $PD//QC$)

$\therefore \quad A\hat{D}C = 180° - 90° - 29°$
$= 61°$

1. Find the exterior angle of a regular polygon with
   (a) 8 sides, **(b)** 12 sides, **(c)** 24 sides.

2. Find the value of an interior angle of a regular polygon with
   (a) 6 sides, **(b)** 10 sides, **(c)** 15 sides.

3. Find the number of sides of a regular polygon whose exterior angles are each
   (a) 5°, **(b)** 8°, **(c)** 12°.

4. Find the number of sides of a regular polygon whose interior angles are each
   (a) 170°, **(b)** 176°, **(c)** 162°.

5. *AB*, *BC* and *CD* are three adjacent sides of a regular polygon of 18 sides. Calculate the value of the following angles.
   (a) $A\hat{B}C$,
   (b) $A\hat{C}D$.

6. The exterior angles of a six-sided polygon are in the ratio 4 : 5 : 6 : 7 : 7 : 7. Calculate the largest interior angle of the polygon.

7. A polygon has n sides and three of its exterior angles are 85°, 76° and 46°. The remaining $(n - 3)$ exterior angles are each 17°. Calculate the value of n.

8. In a regular polygon, each interior angle is 160° greater than each exterior angle. Calculate the number of sides of the polygon.

9. *ABCD* is a quadrilateral in which $\hat{A} = 112°$, $\hat{B} = 86°$, $\hat{C} = 72°$ and $A\hat{D}B = 28°$. Calculate the following angles.
   (a) $A\hat{D}C$,
   (b) $A\hat{B}D$,
   (c) $B\hat{D}C$.

10. One interior angle of a 7-sided polygon is 126°, and each of the other 6 angles is $x°$. Find x.

11. The interior angles of a quadrilateral *ABCD* taken in order are in the ratio 1 : 2 : 3 : 4. Prove that the quadrilateral is a trapezium.

12. $ABCDE$ is a pentagon in which AB is parallel to ED. If $\hat{B} = 155°$, $\hat{C} = 3x°$, $\hat{D} = 2x°$ and $\hat{E} = 75°$, calculate the following.
(a) x
(b) $\hat{A}$

13. Find the number of sides of the polygon whose sum of interior angles is
(a) 1080°
(b) equal to 28 right angles.

14. In the diagram, $HK//PQ//AB$, $C\hat{A}T = 154°$ and $A\hat{B}C = 52°$. Calculate
(a) $H\hat{K}C$,
(b) $Q\hat{C}K$,
(c) $P\hat{Q}B$.

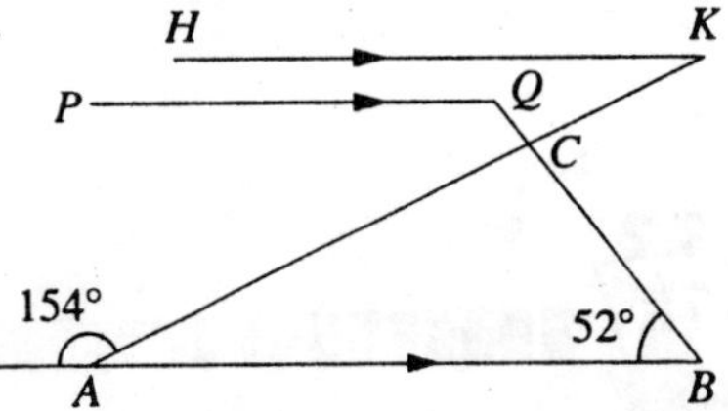

15. In the diagram, $AB//PQ$, $BP//RQ$, $A\hat{B}T = 72°$ and $P\hat{Q}T = 42°$. Calculate
(a) $B\hat{P}Q$,
(b) $P\hat{T}Q$,
(c) $R\hat{Q}T$.

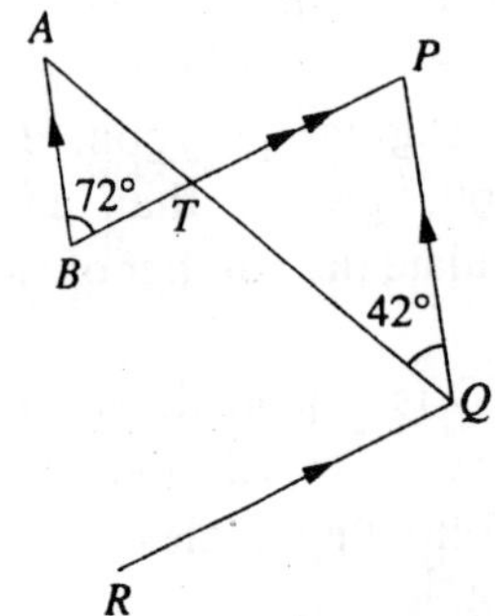

16. In the diagram, $ABCDE$ is parallel to RS, $PC//QD$, $Q\hat{D}E = 156°$ and $R\hat{B}A = 107°$. Calculate
(a) $D\hat{Q}R$,
(b) the reflex angle $B\hat{R}S$.

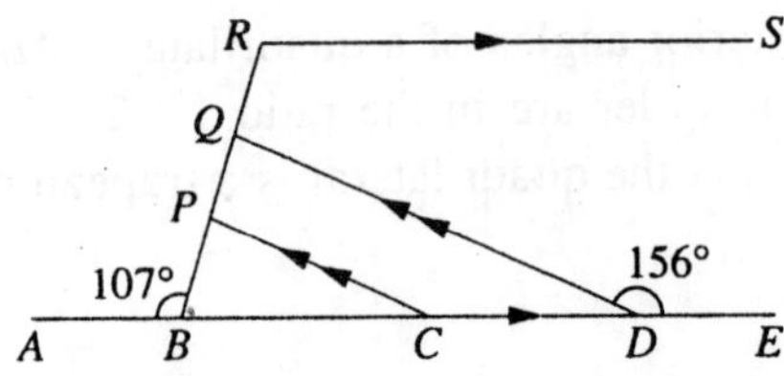

17. In the diagram $BT//HK$, $BP//CQ$, $A\hat{B}T = 16°$, $C\hat{B}H = 46°$ and $B\hat{C}Q = 72°$. Calculate
(a) $P\hat{B}T$,
(b) $B\hat{H}K$.

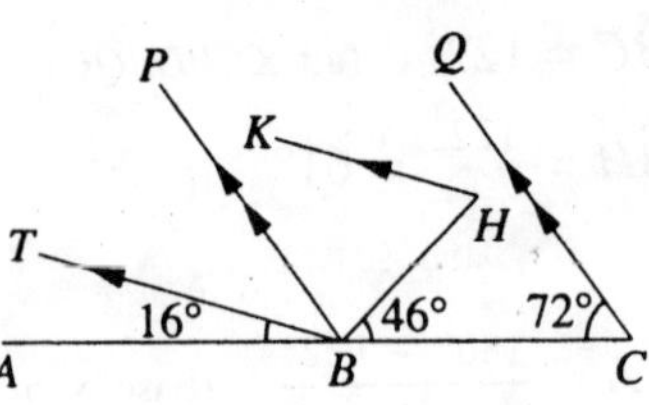

18. In the diagram, $BP//ER$, $CD//EQ$, $Q\hat{E}B = 103°$, $A\hat{B}P = 43°$ and $C\hat{B}D = 78°$. Calculate
(a) $B\hat{D}C$,
(b) $Q\hat{E}R$.

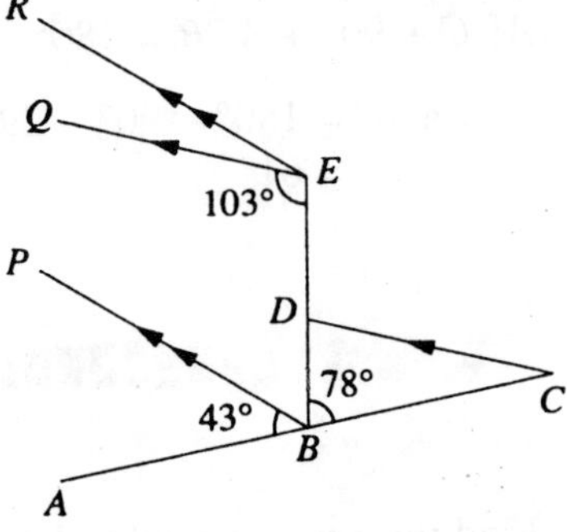

19. In the diagram, $AP = AB$, $\triangle ABQ$ is equilateral and $P\hat{A}B = 82°$, calculate
(a) $A\hat{C}B$,
(b) $P\hat{Q}R$,
(c) $A\hat{R}B$.

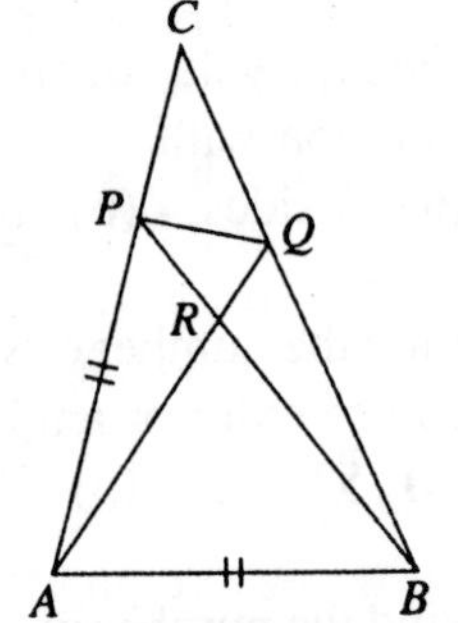

20. In the diagram, $ABCDEF$ is a regular hexagon. PCA is produced to meet EF produced at T. Calculate
(a) $A\hat{T}E$,
(b) $B\hat{C}P$.

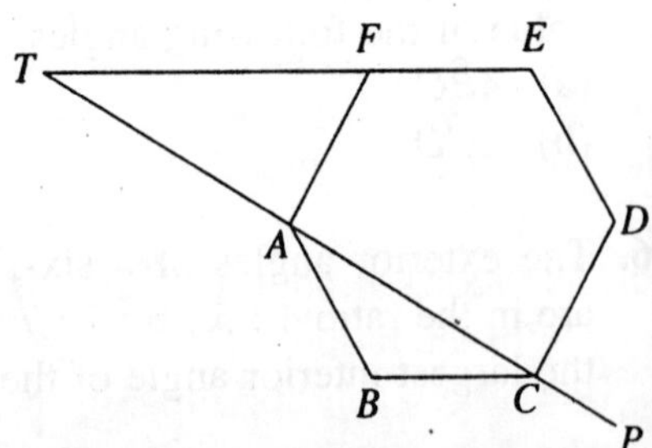

21. In the diagram, $ABCDEF$ is a regular hexagon and $APQRB$ is a regular pentagon. Calculate
(a) $B\hat{A}P$,
(b) $A\hat{B}X$,
(c) $E\hat{X}R$.

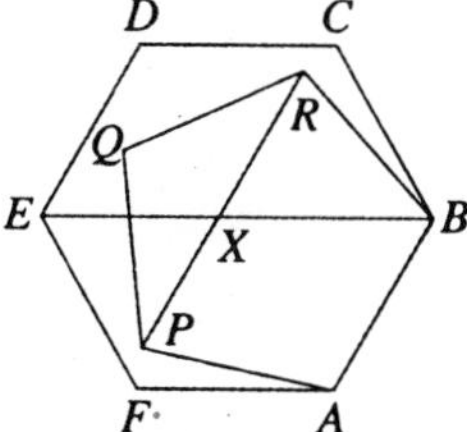

22. (a) Find the number of sides of a polygon if the sum of its interior angles is 2700°.
(b) A polygon has n sides. Three of its exterior angles are 36°, 55°, 65° and the remaining $(n - 3)$ exterior angles are each equal to $8\frac{1}{2}^{\circ}$. Find the value of n.

23.

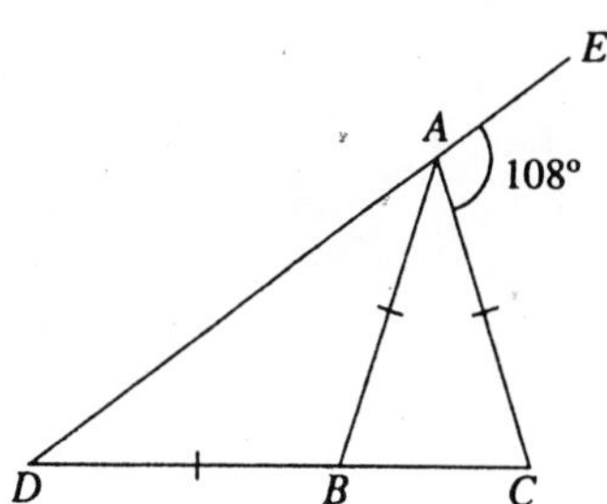

In the figure above, $AB = BD = AC$ and $E\hat{A}C = 108°$. DAE is a straight line. Find the value of
(a) $A\hat{C}B$,
(b) $A\hat{D}B$.

24. (a) Each interior angle of a polygon is 140°. How many sides does the polygon have?
(b) Two exterior angles of a hexagon are $2x°$ and $3x°$ while the other 4 exterior angles are each equal to 65°. Find x.

25. A, B, C, ... are some of the vertices of a regular polygon with N sides. Each interior angle of the polygon is n times as large as each exterior angle, n being an integer.

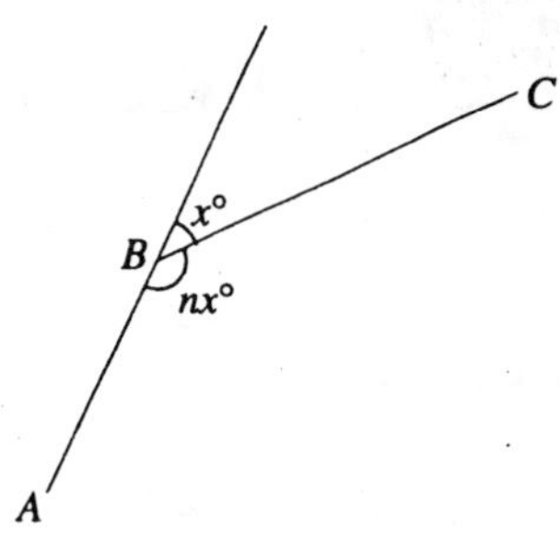

When $n = 1$, $x + x = 180$ (or $x = 90$) and $N = \frac{360}{90} = 4$.

When $n = 2$, $3x = 180$ (or $x = 60$) and $N = \frac{360}{60} = 6$.

When $n = 3$, $4x = 180$ (or $x = 45$) and $N = \frac{360}{45} = 8$.

(a) Complete the table in the answer space, showing the first 5 sets of values of n, x and N.

n	x	N
1	90	$4 = 2(1 + 1)$
2	60	$6 = 2(2 + 1)$
3	45	$8 = 2(3 + 1)$
4		
5		

(b) A regular polygon has each interior angle 49 times as large as each exterior angle. How many sides does this polygon have?
(c) Another regular polygon has 180 sides. What is the size of each of its exterior angles?

Geometry 2: Congruence and Similarity

Example 1

A cone K has a volume of 400 cm³. Calculate the volume of

(a) a cone similar to K but with a height twice that of K,
(b) a cone with a height four times that of K and a base radius one quarter that of K.

(a) $\dfrac{\text{Vol. of } K}{\text{Vol. of new cone}} = \left(\dfrac{1}{2}\right)^3$ or $\dfrac{400}{\text{Vol. of new cone}} = \dfrac{1}{8}$

$\therefore$ Volume of new cone $= 8 \times 400$

$= 3200 \text{ cm}^3$

(b) Let the height of K be h and its base radius be r.

$\therefore \quad \dfrac{1}{3}\pi r^2 h = 400 \text{ cm}^3$

The new cone has a height of $4h$ and a base radius of $\dfrac{1}{4}r$.

Volume of new cone $= \dfrac{1}{3}\pi\left(\dfrac{1}{4}r\right)^2 (4h)$

$= \dfrac{1}{4}\left(\dfrac{1}{3}\pi r^2 h\right)$

$= \dfrac{1}{4}(400)$

$= 100 \text{ cm}^3$

xample 2

The diagram shows a parallelogram PQRS. C is a point on PQ such that 2PC = 3CQ. A is a point on PS such that SA = 3AP and AB is parallel to PQ. Given that the area of $\Delta SPC = 24 \text{ cm}^2$, calculate the area of

(a) parallelogram PQRS,
(b) ΔSAB.

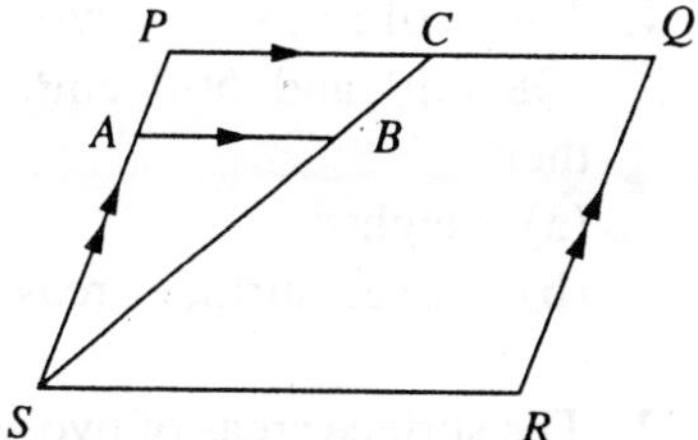

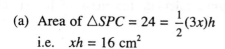

Solution

Let $PC = 3x$, then $CQ = 2x$;
$AP = y$, then $SA = 3y$;
the height of the parallelogram CK be h.

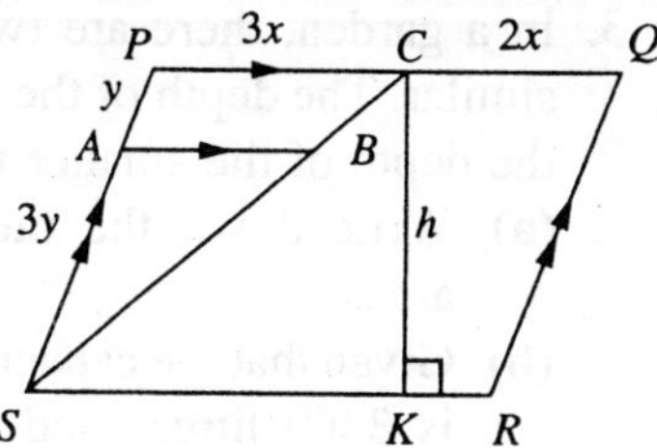

(a) Area of $\Delta SPC = 24 = \frac{1}{2}(3x)h$

i.e. $xh = 16 \text{ cm}^2$

Area of parallelogram $PQRS = 5x \times h = 5 \times 16 = 80 \text{ cm}^2$.

(b) ΔSAB is similar to ΔSPC.

$$\frac{\text{area of } \Delta SAB}{\text{area of } \Delta SPC} = \left(\frac{SA}{SP}\right)^2 \quad \text{or} \quad \frac{\text{area of } \Delta SAB}{24}$$

$$= \left(\frac{3y}{4y}\right)^2$$

$$= \frac{9}{16}$$

$$\therefore \quad \text{area of } \Delta SAB = \frac{24 \times 9}{16} = 13.5 \text{ cm}^2$$

Exercise 71

1. The volumes of two similar bags are 108 cm^3 and 500 cm^3. Find the ratio of their
   (a) heights;
   (b) curved surface areas.

2. The surface areas of two spheres, A and B, are in the ratio of 25 : 144. Find
   (a) the radius of A if the radius of B is 15 cm;
   (b) the volume of A if the volume of B is 864 cm^3.

3. In a garden, there are two ponds which are similar. The depth of the larger pond is twice the depth of the smaller pond.
   (a) Write down the ratio of their surface areas.
   (b) Given that the capacity of the larger pond is 3360 litres, find the capacity of the smaller pond.

4. Two solid spheres have surface areas in the ratio 9 : 16. If the smaller sphere has a radius of 12 cm and a mass of 5 kg, calculate
   (a) the radius of the larger sphere,
   (b) the mass of the larger sphere.

5. The ratio of the surface areas of two similar cones is 4 : 25. If the smaller cone has a height of 6.8 cm and a volume of 500 cm^3, calculate
   (a) the height of the larger cone,
   (b) the volume of the larger cone.

6. A conical flask has a surface area of 50 cm^2 and a capacity of 845 cm^3. Find the volume of a similar conical flask which has a surface area of 32 cm^2.

7. A cone with radius of r cm and a height of h cm has a volume of 420 cm^3. Find the volume of a cone whose height is $\frac{1}{2}h$ cm and whose radius is $3r$ cm.

8. The curved surface area of a cylindrical can of radius r cm and height h cm is 540 cm^2. Find the curved surface area of another cylinder whose height is $\frac{1}{4}h$ cm and whose radius is $5r$ cm.

9. The volume of a solid stone statue 3 m high is V_1 and its surface area is A_1. A wooden model of the statue, 20 cm high has a volume of V_2 and a surface area of A_2. The wooden model weighs 4 kg. Calculate the ratio of
   (a) $V_1 : V_2$,
   (b) $A_1 : A_2$.

   Given that the density of the stone is 3000 kg/m^3 and the density of the wood is 540 kg/m^3, calculate the mass of the stone statue.

10. Two solid spheres have diameters of 35 cm and 14 cm respectively. Find the total surface area of each sphere. Compare the areas in the form of a ratio. If 200 cm^2 of the first sphere is to be painted in red, find the area of the second sphere to be painted in red so that the two spheres will appear similar in design.

11. A suspension bridge is 2500 metres long and a model of it is made on a scale of 1 : 600. If the supporting towers are 34 cm high in the model, find their actual height in metres.
    If it costs \$4 to paint the model, how much will it cost to paint the actual bridge?
    If a steel section weighs 432 tonnes, how much would the section weigh in the model assuming that it is constructed from the same material?

12. Mr Yang buys two cylindrical cans of tonic food drink from a shopkeeper. The cans are similar geometrically. The diameter of one can is 10 cm and that of the other is 15 cm.

(a) The height of the large can is 18 cm. Calculate the height of the small one.

(b) Calculate the following ratios, giving your answer in its lowest term.

(i) Base area of small can : Base area of large can

(ii) Volume of small can : Volume of large can

(c) The shopkeeper's profit for selling tonic food drink is 96 cents for a small can. Calculate his profit from selling a large can, assuming that there is no reduction in profit for doing so.

13. In the diagram, PQ is parallel to BA, P is on BC such that $BP : PC = 2 : 5$ and R is on BA such that $BR : RA = 4 : 3$. If the area of $\triangle BCR = 98$ cm^2, calculate the area of the following.

(a) $\triangle ACR$,

(b) $\triangle CPQ$.

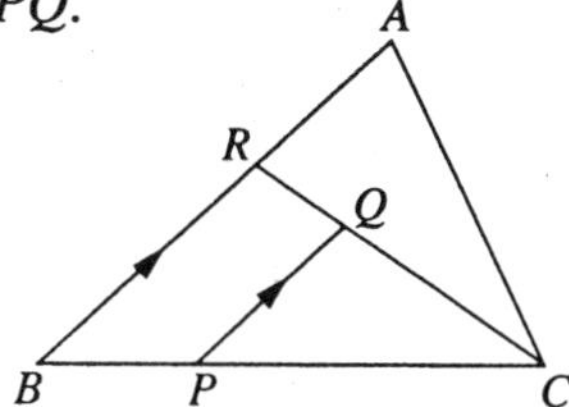

14. In the diagram, the points P and Q lie on the sides AB and AC respectively of triangle ABC. The line PQ is parallel to BC. Given that $AB = 8$ cm, $AP = 2$ cm and $AC = 12$ cm,

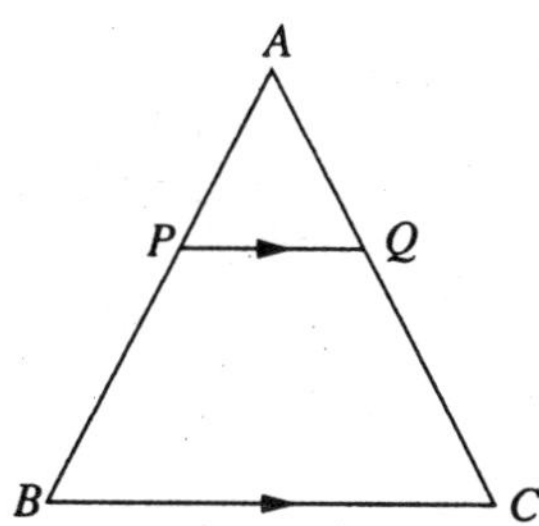

(a) calculate the length of QC,

(b) write down the values of the

(i) $\dfrac{\text{area of } \Delta APQ}{\text{area of } \Delta PQB}$,

(ii) $\dfrac{\text{area of } \Delta ABC}{\text{area of } \Delta APQ}$.

15. In the diagram, BC is parallel to PQ. If $AB = 6$ cm, $BP = 3$ cm and the area of $\triangle ABC = 20$ cm^2, find the area of

(a) $\triangle APQ$,

(b) trapezium $BPQC$.

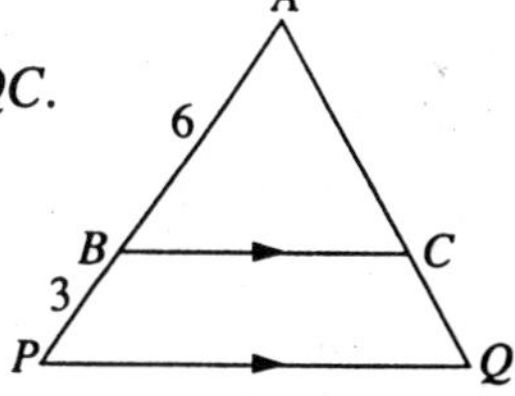

16. In the diagram, $BP : PC = 2 : 3$ and the area of $\triangle APC = 36$ cm^2. Find the area of $\triangle ABP$. If PQ is parallel to BA, find the area of $\triangle CPQ$.

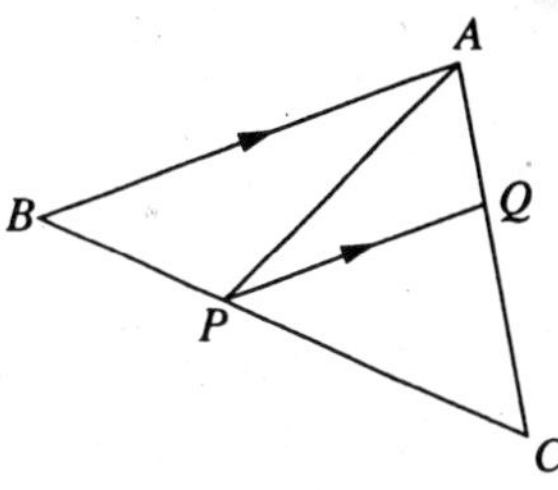

17. In the diagram, $ABCD$ is a parallelogram. If $BC = 4$ cm, $CP = 6$ cm and the area of $ABCD = 40$ cm^2, find the area of $\triangle ABP$.

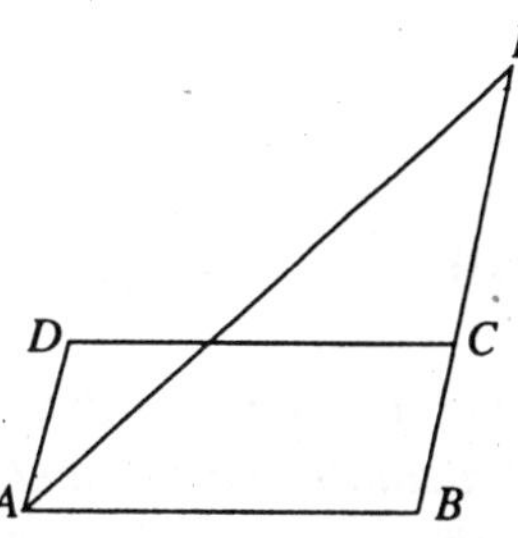

18. In the diagram, $AP = 3$ cm, $PC = 2$ cm, $BC = 4$ cm and PQ is parallel to CB. Find

(a) the length of PQ,

(b) the ratio of the area of $\triangle ABP$ to the area of $\triangle BPC$,

(c) the ratio of the area of $\triangle APQ$ to the area of $PQBC$.

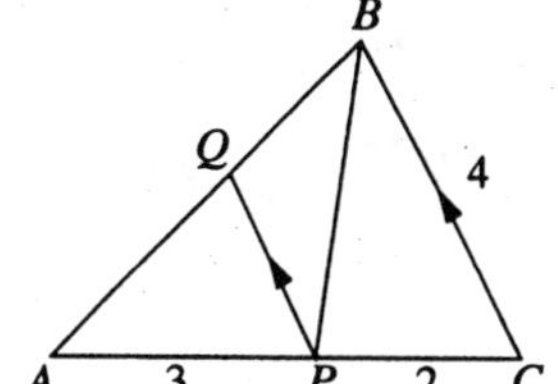

Geometry 3: Angle Properties of Circles

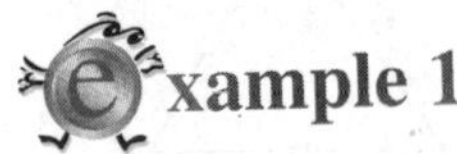

xample 1

In the figure, AB is a diameter of the circle, centre O, $P\hat{A}B = 32°$ and $A\hat{Q}P = 28°$. Calculate the following angles.

(a) $P\hat{O}B$, *(b)* $B\hat{A}Q$, *(c)* $R\hat{B}Q$.

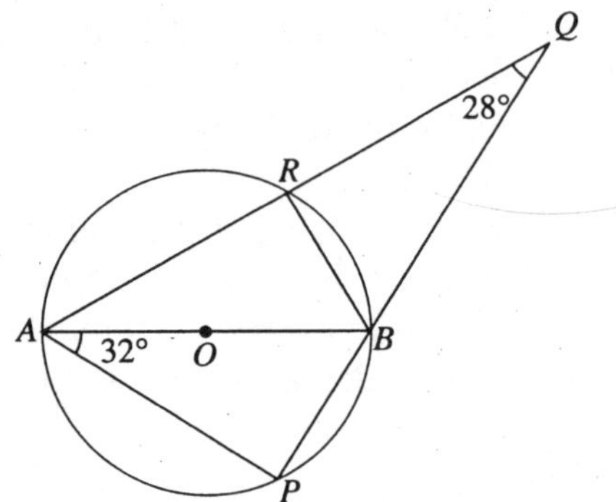

(a) $P\hat{O}B = 2 \times 32°$ (∡ at centre = 2 ∡ at ⊙^{ce})
$= 64°$

(b) $A\hat{P}B = 90°$ (rt. ∡ in semicircle)
∴ $B\hat{A}Q = 180° - 90° - 28° - 32°$ (∡ sum of △)
$= 30°$

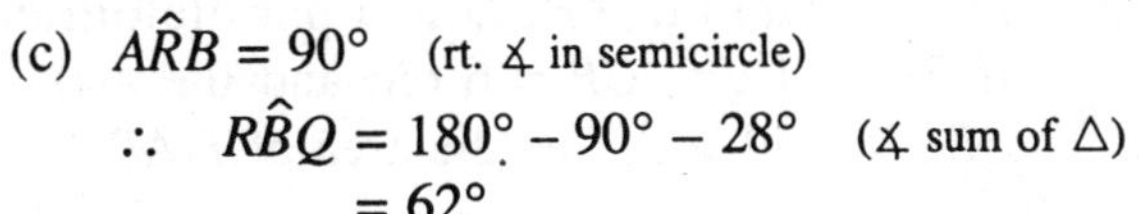

(c) $A\hat{R}B = 90°$ (rt. ∡ in semicircle)
∴ $R\hat{B}Q = 180° - 90° - 28°$ (∡ sum of △)
$= 62°$

xample 2

A chord of length 15 cm is drawn in a circle of radius 12 cm as shown in the figure. Calculate the perpendicular distance from the centre of the circle to the chord.

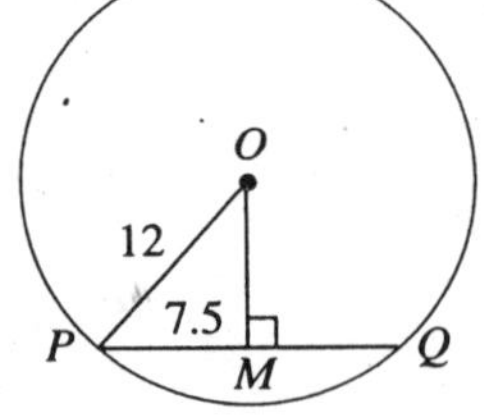

The perpendicular from the centre cuts the chord PQ at its mid-point, i.e. $PM = 7.5$ cm.

$OP^2 = PM^2 + OM^2$

$12^2 = 7.5^2 + OM^2 \Rightarrow OM = \sqrt{12^2 - 7.5^2}$

∴ the perpendicular distance is approximately 9.37 cm.

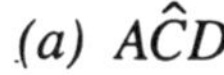

xample 3

In the figure, TAR is a tangent to the circle whose centre is O. The chord AC intersects the diameter BD at X. Given that $A\hat{E}D = 122°$ and $B\hat{D}C = 28°$, calculate the following angles:

(a) $A\hat{C}D$

(b) $A\hat{O}B$

(c) $A\hat{D}O$

(d) $B\hat{A}R$

(e) $A\hat{X}B$

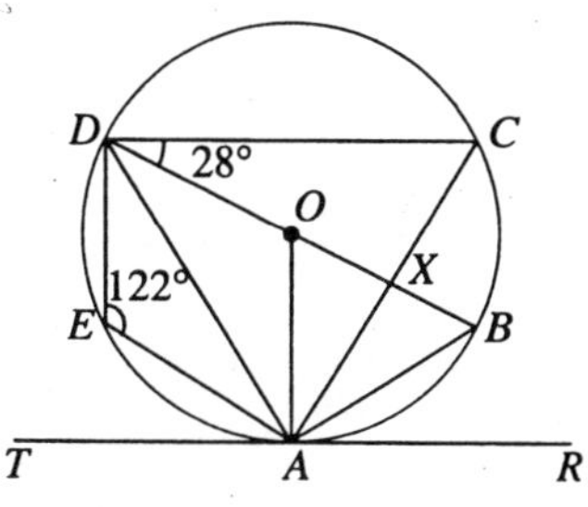

(a) $A\hat{C}D = 180° - 122°$ (angles in opp. segment)
$= 58°$

(b) $A\hat{B}D = 58°$ (∡ in the same segment)
$O\hat{A}B = 58°$ (base ∡ of an isos. △)

$\therefore \quad A\hat{O}B = 180° - 58° - 58°$
$= 64°$

(c) $A\hat{D}O = \frac{1}{2}(64°)$ (∡ at centre = 2 ∡ at ⊙^{ce})

$= 32°$

(d) $O\hat{A}B = 90°$ (radius ⊥ to tangent)

$\therefore \quad B\hat{A}R = 90° - O\hat{A}B = 90° - 58°$
$= 32°$

(e) $B\hat{A}C = B\hat{D}C$ (∡ in the same segment)
$= 28°$

$\therefore \quad A\hat{X}B = 180° - 28° - 58°$
$= 94°$

1. In the diagram, AB is a diameter of the circle, centre O, DC is parallel to AB and $B\hat{A}D = 63°$. Calculate the following angles:
   (a) $A\hat{B}D$,
   (b) $C\hat{B}D$,
   (c) $B\hat{O}C$.

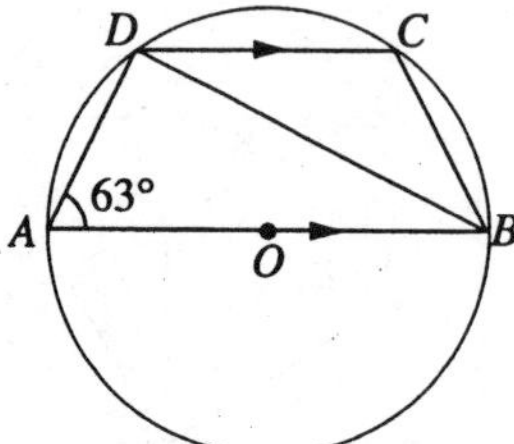

2. In the diagram, ADE, AXC, BXD and BCE are straight lines, $A\hat{E}C = 38°$ and $E\hat{A}C = 23°$. Calculate
   (a) $B\hat{D}A$,
   (b) $B\hat{X}C$.

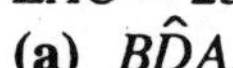

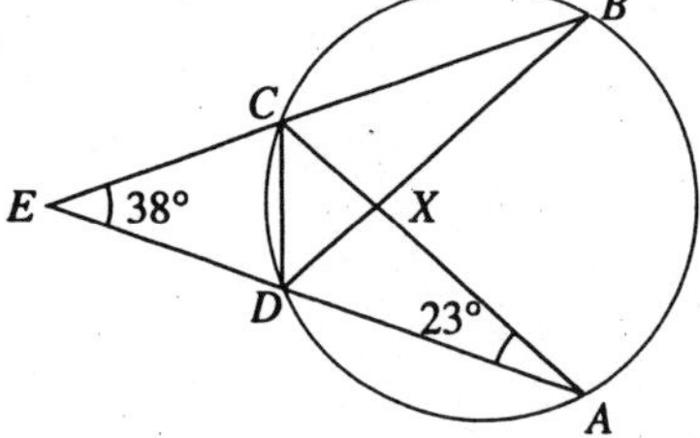

3. In the diagram, O is the centre of the circle, $B\hat{O}C = 98°$ and $A\hat{B}O = 22°$. Calculate the following angles:
   (a) $B\hat{A}C$,
   (b) $A\hat{C}P$.

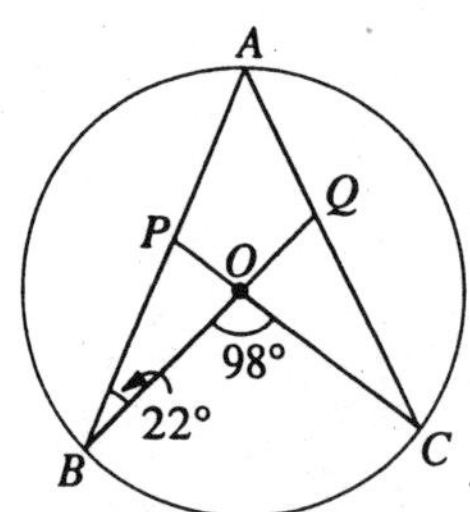

4. In the diagram, $P\hat{A}B = 90°$, $C\hat{B}D = 68°$ and $C\hat{D}Q = 115°$. Calculate
   (a) $A\hat{C}B$,
   (b) $A\hat{C}D$.

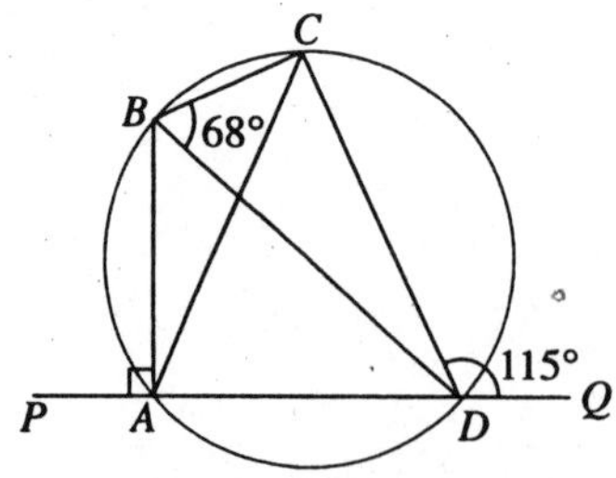

5. In the figure, BC is a diameter of the circle whose centre is O. TA is a tangent to the circle at A and BCT is a straight line. If $A\hat{C}O = 58°$, calculate the following angles:
   (a) $A\hat{O}C$,
   (b) $A\hat{B}C$,
   (c) $C\hat{A}T$,
   (d) $A\hat{T}C$.

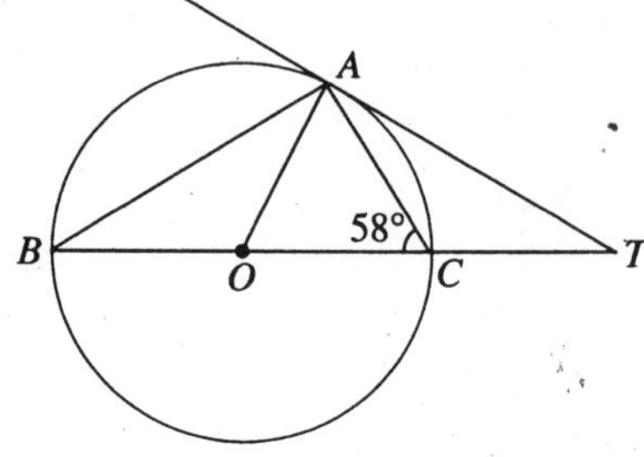

6. In the diagram, TA and TB are tangents to the circle from an external point T. If CB is parallel to AT and $B\hat{A}T = 62°$, calculate the following angles:
   (a) $A\hat{T}B$,
   (b) $B\hat{C}A$,
   (c) $B\hat{A}C$.

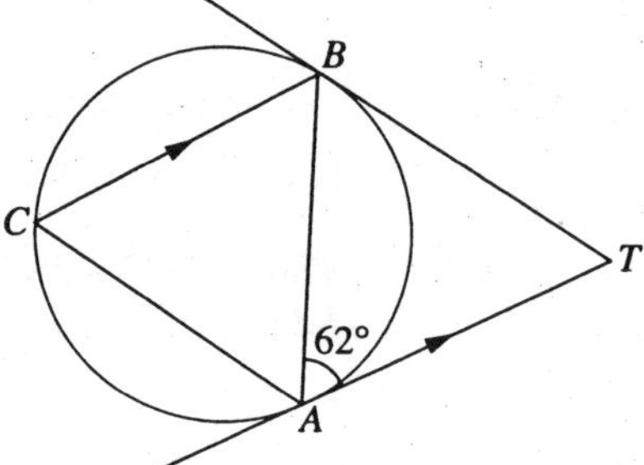

7. In the diagram, O is the centre of the circle and TA is a tangent to the circle. If $A\hat{D}C = 66°$ and $A\hat{C}B = 40°$, calculate the following angles:
   (a) $A\hat{O}C$,
   (b) $B\hat{A}C$,
   (c) $A\hat{C}O$,
   (d) $T\hat{A}B$.

8. In the diagram, AC is a diameter of the circle whose centre is O. AB and DC are produced to meet at T. If $A\hat{T}D = 34°$ and $B\hat{A}C = 32°$, calculate the following angles:

(a) $B\hat{D}C$,

(b) $B\hat{C}D$,

(c) $D\hat{B}C$.

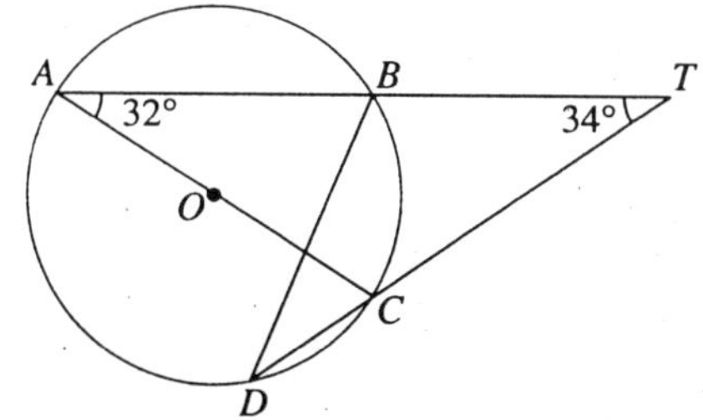

9. In the diagram, O is the centre of the circle and TA is the tangent at A. If $TA = 5$ cm and $TB = 3.2$ cm, calculate the radius of the circle.

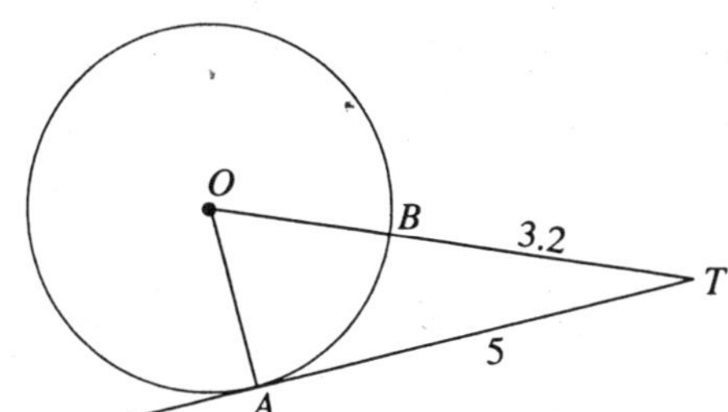

10. In the diagram, TA and TB are the tangents to the circle with centre O and radius 5 cm. If $TA = 17$ cm, calculate

(a) the area of the quadrilateral $ATBO$,

(b) the length of the minor arc APB.

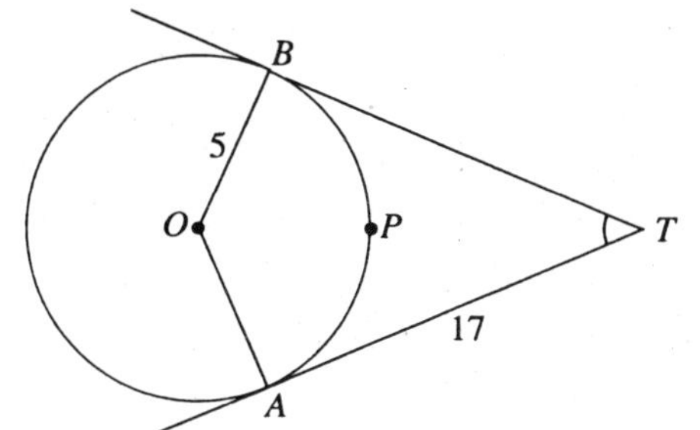

11. A chord of length 18 cm is drawn in a circle of radius 16 cm. Calculate the perpendicular distance from the centre of the circle to the chord.

12. The perpendicular distance from the centre of a circle to a chord drawn in the circle is 7.5 cm. Calculate the radius of the circle if the chord has a length of 12 cm.

13. In the diagram, O is the centre of the circle through A, B, C and D. TA is the tangent at A and AC intersects BD at X. If $A\hat{C}B = 62°$ and $D\hat{A}C = 32°$, calculate the following angles:

(a) $B\hat{A}O$,

(b) $A\hat{O}D$,

(c) $B\hat{X}C$,

(d) $T\hat{A}D$.

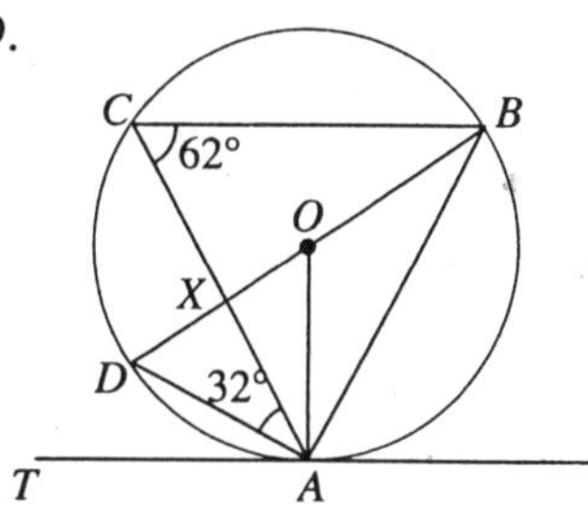

14. A chord 8 cm long is drawn in a circle whose diameter is 10 cm. How far is the chord from the centre of the circle?

15. In the diagram, AD is a diameter of the circle whose centre is O. If $\triangle AOB$ is equilateral, and $O\hat{B}C = 50°$, calculate the following angles:

(a) $B\hat{C}D$,

(b) $O\hat{D}C$,

(c) $C\hat{B}D$,

(d) $C\hat{O}D$.

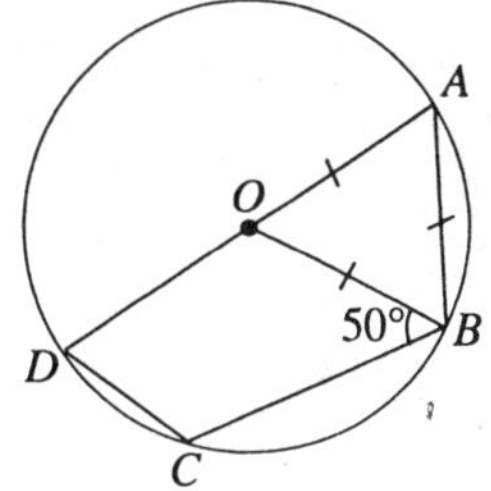

16. In the diagram, ST is the tangent to the circle at S. $S\hat{L}N = 45°$, $N\hat{S}M = 60°$ and $L\hat{N}M = 25°$. Calculate the following angles.

(a) $L\hat{S}T$,

(b) $L\hat{S}M$

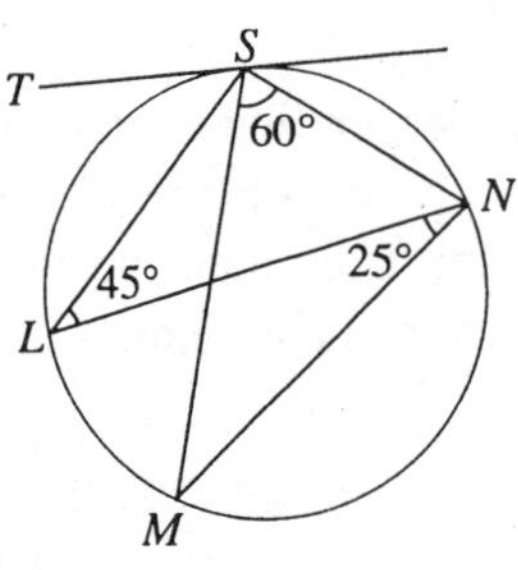

17. In the diagram, AOB is a diameter with O as the centre. Given that $T\hat{A}D = 132°$ and $BC = CD$, find $A\hat{D}C$.

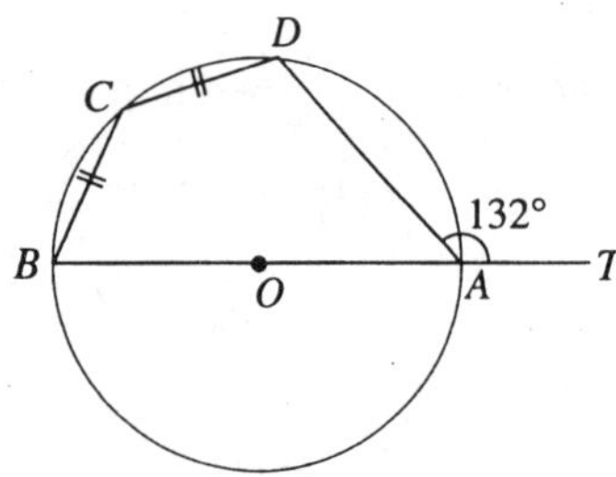

18. In the diagram, O is the centre of the circle. Given that $A\hat{O}B = 110°$ and $B\hat{C}D = 84°$, find $O\hat{A}D$.

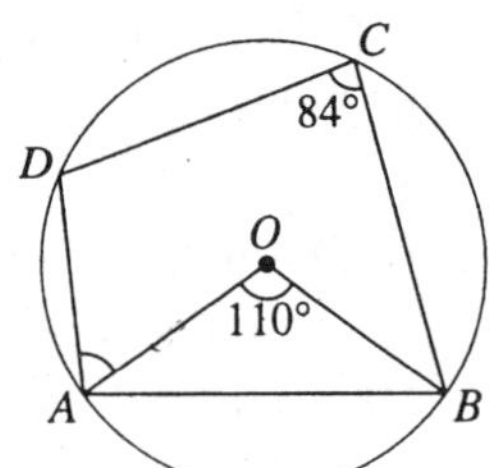

19. In the diagram, O is the centre of the bigger circle ABC and CBP is a straight line. Given that $A\hat{B}C = 132°$, calculate

(a) $A\hat{O}C$,

(b) $A\hat{P}C$.

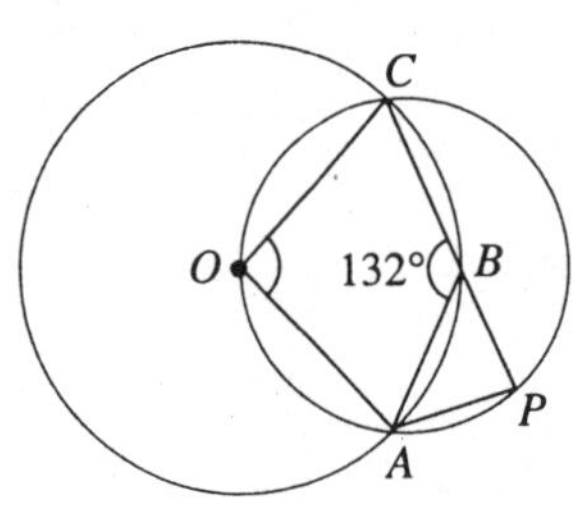

20. In the diagram, AB is a diameter of the circle and PT is the tangent to the circle at P. If $A\hat{P}T = 118°$, calculate $A\hat{B}P$.

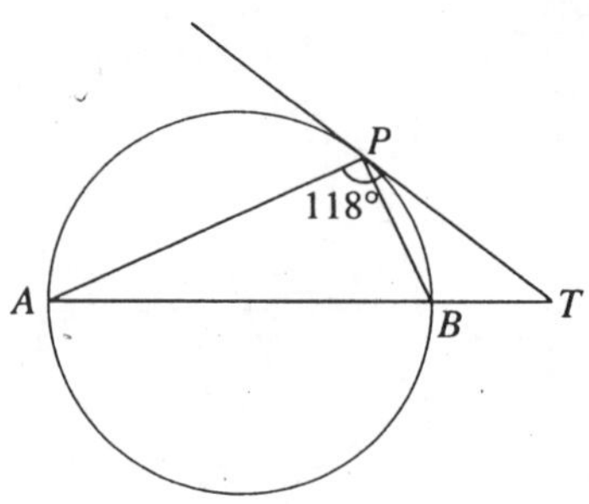

21. In the diagram, O is the centre of the circle and PAQ is the tangent to the circle at A. Given that $B\hat{A}Q = (3x + 4y)°$, $A\hat{O}B = (7x + 6y)°$ and $A\hat{B}O = 40°$, find the value of x and of y and hence state the value of $A\hat{D}B$.

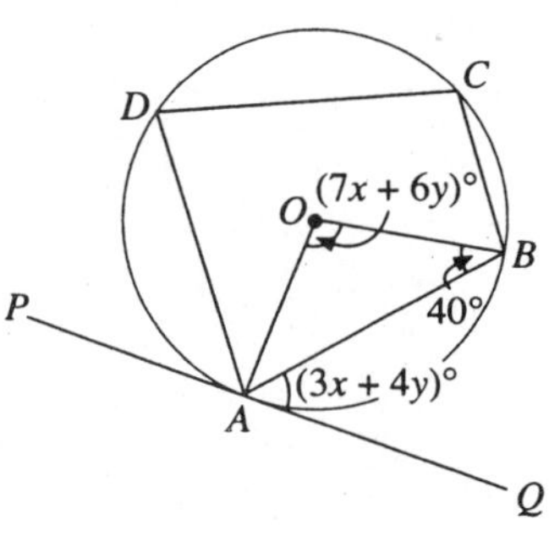

22. In the diagram, TA and TB are tangents to the circle at A and B respectively. The lines PQ and AB intersect at X. Given that $A\hat{T}B = 48°$, $P\hat{B}T = 42°$ and $B\hat{A}Q = 44°$, calculate

(a) $P\hat{B}A$,

(b) $A\hat{P}B$,

(c) $A\hat{X}P$.

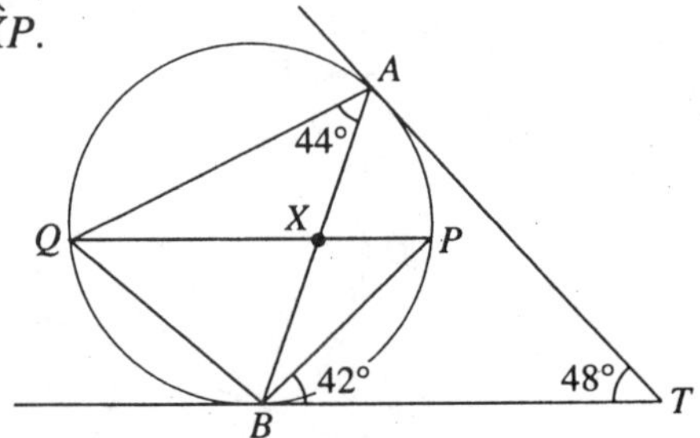

Graphs amd Graphical Solutions

xample 1

The diagram shows part of the curve of $y = \frac{6}{x^2}$.

Write down the equation of the line of symmetry of the curve.

The point $\left(h, 1\frac{1}{2}\right)$ *lies on the curve. Find the possible values of h.*

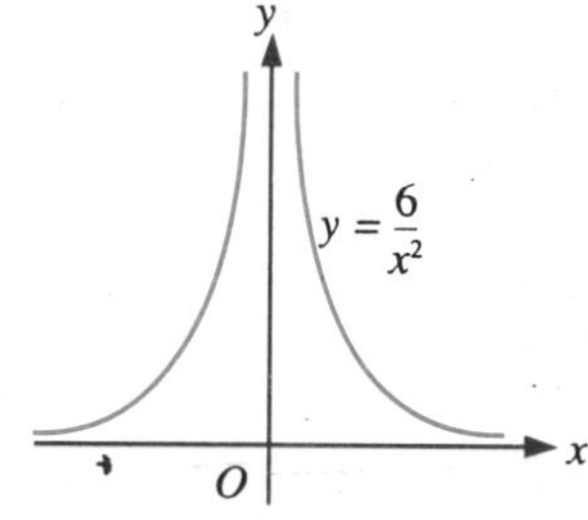

$x = 0$ is the equation of the line of symmetry.

$\left(h, 1\frac{1}{2}\right)$ lies on the curve.

i.e. $1\frac{1}{2} = \frac{6}{h^2} \quad \Rightarrow \quad h^2 = \frac{6}{1\frac{1}{2}} = 4$

$\therefore \quad h = \pm 2$

xample 2

The following is a table of values for the graph of $y = 2(x+1)(x-3)$.

x	−2	−1	0	1	2	3	4
y	h	0	−6	−8	k	0	10

Calculate the value of h and of k.

Using a scale of 1 cm to represent 1 unit on the x-axis and 1 cm to represent 4 units on the y-axis, plot the graph of $y = 2(x + 1)(x - 3)$ *for* $-2 \leqslant x \leqslant 4$.

(a) *Use your graph to solve the equation* $2(x + 1)(x - 3) = 4$.

(b) *By drawing a tangent, find the gradient of the graph at the point* $x = 2$.

(c) *Using the same scale and axes, draw the graph of* $y = 2x - 4$ *and use it to solve the equation* $2(x + 1)(x - 3) = 2x - 4$.

(d) *State the range of values of x for which* $2(x + 1)(x - 3) \leqslant 2x - 4$.

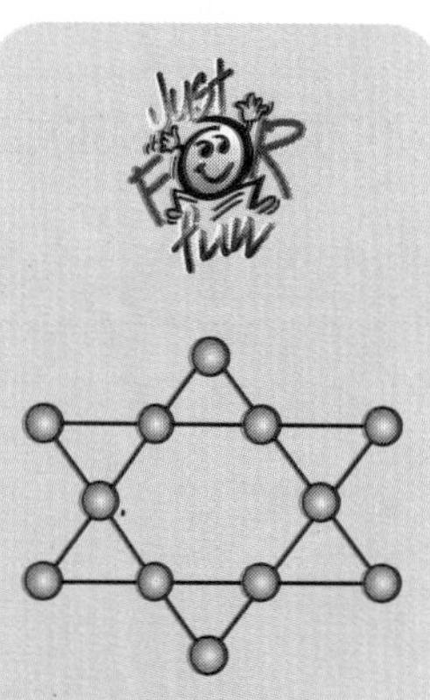

Fill the numbers 1, 2, 3, …, 12 in the circles such that the sum of the numbers in the four circles along each line is equal to 26.

When $x = -2$, $y = 2(-2 + 1)(-2 - 3) = 10$

When $x = 2$, $y = 2(2 + 1)(2 - 3) = -6$,
$\therefore$ $h = 10$ and $k = -6$

(a) The graph of $y = 2(x + 1)(x - 3)$ is plotted as shown below. From the graph, when $y = 4$, $x = -1.45$ or 3.45. Therefore, the solution of $2(x + 1)(x - 3) = 4$ is -1.45 or 3.45.

(b) A tangent is drawn at the point $x = 2$. The gradient of the tangent is approximately $\frac{8}{2}$ or 4. Therefore, the gradient of the curve at $x = 2$ is 4.

(c) The table of values for $y = 2x - 4$ is shown below.

x	0	2	4
y	-4	0	4

The line $y = 2x - 4$ cuts the curve at the points where $x = -0.3$ and $x = 3.3$.
$\therefore$ the solution of the equation $2(x + 1)(x - 3) = 2x - 4$ is $x = -0.3$ or $x = 3.3$.

(d) The range of values of x for which $2(x + 1)(x - 3) \leqslant 2x - 4$ is $-0.3 \leqslant x \leqslant 3.3$.

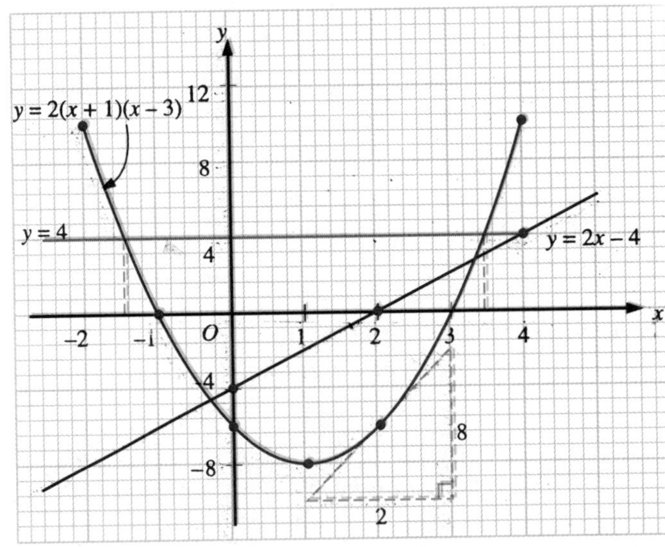

1. In the figure, the curve $y = (x + 1)(2 - x)$ cuts the x-axis at points A and C and the y-axis at B.
   (a) Find the coordinates of the points A, B and C.
   (b) Find the equation of the line of symmetry of the curve.

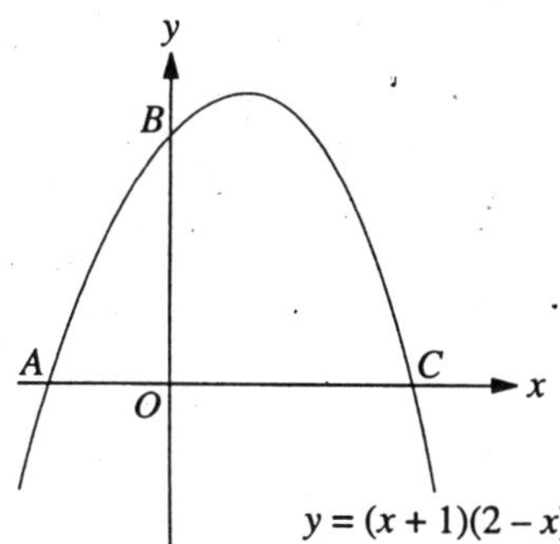

2. On separate diagrams, sketch the graph of each of the following functions:
   (a) $y = x^2 + 2$
   (b) $x + y = 2$
   (c) $y = x^2$
   (d) $y = 4 - x^2$
   (e) $y = x^3 + 2$
   (f) $y = \frac{2}{x}$
   (g) $y = \frac{3}{x^2}$
   (h) $y = 3 - x^3$

3. The curve $y = x^2 + kx - 5$ cuts the y-axis at A and passes through the point $(1, -2)$.
   (a) Find the coordinates of A.
   (b) Calculate the value of k.

4. The figure shows part of the graph of $y = x^2 + kx + p$. Find the value of k and of p.

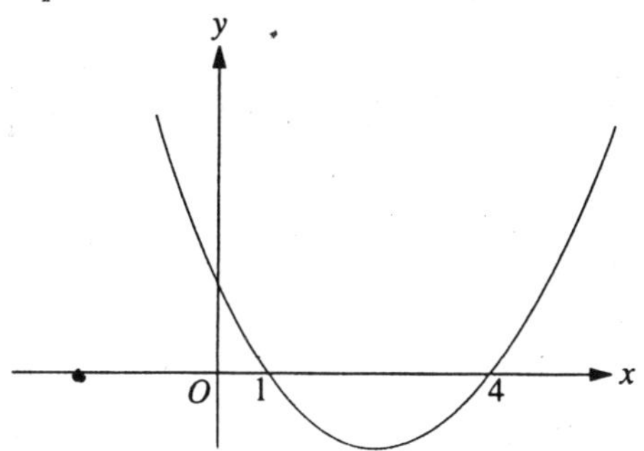

5. A table of values for the graph of $y = x^2 - 3x + 9$ is given below.

x	–2	–1	0	1	2	3	4	5
y	a	13	9	7	7	b	13	19

Calculate the values of a and b.
Using a scale of 2 cm to represent 1 unit on the x-axis and a scale of 1 cm to represent 1 unit on the y-axis, draw the graph of $y = x^2 - 3x + 9$.

Use your graph to solve the equations:
(a) $x^2 - 3x + 9 = 11$
(b) $x^2 - 3x = 7$

By drawing a suitable straight line graph on the same axes, solve the equation $x^2 - 4x + 3 = 0$.

6. The following is an incomplete table of values for the graph of $y = (x + 2)(4 - x)$.

x	–2	–1	0	1	2	3	4
y	0			9			0

   (a) Calculate the missing values of y.
   (b) Using a scale of 2 cm to represent 1 unit on the x-axis and 1 cm to represent 1 unit on the y-axis, draw the graph of $y = (x + 2)(4 - x)$ for $-2 \leqslant x \leqslant 4$.
   (c) Use your graph to find two values of x which satisfy the equation $(x + 2)(4 - x) = 3$.
   (d) Use your graph to estimate the biggest value of y.
   (e) State the range of values of x for which $(x + 2)(4 - x)$ is greater than 8.

7. The variables x and y are connected by the equation $y = x^2 + 3x - 3$. Some corresponding values of x and y are given in the following table.

x	–5	–4	–3	–2	–1	0	1	2
y	7	1	–3	–5	–5	–3	1	7

(a) Using a scale of 2 cm to represent 1 unit on the x-axis and 2 cm to represent 2 units on the y-axis, draw the graph of $y = x^2 + 3x - 3$ for $-5 \leqslant x \leqslant 2$.
(b) Use your graph to find the values of x for which
(i) $x^2 + 3x = 8$,
(ii) $x^2 + 3x - 3 \leqslant x$,
(iii) $x^2 + 4x = 2$.
(c) By drawing a suitable tangent to your curve, find the coordinates of the point at which the gradient of the tangent is equal to 1.

8. The following is an incomplete table of values of the graph of $y = x^2(x - 2)$.

x	–2	–1	0	1	2	3	4
y	–16		0		0		

(a) Calculate the missing values of y.
(b) Using scales of 2 cm to 1 unit on the x-axis and 2 cm to 4 units on the y-axis, draw the graph of $y = x^2(x - 2)$, for $-2 \leqslant x \leqslant 4$.
(c) By drawing a tangent, estimate the gradient of the curve when $x = 1\frac{1}{2}$.
(d) Use your graph to solve the equation $x^2(x - 2) = -1$.
(e) By drawing a suitable straight line on the same axes, use your graph to find three values of x which satisfy the equation $x^2(x - 2) = x - 2$.

9. The following is an incomplete table of values for the graph of $y = x^2 + \frac{10}{x} - 8$.

x	$\frac{1}{2}$	1	$1\frac{1}{2}$	2	3	4
y	$12\frac{1}{4}$				$4\frac{1}{3}$	10.5

(a) Fill in the missing values of y.
(b) Using scales of 4 cm to represent 1 unit on the x-axis and 1 cm to represent 1 unit on the y-axis, draw the graph of $y = x^2 + \frac{10}{x} - 8$, for $\frac{1}{2} \leqslant x \leqslant 4$.
(c) Use your graph to find
(i) the minimum value of y;
(ii) the two values of x for which $y = 2$.
(d) By drawing a suitable straight line, find the solution to the equation $x^2 + \frac{10}{x} = 16 - 2x$.

10. Given that $y = \frac{5}{x} + 2x - 3$, copy and complete the following table.

x	0.5	1	2	4	5	6	7
y	8						11.7

Taking 2 cm to represent 1 unit on the x-axis and 1 cm to represent 1 unit on the y-axis, draw the graph of $y = \frac{5}{x} + 2x - 3$ from $x = 0.5$ to $x = 7$.

(a) By drawing a tangent, find the gradient of the graph at the point where $x = 3$.

(b) Using your graph, estimate the solutions to the equation

(i) $\frac{5}{x} + 2x - 8 = 0$;

(ii) $\frac{5}{x} + x - 6 = 0$.

11. Set up a table of values for $y = 2^x - 5$, such that $-1.5 \leqslant x \leqslant 2.5$. Draw the graph of $y = 2^x - 5$ using a scale of 4 cm to represent 1 unit on the x-axis and 2 cm to represent 1 unit on the y-axis. Use your graph to find

(a) the value of y when $x = 0.8$;

(b) the value of x when $y = -1.5$.

12. The following table gives corresponding values of x and y which are connected by the equation $y = 8(0.6)^x$.

x	0	0.5	1	1.5	2	3	4	5	6	7
y	8	6.2	4.8	h	2.9	k	1.0	0.6	0.4	0.2

(a) Calculate the value of h and of k correct to 1 decimal place.

(b) Using a scale of 2 cm for 1 unit on both axes, plot the graph of $y = 8(0.6)^x$ for $0 \leqslant x \leqslant 7$.

(c) By drawing a tangent, find the gradient of the curve at the point $x = 1.5$.

(d) Use your graph to find

(i) the value of y when $x = 2.5$,

(ii) the solution of the equation $(0.6)^x = 0.5$,

(iii) the solution of the equation $8(0.6)^x = x$,

(iv) the range of values of x for which $8(0.6)^x > x + 3$.

Graphs in Practical Situations

Example 1

The diagram is the speed-time graph of an MRT train. Given that the distance travelled in the first 50 seconds is 850 m, calculate

(a) the maximum speed, V m/s,
(b) the acceleration of the train during the first 15 seconds,
(c) the further distance travelled before the train comes to a stop.

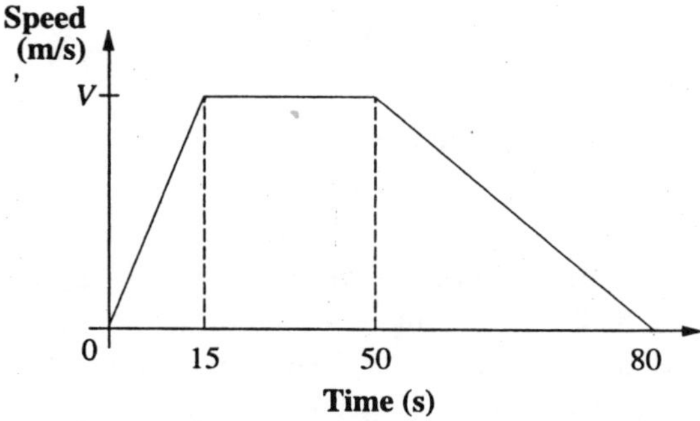

(a) The distance moved is given by the area under the speed-time graph

$$850 = \frac{1}{2}(15)V + (50 - 15)V$$

$$850 = 7.5V + 35V$$

$$\therefore \quad V = 850 \div 42.5 = 20$$

(b) The acceleration of the train during the first 15 seconds is given by the gradient of the graph for that period.

$$\therefore \quad \text{acceleration} = \frac{20}{15}$$

$$= 1\frac{1}{3} \text{ m/s}^2$$

(c) The train slows down for 30 seconds before it comes to rest.

The further distance travelled $= \frac{1}{2} \times 20 \times 30$

$= 300$ m

To promote greater usage of mobile phone services, a mobile phone company devises the following structure of charges for its users as follows.

> *First 40 minutes at 18 cents per minute.*
> *Next 40 minutes at 12 cents per minute.*
> *Any additional units at 6 cents per minute.*

Using a horizontal axis marked 0 to 150 minutes, with a scale of 1 cm to 10 minutes and a vertical scale of 1 cm to 2 dollars, draw a graph of cost against the number of minutes used. Use your graph to find

(a) the cost of using the mobile phone for (i) 32 minutes, (ii) 68 minutes.
(b) the number of minutes used when the cost is (i) \$8, (ii) \$16.

The graph is as shown below.

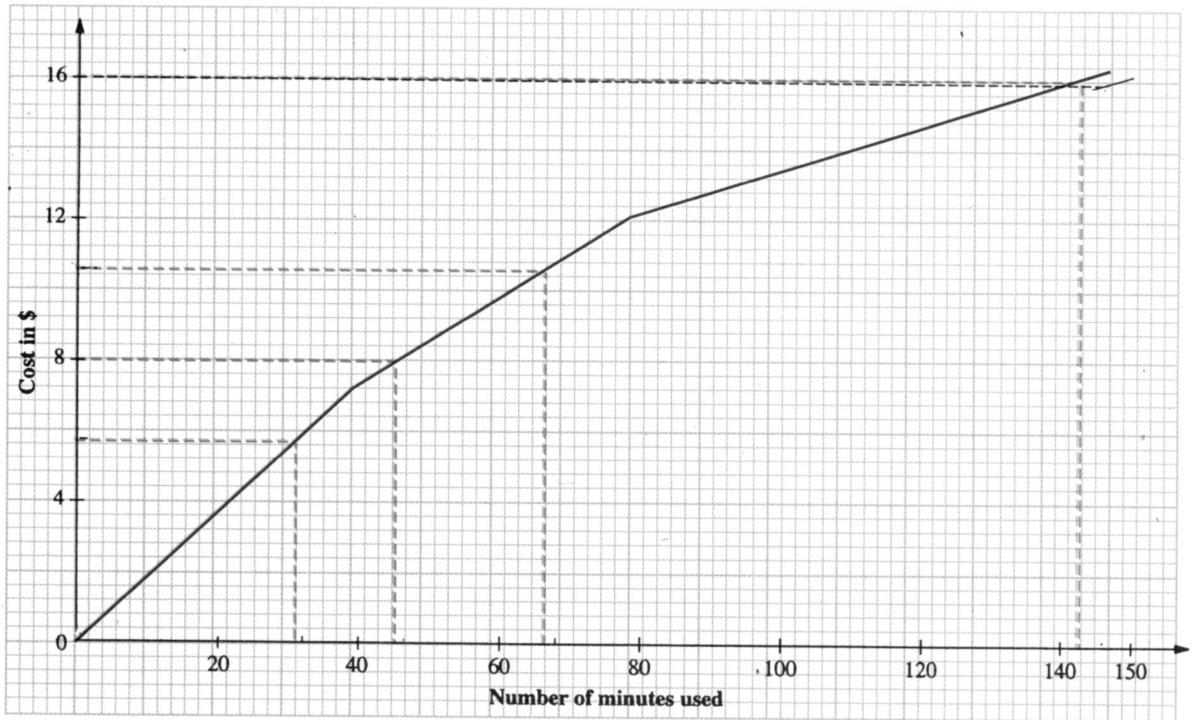

From the graph

(a) the cost of using the mobile phone for
  (i) 32 minutes is approximately \$5.80,
  (ii) 68 minutes is approximately \$10.80.

(b) (i) when the total cost is \$8, the number of minutes is approximately 47.
  (ii) when the total cost is \$16, the number of minutes used is approximately 146.

Exercise 7o

1. A car uses 2 litres of petrol for every 25 km it travels. Draw a graph to show the relationship between the distance travelled (d) and the number of litres of petrol used (l). Use your graph to find
   (a) the amount of petrol used after travelling 75 km,
   (b) the distance travelled after 5 litres of petrol had been used.

2. On a certain day in 1999, the exchange rate for RM100 is S$45. Draw a graph to convert Malaysian ringgit to Singapore dollars. Use your graph to find the approximate values of
   (a) **(i)** RM12,
   (ii) RM38 in S$,
   (b) **(i)** S$42,
   (ii) S$75 in RM.

3. The relationship between degrees Celsius (°C) and degrees Fahrenheit (°F) is given by the formula $F = \frac{9}{5}C + 32$. Plot a graph of F against C for $0° \leq C \leq 100°$. Use your graph to find
   (a) the value of C when $F = 98$,
   (b) the value of F when $C = 50$,
   (c) the change in C when F increases from 70 to 120.

4. The charges for household electricity are as follows:
   first 30 units at 25 cents per unit,
   next 30 units at 12 cents per unit,
   any additional unit at 7 cents per unit.
   Using a horizontal axis marked from 0 to 100 units, with a scale of 1 cm to 5 units, and a vertical scale of 1 cm to 1 dollar, draw a graph of cost against number of units used. Use your graph to find the
   (a) the cost of 84 units;
   (b) the number of units used if the charge is $8.70;
   (c) the number of units used if the charge is $12.15.

5. The velocity-time graph shows a motorist travelling with constant acceleration.
   (a) What is the initial velocity?
   (b) What is the acceleration?
   (c) What is the distance moved in the first 30 seconds?

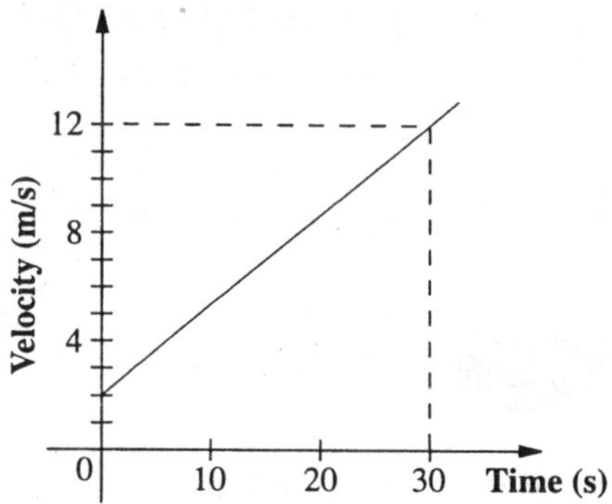

6. The diagram shows the speed-time graph of a body over a period of 90 seconds. Given that the total distance moved is 1.84 km, find
   (a) the value of v,
   (b) the acceleration during the first 10 seconds,
   (c) the distance moved during the first 10 seconds of its motion.

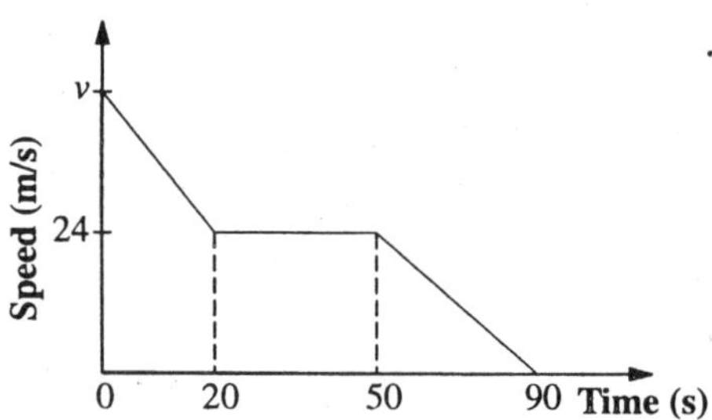

7. The diagram shows the speed-time graph of a body moving in a straight line.
   (a) Calculate the acceleration of the body during the first 15 seconds.
   (b) Calculate the distance moved by the body in the first 40 seconds of its motion.
   (c) Given that the body decelerates at 1.25 m/s², find the value of t.

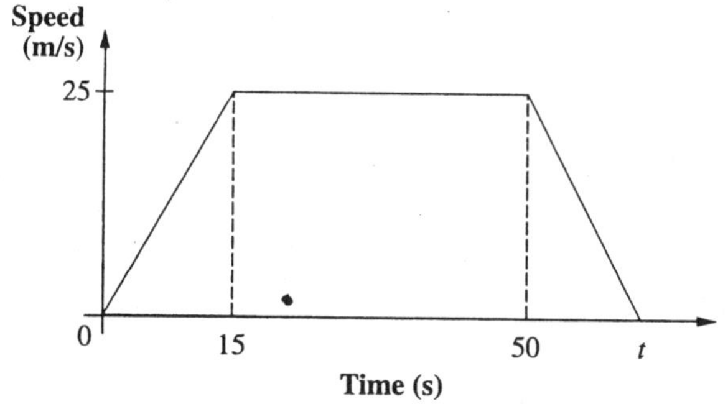

8. The diagram shows the speed-time graphs of a goods train and a lorry during a period of 100 seconds. Calculate
   (a) the acceleration of the lorry in the first 20 seconds,
   (b) the distance travelled by the lorry during the 100 seconds,
   (c) the distance travelled by the train during the 100 seconds,
   (d) the time when the lorry overtakes the train.

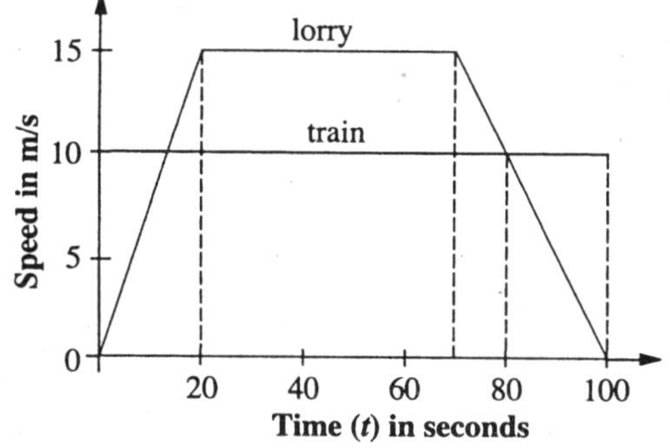

9. The force F in newtons (N) applied to a pulley to raise a load L kg is given in the table below.

L (kg)	20	40	80	120	160	200
F (N)	70	90	130	170	210	250

Using a scale of 2 cm to 40 kg on the horizontal axis and 2 cm to 40 N on the vertical axis, plot the graph of F (N) against L (kg).

Use your graph to find
   (a) the force required to raise a load of
      (i) 50 kg,
      (ii) 190 kg,
   (b) the initial force required to operate the pulley.

10. The distance-time graphs show the journeys of two cyclists A and B. A travelled from P to Q while B travelled from Q to P.

Use the graph to answer the following questions:

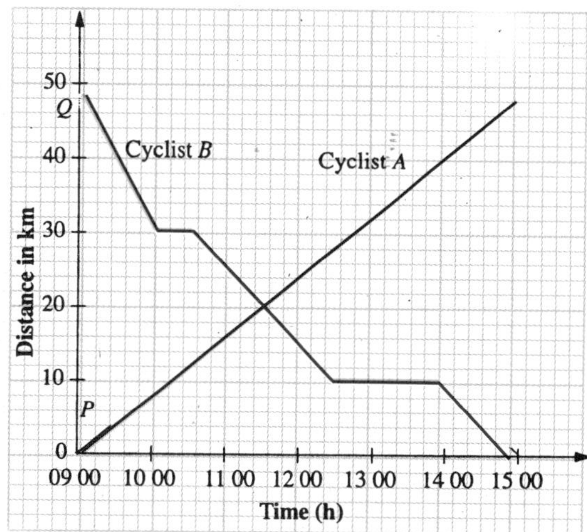

   (a) Find the distance of PQ.
   (b) How long did B rest during the journey?
   (c) How far from Q did the two cyclists meet?
   (d) During which period of time did B travel the fastest?
   (e) Find the average speed of cyclist B for the whole journey.

11. The diagram shows the speed-time graph of a moving particle. The graph consists of 3 line segments BC, CD, DE and a quadrant with centre A.

(a) Write down the acceleration of the particle at time $t = 10$.

(b) Calculate the acceleration of the particle during the last 5 seconds.

(c) Calculate the total distance covered in the first 20 seconds of the journey. (Take $\pi = 3.14$)

(d) Calculate the average speed for the whole journey.

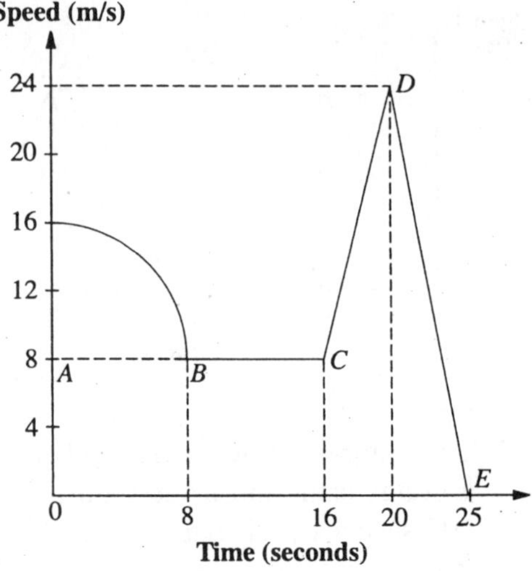

12. The table below shows the speed of a car over a period of 8 seconds.

Time (s)	0	1	2	3	4	5	6	7	8
Speed (m/s)	0	4.5	7.8	10.1	11.6	12.4	13	13.4	14

After the 8th second, the car moves with a constant speed of 14.0 m/s. Using a scale of 2 cm to represent 1 second on the horizontal axis and 2 cm to represent 2 m/s on the vertical axis, plot the graph of the motion of the car.

A sports car starts from rest at $t = 2$ and moves with an acceleration of 3 m/s^2. Plot the graph of the motion of the sports car for $2 \leqslant t \leqslant 8$ and find, graphically,

(a) the time at which the two cars have the same speed,

(b) the acceleration of the car at the time $t = 5$.

13. The volume of an **open** rectangular box, made of thin metal, is 35 cm^3. The base of the box is a square of side x cm.

(a) Find, in terms of x, an expression for the height of the box.

(b) The total external area, of the base and the four sides, is A cm^2. Show that $A = x^2 + \dfrac{140}{x}$.

(c) Complete the following table which gives the values of x and the corresponding values of A.

x	2	2.5	3	3.5	4	4.5	5	5.5	6
A	74			52.3	51	51.4		55.7	

(d) Using a scale of 4 cm to 1 unit, draw a horizontal x-axis for $2 \leq x \leq 6$. Using a scale of 4 cm to 5 units, draw a vertical A-axis for $50 \leq A \leq 75$. Draw the graph of A against x.

(e) Use your graph to find

(i) the side of the largest base, which will give a total surface area of 55 cm^2,

(ii) the minimum value of A,

(iii) the height of the box for which the least amount of metal is used,

(iv) the total surface area when the base has side 2.6 cm.

Pythagoras' Theorem and Trigonometry

Example 1

The figure shows a triangle ABC, where AB = 19 cm, AC = 15 cm and $B\hat{A}C = 46°$. Calculate the following:

(a) BC *(b) the area of $\triangle ABC$*

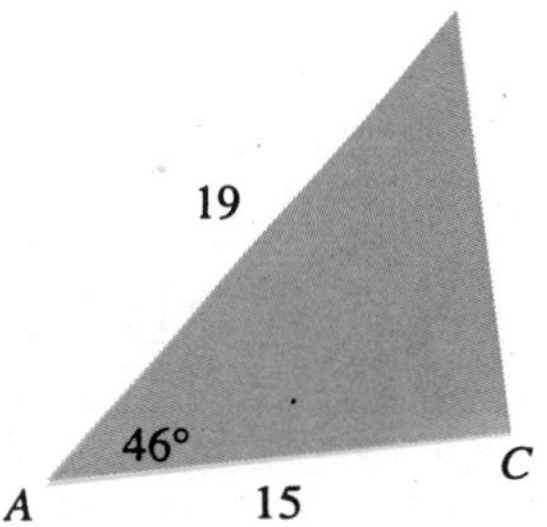

(a) $BC^2 = AC^2 + AB^2 - 2(AC)(AB)\cos B\hat{A}C$

$= 15^2 + 19^2 - 2(15)(19)\cos 46° = 190.04$ (correct to 2 decimal places)

$\therefore \quad BC = \sqrt{190.04} = 13.8$ cm (correct to 1 decimal place)

(b) Area of $\triangle ABC = \frac{1}{2}(15)(19)\sin 46° = 102.5 \text{ cm}^2$ (correct to 1 decimal place)

Example 2

In $\triangle ABC$, AB = 8 cm, AC = 15 cm, $B\hat{A}C = 90°$ and AC is produced to D. Find

(a) the length of BC, *(b) $\sin A\hat{C}B$,* *(c) $\cos B\hat{C}D$.*

(a) $BC^2 = 15^2 + 8^2$

$= 225 + 64 = 289$

$\therefore \quad BC = \pm\sqrt{289} = \pm 17$

i.e. $BC = 17$ cm (negative value is ignored here)

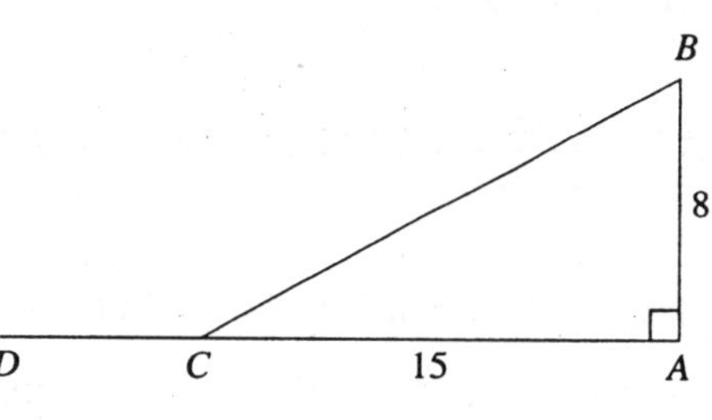

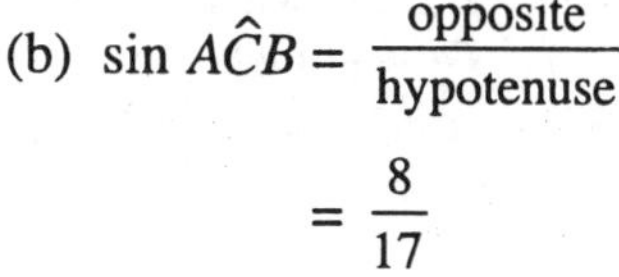

(b) $\sin A\hat{C}B = \dfrac{\text{opposite}}{\text{hypotenuse}}$

$= \dfrac{8}{17}$

(c) $\cos B\hat{C}D = -\dfrac{15}{17}$

Example 3

From the top of a building 46 m high, the angles of depression of two points on the ground both due east of the tower are 58° and 32°.

Calculate the distance between the two points.

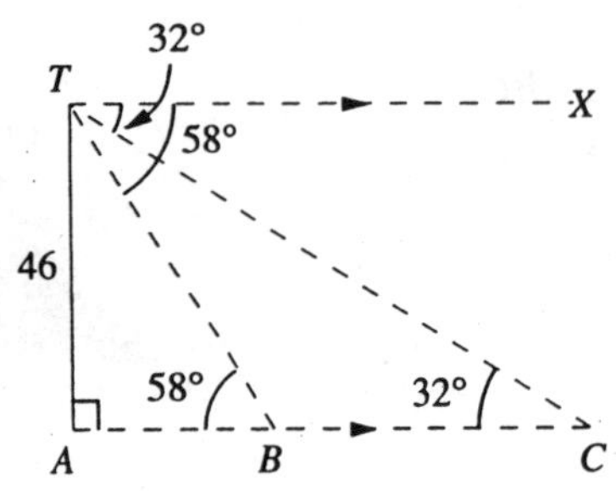

The trigonometric ratio of an angle remains constant whatever the length of the radius may be.

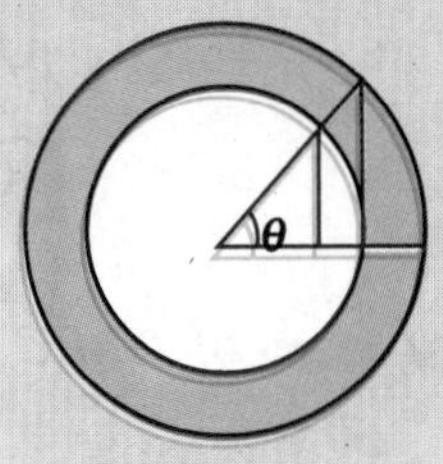

Solution

Let AT be the building and B and C the two points on the ground.

$T\hat{C}A = 32°$, $T\hat{B}A = 58°$ (alternate ∡s)

In $\triangle ABT$, $\tan 58° = \frac{AT}{AB} = \frac{46}{AB}$

$\therefore \quad AB = \frac{46}{\tan 58°} = 28.74$ m (correct to 2 decimal places)

In $\triangle ACT$, $\tan 32° = \frac{AT}{AC} = \frac{46}{AC}$

$\therefore \quad AC = \frac{46}{\tan 32°} = 73.62$ m (correct to 2 decimal places)

$\therefore$ distance between B and $C = 73.62 - 28.74$

$= 44.88$ m

What is the angle of rotation made by the Earth in 1 hour?

Exercise 7p

1. In $\triangle ABD$, $A\hat{B}D = 90°$. AC bisects $B\hat{A}D$. Given that $AC = 6$ cm and $A\hat{C}B = 60°$, calculate the length of
   (a) AB;
   (b) AD.

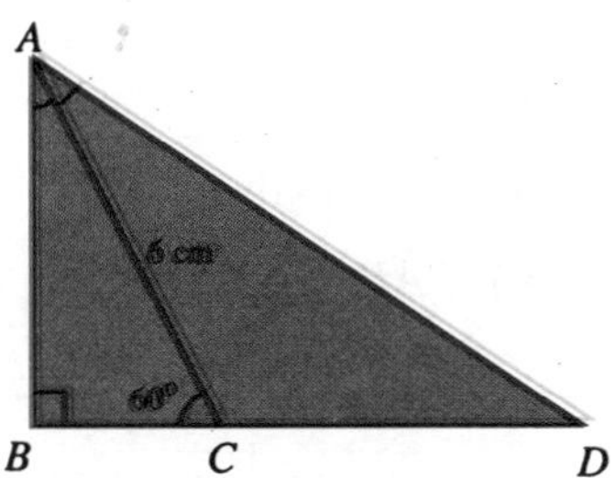

2. If A is an obtuse angle and $\sin A = \frac{7}{25}$, find the values of:
   (a) $\tan A$
   (b) $\cos A$

3. (a) Calculate the area of the semicircle BDC in the diagram.
   (Take $\pi = 3.142$.)

   (b) The vertical angle of an isosceles triangle is 54° and the height is 32 cm. Find the length of the base of the triangle and its area.

   (c) In the isosceles triangle ABC, $AB = AC = 6$ cm and $B\hat{A}C = 94°$. Calculate the length of BC.

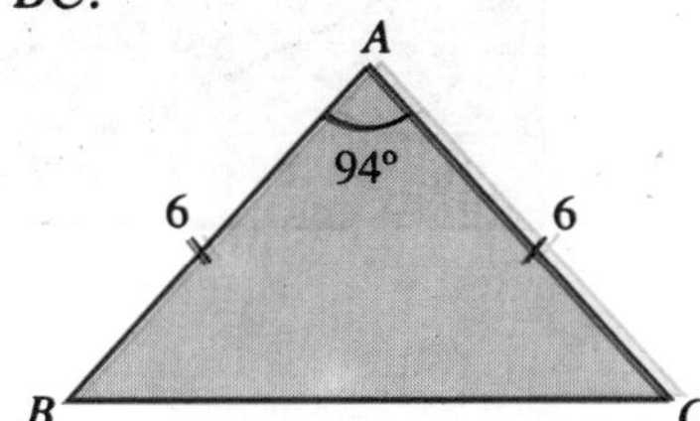

4. From the figure, calculate
   (a) the length of BC (correct to 3 significant figures),
   (b) $B\hat{A}X$.

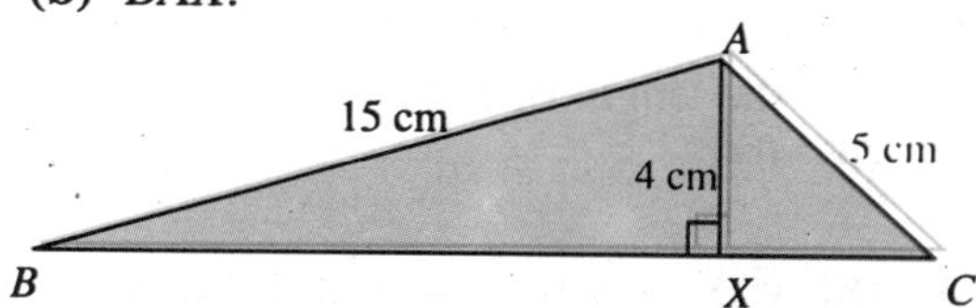

5. (a) Find the length of AB and the angle AOB in the figure below.

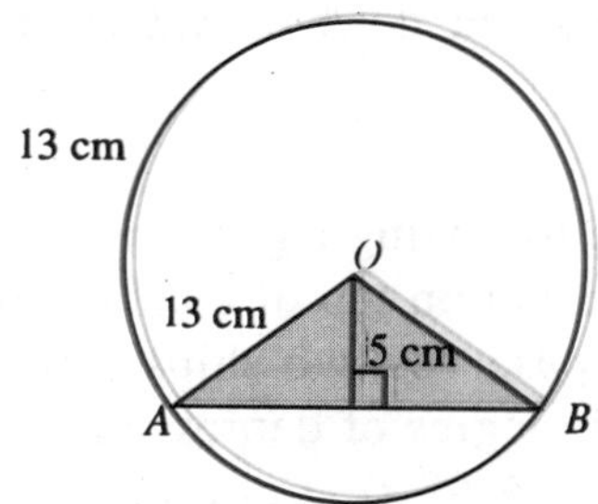

   (b) From a point 10 m away from the base of a building, the angles of elevation of the top and bottom of a window are 40° and 30° respectively. How tall is the window? (Give your answer correct to 2 significant figures.)

6. If $\tan\theta = 2\frac{2}{5}$ where θ is acute, find the value of
   (a) $5\cos\theta$,
   (b) $\sin(90° - \theta)$.

7. (a) A ladder 12 m long leans against a wall. Its foot on the ground is 8 m from the wall.
   (i) Calculate the angle the ladder makes with the ground.
   (ii) How high up the wall does the ladder reach?

   (b) A tower 60 m high has a shadow 75 m long. Find the angle of elevation of the sun.

8. In $\triangle ABC$, $\hat{C} = 90°$, $AC = 8$ cm and $BC = 6$ cm.

(a) Find the length of AB.
(b) If CD is the perpendicular from C to AB, find the length of CD.

9. In triangle ABC, $\hat{C} = 90°$ and $AC = 12$ cm. If its area is 48 cm^2, calculate

(a) the length of BC,
(b) $B\hat{A}C$.

10. (a) Given $\sin x = \sin 32°$, such that $90° < x < 180°$, write down the value of x.

(b) Given $\sin x = \frac{3}{5}$, such that $90° < x < 180°$, write down the values of $\cos x$ and $\tan x$.

11. (a) The following figure shows a man M standing on top of a cliff 250 m high. He observes two ships, A and B, and their angles of depression to be 58.5° and 34.6° respectively. Find the distance between A and B.

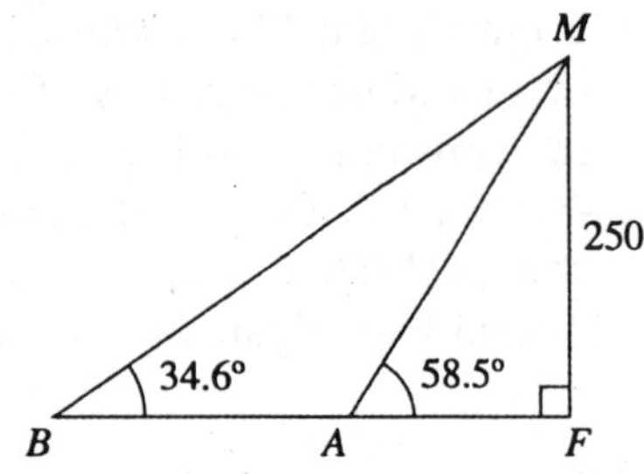

(b) The angles of elevation of the top and bottom of a window from a point 7.2 m from its foot are 43° and 32° respectively. Calculate the height of the window.

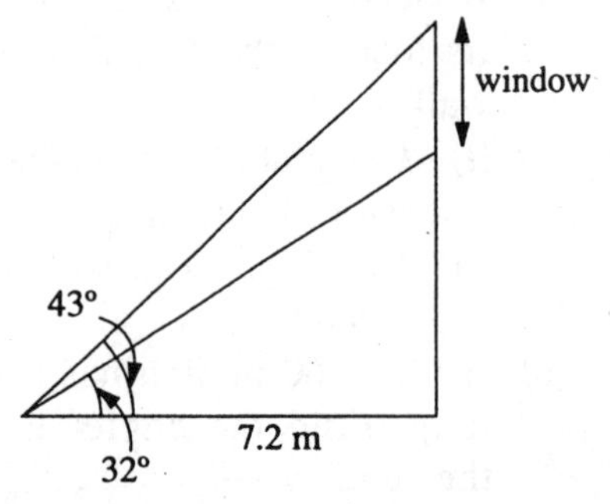

12. In $\triangle ABC$, $A\hat{B}C = 42°$, $B\hat{A}C = 41°$ and $BC = 8.6$ cm. Calculate

(a) the length of AB,
(b) the area of $\triangle ABC$.

13. In the diagram, r_1 and r_2 are the radii of the circles whose centres are A and B respectively and PQ is a common tangent. If r_1 is 5 cm and r_2 is 8 cm, calculate

(a) the length of PQ,

(b) $P\hat{A}B$.

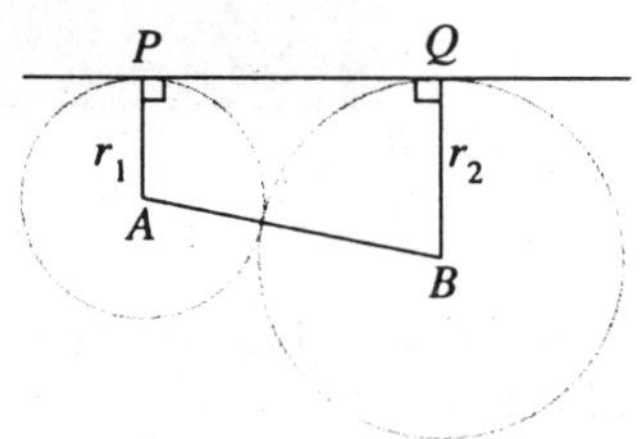

14. The area of $\triangle ABC$ is 8 cm^2. If $AB = 6$ cm and $AC = 5$ cm, calculate the following:

(a) $B\hat{A}C$,
(b) the length of BC.

15. ABC is a triangle in which $B\hat{A}C = 90°$, $A\hat{B}C = 35°$ and $AC = 6$ cm. Calculate the length of BC. If BA is produced to a point D such that $CD = 11$ cm, calculate $A\hat{D}C$ and the length of BD.

16. In the diagram, $ABCD$ is a trapezium in which AB is parallel to DC and $B\hat{A}D = 90°$. If $D\hat{A}C = 64°$, $AC = 5.4$ cm and $AB = 3.6$ cm, calculate

(a) the length of CD,
(b) $A\hat{B}D$.

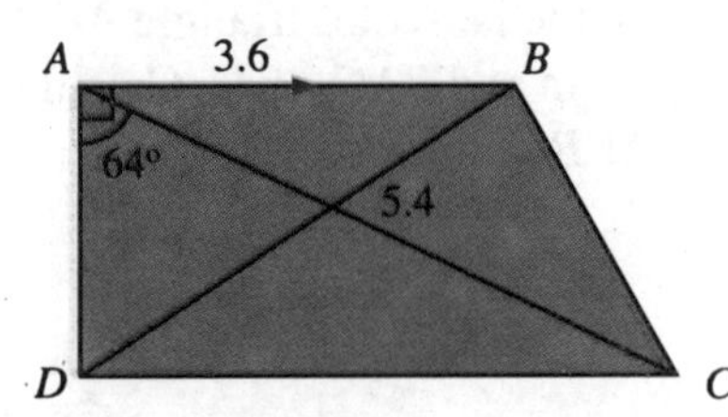

17. In the diagram, AB is a common tangent to the two circles whose centres are P and Q and whose radii are 4 cm and 5 cm respectively. Calculate

(a) the length of AB,

(b) $P\hat{Q}B$.

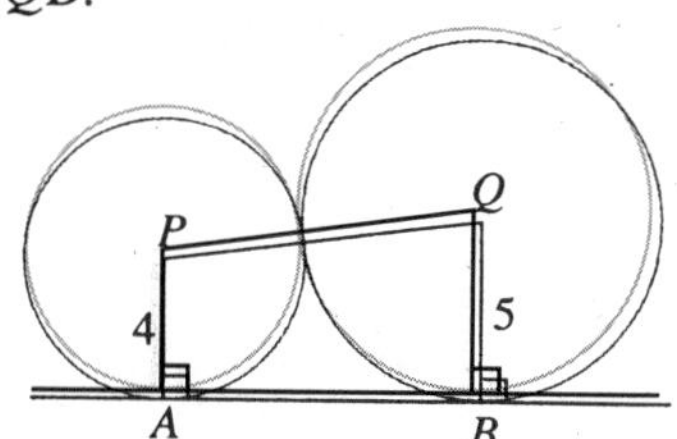

18. In the following diagram, $ABCD$ is a trapezium in which BA is parallel to CD. $BA = 8.6$ cm, $BD =$, $CD = 12.4$ cm and $B\hat{D}C = x°$. The line BE is perpendicular to CD. Write down expressions in x for

(a) BE;

(b) the area of the trapezium $ABCD$.

Given that the area of the trapezium $ABCD$ is 73.5 cm², calculate $x°$.

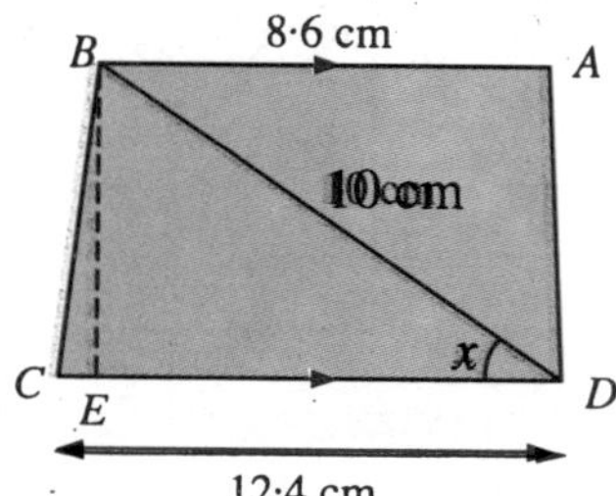

19. (a) In the diagram, O is the centre of the circle and PA is the tangent to the circle at A. If $OA = 7$ cm and $P\hat{A}B = 26°$, calculate

(i) $A\hat{O}B$;

(ii) the length of AP;

(iii) the area of the minor sector AOB.

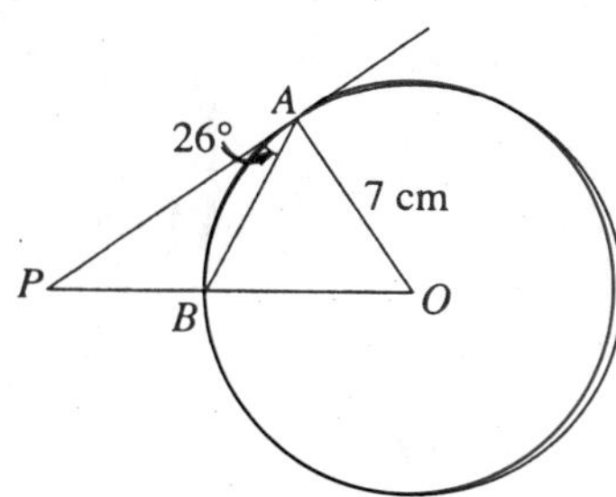

(b) In the diagram, O is the centre of the sector OAB of radius 12 cm. K is a point on OB such that $KB = 4$ cm. If $A\hat{O}B = 56°$, calculate the area of the shaded region, giving your answer correct to 2 decimal places.
[Take $\pi = 3.142$]

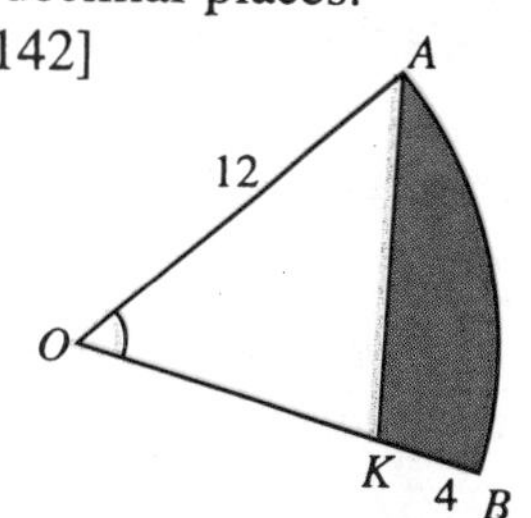

20. $ABCDE$ is a regular pentagon of side 14 cm. Calculate

(a) the length of AC,

(b) the area of the pentagon $ABCDE$.

21. In the diagram, $A\hat{C}B = A\hat{D}C = 90°$, $B\hat{A}C = 54.6°$, $AD = 4.8$ cm and $DC = 7.6$ cm. Calculate the following:

(a) $A\hat{C}D$, **(b)** AC,

(c) AB.

Given that E is the point on AB such that $AE = 7$ cm, calculate the area of $\triangle ACE$.

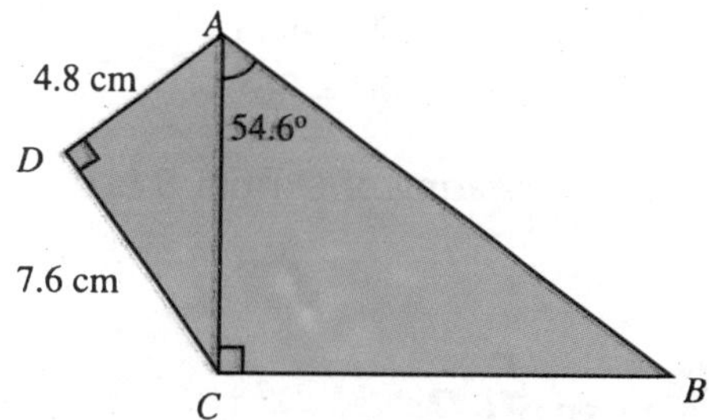

22. In the acute-angled triangle ABC, $\hat{A} = 47°$, $AC = 12.4$ cm and $BC = 10.5$ cm.

(a) Calculate $\hat{B}$.

(b) It is also possible to draw an obtuse-angled triangle with the given dimensions. What is the size of the obtuse angle of this triangle?

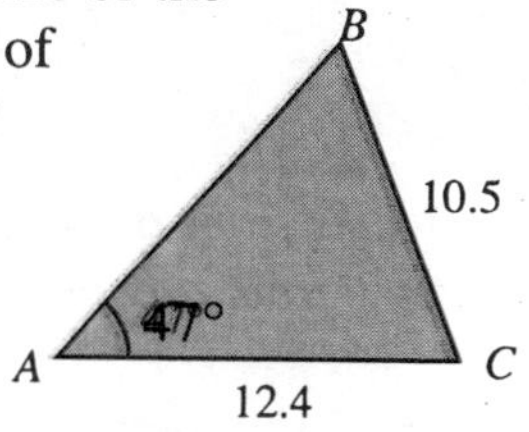

Bearing and Trigonometry

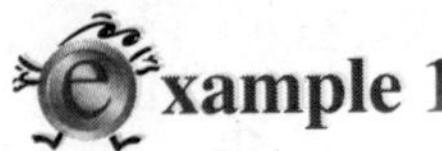

xample 1

In the diagram, A, B and C represent three points on a map. Calculate

(a) the bearing of C from A,
(b) the bearing of C from B.

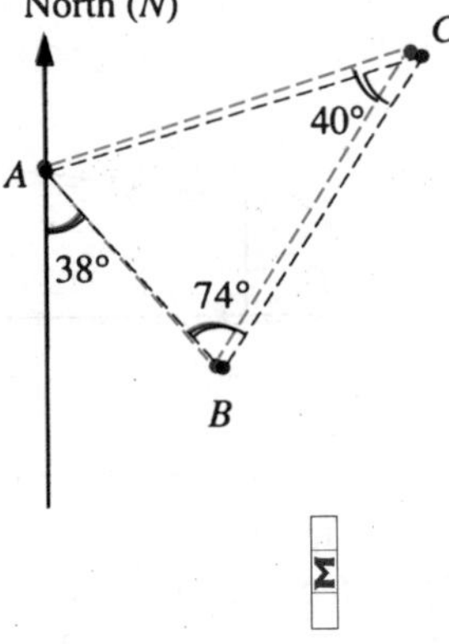

(a) $B\hat{A}C = 180° - 74° - 40°$ ($\measuredangle$ sum of a $\triangle$)
$= 66°$

$\therefore$ $N\hat{A}C = 180° - 66° - 38°$ ($\measuredangle$s on a straight line)
$= 76°$

$\therefore$ the bearing of C from A is 076°.

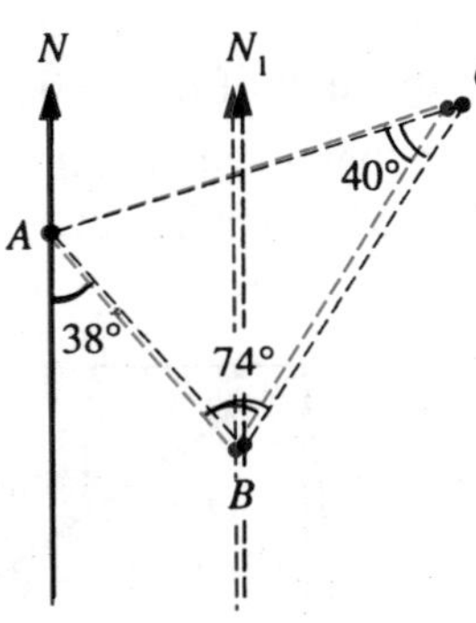

(b) Construct a line parallel to AN and passing through B.
$A\hat{B}N = 38°$ (alt. $\measuredangle$s),
$N_1\hat{B}C = 74° - 38° = 36°$

$\therefore$ the bearing of C from B is 036°.

xample 2

A, B and C are three points on level ground. B is due south of A and the bearing of C from A is 085°. A vertical mast AT of height 50 m stands at A. The angle of elevation of T from B is 44° and the angle of elevation of T from C is 28°. Calculate the following, giving your answer correct to 2 decimal places.

(a) AB *(b) AC*
(c) BC *(d) the bearing of C from B*

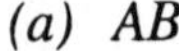

A man walks from B to C, find the greatest angle of elevation T from any point along BC.

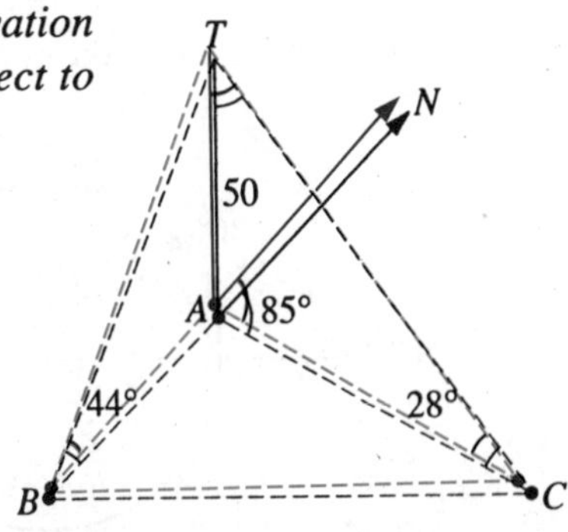

(a) In $\triangle ABT$, $\tan 44° = \dfrac{AT}{AB} = \dfrac{50}{AB}$

$\therefore \quad AB = \dfrac{50}{\tan 44°} \approx 51.777 = 51.78$ m (correct to 2 decimal places)

(b) In $\triangle ACT$, $\tan 28° = \dfrac{AT}{AC} = \dfrac{50}{AC}$

$\therefore \quad AC = \dfrac{50}{\tan 28°} \approx 94.036 = 94.04$ m (correct to 2 decimal places)

(c) In $\triangle ABC$, $B\hat{A}C = 180° - 85°$ (∡s on a straight line)
$= 95°$

$BC^2 = AB^2 + AC^2 - 2(AB)(AC)\cos 95°$
$= 51.777^2 + 94.036^2 - 2(51.777)(94.036)\cos 95° \approx 12\ 372.3$

$\therefore \quad BC = 111.23$ m (correct to 2 decimal places)

(d) In $\triangle ABC$, $\dfrac{AC}{\sin A\hat{B}C} = \dfrac{BC}{\sin B\hat{A}C}$

$$\frac{94.036}{\sin A\hat{B}C} = \frac{111.23}{\sin 95°}$$

$$\sin A\hat{B}C = \frac{94.036 \sin 95°}{111.23}$$

$$A\hat{B}C = 57.37°$$

$\therefore$ the bearing of C from B is 057.37°. (correct to 2 decimal places)

In country Y, only 5¢ and 8¢ coins are available. Jonathan has a big bag of 5¢ and 8¢ coins. He goes to a shop which also has a plentiful supply of 5¢ and 8¢ coins. Can Jonathan buy any product of value from 1¢ to 99¢ (To buy an item worth 1¢, Jonathan can give the shop-keeper two 8¢ coins and the shopkeeper gives him back three 5¢ coins.)

The greatest angle of elevation of T from the path of BC occurs at the point K on BC where AK is perpendicular to BC.

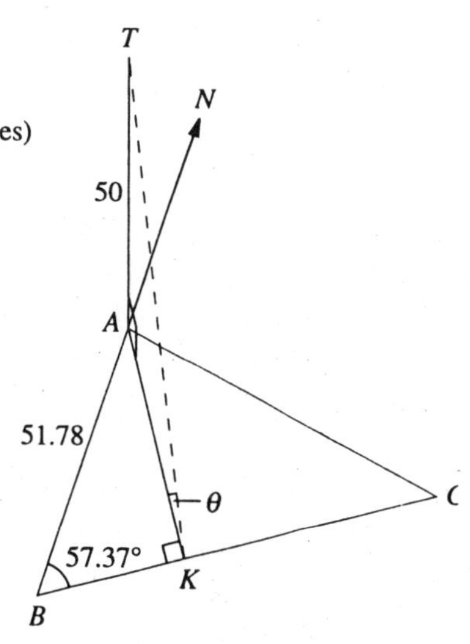

$\sin 57.37° = \dfrac{AK}{51.78}$

$AK = 51.78 \sin 57.37° = 43.61$ m (correct to 2 decimal places)

$\tan A\hat{K}T = \dfrac{50}{43.61}$

$\therefore \quad A\hat{K}T = 48.91°$ (correct to 2 decimal places)

$\therefore$ the greatest angle of elevation of T from any point along BC is 48.91°.

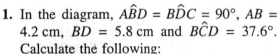

1. In the diagram, $A\hat{B}D = B\hat{D}C = 90°$, $AB = 4.2$ cm, $BD = 5.8$ cm and $B\hat{C}D = 37.6°$. Calculate the following:
   (a) $B\hat{A}D$,
   (b) CD,
   (c) BC.

   If X is the foot of the perpendicular from D to BC, calculate the length of BX.

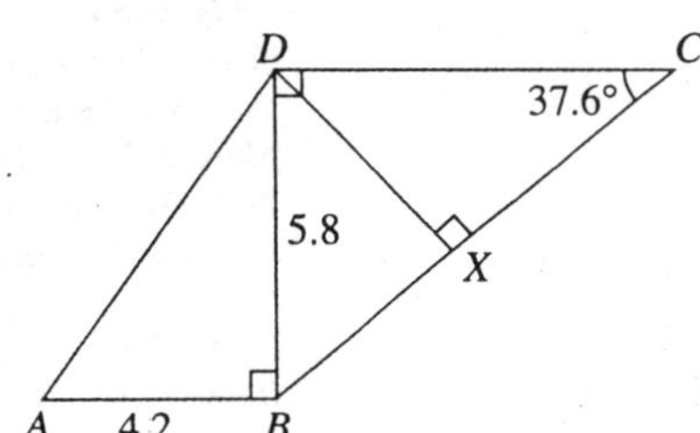

2. The points P, Q and R are on level ground and $P\hat{Q}R = 101°$. R is due north of P, and Q is on a bearing 049° from P. Find
   (a) the bearing of Q from R,
   (b) the bearing of R from Q.
   (c) If $PQ = 1.45$ km, calculate the length of PR.

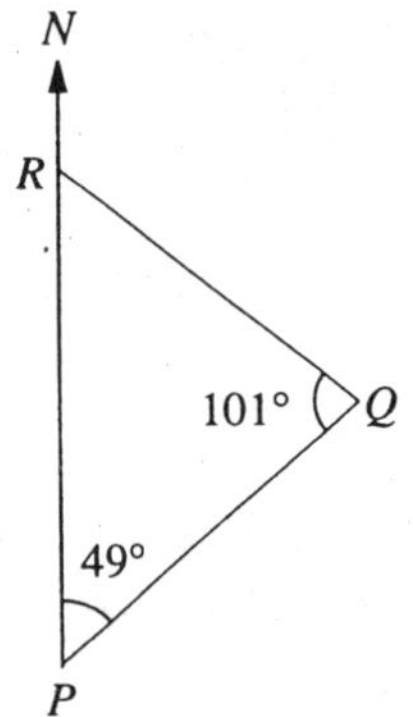

3. In the diagram, the points A, B and C form an equilateral triangle, and the bearing of B from A is 042°. Find
   (a) the bearing of C from A,
   (b) the bearing of C from B.

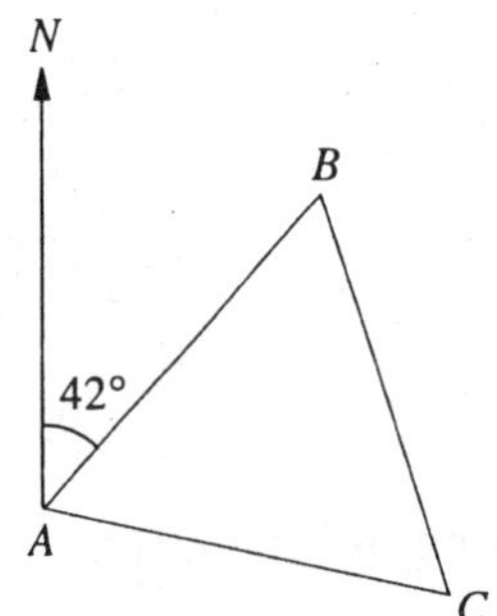

4. Three points A, B and C are on level ground, A is due south of B and C is 25 m due east of B. BT is a vertical flagpole.
   (a) If the angle of elevation of T from C is 18°, calculate the height of the flagpole.
   (b) If the bearing of C from A is 036°, find the angle of elevation of T from A.

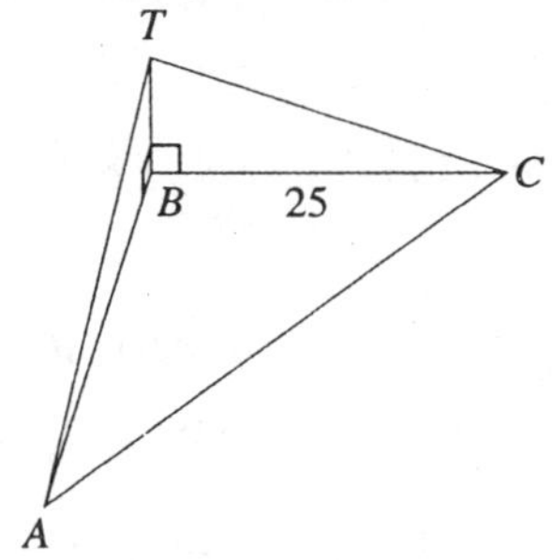

5. Two ships A and B leave a port P at 12 00. A sails at 15 km/h on a bearing 040° and B at 24 km/h on a bearing 100°. Calculate, at 14 00,
   (a) the distance between the ships,
   (b) $P\hat{A}B$, to the nearest degree,
   (c) the bearing of B from A.

6. A and B are two points on the coast. A is due north of B and $AB = 450$ m. A ship S is due east of A and the bearing of S from B is 038°. A second ship R is due east of B and the bearing of R from A is 128°. Calculate the distance of SR and find the bearing of R from S.

7. Three points A, B and C are on level ground. The bearing of B and C from A are 195° and 305° respectively. Given that $AB = 3.4$ km and $AC = 4.5$ km, calculate
   (a) the distance of BC in km,
   (b) the bearing of C from B,
   (c) the area of $\triangle ABC$ in hectares. [1 hectare = 10 000 m^2]

8. In the figure, A, B, C and D are four points on level ground. D is due south of C and A is due west of D. If $CD = 24$ m, $AC = 43$ m, $AB = 25$ m, $B\hat{A}X = 108°$ and $A\hat{B}X = 40°$, calculate

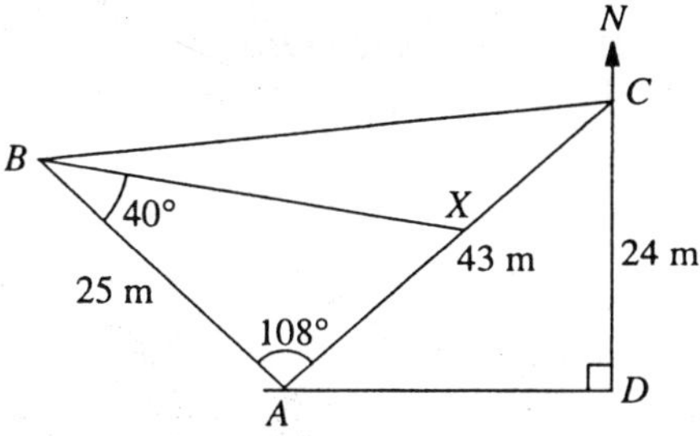

(a) the bearing of C from A,
(b) the length of CX,
(c) the length of BC,
(d) the area of the quadrilateral $ABCD$.

9. A, B, C and D are four points on horizontal ground with D due east of A. Given that $AB = 70$ m, $BC = 80$ m, $CD = 110$ m and $AD = 190$ m, calculate

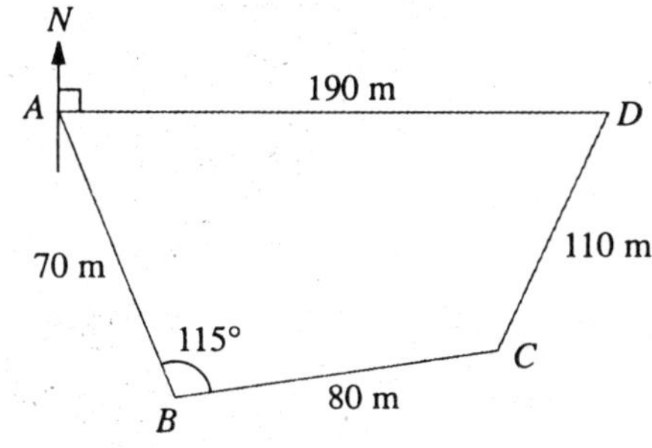

(a) the length of AC,
(b) $A\hat{D}C$,
(c) $A\hat{C}B$,
(d) the bearing of B from A,
(e) the area of the quadrilateral $ABCD$ in m^2.

10. A ship sailed from a port A at 09 00 on a bearing of 055° towards port B. It sailed at an average speed of 12 kmh^{-1}, reaching port B at 11 15. It rested for 30 minutes and then sailed at the same average speed of 12 kmh^{-1} to port C which is 30 km away from port B. At port C, the ship took 45 minutes to unload some goods before it set sail again at an average speed of 14 kmh^{-1} to port D, which is due north of port B. Given that $A\hat{B}C = 80°$ and $B\hat{C}D = 75°$, calculate

(a) the bearing of C from B,
(b) the distance of AC,
(c) the time when the ship reached D,
(d) the distance of BD,
(e) the bearing of D from A.

11. A harbour H and an oil rig P are 62 km apart with P due east of H. A supply ship leaves H for a second oil rig Q which is 44 km from P on a bearing 048° from H.

Find

(a) the bearing of Q from P,
(b) the distance HQ.

A seaside resort R is situated west of the line HQ. R is 45 km and 61 km from H and Q respectively.

(c) The supply ship leaves H at 11 15. It sails directly to R, where it stays for 40 minutes. Then it returns to H. When moving, it may be assumed that it travels at a constant speed of 15 km/h. At what time does it return to H?
(d) Calculate the angle HQR.
(e) What is the shortest distance from R to HQ?
(f) Find the area of quadrilateral $HPQR$.

12. The diagram shows a point A which lies 9 km south of a point B. The points C and D are both 6 km from B and the bearing of C from A is 036.3°. The points A, C, D and E all lie on a straight line. Calculate

(a) $A\hat{C}B$,

(b) the bearing of C from B,

(c) the length of CD,

(d) the shortest distance from B to the line ACD.

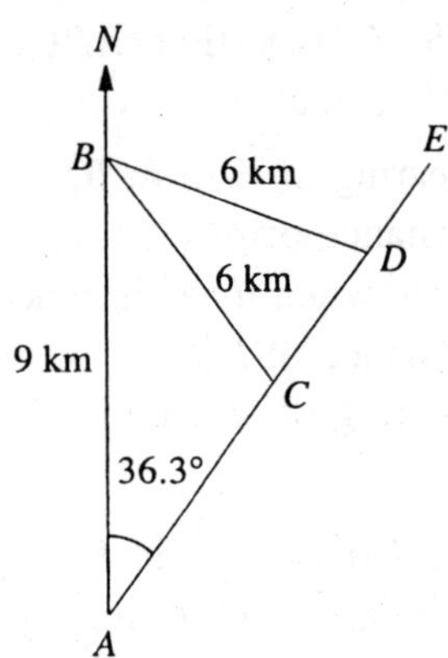

13. The diagram shows the positions A, B, C and D of four oil rigs. C, A and D lie in a straight line. Given that $AD = AB = 60$ km, $C\hat{A}B = 115°$, $A\hat{B}C = 35°$ and B is due east of C, calculate

(a) the distance of CB,

(b) the distance of BD.

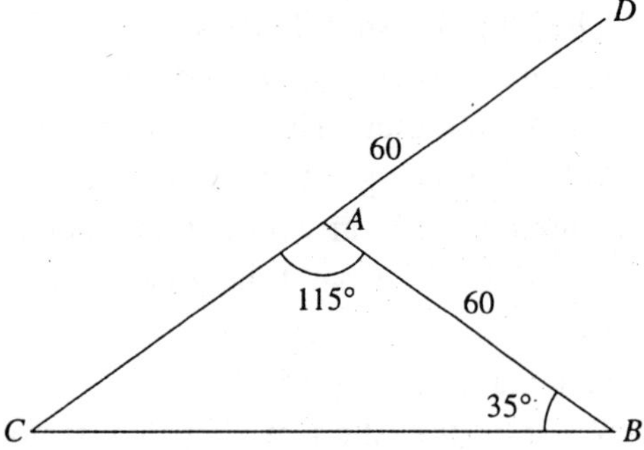

A supply ship S sets sail from C to B in a straight line. Find the distance the ship S must move such that it will be closest to A.

14. The points P, Q and R are on level ground such that Q is due north of P, the bearing of R from P is 018° and the bearing of R from Q is 063°.

(a) Given that the distance $PQ = 250$ m, calculate

(i) the distance QR,

(ii) the bearing of P from R.

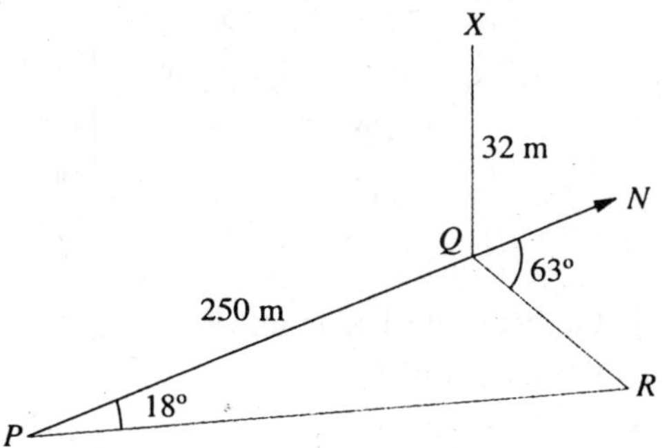

(b) Given that the vertical post XQ is 32 m high, calculate the angle of elevation of X from P.

15. (a) In the diagram, O is the centre of the sector BOC. Given that $B\hat{O}C = 124°$, $B\hat{A}O = 34.5°$, $A\hat{O}B = 90°$ and $OC = 6.8$ cm,

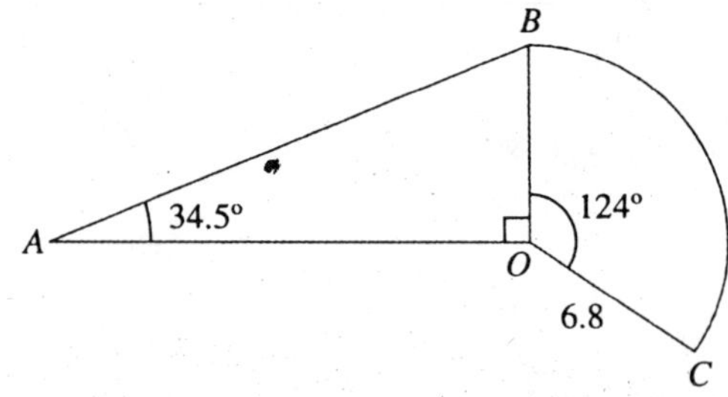

calculate

(i) AO,

(ii) AB,

(iii) the area of the sector BOC.

(b) Three points A, B and C lie on level ground. The bearing of B from A is 057° and the bearing of C from A is 126°. If $BC = 84$ m and $AB = 65$ m, find the bearing of B from C.

Number Sequence and Problem Solving

xample 1

The table below refers to a certain series.

(a) *Study the table and then fill in the blank spaces.*

Series	S Sum of series	N Base of last term of series	N + 1	M N(N + 1)
$1^3 + 2^3$	9	2	3	6
$1^3 + 2^3 + 3^3$	36	3	4	
$1^3 + 2^3 + 3^3 + 4^3$		4	5	20
$1^3 + 2^3 + 3^3 + 4^3 + 5^3$	225			
$1^3 + 2^3 + 3^3 + 4^3 + 5^3 + 6^3$				42

(b) *Express the relationship between the numbers in column S and those in column M as a formula connecting S and M.*

(c) (i) *Use your answer to part (b) to find the value of S when $N = 8$.*

(ii) *Verify this by evaluating $1^3 + 2^3 + 3^3 + 4^3 + 5^3 + 6^3 + 7^3 + 8^3$.*

(d) *Use your answer to part (b) to evaluate*

(i) $1^3 + 2^3 + 3^3 + \ldots + 3375$,

(ii) $1^3 + 2^3 + 3^3 + \ldots + 24^3$.

(e) *Suggest a formula, in terms of n, for the sum of the series $1^3 + 2^3 + 3^3 + \ldots + n^3$.*

How many squares (of varying sizes) are there in a standard 8 × 8 chess board?

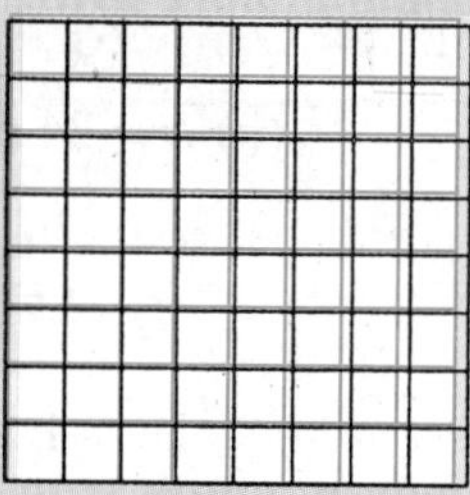

(a)

Series	S Sum of series	N Base of last term of series	N + 1	M N(N + 1)
$1^3 + 2^3$	9	2	3	6
$1^3 + 2^3 + 3^3$	36	3	4	12
$1^3 + 2^3 + 3^3 + 4^3$	100	4	5	20
$1^3 + 2^3 + 3^3 + 4^3 + 5^3$	225	5	6	30
$1^3 + 2^3 + 3^3 + 4^3 + 5^3 + 6^3$	441	6	7	42

(b) $S = \left(\frac{M}{2}\right)^2 = \frac{M^2}{4}$

(c) (i) When $N = 8$, $M = N(N + 1) = 8 \times 9 = 72$

$\therefore \quad S = \left(\frac{72}{2}\right)^2 = 1296$

(ii) $1^3 + 2^3 + 3^3 + 4^3 + 5^3 + 6^3 + 7^3 + 8^3$

$= 1 + 8 + 27 + 64 + 125 + 216 + 343 + 512$

$= 1296$

(d) (i) $3375 = 15^3$

$\therefore \quad N = 15$ and $M = 15 \times 16 = 240$

$S = \left(\frac{240}{2}\right)^2 = 14\,400$

$\therefore \quad 1^3 + 2^3 + 3^3 + \ldots + 3375 = 14\,400$

(ii) $N = 24$ and $M = 24 \times 25 = 600$

$\therefore \quad S = \left(\frac{600}{2}\right)^2 = 90\,000$

i.e. $1^3 + 2^3 + 3^3 \ldots + 24^3 = 90\,000$

(e) $1^3 + 2^3 + 3^3 + \ldots + n^3 = \left[\frac{n(n + 1)}{2}\right]^2$ or $\frac{n^2(n + 1)^2}{4}$

*Start with any counting number. If it is even, **divide it by 2**; if it is odd, **multiply it by 3 and add 1 to it**. Write down the result on a piece of paper. Repeat this with the number you have written down. For example, starting with 9 which is odd, multiply it by 3 and add 1 to obtain 28 which is even. Divide it by 2. Divide the even number 14 by 2. Obtaining 7, multiply it by 3 and add 1 to it and so on. If you continue this often enough, what interesting result will you observe? Repeat the procedure, starting with different counting numbers. Did you obtain the same result each time? Can you think of an explanation for this?*

Example 2

All the members of a family of chemical compounds contain Carbon atoms, C, and Hydrogen atoms, H. Some of the members of the family are represented in the diagrams below.

```
        H                            H   H
        |                            |   |
H — C = C — H                H — C = C — C — H
    |                            |       |
    H                            H       H

        H   H   H                    H   H   H   H
        |   |   |                    |   |   |   |
H — C = C — C — C — H        H — C = C — C — C — C — H
    |       |   |                |       |   |   |
    H       H   H                H       H   H   H
```

(a) Draw the next pattern in the series.

(b) If a member of the family of chemical compounds contains x Carbon atoms and y Hydrogen atoms, then the chemical formula of this member is written as C_xH_y.

(i) Write down the chemical formulas of the first five members of the family represented in the diagrams above and your diagram.

(ii) A member contains 10 Carbon atoms. Write down the number of Hydrogen atoms it contains.

(iii) Another member contains 64 Hydrogen atoms. How many Carbon atoms does it contain?

(iv) Give a formula that connects x and y.

(a) The next member of the family is represented in the diagram below.

```
        H   H   H   H   H
        |   |   |   |   |
H — C = C — C — C — C — C — H
    |       |   |   |   |
    H       H   H   H   H
```

(b) (i) The first five members of the family are C_2H_4, C_3H_6, C_4H_8, C_5H_{10} and C_6H_{12}.

(ii) The number of Hydrogen atoms = 2(10) = 20.

(iii) The number of Carbon atoms = $\frac{1}{2}(64) = 32$.

(iv) $y = 2x$.

1. (a) Write down the next two terms in the sequence

   120, 110, 101, 93, …

   (b) Write down an expression, in terms of n, for the nth term in the sequence

   0, –1, –8, –27, –64, …

2. Copy and complete the following sequence of numbers.

   (a) 0, 3, 8, 15, 24, ______, ______

   (b) 1, 1, $\sqrt{2}$, $\sqrt{3}$, $\sqrt{5}$, $\sqrt{8}$, $\sqrt{13}$, ______, ______

   (c) $\frac{1}{6}$, $\frac{5}{12}$, $\frac{2}{3}$, $\frac{11}{12}$, ______, ______

3. Consider the pattern

   $1^2 - 1 = 0$
   $2^2 - 2 = 2$
   $3^2 - 3 = 6$
   $4^2 - 4 = 12$
   $5^2 - 5 = 20$
   ⋮
   $x^2 - x = 110$
   ⋮

   (a) Write down the 8th line in the pattern.
   (b) Find the positive integer value of x satisfying the equation $x^2 - x = 110$.

4. (a) Write down the next two terms in the sequence

   2, 3, 7, 16, 32, 57, _____, _____.

   (b) Write down an expression, in terms of n, for the nth term of the sequence

   3, 5, 9, 17, 33, 65, … .

5. Squares are placed to enclose numbers in the number array as shown in the diagram.

1	2	3	4	5	6	· · ·
2	4	6	8	10	12	· · ·
3	6	9	12	15	18	· · ·
4	8	12	16	20	24	· · ·
5	10	15	20	25	30	· · ·

The sum of the numbers in the first square, $S_1 = 1 = 1^2$.
The sum of the numbers in the second square, $S_2 = 1 + 2 + 2 + 4 = 9 = 3^2$.

(a) Find S_3, S_4 and S_5.
(b) Find a formula for S_n in terms of n.
(c) The sum of the numbers in the kth square is 44 100. Find k.

6. A boy arranged small cubes of 1 cm to form cubes with sides 2 cm, 3 cm, 4 cm, etc.

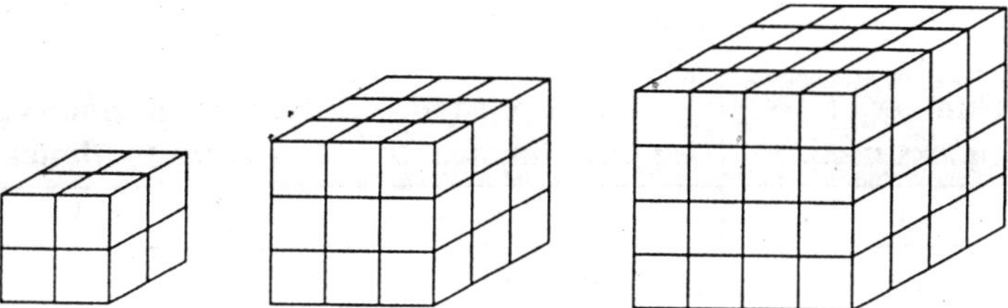

He then painted the outer surfaces of each cube. He observed that for cubes with side 2 cm ($n = 2$), there are 8 cubes with 3 faces painted. For cubes with side 3 cm ($n = 3$), there are 8 cubes with 3 faces painted, 12 cubes with 2 faces painted, 6 cubes with only 1 face painted and 1 cube not painted at all. He tabulated his findings as shown in the table below.

Size of cubes	**Number of faces painted**			
	3	*2*	*1*	*0*
$n = 2$	8	0	0	0
$n = 3$	8	12	6	1
$n = 4$	a	b	c	d
$n = 5$				
⋮				

(a) Find the values of a, b, c and d.
(b) When $n = 10$, how many cubes will have 3 faces painted?
(c) When $n = 5$, how many cubes will not be painted?
(d) When a cube has size n cm, find in terms of n the number of cubes with
  (i) 2 faces painted,
  (ii) 1 face painted,
  (iii) none of the faces painted.

7. John used toothpicks to make a series of squares.

The first four squares he constructed are as shown.

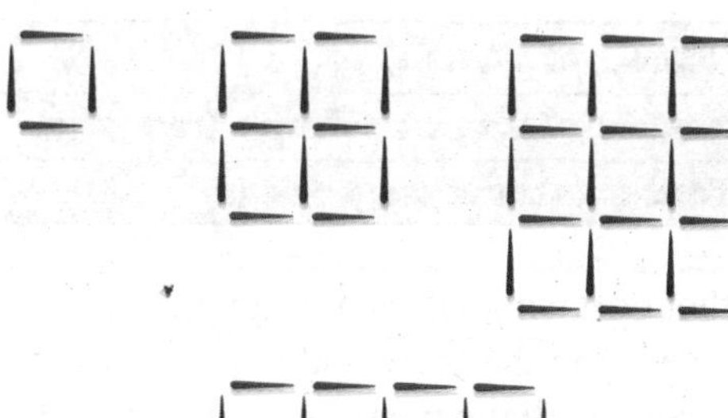

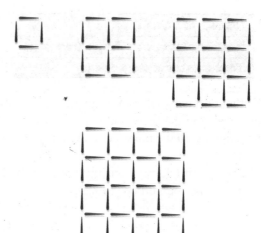

For each square, let T represent the number of toothpicks used, S the total number of small squares formed and P the number of points at which 2 or more toothpicks meet. The values of T, S and P are tabulated as shown in the following.

Number of toothpicks used, T	Number of small squares formed, S	Number of points at which 2 or more toothpicks meet, P
4	1	4
12	4	9
24	9	16
40	16	25
l	m	n

Study the number patterns in the table above and answer the following questions.

(a) Find the values of l, m and n in the fifth line of the table.

(b) Form and write down, a formula connecting T, S and P.

(c) Use your answer to part **(b)** to find the value of P when $T = 364$ and $S = 169$.

(d) Give a simple reason why the number 112 can neither appear in the S column nor in the P column.

(e) Give a simple reason why the number 4442 cannot appear in the T column.

8. The total number of diagonals (d) that can be drawn in polygons with a given number of sides (n) and the number of diagonals (v) that can be drawn from a vertex V are being investigated. The diagram below and the table show the total number of diagonals that can be drawn and the number of diagonals that can be drawn from a vertex V in a triangle, a quadrilateral, a pentagon and a hexagon.

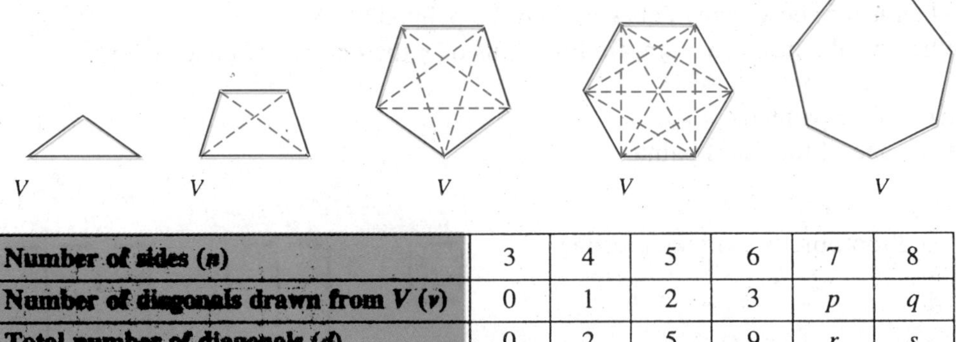

Number of sides (n)	3	4	5	6	7	8
Number of diagonals drawn from V (v)	0	1	2	3	p	q
Total number of diagonals (d)	0	2	5	9	r	s

(a) Without drawing all the possible diagonals or considering the number patterns, find the values of p and q in the table and explain how you find them.

(b) By drawing all the possible diagonals or by considering the number patterns, find the values of r and s.

(c) There is a simple relationship between the number of diagonals drawn from a vertex V of a polygon and the number of sides n.
Express this relationship as a formula connecting n and v.

(d) By studying the three rows of numbers in the table, find an equation that connects n, v and d and hence, express d in terms of n using the result in **(c)**.

(e) Using the result in **(d)**, find the total number of diagonals in a polygon with 30 sides.

Sets and Venn Diagrams

Example 1

It is given that $\mathcal{E} = \{1, 2, 3, 4, 5, 6, 7, 8\}$, $A = \{2, 5, 6\}$ and $B = \{1, 2, 4, 6, 8\}$.

(i) Find $n(A \cap B)$.
(ii) List the members of (a) $A' \cap B$
(b) $(A \cup B)'$.

(i) $A \cap B = \{2, 6\}$
$\therefore \quad n(A \cap B) = 2$

(ii) (a) $A' \cap B = \{1, 3, 4, 7, 8\} \cap \{1, 2, 4, 6, 8\} = \{1, 4, 8\}$
(b) $(A \cup B)' = (\{1, 2, 4, 5, 6, 8\})' = \{3, 7\}$

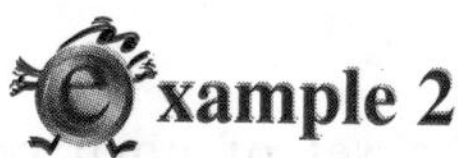

Example 2

Given that $\mathcal{E} = \{x : x \text{ is an integer}, 12 \leq x \leq 25\}$, $A = \{x : x \text{ is a prime number}\}$ and $B = \{x : x \text{ is an odd number}\}$.
(i) Find $n(A \cap B)$.
(ii) List the members of the following set (a) $A' \cap B'$
(b) $A' \cap B$.

(i) $A = \{13, 17, 19, 23\}$
$B = \{13, 15, 17, 19, 21, 23, 25\}$
$A \cap B = \{13, 17, 19, 23\}$
$\therefore \quad n(A \cap B) = 4$

(ii) $A' = \{12, 14, 15, 16, 18, 20, 21, 22, 24, 25\}$
$B' = \{12, 14, 16, 18, 20, 22, 24\}$
(a) $A' \cap B' = \{12, 14, 16, 18, 20, 22, 24\}$
(b) $A' \cap B = \{15, 21, 25\}$

The sets A, B and C satisfy the following conditions:

$$B \subseteq A, \quad B \cap C \neq \varnothing, \quad A \cap C = C.$$

Represent these sets on a clearly-labelled Venn diagram.

Since $A \cap C = C$, $C \subseteq A$. Also $B \subseteq A$ and $B \cap C \neq \varnothing$. Thus the Venn diagram is

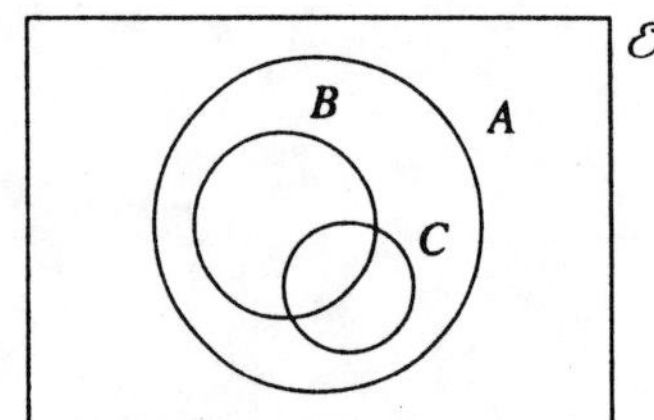

1. If $\mathcal{E} = \{2, 3, 4, 5, 6, 7, 8, 9\}$, $A = \{2, 4, 7, 8\}$ and $B = \{5, 6, 7, 8\}$,
   (a) list the members of $A \cap B$,
   (b) find the value of $n(A \cap B')$.

2. If $\mathcal{E} = \{a, b, c, d, e, f\}$, $A = \{a, c, d\}$, $B = \{c, f\}$ and $C = \{d, e\}$,
   (a) list the members of
   (i) $A \cap B$, **(ii)** $A \cup C$.
   (b) find the value of
   (i) $n(A \cap B')$, **(ii)** $n(B \cup C)'$.

3. If $\mathcal{E} = \{x : x \text{ is an integer and } 1 \leq x \leq 10\}$, A = {prime numbers}, B = {even numbers} and C = {multiples of 3}, list the members of the following.
   (a) $A \cap B$
   (b) $A \cup B'$
   (c) $A \cap C'$

4. The universal set is the set of positive integers greater than 10 but less than 34. $A = \{x : 15 \leq x \leq 32\}$, $B = \{x : x \text{ is an odd number}\}$ and $C = \{x : x \text{ is a prime number}\}$.
   Find the values of the following.
   (a) $n(A)$
   (b) $n(B)$
   (c) $n(C)$
   (d) $n(A \cap B)$
   (e) $n(B \cap C)$
   (f) $n(B \cap C')$

5. Two sets, P and Q, satisfy the following conditions $P = \{(x, y) : y = 2x + 5\}$, $Q = \{(x, y) : y = mx + c\}$ and $P \cap Q = \varnothing$. Write down the value of m and a possible value for c.

6. A and B are distinct sets such that $A \subset B$. Simplify the following.

(a) $A \cap B$
(b) $A \cup B$

7. Given that $A = \{x : x \text{ is an integer and } 50 \leq x \leq 100\}$, $B = \{x : x \text{ is a positive integer and } x^2 \in A\}$ and $C = \{x : \sqrt{x} \text{ is a positive integer}\}$,

(a) find the value of n(A),
(b) list the members of the set $A \cap C$,
(c) list the members of the set B.

8. If n(A) = 8, n(B) = 6 and n($A \cup B$) = 12, find the value of n($A \cap B$).

9. Given that $\mathcal{E} = \{x : x \text{ is a positive integer}, x \leq 25\}$, $A = \{x : x \leq 15\}$ and $B = \{x : 10 \leq x \leq 25\}$,

(a) list the elements of the following,
 (i) A'
 (ii) $A' \cap B'$
(b) find the value of the following.
 (i) n(B')
 (ii) n($A' \cap B'$)

10. If $\mathcal{E} = \{x : x \text{ is an integer}, 1 \leq x \leq 12\}$, $A = \{x : x \text{ is a factor of } 12\}$ and $B = \{x : x \text{ is odd}\}$, list the members of the following.

(a) A
(b) $A' \cap B$
(c) $A \cup B$

11. If $\mathcal{E} = \{x : x \text{ is an integer}, 1 \leq x \leq 40\}$, $A = \{x : x \text{ is a factor of } 36\}$ and $B = \{x : x \text{ is a multiple of } 3\}$, list the members of the following.

(a) $A \cap B$
(b) $A \cap B'$

12. If $\mathcal{E} = \{x : x \text{ is an integer}, 1 \leq x \leq 20\}$, $A = \{x : x \text{ is a factor of } 60\}$ and $B = \{x : x \text{ is a prime number}\}$, list the members of the following.

(a) A
(b) B
(c) $A \cap B$

13. Given that $\mathcal{E} = \{x : x \text{ is an integer}, 1 \leq x \leq 24\}$, $A = \{x : x \text{ is prime}\}$, $B = \{x : x \text{ is a multiple of } 3\}$ and $C = \{x : x \text{ is a factor of } 24\}$, list the members of the following.

(a) C
(b) $A \cap C$
(c) $B' \cap C$
(d) $A \cap B'$

14. P and Q are two non-empty subsets of the universal set $\mathcal{E}$. If $P \cap Q \neq \varnothing$, draw separate Venn diagrams to illustrate by shading, the following.

(a) Q'
(b) $P \cup Q'$

15. The Venn diagram represents subsets A and B of the universal set $\mathcal{E}$. Shade on separate copies of the Venn diagram the region representing the following.

(a) $A \cap B'$
(b) $A' \cap B'$

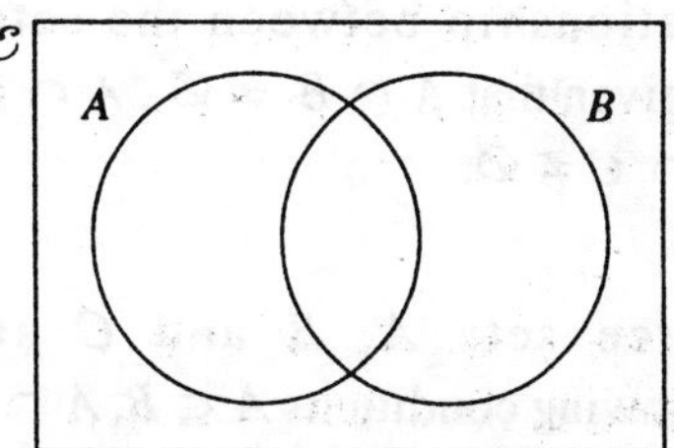

16. Identify the set shaded in each of the following Venn diagrams.

(a)

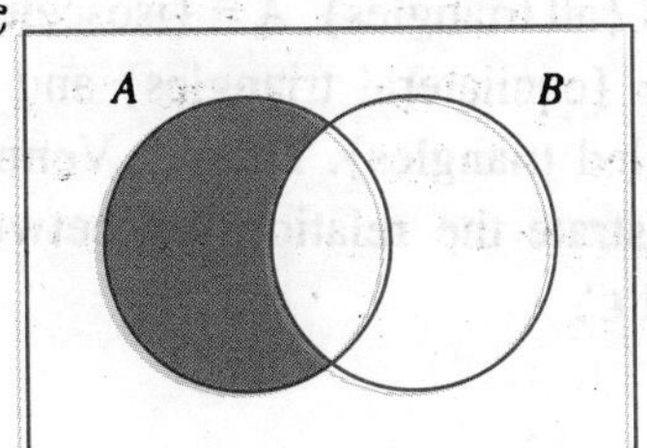

(b) 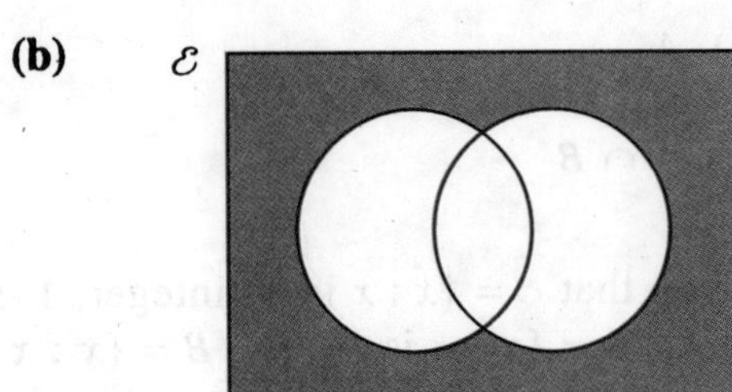

(c) 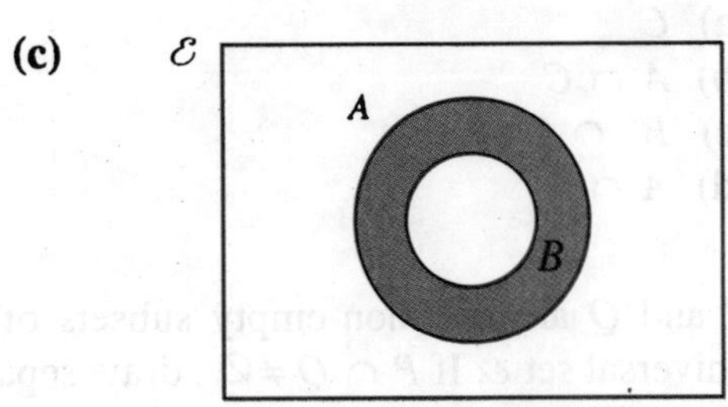

(d) 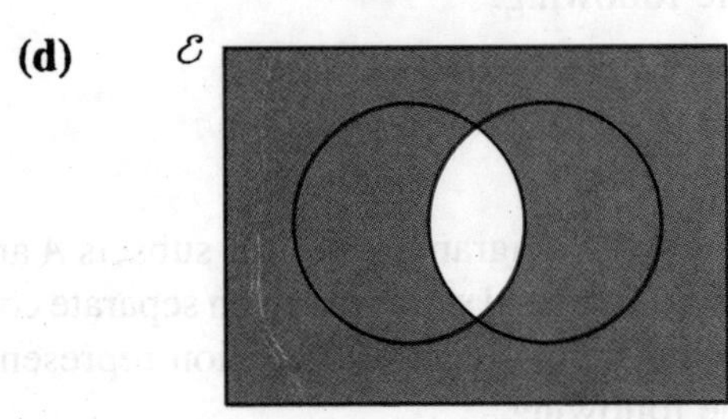

17. Illustrate, on a Venn diagram, the relationship between the sets A, B and C, given that $A \cap B \neq \emptyset$, $A \cap C = \emptyset$ and $B \cap C \neq \emptyset$.

18. Three sets A, B and C satisfy the following conditions $A \subseteq B$, $A \cap B \cap C \neq \emptyset$ and $B' \cap C \neq \emptyset$.
Illustrate the relationship between the sets by a Venn diagram.

19. $\mathcal{E}$ = {all triangles}, A = {isosceles triangles}, B = {equilateral triangles} and C = {right-angled triangles}. Draw a Venn diagram to illustrate the relationship between $\mathcal{E}$, A, B and C.

20. $\mathcal{E}$ = {quadrilaterals}, A = {rectangles}, B = {parallelograms} and C = {squares}. Draw a clearly labelled diagram to show the relationship between the sets $\mathcal{E}$, A, B and C.

21. It is given that $\mathcal{E} = \{1, 2, 3, 4, 5, 6, 7, 8\}$, $A = \{1, 2, 3, 6\}$, $B = \{2, 3, 4, 7\}$ and $C = \{3, 4, 5, 8\}$. Copy the Venn diagram given below and insert the numbers 1, 2, 3, 4, 5, 6, 7 and 8 in the appropriate regions.

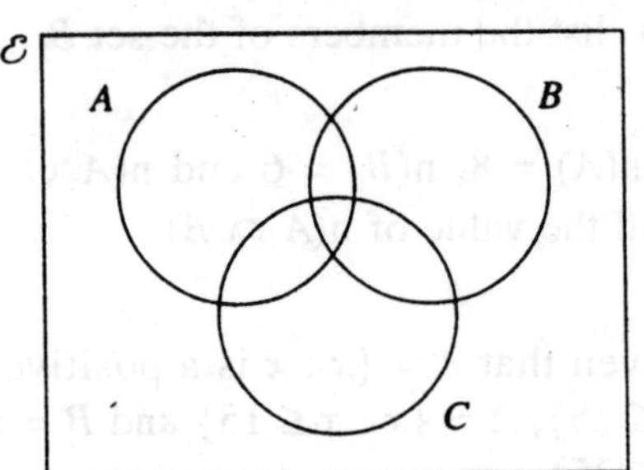

Matrices

xample 1

Evaluate the following matrix products.

(a) $\begin{pmatrix} 2 & 1 \\ 3 & 5 \end{pmatrix}\begin{pmatrix} -2 & 3 \\ 1 & 0 \end{pmatrix}$ (b) $\begin{pmatrix} 3 \\ 1 \end{pmatrix}(1 \quad 3)$ (c) $(1 \quad 5)\begin{pmatrix} 2 \\ 4 \end{pmatrix}$

(d) $\begin{pmatrix} 2 & 1 & 3 \\ 0 & -1 & 4 \end{pmatrix}\begin{pmatrix} 2 \\ -1 \\ 1 \end{pmatrix}$ (e) $\begin{pmatrix} 2 & 1 \\ 3 & 0 \\ -1 & -2 \end{pmatrix}\begin{pmatrix} 4 \\ -1 \end{pmatrix}$

(a) $\begin{pmatrix} 2 & 1 \\ 3 & 5 \end{pmatrix}\begin{pmatrix} -2 & 3 \\ 1 & 0 \end{pmatrix} = \begin{pmatrix} 2(-2) + 1(1) & 2(3) + 1(0) \\ 3(-2) + 5(1) & 3(3) + 5(0) \end{pmatrix} = \begin{pmatrix} -3 & 6 \\ -1 & 9 \end{pmatrix}$

(b) $\begin{pmatrix} 3 \\ 1 \end{pmatrix}(1 \quad 3) = \begin{pmatrix} 3 \times 1 & 3 \times 3 \\ 1 \times 1 & 1 \times 3 \end{pmatrix} = \begin{pmatrix} 3 & 9 \\ 1 & 3 \end{pmatrix}$

(c) $(1 \quad 5)\begin{pmatrix} 2 \\ 4 \end{pmatrix} = (1 \times 2 + 5 \times 4) = (22)$

(d) $\begin{pmatrix} 2 & 1 & 3 \\ 0 & -1 & 4 \end{pmatrix}\begin{pmatrix} 2 \\ -1 \\ 1 \end{pmatrix} = \begin{pmatrix} 2 \times 2 + 1 \times (-1) + 3 \times 1 \\ 0 \times 2 + (-1) \times (-1) + 4 \times 1 \end{pmatrix} = \begin{pmatrix} 6 \\ 5 \end{pmatrix}$

(e) $\begin{pmatrix} 2 & 1 \\ 3 & 0 \\ -1 & -2 \end{pmatrix}\begin{pmatrix} 4 \\ -1 \end{pmatrix} = \begin{pmatrix} 2(4) + 1(-1) \\ 3(4) + 0(-1) \\ -1(4) + (-2)(-1) \end{pmatrix} = \begin{pmatrix} 7 \\ 12 \\ -2 \end{pmatrix}$

Given that $\mathbf{A} = \begin{pmatrix} 4 & 0 \\ 2 & 1 \end{pmatrix}$ and $\mathbf{B} = \begin{pmatrix} 2 & 3 \\ -1 & 1 \end{pmatrix}$.

(a) find $2\mathbf{A} + \mathbf{B}$,

(b) if $\mathbf{A}\begin{pmatrix} 1 \\ x \end{pmatrix} = \begin{pmatrix} 4y \\ 10 \end{pmatrix}$, *find the values of x and y.*

(a) $$2\mathbf{A} + \mathbf{B} = 2\begin{pmatrix} 4 & 0 \\ 2 & 1 \end{pmatrix} + \begin{pmatrix} 2 & 3 \\ -1 & 1 \end{pmatrix}$$
$$= \begin{pmatrix} 8 & 0 \\ 4 & 2 \end{pmatrix} + \begin{pmatrix} 2 & 3 \\ -1 & 1 \end{pmatrix}$$
$$= \begin{pmatrix} 10 & 3 \\ 3 & 3 \end{pmatrix}$$

(b) $$\begin{pmatrix} 4 & 0 \\ 2 & 1 \end{pmatrix}\begin{pmatrix} 1 \\ x \end{pmatrix} = \begin{pmatrix} 4y \\ 10 \end{pmatrix}$$
$$\begin{pmatrix} 4 \times 1 + 0 \times x \\ 2 \times 1 + 1 \times x \end{pmatrix} = \begin{pmatrix} 4y \\ 10 \end{pmatrix}$$
$$\begin{pmatrix} 4 \\ 2 + x \end{pmatrix} = \begin{pmatrix} 4y \\ 10 \end{pmatrix}$$
$4 = 4y$ and $2 + x = 10$

$\therefore$ $y = 1$ and $x = 8$

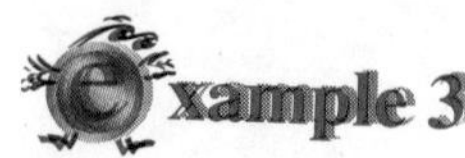

Given that $\mathbf{A}$ is a 2×2 matrix such that $2\mathbf{A} + \begin{pmatrix} 3 & 0 \\ 0 & 3 \end{pmatrix}\mathbf{A} = \begin{pmatrix} 4 & 5 \\ 6 & 7 \end{pmatrix}$, *find the matrix* $\mathbf{A}$.

$$2\mathbf{A} + \begin{pmatrix} 3 & 0 \\ 0 & 3 \end{pmatrix}\mathbf{A} = \begin{pmatrix} 4 & 5 \\ 6 & 7 \end{pmatrix}$$
$$2\mathbf{A} + 3\begin{pmatrix} 1 & 0 \\ 0 & 1 \end{pmatrix}\mathbf{A} = \begin{pmatrix} 4 & 5 \\ 6 & 7 \end{pmatrix}$$
$$5\mathbf{A} = \begin{pmatrix} 4 & 5 \\ 6 & 7 \end{pmatrix}$$
$$\therefore \quad \mathbf{A} = \frac{1}{5}\begin{pmatrix} 4 & 5 \\ 6 & 7 \end{pmatrix}$$

Example 4

There are three transport operators that ply the route from Johor Bahru to downtown Singapore; SBS, Causeway Link and Singapore Express. The bus operator uses three different type of buses-Big, Medium and Standard. The table below shows the number of bus trips run per day by the different operators and the capacity of each bus as well as the ticket prices of each bus trip.

Bus Operator	*Big Buses*	*Medium Buses*	*Standard Buses*	*Cost per Passenger*
SBS	*220*	*110*	*30*	*$2.40*
Causeway Link	*110*	*60*	*20*	*$3.20*
Singapore Express	*80*	*40*	*40*	*$4.00*
Maximum no. of passengers per bus	*60*	*40*	*52*	

(a) Write down two matrices such that their product shows the greatest number of passengers that each bus operator can carry per day. Hence, calculate this product.

(b) Using the result of (a), express the total maximum revenue for each of the bus operators as a product of two matrices and hence, calculate the maximum total revenue of each of the three operators.

(a) As there are three bus operators, to find the maximum number of passengers each bus operator can carry, we can either find a solution that will result in a 3 × 1 matrix or a 1 × 3 matrix.

Maximum number of passengers each bus operator can carry

$$= \begin{pmatrix} 220 & 110 & 30 \\ 110 & 60 & 20 \\ 80 & 40 & 40 \end{pmatrix}\begin{pmatrix} 60 \\ 40 \\ 52 \end{pmatrix} = \begin{pmatrix} 19\,160 \\ 10\,040 \\ 8480 \end{pmatrix}$$

or

$$\begin{pmatrix} 60 & 40 & 52 \end{pmatrix}\begin{pmatrix} 220 & 110 & 30 \\ 110 & 60 & 20 \\ 80 & 40 & 40 \end{pmatrix} = \begin{pmatrix} 19\,160 & 10\,040 & 8480 \end{pmatrix}$$

i.e. SBS can carry a maximum of 19 160 passengers, Causeway Link can carry a maximum of 10 040 passengers and Singapore Express can carry a maximum of 8480 passengers.

(b) To obtain the total maximum revenue, we must obtain either a 3×1 matrix or a 1×3 matrix for the three bus operators. We can do this by either pre-multiplying the 3×1 matrix obtained in (a) by a 3×3 matrix or post-multiplying the 1×3 matrix by a 3×3 matrix. As there are only 3 prices for passengers of each company, we put the prices per passenger on the leading diagonal and 0 for the other entries. i.e.

$$\begin{pmatrix} 2.40 & 0 & 0 \\ 0 & 3.20 & 0 \\ 0 & 0 & 4.00 \end{pmatrix}\begin{pmatrix} 19\,160 \\ 10\,040 \\ 8480 \end{pmatrix} = \begin{pmatrix} 45\,984 \\ 32\,128 \\ 33\,920 \end{pmatrix}$$

or

$$(19\,160 \quad 10\,040 \quad 8480)\begin{pmatrix} 2.40 & 0 & 0 \\ 0 & 3.20 & 0 \\ 0 & 0 & 4.00 \end{pmatrix} = (45\,984 \quad 32\,128 \quad 33\,920)$$

i.e. SBS's total maximum revenue is \$45 984, Causeway Link's total maximum revenue is \$32 128 while that of Singapore Express is \$33 920.

1. Evaluate the following matrices.

(a) $\begin{pmatrix} 2 \\ 0 \\ 1 \end{pmatrix} + \begin{pmatrix} 3 \\ -2 \\ -5 \end{pmatrix}$

(b) $\begin{pmatrix} 2 & 4 & 5 \\ 1 & -1 & 0 \end{pmatrix} + \begin{pmatrix} 5 & 4 & 7 \\ 3 & 0 & 9 \end{pmatrix}$

(c) $\begin{pmatrix} 2 & -1 \\ 4 & 2 \\ 7 & 0 \end{pmatrix} - \begin{pmatrix} 2 & -2 \\ 3 & 4 \\ -7 & 0 \end{pmatrix}$

(d) $2\begin{pmatrix} 2 & 4 \\ 5 & 0 \end{pmatrix} + \frac{1}{2}\begin{pmatrix} -2 & 6 \\ 4 & 2 \end{pmatrix}$

2. Find the product of the given matrices.

(a) $(2 \quad -1 \quad 4)\begin{pmatrix} 0 \\ -3 \\ \frac{1}{2} \end{pmatrix}$

(b) $\begin{pmatrix} 2 & -1 & 5 \\ 1 & 2 & 3 \end{pmatrix}\begin{pmatrix} 1 \\ 3 \\ -1 \end{pmatrix}$

(c) $\begin{pmatrix} 5 & 2 & 5 \\ 2 & 2 & 2 \\ 0 & 1 & 0 \end{pmatrix}\begin{pmatrix} 1 & 2 \\ 0 & 4 \\ 1 & -2 \end{pmatrix}$

(d) $(1 \quad 2 \quad 3)\begin{pmatrix} 1 & 8 & 7 \\ 7 & 0 & -8 \\ 0 & 2 & 3 \end{pmatrix}$

(e) $\begin{pmatrix} 4 & -1 \\ 2 & 1 \end{pmatrix}\begin{pmatrix} 2 & 5 \\ 4 & 0 \end{pmatrix}\begin{pmatrix} -1 & 0 \\ 2 & 8 \end{pmatrix}$

(f) $(7 \quad -2 \quad 3)\begin{pmatrix} -1 & 2 \\ 3 & 5 \\ 0 & 2 \end{pmatrix}\begin{pmatrix} 1 & 3 \\ 5 & 4 \end{pmatrix}$

(g) $\begin{pmatrix} 4 & 1 \\ 3 & 5 \end{pmatrix}\begin{pmatrix} 3 & -1 & 0 \\ 6 & 2 & 5 \end{pmatrix}\begin{pmatrix} -2 \\ 6 \\ -2 \end{pmatrix}$

(h) $(7 \quad 5)\begin{pmatrix} 1 & 0 & 1 \\ 3 & 1 & 0 \end{pmatrix}\begin{pmatrix} 2 \\ 6 \\ 2 \end{pmatrix}$

3. Solve the following equations.

(a) $2\begin{pmatrix} x \\ y \end{pmatrix} - 4\begin{pmatrix} 2 \\ 5 \end{pmatrix} = \begin{pmatrix} 4x \\ 3y \end{pmatrix}$

(b) $\begin{pmatrix} x \\ y \end{pmatrix} = \begin{pmatrix} 3 & -1 \\ 0 & 2 \end{pmatrix}\begin{pmatrix} 2 \\ 3 \end{pmatrix} + \begin{pmatrix} 5 \\ 2 \end{pmatrix}$

(c) $x\begin{pmatrix} 2 \\ 4 \end{pmatrix} + y\begin{pmatrix} 5 \\ 7 \end{pmatrix} = \begin{pmatrix} -5 \\ -1 \end{pmatrix}$

(d) $\begin{pmatrix} 0 & 2 \\ -1 & 4 \end{pmatrix}\begin{pmatrix} x \\ y \end{pmatrix} = \begin{pmatrix} 2 \\ 3 \end{pmatrix}$

(e) $(x \quad y \quad z)\begin{pmatrix} 3 & 0 & 1 \\ 0 & 4 & 0 \\ 2 & 0 & -2 \end{pmatrix} = (2 \quad 4 \quad 5)$

(f) $2\begin{pmatrix} 2x \\ y \end{pmatrix} + \begin{pmatrix} x \\ 3y \end{pmatrix} = \begin{pmatrix} -20 \\ 30 \end{pmatrix}$

4. Find the value of the unknown in each of the following equations.

(a) $\begin{pmatrix} 2 & 1 \\ 4 & x \end{pmatrix}\begin{pmatrix} y \\ 2 \end{pmatrix} = \begin{pmatrix} 6 \\ 10 \end{pmatrix}$

(b) $\begin{pmatrix} 3 & 1 \\ x & 4 \end{pmatrix}\begin{pmatrix} y \\ 1 \end{pmatrix} = \begin{pmatrix} -2 \\ 1 \end{pmatrix}$

(c) $\begin{pmatrix} 1 & 2 & 3 \\ 0 & 1 & 4 \end{pmatrix}\begin{pmatrix} x \\ 0 \\ 2 \end{pmatrix} = \begin{pmatrix} 2 \\ 2y \end{pmatrix}$

5. Find matrices $\boldsymbol{A}$ and $\boldsymbol{B}$ which satisfy the following matrix equations.

$$\boldsymbol{A} + \boldsymbol{B} = \begin{pmatrix} 2 & -1 \\ 3 & 6 \end{pmatrix}, \quad 2\boldsymbol{A} - \boldsymbol{B} = \begin{pmatrix} 1 & 2 \\ 7 & 5 \end{pmatrix}$$

6. If $A = \begin{pmatrix} 2 & -3 \\ 6 & 1 \end{pmatrix}$, find

(a) $\boldsymbol{A}^2 - 4\boldsymbol{A}$, **(b)** $\boldsymbol{A}^4 + 3\boldsymbol{I}_2$

(c) $3A^2 + 2A - 4\boldsymbol{I}_2$,
where $\boldsymbol{I}_2$ is the 2×2 identity matrix.

7. Given that $\begin{pmatrix} 3 & 2 \\ 1 & a \end{pmatrix}\begin{pmatrix} 5 & c \\ b & 0 \end{pmatrix} = 3\begin{pmatrix} b & 4 \\ -1 & 0 \end{pmatrix} - \begin{pmatrix} 3 & 0 \\ 1 & -1 \end{pmatrix}\begin{pmatrix} -1 & 0 \\ -2 & 4 \end{pmatrix}$, find the values of a, b and c.

8. Given that $\boldsymbol{A} = \begin{pmatrix} -4 & p \\ -1 & 2 \end{pmatrix}$, $\boldsymbol{B} = \begin{pmatrix} q & 0 \\ 2 & 3 \end{pmatrix}$ and $\boldsymbol{AB} = \boldsymbol{BA}$, find the values of p and q.

9. The table below shows different types of vehicles parked at a car park on each of the days of a particular week.

	Cars	Motorcycles	Lorries	Buses
Monday	560	240	30	20
Tuesday	580	220	40	22
Wednesday	480	200	36	25
Thursday	450	180	45	18
Friday	460	210	38	16
Saturday	640	180	42	26

(a) If the average amount paid by each car is \$2.40, each motorcycle is 80 cents, each lorry is \$3.20 and each bus is \$3.60, write down two matrices such that their product gives the total amount collected for each of the days of the week and hence calculate the product.

(b) Using the result obtain in **(a)**, write down two matrices such that their product gives the total amount of parking fees collected for the week. Calculate this total amount.

10. A renovation contractor tendered a job to refurbish an upgrading project under the government's main upgrading programme. For the project, he needs to supply three different types of flooring material. The areas of flooring material needed for each type of flats are given in the table below.

Type of flats \ Material	Durable	Heavy Duty	Supreme
3 Room	24 m^2	12 m^2	22 m^2
4 Room	32 m^2	16 m^2	25 m^2
5 Room	42 m^2	20 m^2	26 m^2
Executive	48 m^2	28 m^2	34 m^2
Cost per m^2	\$12	\$15	\$18

There are 46 3-Room, 58 4-Room, 65 5-Room and 34 Executive flats.
Using matrix multiplication twice, find the total cost that the contractor had to pay for the flooring material for the project.

11. Tour coaches come in three different types – Luxury has 48 seats, Comfort has 32 seats and Mini has 26 seats.
Robert Tours has 12 Luxury, 8 Comfort and 11 Mini coaches.
Chartered Tours has 18 Luxury, 11 Comfort and 7 Mini coaches.
Boat Quay Tours has 8 Luxury, 9 Comfort and 15 Mini coaches.

(a) Write down two matrices whose product will show the greatest number of tourists that each tour company can take on a day when each coach is used once. Hence, evaluate this product.

(b) Robert Tours charges \$9.80 per seat, Chartered Tours \$10.40 per seat and Boat Quay Tours \$9.90 per seat. Express the maximum total earnings for the companies as a product of two matrices and hence, find the total earning.

Vectors

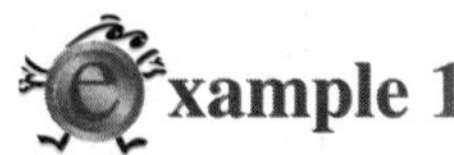

example 1

It is given that P is the point (5, 6), Q is the point (13, 10) and X is the point on $\overrightarrow{PQ}$ *such that* $\overrightarrow{PX} = \frac{1}{3}\overrightarrow{XQ}$.

(a) Express as column vectors the following:

(i) $\overrightarrow{PQ}$, *(ii)* $\overrightarrow{PX}$,

(iii) the position vector of X relative to the origin O.

(b) If O, P and Q are three of the vertices of a parallelogram, find the coordinates of the two possible positions of the fourth vertex.

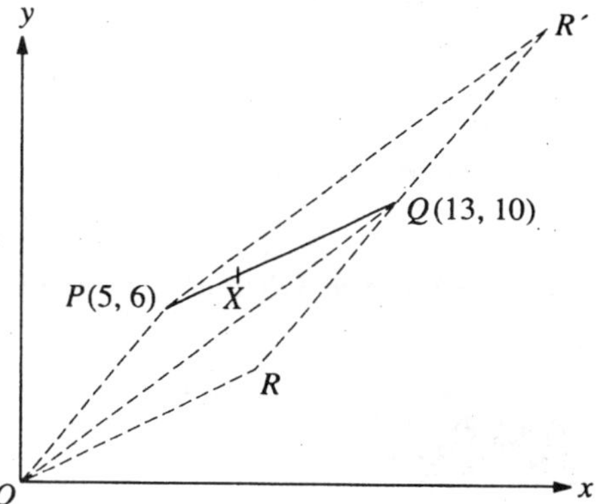

Solution

(a) We have $\overrightarrow{OP} = \begin{pmatrix} 5 \\ 6 \end{pmatrix}$, $\overrightarrow{OQ} = \begin{pmatrix} 13 \\ 10 \end{pmatrix}$.

(i) $\overrightarrow{PQ} = \overrightarrow{OQ} - \overrightarrow{OP}$

$= \begin{pmatrix} 13 \\ 10 \end{pmatrix} - \begin{pmatrix} 5 \\ 6 \end{pmatrix} = \begin{pmatrix} 8 \\ 4 \end{pmatrix}$

(ii) Given that $\overrightarrow{PX} = \frac{1}{3}\overrightarrow{XQ}$, we have $\overrightarrow{PX} = \frac{1}{4}\overrightarrow{PQ} = \frac{1}{4}\begin{pmatrix} 8 \\ 4 \end{pmatrix} = \begin{pmatrix} 2 \\ 1 \end{pmatrix}$

(iii) $\overrightarrow{OX} = \overrightarrow{OP} + \overrightarrow{PX}$

$\overrightarrow{OX} = \begin{pmatrix} 5 \\ 6 \end{pmatrix} + \begin{pmatrix} 2 \\ 1 \end{pmatrix} = \begin{pmatrix} 7 \\ 7 \end{pmatrix}$

$\therefore$ the position vector of X relative to the origin O is $\overrightarrow{OX} = \begin{pmatrix} 7 \\ 7 \end{pmatrix}$.

(b) In the figure shown, R and R' are the two possible positions of the fourth vertex.

In parallelogram $OPQR$, $\overrightarrow{OR} = \overrightarrow{PQ} = \begin{pmatrix} 8 \\ 4 \end{pmatrix}$.

In parallelogram $OPR'Q$, $\overrightarrow{OR'} = \overrightarrow{OP} + \overrightarrow{OQ} = \begin{pmatrix} 5 \\ 6 \end{pmatrix} + \begin{pmatrix} 13 \\ 10 \end{pmatrix} = \begin{pmatrix} 18 \\ 16 \end{pmatrix}$

$\therefore$ the coordinates of the two possible positions of the fourth vertex are (8, 4) and (18, 16).

Example 2

In the diagram, $\overrightarrow{OA} = \mathbf{a}$ *and* $\overrightarrow{OB} = \mathbf{b}$.

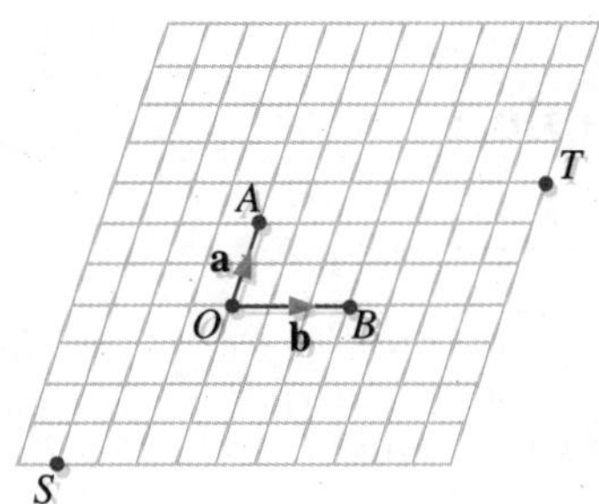

(a) Mark clearly on the diagram,

(i) the point P, such that $\overrightarrow{OP} = 3\mathbf{a} + 2\mathbf{b}$,

(ii) the point Q, such that $\overrightarrow{OQ} = 2\mathbf{b} - \mathbf{a}$,

(iii) the point R, such that $\overrightarrow{OR} = -(\mathbf{b} - 3\mathbf{a})$.

(b) Write down $\overrightarrow{OS}$ *and* $\overrightarrow{OT}$ *in terms of* **a** *and* **b**.

Solution

(a)

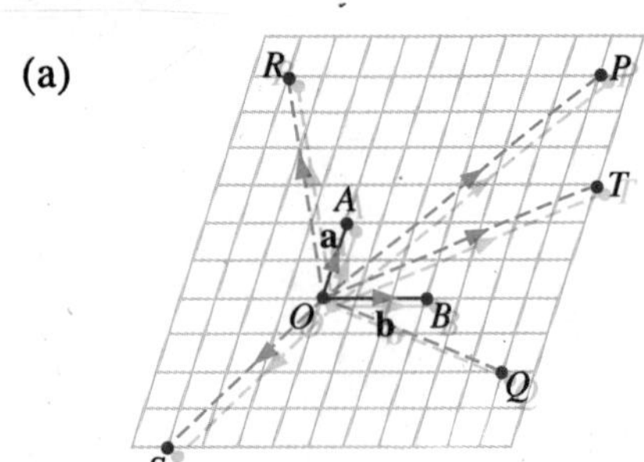

(b) $\overrightarrow{OS} = -2\mathbf{a} - \mathbf{b}$

$= -(2\mathbf{a} + \mathbf{b})$

$\overrightarrow{OT} = 1\frac{1}{2}\mathbf{a} + 2\frac{1}{3}\mathbf{b}$

$= \frac{3}{2}\mathbf{a} + \frac{7}{3}\mathbf{b}$

$= \frac{1}{6}(9\mathbf{a} + 14\mathbf{b})$

Example 3

In the diagram, BC = 3BD and CA = 4FA. E is the mid-point of DA. $\overrightarrow{BD} = \mathbf{p}$ *and* $\overrightarrow{FA} = \mathbf{q}$.

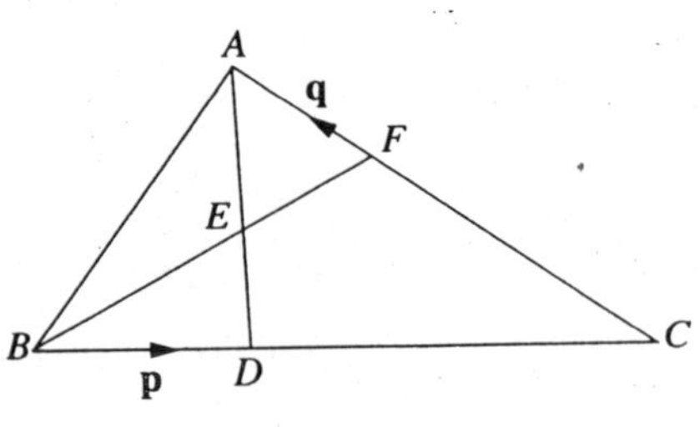

(a) Express, as simply as possible, in terms of **p** *and/or* **q**,

(i) $\overrightarrow{DC}$, *(ii)* $\overrightarrow{DA}$,

(iii) $\overrightarrow{DE}$.

(b) Show that $\overrightarrow{BE} = 2(\mathbf{p} + \mathbf{q})$.

(c) Express $\overrightarrow{BF}$ *as simply as possible, in terms of* **p** *and* **q**.

(d) Calculate the value of

(i) $\frac{BE}{BF}$, *(ii)* $\frac{\text{area of } \Delta ABE}{\text{area of } \Delta ABF}$, *(iii)* $\frac{\text{area of } \Delta ABE}{\text{area of } \Delta ABC}$.

Solution

(a) (i) $DC = 2BD$ $(BC = 3BD)$

$\therefore \overrightarrow{DC} = 2\mathbf{p}$

(ii) $CA = 4FA$

$\therefore \overrightarrow{CA} = 4\mathbf{q}$

$\overrightarrow{DA} = \overrightarrow{DC} + \overrightarrow{CA}$

$= 2\mathbf{p} + 4\mathbf{q}$

$= 2(\mathbf{p} + 2\mathbf{q})$

(iii) $DE = \frac{1}{2}DA$ (*E* is the mid-point of *DA*)

$\therefore \overrightarrow{DE} = \frac{1}{2} \times 2(\mathbf{p} + 2\mathbf{q})$

$= \mathbf{p} + 2\mathbf{q}$

(b) $\overrightarrow{BE} = \overrightarrow{BD} + \overrightarrow{DE}$

$= \mathbf{p} + \mathbf{p} + 2\mathbf{q}$

$= 2\mathbf{p} + 2\mathbf{q}$

$= 2(\mathbf{p} + \mathbf{q})$

(c) $\overrightarrow{BF} = \overrightarrow{BC} + \overrightarrow{CF}$

$= 3\mathbf{p} + 3\mathbf{q}$

$= 3(\mathbf{p} + \mathbf{q})$

(d) (i) From (b) and (c), we have $\overrightarrow{BE} = \frac{2}{3}\overrightarrow{BF}$.

$\therefore \frac{BE}{BF} = \frac{2}{3}$

(ii) $\frac{\text{area of } \Delta ABE}{\text{area of } \Delta ABF} = \frac{BE}{BF}$

$= \frac{2}{3}$

(iii) $\frac{\text{area of } \Delta ABF}{\text{area of } \Delta ABC} = \frac{1}{4}$

$= \frac{3}{12}$

$\therefore \frac{\text{area of } \Delta ABE}{\text{area of } \Delta ABC} = \frac{2}{12}$

$= \frac{1}{6}$

1. It is given that P is the point $(-2, -1)$, Q is the point $(4, 2)$ and R is the point $(2, 6)$. Express as column vectors the position vector of
   (a) the point M, which is the mid-point of QR,
   (b) the point N on PM such that $4\overrightarrow{PN} = \overrightarrow{NM}$.

2. In the quadrilateral $OPQR$, the points M, N, X and Y are the mid-points of OP, PQ, QR and RO respectively.

   Given that $\overrightarrow{OP} = \begin{pmatrix} 6 \\ -1 \end{pmatrix}$, $\overrightarrow{OQ} = \begin{pmatrix} 5 \\ 7 \end{pmatrix}$ and $\overrightarrow{OR} = \begin{pmatrix} 2 \\ 6 \end{pmatrix}$, find the vectors $\overrightarrow{PQ}$, $\overrightarrow{RQ}$, $\overrightarrow{MN}$ and $\overrightarrow{XY}$. State the geometrical facts concerning MN and XY.

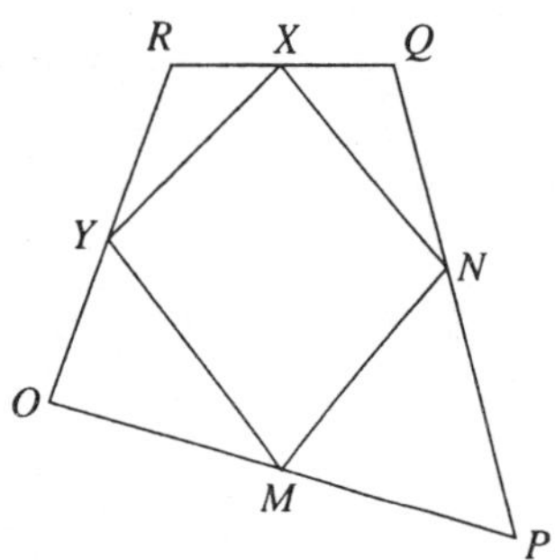

3. It is given that P is the point $(0, 2)$, Q is the point $(8, 0)$ and $\overrightarrow{QR} = \begin{pmatrix} -2 \\ 4 \end{pmatrix}$. Find the following:
   (a) $|\overrightarrow{PQ}|$,
   (b) the coordinates of the point R,
   (c) $|\overrightarrow{PR}|$.

4. It is given that $\mathbf{a} = \begin{pmatrix} 4 \\ 1 \end{pmatrix}$, $\mathbf{b} = \begin{pmatrix} -5 \\ 12 \end{pmatrix}$ and $\mathbf{c} = \begin{pmatrix} p \\ q \end{pmatrix}$.
   (a) Find $|\mathbf{b}|$.
   (b) Express $3\mathbf{a} + 2\mathbf{b}$ as a column vector.
   (c) Given that $2\mathbf{a} - \mathbf{b} = 2\mathbf{c}$, find the value of p and the value of q.

5. A is the point $(-3, 4)$ and O is the origin.

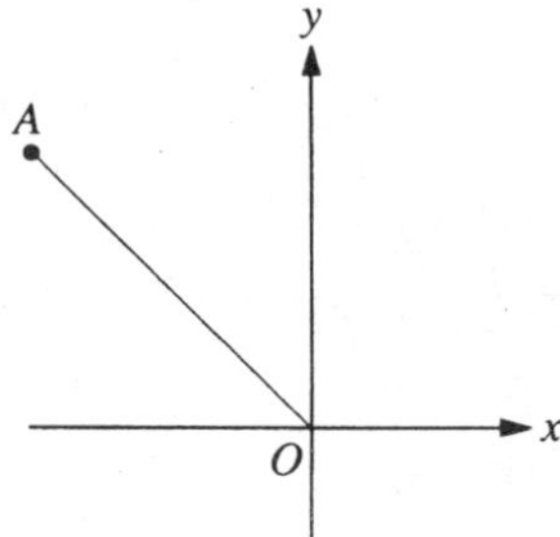

   (a) The point B lies on OA produced. Given that $\overrightarrow{OB} = 3\overrightarrow{OA}$, express $\overrightarrow{OB}$ as a column vector.
   (b) C is the point $(2, 16)$. Express $\overrightarrow{AC}$ as a column vector and find $|\overrightarrow{AC}|$.
   (c) D is the reflection of A in the line $y = x$. Express $\overrightarrow{OD}$ as a column vector.
   (d) OA is rotated in an anticlockwise direction about O so that A is mapped onto E, where E is a point on the negative x-axis.

   Express $\overrightarrow{OE}$ as a column vector.

6. $PQRS$ is a parallelogram. The point T, on SR, is such that $TR = \frac{2}{3}SR$. The lines PT and QR are produced to meet at U.
$\overrightarrow{PQ} = \begin{pmatrix} 6 \\ 0 \end{pmatrix}$ and $\overrightarrow{QR} = \begin{pmatrix} 1 \\ 5 \end{pmatrix}$.

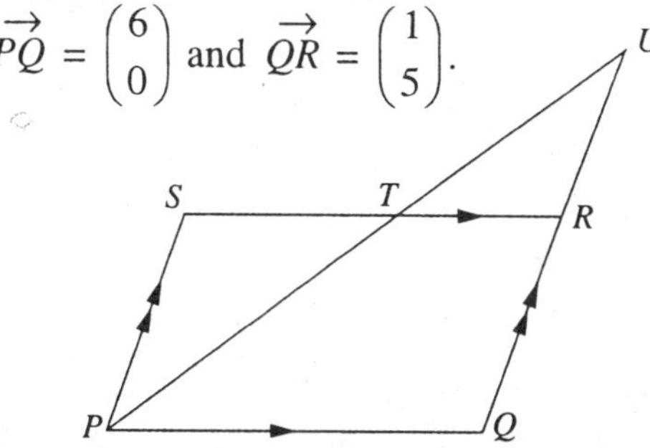

(a) Find $|\overrightarrow{QR}|$, giving your answer correct to the nearest whole number.

(b) Express each of the following as a column vector:

(i) $\overrightarrow{SP}$ (ii) $\overrightarrow{ST}$

(iii) $\overrightarrow{RT}$ (iv) $\overrightarrow{UT}$

7. The quadrilateral $PQRS$ is such that $\overrightarrow{PQ} = 3\mathbf{a}$, $\overrightarrow{QR} = \mathbf{b}$ and $\overrightarrow{RS} = -2\mathbf{a}$.

(a) What is the special name given to the quadrilateral $PQRS$?

(b) Express $\overrightarrow{SP}$ in terms of **a** and **b**, giving your answer in the simplest form.

8. In the diagram, P is (0, 2), Q is (3, 3) and O is the origin.

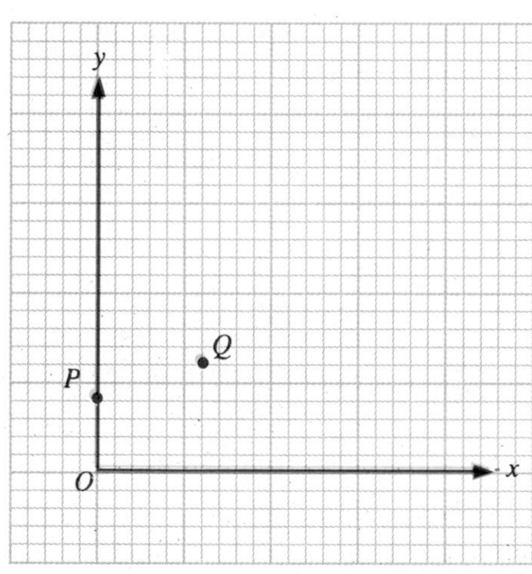

(a) Express $\overrightarrow{PQ}$ as a column vector.

(b) Calculate the coordinates of the point R, where $\overrightarrow{QR} = 2\overrightarrow{PQ}$.

(c) It is given that $\overrightarrow{PS} = \begin{pmatrix} 6 \\ -1 \end{pmatrix}$.

(i) Calculate the length of PS.

(ii) Write down the gradient of the line PS.

(iii) Write down the equation of the line PS.

(iv) The point T lies on PS and TQ is parallel to the y-axis. Calculate the coordinates of T.

9. In the diagram, $\overrightarrow{AB} = \mathbf{p}$, $\overrightarrow{AD} = \mathbf{q}$ and X is the point on DB such that $DX = \frac{1}{4}DB$.

(a) Given that DC is parallel to AB and that it is three-quarters as long as AB, express $\overrightarrow{CD}$ in terms of **p** and/or **q**.

(b) Express the following, as simply as possible, in terms of **p** and/or **q**.

(i) $\overrightarrow{AC}$ (ii) $\overrightarrow{DB}$ (iii) $\overrightarrow{AX}$

(c) Given further that $\overrightarrow{AX} = h\mathbf{p} + k\mathbf{q}$, and that Y is the point such that $\overrightarrow{AY} = h\mathbf{p}$, mark and label the point Y on the diagram.

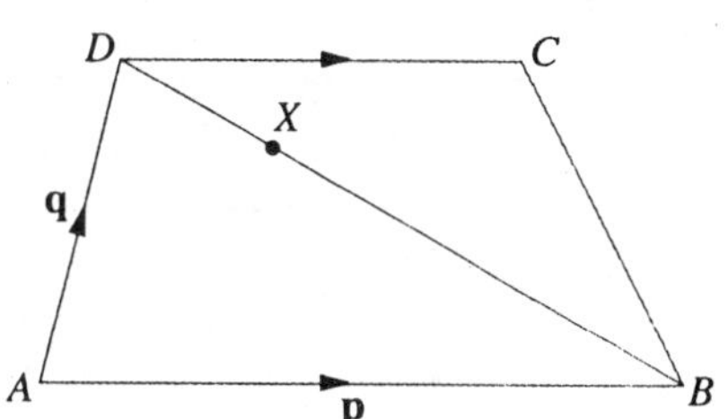

★10. In the diagram, $\overrightarrow{PQ} = \mathbf{a}$, $\overrightarrow{PR} = \mathbf{b}$ and M is the mid-point of QR.

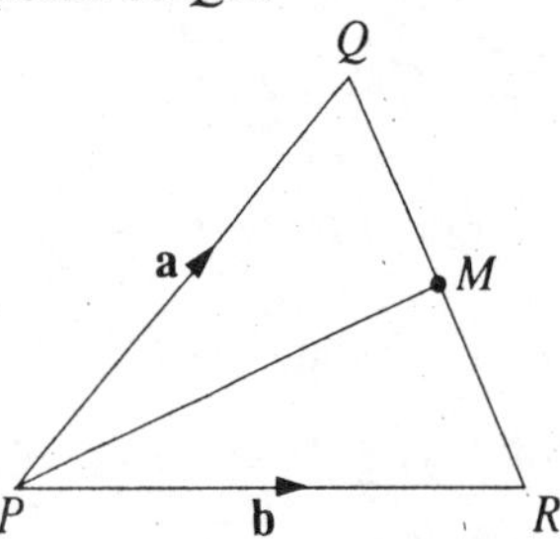

(a) Express the following as simply as possible, in terms of **a** and/or **b**.

(i) $\overrightarrow{QR}$ (ii) $\overrightarrow{QM}$ (iii) $\overrightarrow{PM}$

(b) Given further that $\overrightarrow{PM} = \lambda\mathbf{a} + \mu\mathbf{b}$, and N is the point such that $\overrightarrow{PN} = \mu\mathbf{b}$, mark and label the point N on the diagram.

(c) The point S lies on PM produced. Given that $\overrightarrow{PS} = 2\overrightarrow{PM}$, express the following as simply as possible, in terms of **a** and/or **b**.

(i) $\overrightarrow{PS}$ (ii) $\overrightarrow{QS}$

(iii) $\overrightarrow{RS}$

State what sort of quadrilateral $PRSQ$ is.

11. In the diagram, $\overrightarrow{OS} = \mathbf{s}$ and $\overrightarrow{OT} = \mathbf{t}$.

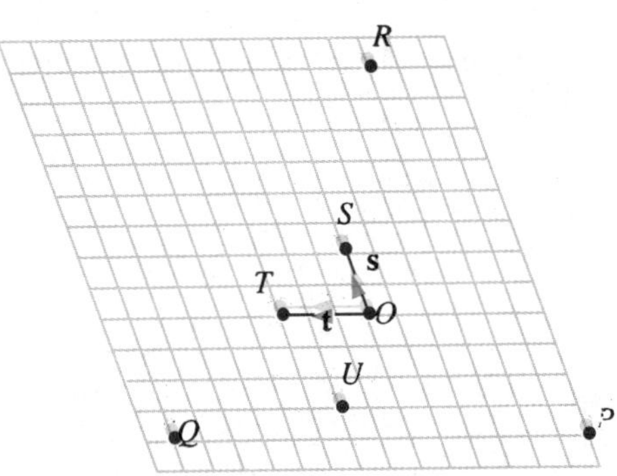

(a) Mark clearly on the diagram

(i) the point A, such that $\overrightarrow{OA} = 2\mathbf{s} + 3\mathbf{t}$,

(ii) the point B, such that $\overrightarrow{OB} = -2(\mathbf{t} - \mathbf{s})$,

(iii) the point C, such that $\overrightarrow{OC} = 3\mathbf{t} - \mathbf{s}$.

(b) Write down $\overrightarrow{OP}$, $\overrightarrow{OQ}$, $\overrightarrow{OR}$ and $\overrightarrow{OU}$ in terms of **s** and **t**.

12. In the diagram, $PQRS$ is a parallelogram, M is the mid-point of QS, N is the mid-point of QM and L is the point on QR such that $QL = \frac{2}{3}QR$.

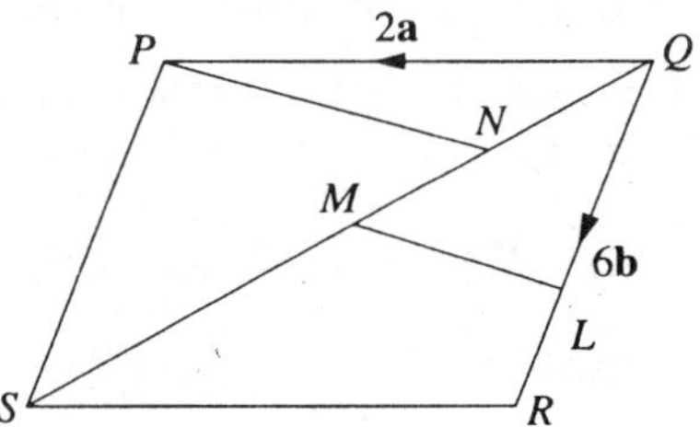

(a) Given that $\overrightarrow{QP} = 2\mathbf{a}$ and $\overrightarrow{QR} = 6\mathbf{b}$, express, as simply as possible, in terms of **a** and/or **b**,

(i) $\overrightarrow{QS}$, (ii) $\overrightarrow{QM}$,

(iii) $\overrightarrow{PN}$, (iv) $\overrightarrow{ML}$.

(b) What do your answers to **(a)(iii)** and **(a)(iv)** tell you about PN and ML?

(c) What is the special name given to the quadrilateral $PMLN$?

(d) Write down the value of each of the following:

(i) $\dfrac{\text{Area of } \triangle PNQ}{\text{Area of } \triangle PSN}$

(ii) $\dfrac{\text{Area of } \triangle PSN}{\text{Area of } \triangle QML}$

Statistics 1: Data Handling and Averages

xample 1

720 pupils were asked which of the four subjects, Mathematics, Science, History and English, they preferred. The pie chart illustrates the results.

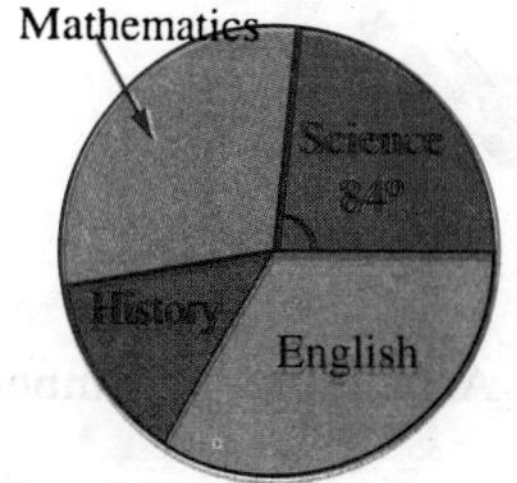

(a) How many pupils preferred Science?
(b) Given that 204 pupils preferred Mathematics, calculate the angle of the sector representing this.
(c) Given that 35% preferred English, find the angle of the sector representing this.
(d) Draw a bar graph to illustrate the data.

Solution

(a) No. of pupils who preferred Science $= \frac{84°}{360°} \times 720 = 168$

(b) The angle of the Mathematics sector $= \frac{204}{720} \times 360° = 102°$

(c) The angle of the English sector = 35% of 360° $= \frac{35}{100} \times 360° = 126°$

(d) No. of pupils who preferred English $= \frac{126°}{360°} \times 720 = 252$

No. of pupils who preferred History $= 720 - 168 - 204 - 252 = 96$

The table below shows how the pupils voted.

Subject	No. of pupils
English	252
History	96
Mathematics	204
Science	168

The bar graph shows the number of pupils voting for various subjects.

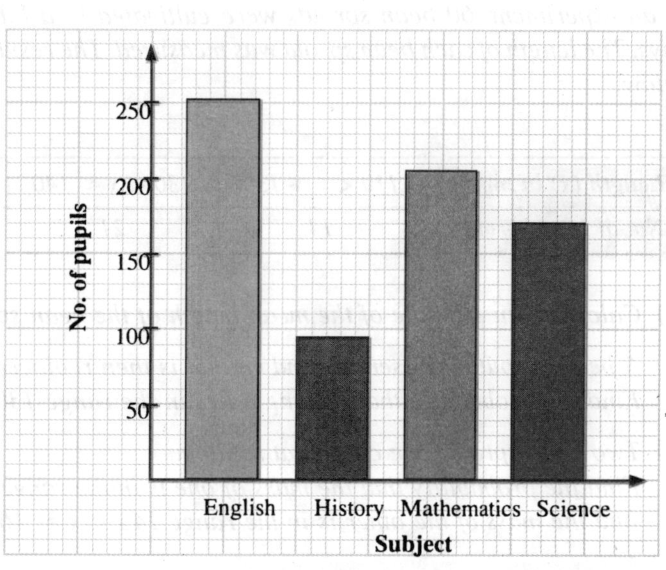

Example 2

For the distribution 6, 8, 15, 11, 4, 6, 7, 11, 21, 6, find the following:

(a) Mode
(b) Median
(c) Mean

In 1996, Singaporeans spent a whopping \$5 billion on legal betting alone. \$2.8 billion was spent on four-digit lottery, \$1.26 billion on horse-racing, \$310 million on Toto, \$72 million on Singapore Sweep and another 500 million on Jackpot machines in private clubs. The government collected a total of \$1.144 billion taxes from betting, sweepstakes and private lotteries in 1996. Singaporeans were ranked top gamblers in South-East Asia on per capital basis. Do you think we should celebrate this great achievement?

(a) The mode is 6.

(b) Arranging the numbers in order of size, we have

$$4, 6, 6, 6, 7, 8, 11, 11, 15, 21.$$

The median is the average of 7 and 8.

$\therefore$ the median is $\dfrac{7 + 8}{2} = 7.5$

(c) The mean $= \dfrac{4 + 6 + 6 + 6 + 7 + 8 + 11 + 11 + 15 + 21}{10}$

$= \dfrac{95}{10}$

$= 9.5$

Example 2

In an experiment, 60 bean sprouts were cultivated in a laboratory for six days. The length of each bean sprout was measured. The results are tabulated below.

Length (x) in mm	$110 < x \leqslant 130$	$130 < x \leqslant 140$	$140 < x \leqslant 145$	$145 < x \leqslant 160$
No. of bean sprouts	14	21	10	15

(a) Calculate an estimate of the mean length of the bean sprouts.

(b) A bean sprout is chosen at random and is then replaced.
Find the probability that its length lies in the range $130 < x \leqslant 140$.

(c) Two bean sprouts are chosen at random.
Find the probability that the mass of one is in the range $130 < x \leqslant 140$ and the mass of the other is in the range $145 < x \leqslant 160$.

(a)

Length (x mm)	120	135	142.5	152.5
Frequency	14	21	10	15

$$\text{The estimate of the mean length} = \frac{120 \times 14 + 135 \times 21 + 142.5 \times 10 + 152.5 \times 15}{60}$$

$= 137.125$ mm

$= 137$ mm (correct to the nearest mm)

(b) Required probability $= \frac{21}{60} = \frac{7}{20}$.

(c) Required probability $= \frac{21}{60} \times \frac{15}{59} \times 2 = \frac{21}{118}$.

1. The pie chart illustrates the value of various goods sold by a certain shop.

(a) Calculate the value of x.

(b) Given that the total value of the sales was \$21 600, find the sales value of the following:

(i) food

(ii) stationery

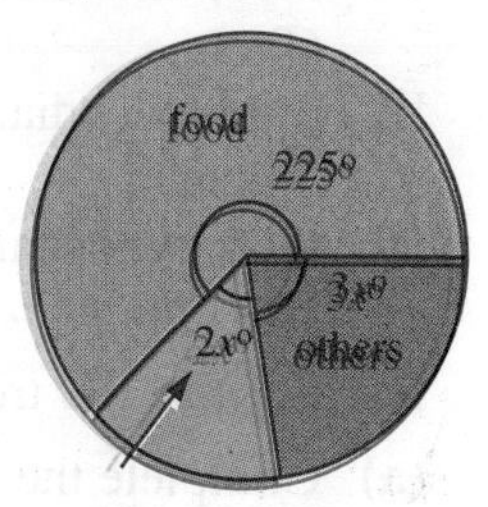

2. The bar graph shown in the figure illustrates the production of edible oils in a certain country.

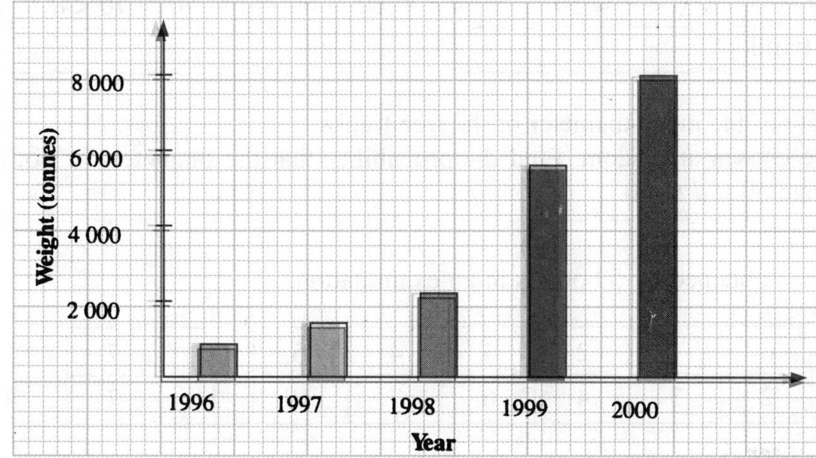

(a) Calculate the total production of edible oils from 1996 to 2000.

(b) Illustrate the information on a clearly-labelled pie chart.

3. The pie chart shows the number of road deaths in a certain country during one year for boys aged up to and including 19 years. Given that the total number of road deaths was 120, find the number of road deaths for each category. Hence, illustrate the information on a clearly-labelled bar graph.

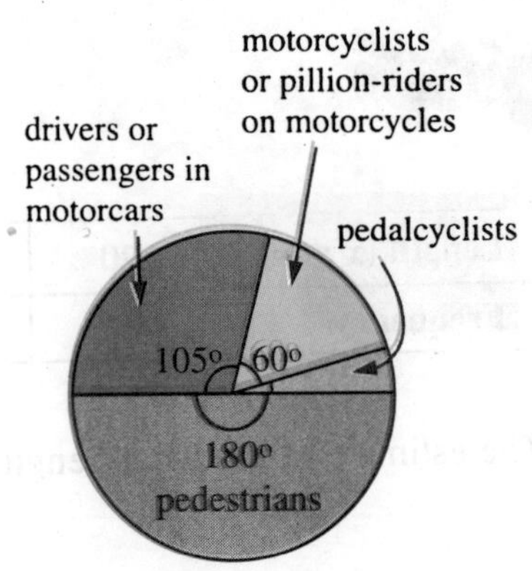

4. The following is a set of twelve numbers.

6, 7, 14, 7, 4, 9, 4, 4, 3, 4, 5, 17

(a) Find the following:
(i) Mode (ii) Median (iii) Mean

(b) When the number a is added to the above set, the new mean is 9. Calculate the value of a.

5. Diameters of 100 tree trunks were measured and were divided into four groups.

I: those with diameter less than 50 cm,
II: those with diameter greater than or equal to 50 cm, but less than 60 cm,
III: those with diameter greater than or equal to 60 cm, but less than 70 cm,
IV: those with diameter greater than or equal to 70 cm, but less than 100 cm.

Each of the 100 tree trunks is in one of the four groups, as shown on the given pie chart.

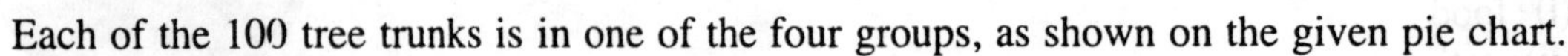

(a) Complete the table in the answer space.

	Group I	Group II	Group III	Group IV
Diameter (d cm)	$0 < d \leqslant 50$	$50 < d \leqslant 60$	$60 < d \leqslant 70$	$70 < d \leqslant 100$
Number of tree trunks		18		

(b) Calculate an estimate of the mean diameter of the tree trunks.

(c) Two tree trunks are chosen at random. Find the probability that the diameters of both tree trunks lie in the range $50 < d \leqslant 60$.

6. The following marks were obtained by 50 pupils in an examination.

Marks	0	1	2	3	4	5	6	7
No. of pupils	2	3	4	6	7	10	11	7

(a) Draw a histogram to represent the data given in the table.

(b) For this distribution, find the following:
(i) Mode (ii) Median (iii) Mean

7. The marks obtained by 48 students in a Science test are as follows:

48 37 78 90 51 76 88 94 33 35 74 78
23 36 54 60 65 46 42 43 45 28 32 36
37 44 68 72 59 48 43 89 78 32 76 84
53 39 39 67 68 83 27 43 75 67 83 57

(a) Construct a frequency table for the above marks using class intervals 21–30, 31–40, 41–50, and so on.
(b) Use your table to calculate the mean.

8. There are 100 houses in a certain housing estate. The following table shows the number of children living in each house:

Number of children	1	2	3	4	more than 4
Number of houses	13	37	17	5	7

(a) How many houses in the estate do not have any children?
(b) Explain clearly why it is not possible to calculate the mean number of children living in each house in the housing estate.
(c) There are altogether 200 children in the estate. A house is considered "overcrowded" if it has more than 4 children living in it. Find the mean number of children in "overcrowded" houses.

9. The mass of each of the 40 students in a class, correct to the nearest kg, are as follows:

52 67 65 57 52 60 58 59
53 42 51 72 69 57 54 54
58 52 44 47 73 58 62 56
63 57 68 59 63 47 68 58
48 50 64 54 57 59 44 55

(a) Construct a frequency table, using a class interval of 5 kg, starting with 41 kg.
(b) Use this frequency table to estimate the mean mass.
(c) List all the possible masses of the students in the class which contains the median and, hence, find the median.

10. (a) The fares paid by bus passengers in one day are shown in the following frequency distribution:

Fare in cents	45	64	85	105	115	125
Number of passengers	47	165	72	34	46	26

Calculate the mean fare per passenger. What is the modal fare?

(b) Pupils in a class of 44 were asked how many children there were in their families and the following data shows their replies:

1 4 7 4 2 3 4 2 3 4 4
2 3 2 3 1 2 3 2 4 5 2
3 4 1 2 1 6 2 5 3 2 1
5 5 1 3 2 1 1 1 6 3 3

(i) Rewrite the above data in a frequency distribution table.
(ii) Draw a histogram to illustrate the data and write down the mode.
(iii) Calculate the percentage of families that had fewer than three children.

Statistics 2: Data Analysis

xample 1

The mass of each of the 90 oranges of a certain variety was recorded. The cumulative frequency curve was drawn as shown below.

A former Prime Minister of Britain, Mr Disraeli, once said: 'There are three kinds of lies — lies, damned lies and statistics'. It is very true that statistical information can be distorted to mislead people to support a particular case.

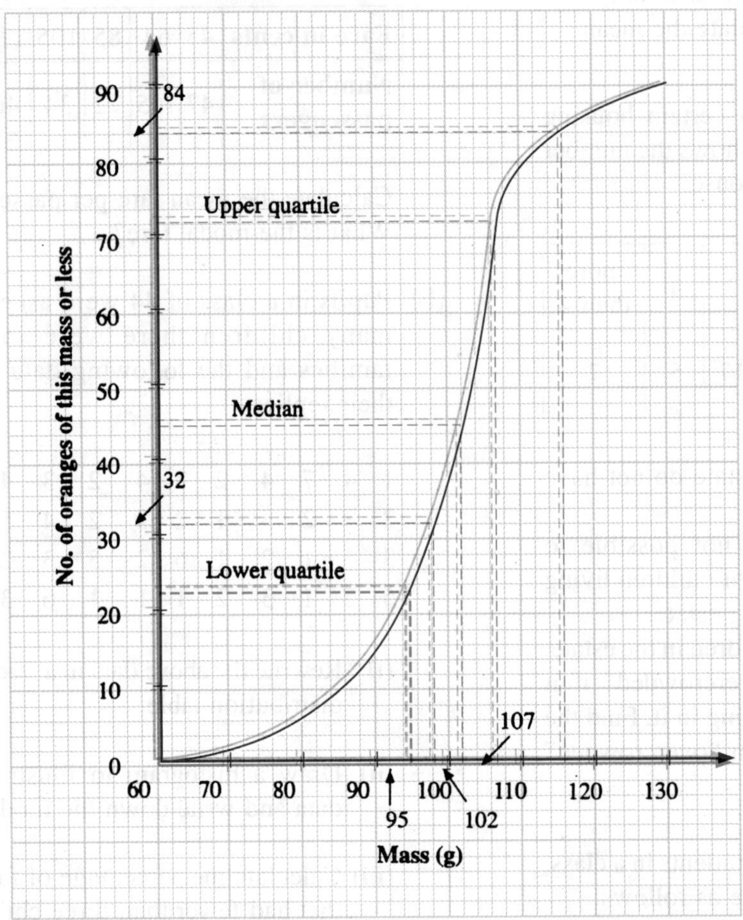

(a) Use the graph to estimate the following for this distribution.
  (i) the median,
  (ii) the interquartile range.

(b) Use the graph to find, as accurately as possible, the probability that an orange chosen at random from the sample has a mass of
  (i) 98 g or less,
  (ii) more than 98 g but not more than 116 g.

(c) Find the probability that one orange, chosen at random, has a mass of more than 110 g.

(d) Two oranges are chosen at random from these 90 oranges. Find the probability that neither has a mass of more than 90 g.

(a) From the graph,
the median = 102 g
the interquartile range = 107 – 95 = 12 g.

(b) (i) From the graph, the estimated number of oranges having a mass of 98 g or less is 32.

$\therefore$ P(an orange chosen at random has mass 98 g or less)

$= \frac{32}{90} = \frac{16}{45}$

(ii) No. of oranges having a mass of not more than 116 g = 84

$\therefore$ no. of oranges having a mass of more than 98 g but not more than 116 g = 84 – 32
= 52

$\therefore$ the required probability $= \frac{52}{90} = \frac{26}{45}$

(c) No. of oranges having a mass of more than 110 g = 8 + 4 = 12

$\therefore$ the required probability $= \frac{12}{90} = \frac{2}{15}$

(d) No. of oranges having a mass of 90 g or less = 4 + 9 = 13

$\therefore$ the required probability $= \frac{13}{90} \times \frac{12}{89}$

$= \frac{26}{1335}$

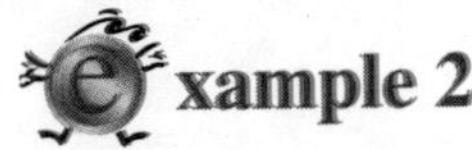

xample 2

A class of 50 pupils sat for a Physical Science examination. The marks obtained by the pupils were tabulated and a cumulative frequency curve was drawn as shown below.

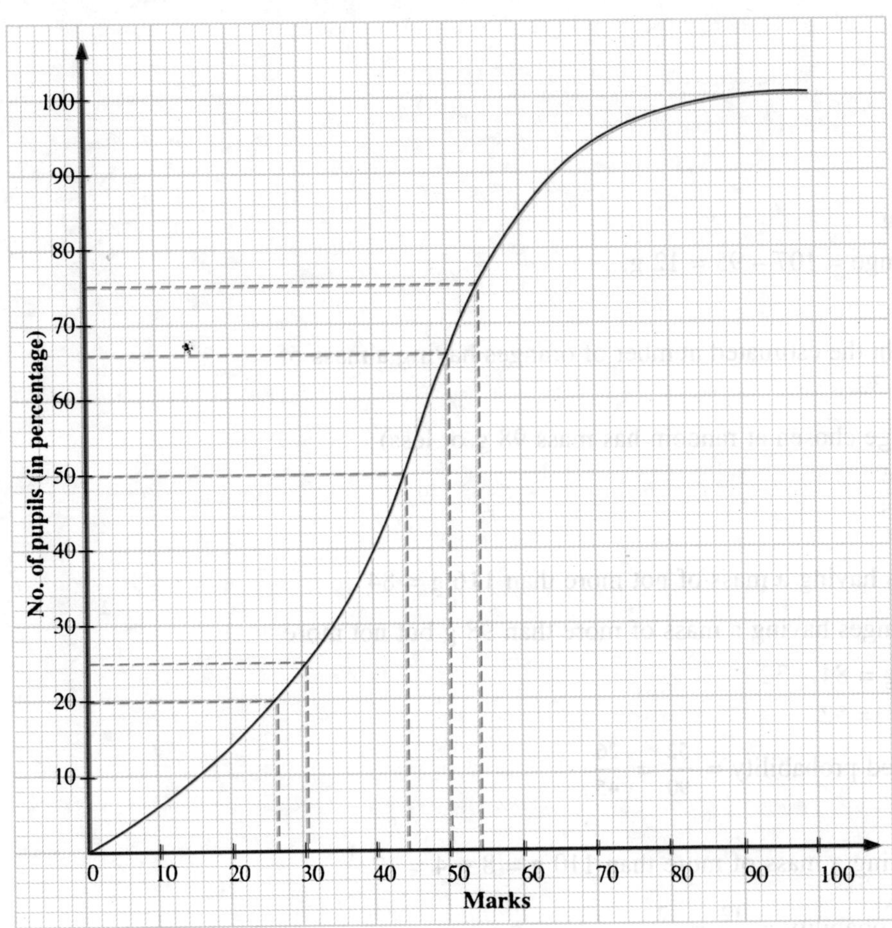

Study the graph and answer the following.

(a) Find the following:

(i) the lower quartile, *(ii) the median,*

(iii) the upper quartile, *(iv) the interquartile range.*

(b) If 75% of the pupils passed the test, what was the passing mark?

(c) If not more than 20% failed, what was the passing mark?

(d) How many pupils passed the test if the passing mark is 50?

(a) From the graph,

(i) lower quartile = 30,
(ii) median = 44,
(iii) upper quartile = 54,
(iv) interquartile range = 54 – 30 = 24.

(b) If 75% of the boys passed the test, then the passing mark = the lower quartile = 30.

(c) The passing mark = the 20th percentile = 26.

(d) 66th percentile = 50, so 34% of the pupils passed the test.

$\therefore$ Number of pupils who passed = $\frac{34}{100} \times 50 = 17$.

xample 3

The box-and-whisker plot below represents the scores of 17 pupils in a Mathematics quiz. Find the upper limit, the lower limit, the range, the median, the upper quartile, the lower quartile and the interquartile range.

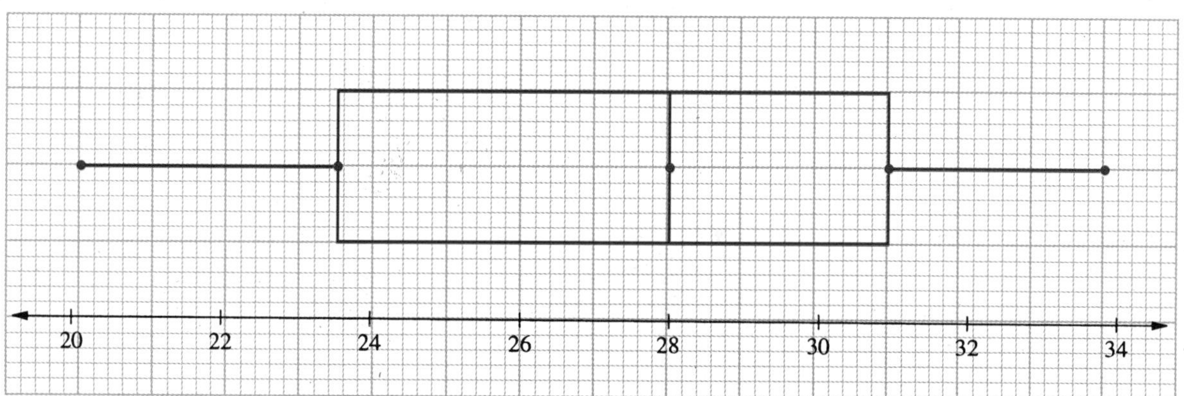

From the box-and-whisker plot, we know that

the upper limit = 34, the lower limit = 20, the median = 28,

the upper quartile = 31, the lower quartile = $23\frac{1}{2}$.

Then,

the range = the upper limit – the lower limit = 34 – 20 = 14.

the interquartile range = the upper quartile – the lower quartile = $31 - 23\frac{1}{2} = 7\frac{1}{2}$.

1. The diagram shows the cumulative frequency curve for the distance travelled to work by a number of commuters. Use the curve to estimate, as accurately as possible,

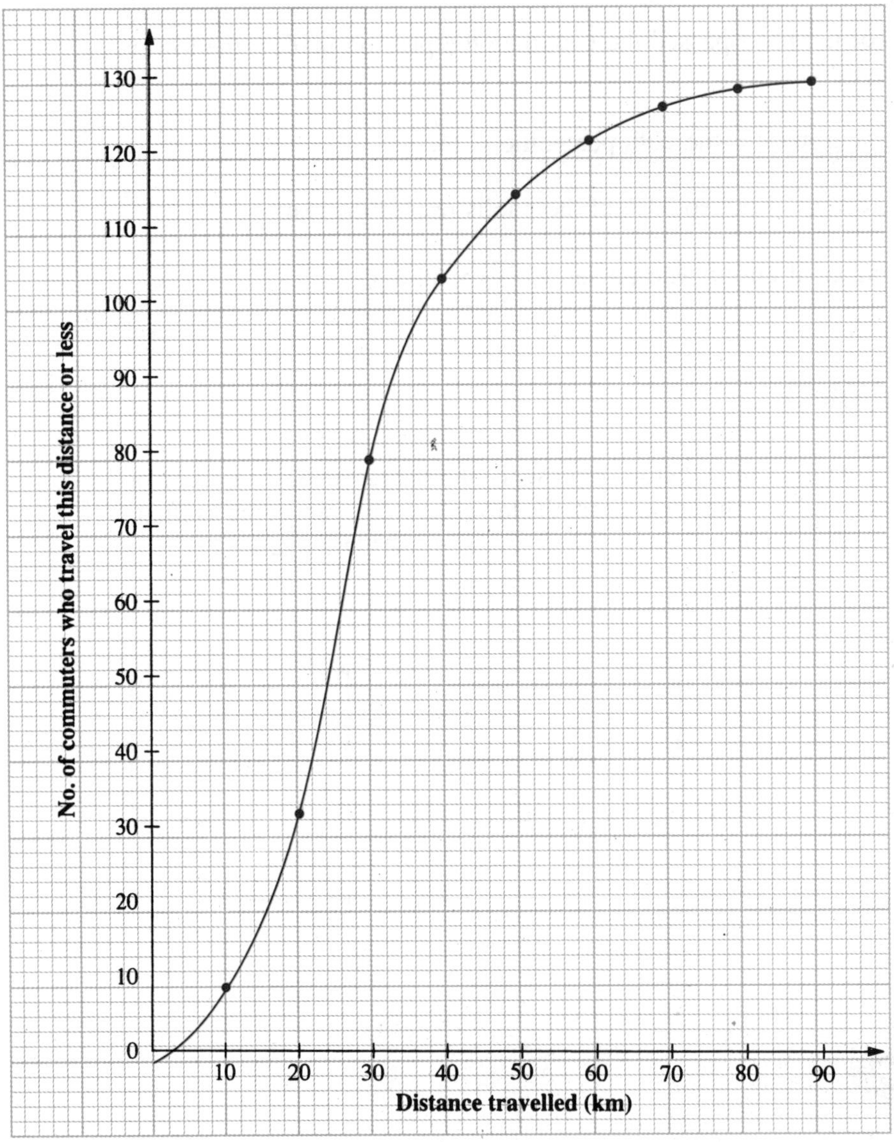

(a) the median distance,

(b) the interquartile range,

(c) the probability that a commuter selected at random travels 34 km or less to work.

2. The diagram shows the cumulative frequency curve for the length of 100 leaves of a plant.

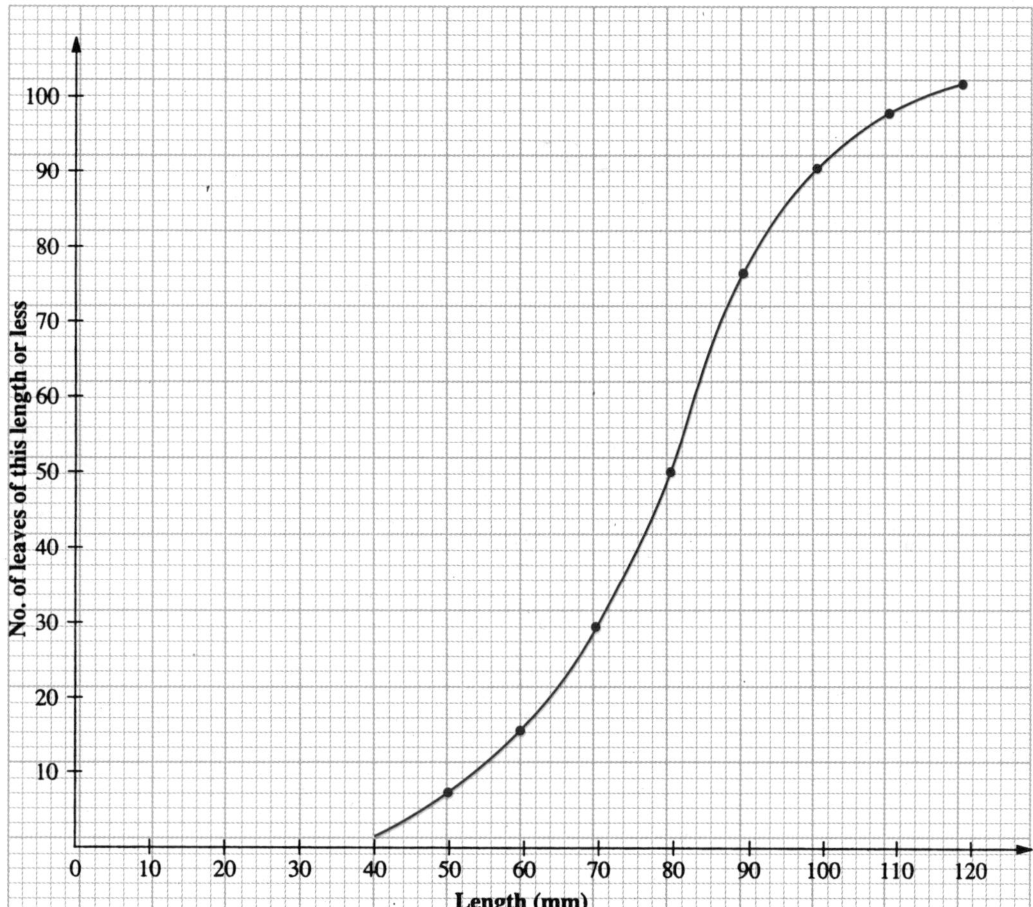

(c) Using the graph to estimate, showing your method clearly for this distribution,
 (i) the median,
 (ii) the interquartile range.

(d) Find the probability that a leaf chosen at random has a length of more than 80 mm.

(e) A leaf is chosen at random from those having lengths more than 80 mm. Find the probability that its length is greater than 100 mm.

3. The diagram shows the cumulative frequency curve for the distance travelled from home to school by 560 pupils in a girls' school.

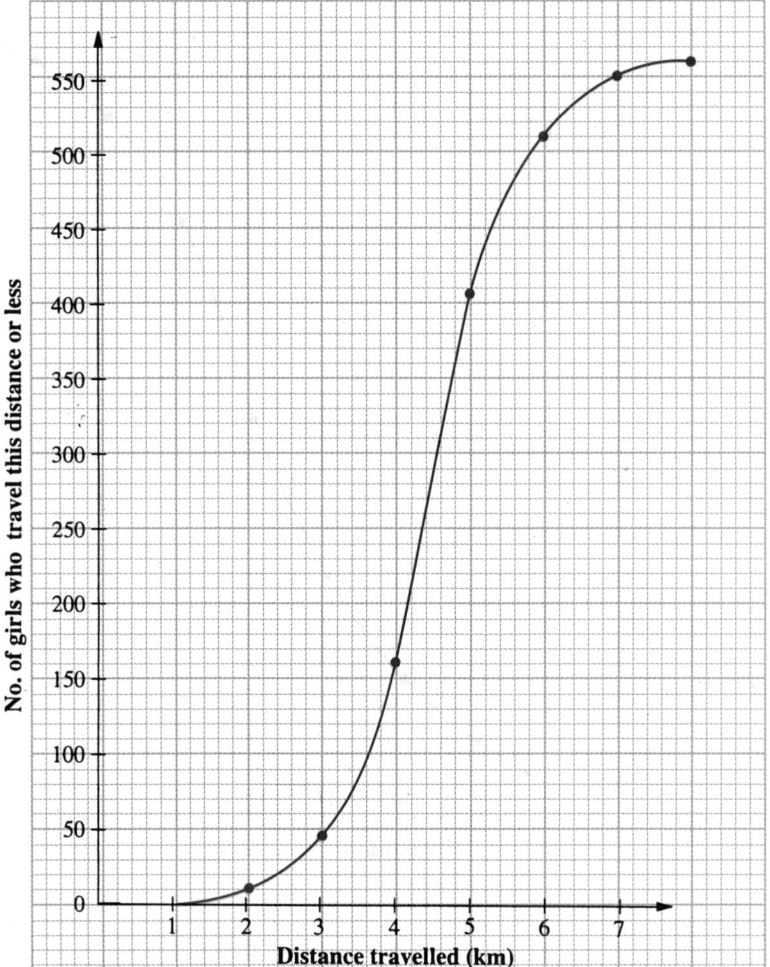

(a) Use the graph to estimate the number of girls who travel 4.5 km or more.

(b) Use the graph to estimate, showing your method clearly,
  (i) the median,
  (ii) the interquartile range of this distribution.

(c) A girl is selected at random from the 560.
  (i) Find the probability that the distance she travels is less than or equal to 3 km.
  (ii) If the probability that she travels more than y kilometres is $\frac{5}{56}$, find y.

(d) Two girls are selected at random from the 560. Find the probability that they each travel a distance less than or equal to 1 km.

4. (a) The mass of each of the 100 members of a sports club are given in the following table.

Mass (x kg)	Number of members
$45 < x \leq 55$	5
$55 < x \leq 65$	10
$65 < x \leq 75$	21
$75 < x \leq 85$	45
$85 < x \leq 95$	16
$95 < x \leq 105$	3

Find an estimate for the mean mass for these members.

(b) In a pie chart drawn to represent the number of animals in a farm, the angle representing the number of deer is 165°. A quarter of the animals are goats and there are 287 cows. Given that there are no other animals, calculate

(i) the percentage of deer on the farm, giving your answer correct to the nearest whole number,

(ii) the total number of animals on the farm.

5.

Life in hours	Frequency
4 – 5	0
5 – 6	3
6 – 7	5
7 – 8	8
8 – 9	14
9 – 10	30
10 – 11	48
11 – 12	32
12 – 13	10
13 – 14	6
14 – 15	4

The frequency table shows the life of a sample of 160 batteries where 5 – 6 means ≥ 5 hours but < 6 hours. Estimate the mean life of the batteries.

6. Find the range, median and the interquartile range for the box-and-whisker plot shown below.

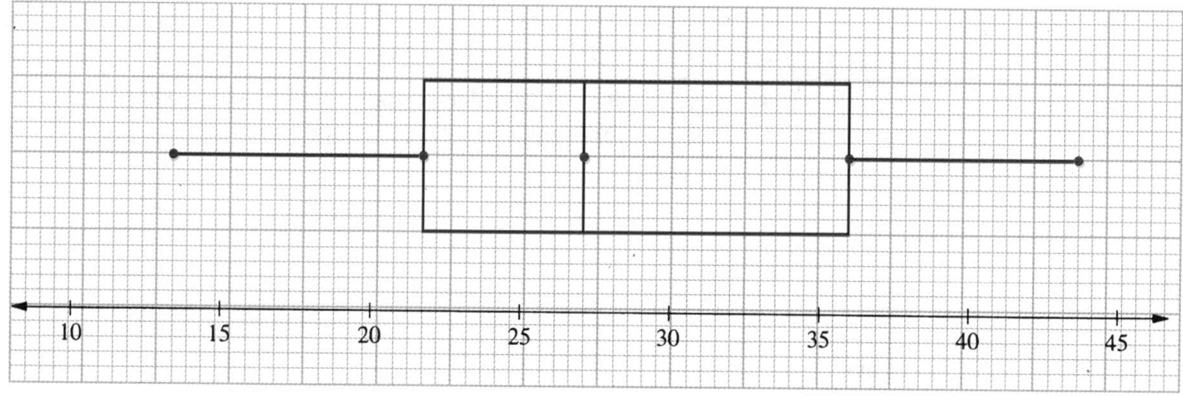

7. The diagram shows the cumulative frequency curve for the mass of 450 star fruits.

(a) Use the graph to estimate
 (i) the median,
 (ii) the interquartile range,
 (iii) the 80th percentile.

(b) The star fruits are graded "A grade" or "B grade" according to mass. In order to be graded "A grade", a star fruit must have a mass exceeding a certain value. Given that there are 150 "A grade" star fruits, find the value of this mass.

(c) If a star fruit is chosen at random from these 450 star fruits, find the probability that its mass is between 150 g and 195 g.

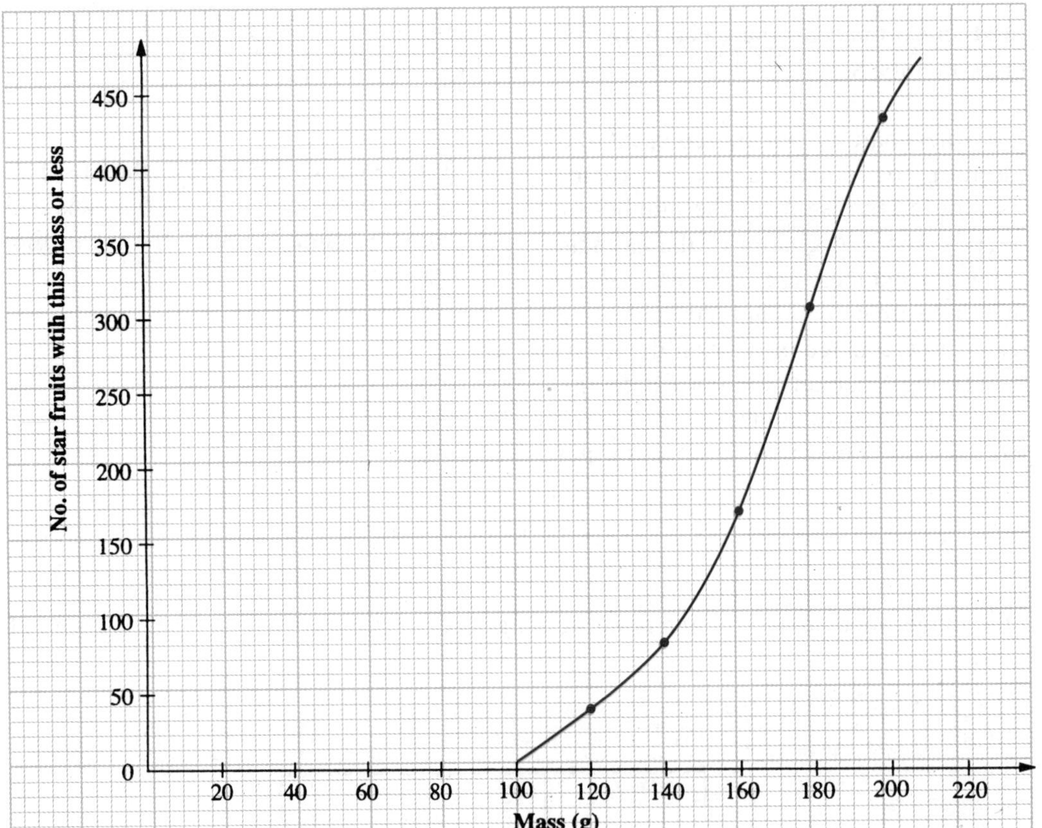

Probability

xample 1

A bag contains 52 cards numbered from 1 to 52 inclusive. A card is chosen at random from the bag. Write down the probability that the number on the chosen card will

(a) have a single digit,
(b) be a perfect square,
(c) have at least one figure 4,
(d) ***not*** *be divisible by either 3 or 4.*

(a) There are 9 single digit numbers from 1 to 52 inclusive.

$\therefore$ P(number on the card chosen will contain a single digit) = $\frac{9}{52}$.

(b) The numbers from 1 to 52 inclusive which are perfect squares are 1, 4, 9, 16, 25, 36, 49.

$\therefore$ P(number on the card chosen will be a perfect square) = $\frac{7}{52}$.

(c) The numbers from 1 to 52 inclusive which contains at least one figure 4 are 4, 14, 24, 34, 40, 41, 42, 43, 44, 45, 46, 47, 48, 49.

$\therefore$ P(number on the card chosen will contain at least one figure 4)

$= \frac{14}{52} = \frac{7}{26}$.

(d) Number of numbers from 1 to 52 that are
divisible by 3 is 17 ($3 \times 17 = 51 < 52$),
divisible by 4 is 13 ($4 \times 13 = 52$),
divisible by 12 is 4 ($12 \times 4 = 48 < 52$).

Both the 17 numbers and the 13 numbers that are divisible by 3 and 4 respectively include the 4 numbers that are divisible by 12, namely 12, 24, 36 and 48. By simply adding 17 and 13 will result in double counting of the numbers that are divisible by 12.

$\therefore$ there are $17 + 13 - 4 = 26$ numbers which are divisible by either 3 or 4.
P(number on the card chosen will *not* be divisible by either 3 or 4)

$= 1 - \frac{26}{52} = \frac{1}{2}$

If you bet $1 'small' on a 4D number, you may win the first prize of $3000, the second prize of $2000 or the third prize of $1000 each with the probability of $\frac{1}{10\,000}$. However, you stand to lose your bet of $1 with the probability of $\frac{9997}{10\,000}$. The table below displays your possible gains.

Gain (in dollars)	Probability
3000	$\frac{1}{10\,000}$
2000	$\frac{1}{10\,000}$
1000	$\frac{1}{10\,000}$
–	$\frac{9997}{10\,000}$

Note: *–1 indicates a loss of your bet of $1.*

Multiplying each gain by the corresponding probability and summing up, a value which we call the expected gain is obtained.

In this case, the expected gain $\frac{1}{10\,000}$ *. (3000 + 2000 + 1000) + (–1) ×* $\frac{9997}{10\,000}$ *= –0.40 (correct to two decimal places)*

$X = \{G, E, R, M, A, N\}$ *and* $Y = \{E, N, G, L, I, S, H\}$.

(a) If one element is selected at random from X, write down the probability that it is a vowel.

(b) If one element is selected at random from each set, construct a possibility diagram to show all possible outcomes. How many possible outcomes are there altogether?

(c) Using the diagram, find the probability that both elements are
(i) vowels,
(ii) the same.

The negative value of the expected gain can be interpreted as follows:

you expect to lose 40 cents for every \$1 you bet in the long run, i.e. if you bet often enough.

Find out the expected gain if you bet \$1 'big' on a 4D number and interpret the value obtained.

(a) There are two vowels in the set X.

$$\therefore \quad \text{P(selecting a vowel from } X) = \frac{2}{6} = \frac{1}{3}$$

(b) From the possibility diagram, there are $6 \times 7 = 42$ possible outcomes.

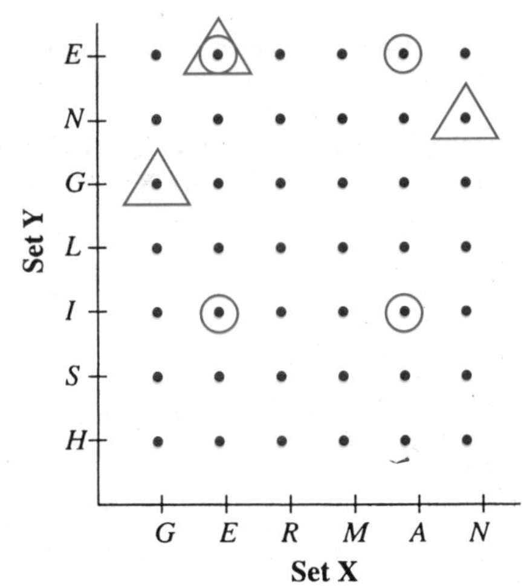

(c) (i) There are 4 outcomes, EI, EE, AI and AE (shown circled) involving 2 vowels.

$$\therefore \quad \text{P(both elements are vowels)} = \frac{4}{42} = \frac{2}{21}$$

(ii) There are 3 outcomes, GG, EE and NN (shown enclosed in triangles) in which the two elements are the same.

$$\text{P(both elements are the same)} = \frac{3}{42} = \frac{1}{14}$$

Example 3

On a mini-market shelf there are 15 boxes containing white table-tennis balls and 6 boxes containing orange table-tennis balls. A boy picks any two boxes at random. Use a tree diagram to determine the probability of picking

(a) two boxes containing white table-tennis balls,
(b) two boxes containing orange table-tennis balls,
(c) a box containing white table-tennis balls followed by one containing orange table-tennis balls,
(d) two boxes that are different.

Let W denote the event of picking a box containing white table-tennis balls and O denote the event of picking a box containing orange table-tennis balls. The tree diagram is shown below.

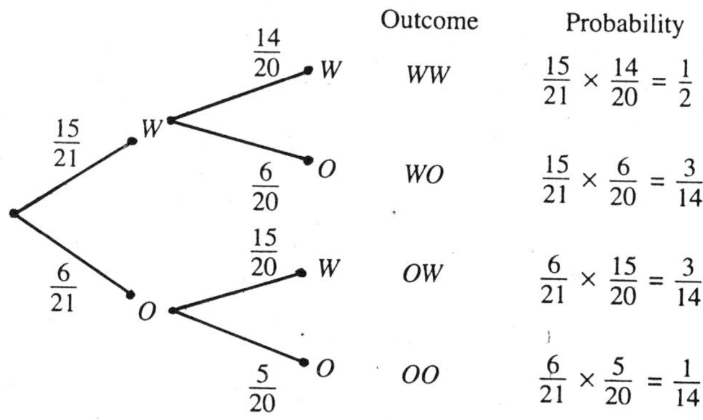

(a) P(two boxes of white table-tennis balls) = $P(WW) = \frac{1}{2}$

(b) P(two boxes of orange table-tennis balls) = $P(OO) = \frac{1}{14}$

(c) P(one box of white table-tennis balls followed by one of orange table-tennis balls) = $P(WO) = \frac{3}{14}$

(d) P(two boxes with table-tennis balls of different colours)

$= P(WO \text{ or } OW)$

$= P(WO) + P(OW)$

$= \frac{3}{14} + \frac{3}{14}$

$= \frac{3}{7}$

1. Each of the letters of the word '*EXCELLENCE*' is printed on a separate card and the cards are put into a box. Two cards are drawn at random from the box, one at a time, without replacement. Find the probability that
   (a) both cards contain vowels,
   (b) the first card drawn contains a vowel,
   (c) the second card drawn contains a vowel,
   (d) one of the two cards drawn contains a vowel,
   (e) the letters on the two cards drawn are the same.

2. Two bags, X and Y, contain red and black marbles only. Bag X contains 4 red marbles and 2 black marbles. Bag Y contains 3 red marbles and 1 black marble.
   A bag is to be chosen by flipping a coin. If the coin shows head, bag X is chosen; otherwise bag Y is chosen. A marble is then selected at random from the chosen bag.
   (a) Draw a tree diagram to illustrate this experiment.
   (b) Calculate the probability of selecting a red marble.

3. In an election with only two candidates, x voters voted for candidate A and 36 voters voted for candidate B. If a voter is to be chosen at random, write down an expression for the probability that a voter who voted for candidate A will be chosen. Given that the probability of a voter who voted for candidate A will be chosen is $\frac{2}{5}$, find the value of x.

4. The questions on an examination paper are numbered from 1 to 50 inclusive. A question is chosen at random.
   Write down, giving your answer as a fraction, the probability that the number of the question chosen will
   (a) contain more than a single digit,
   (b) be a perfect square,
   (c) contain at least one figure 3,
   (d) not be divisible by either 2 or 3.

5. A box contains 33 table-tennis balls, 12 of which are white and 21 of which are orange. One ball is taken at random from the box and not replaced. A second ball is then picked. Use a tree diagram to find the probability that
   (a) both balls are orange,
   (b) both balls are of the same colour,
   (c) the balls are of different colours.

6. A bag contains 4 counters, one marked with the letter A, one with the letter B and two with the letter L. The counters are drawn at random from the bag, one at a time, without replacement.
   In each of the following cases, calculate the probability that
   (a) the first two counters drawn will each have the letter L marked on them,
   (b) the second counter to be drawn will have the letter B marked on it,
   (c) the order in which the counters are drawn will spell out the word *BALL*.

7. The faces of a cubical die are numbered from 3 to 8. Two such dice are thrown and the product of the resulting numbers is shown in the possibility diagram given below.

×	3	4	5	6	7	8
3			15			
4		16				
5				30		
6	18					
7						56
8		32				

(a) Copy and complete the possibility diagram.

(b) Using the diagram or otherwise, find the probability that the product of the two numbers is
(i) odd,
(ii) less than or equal to 23,
(iii) a prime number,
(iv) divisble by 14,
(v) greater than 8.

8. John has fifteen coins in his pocket. He has eight 20¢ coins, four 50¢ coins and three $1 coins. He takes two coins at random from his pocket, one after the other without replacement.

(a) Complete the probability tree diagram shown below.

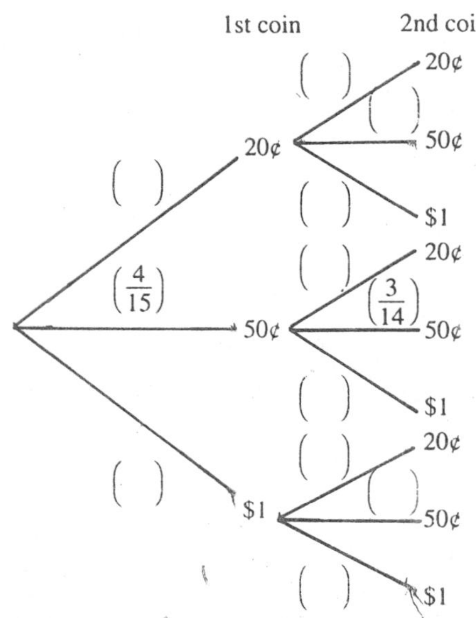

(b) Find the probability that
(i) the first coin is a 20¢ coin and the second is a $1 coin,
(ii) the two coins have different denominations,
(iii) the second coin he takes from his pocket is a 50¢ coin,
(iv) the total value of the two coins is more than one dollar

9. A bag contains 1 red ball, 2 black balls and 3 white balls.

(a) A ball is drawn at random from the bag. What is the probability that the ball drawn is
(i) red,
(ii) white.

(b) The first ball drawn is replaced and a ball is again drawn at random. What is the probability that the two balls drawn are of different colours?

(c) If, instead, the first ball drawn is not replaced and then a second ball is drawn at random, what is the probability in this case of drawing two balls of the same colour?

10. There are 24 white marbles, x red marbles and y blue marbles in a box. One marble is drawn at random. Given the probability that a red marble is drawn is $\frac{1}{5}$ and that a blue marble is drawn is $\frac{2}{5}$, calculate the value of x and of y.

With these values of x and y, calculate the probability that two marbles drawn in succession without replacement are

(a) of the same colour,

(b) a white marble followed by a red marble.

Answers

Exercise 1a

1. −27, −1, 0, 8
   (a) 3.4 (b) −2.3
2. −13, −5, −4, 3
   (a) −15.6 (b) 2.7
3. −2, 2, 0, −2
   (a) 0.2 (b) 2.4
4. 8, 4, 1.3, 0.8
   (a) 1.1 (b) 2.7
5. 2.5, 1.1, 0.4
   (a) 1.3 (b) 1.5
6. −5, −2.3, −1.7, −1.5
   (a) − 1.8 (b) 3.3
7. 1, −1, 1.81, 1.88
   (a) 0.67
   (b) 2.45
8. (a) −5, −1, −2, 20
   (b) (i) −1 or 1.6, −2.4, 2.8
   (ii) −11.6, −1.9, 5.2
9. (a) 0, 10, 20
   (b) (i) 9.4, 15, 27
   (ii) 0.8, 3.5, 4.15
10. (a) $h = 2$, $k = 5.5$
    (b) (i) 0.9, 1.75, 5.2
    (ii) −0.3, 2.5, 4.7
11. (a) 24, 20, 19.2
    (b) (i) 5.4, 3.2, 1.15
    (ii) 27, 20.7, 19
12. 2.5, 7.7
    (b) (i) 2.6, 8.5
    (ii) 1.72, 2.46
13. 2.4, 5.8, 10.7
    (b) (i) 3, 9.5
    (ii) 0.18, 1.62
    $p = 2$, $q = -1.8$

Exercise 1b

3. (a) −4, 2
   (b) −3.45, 1.45
   (c) 2.83, −2.83
   (d) 1.41
4. (a) −2, 3
   (b) 2.79, −1.79
   (c) 3.37, −2.37
   (d) 0.56, −3.56
5. (a) 1, 3 (b) 2.6, −2.6
   (c) no real x
   (d) no real x
   (e) −3.3, 0.3
6. (a) 4.65, −0.65
   (b) 3.42, 0.59
   (c) 5.32, −1.32
   (d) 2.82, 1.18
   (e) 0.5, 4
7. (a) 6.2 (b) 1.7, −1.2
8. (a) $a = -77$, $b = 163$
   (b) 24.4, 5.65
9. (a) −5.13 (b) 2.85, −0.35
   (c) 4.21, −0.71
10. (a) 5.7, −0.7 (b) −2.3, 1.3
    (c) 0, −7

Review Questions 1

1. (a) −12, −8, −12, −8
   (b) (i) −9.6 (ii) 3.1
2. (a) 3, 0, 15
   (b) (i) −2.9 (ii) 2.4
   (iii) −2, 0 or 2
3. (a) 7.3, 5.5, 4
   (b) (i) −2.85, −3.9
   (ii) 3.8, 6.4, 8.8
4. −1.7, −1.4, −0.3, 1
   (b) (i) −1.2, 1.7
   (ii) 0.6, 1.8
5. 2.3, 0.2
   (b) (i) −1.9, 1.8
   (ii) 2.6, 0.3
6. (b) 303, 235, 134, 101, 81, 72
   (c) 5.3.
7. $x = 0.4$, $y = 0.1$

Exercise 2a

1. (a) 86.4 km/h (b) 64.8 km/h
   (c) 144 km/h (d) $3.6a$ km/h
2. (a) 4.44 m/s (b) 8.89 m/s
   (c) 12.5 m/s (d) $0.28b$ m/s
3. (a) 29.63 (b) 8.23
4. 39.59 km/h
5. 19.44 m/s
6. (a) 60 km (b) 56 km/h
   (c) $1\frac{1}{2}$ h (d) 52.6 km/h
7. 39.59 km/h
8. (a) 120° (b) 83.8 cm
9. 65 min
10. (a) from $1\frac{1}{2}$ h to $2\frac{1}{2}$ h
    (b) 30 km/h (c) 30 km/h
11. (b) $v = 45$ km/h, $u = 72$ km/h
12. 10 45
13. 1 h 11 min, 1 h and 1 h 22 min
14. 10 11, 8.3 km
15. (a) 5, 8, 5 (c) 4
    (d) 2.8 or −1.8
    (e) $0 < x < 3$
16. −1, 15, 4, −13
    (b) 10, −14
    (c) $-1.1 \leqslant x \leqslant 4.1$
17. (b) 3.6 m/s (c) 19 m
18. 0.65 km/min, 2.88 km
19. (a) 2.3 min (b) 0.38 km/min
    (c) 2.75 min

Exercise 2b

1. (a) 5 m/s^2 (b) 30 m
   (c) 7.5 m/s
2. (a) 2 m/s^2 (b) 3 m/s^2
   (c) 26 m (d) $4\frac{1}{3}$ m/s
3. (a) 9 (b) 30 m/s
4. (a) acceleration
   (b) 7 m/s (c) 420 m
5. (a) 4 m/s^2 (b) 65 m
   (c) 10.83 m/s
6. (a) 32.5 km (b) 78 km/h
7. (a) 1.5 m/s^2 (b) 1 500 m
   (c) 100 s
9. (a) 2 m/s^2 (b) 153 m
10. 70 m
11. (a) $6\frac{2}{3}$ m/s (b) 2 925 m
12. (a) 42 km/h (b) 126 km
    (c) 36 km/h
13. (a) $\frac{1}{3}$ m/s^2 (b) 720 m
    (c) 25.7 m/s (d) 18 m/s
14. (a) 12 m/s (b) 2 m/s^2
    (c) 10 m/s (d) 13 m/s
15. (a) 2.4 m/s^2, 4.8 m/s^2
    (b) 9.5 m/s, 34 m/s
16. (a) 5.2 m/s^2, −3.5 m/s^2
    (b) $t = 3.5$ s

Review Questions 2

1. (a) 60 km/h (b) 30 km/h
   (c) 22 km/h
2. (a) $1 \leqslant t \leqslant 2$ (b) 40 km/h
   (c) 17.14 km/h
3. 70.4 m/min
4. 2 376 km/h
5. (a) 15 km (b) 15 min

6. 17 00, 360 km
7. 62.5 km/h, 12 42
8. $a = 54$, $b = 45$
(a) 6.7 s (b) 2.3 s
(c) 5 m/s²
9. 1.5, 2 (b) 1.5, 1.7
(c) $0.9 < x < 3.3$
(d) 0.67 (e) 3.6
10. (a) $a = 3$, $b = 4.4$
(c) 1.3 or 4.7
(d) $1.6 \leqslant x \leqslant 5.1$
(e) 1.25
11. 0, 50
(a) 4.2 (b) 2
(c) −4 m/s², 12 m/s²
12. (a) 2.5 m/s² (b) 20 m
13. (a) 60 km/h (c) 7.13 a.m.
(d) 4
14. 5 min 24 sec
15. 16 sec
17. (a) 11.25 m/s
(b) 330 m
(c) $36\frac{2}{3}$ m/s
18. (b) 0.125 m/s² (c) 200 m

Exercise 3a

1. $\overrightarrow{AB} = \begin{pmatrix} 1 \\ 3 \end{pmatrix}$, $\overrightarrow{BA} = \begin{pmatrix} -1 \\ -3 \end{pmatrix}$,
$\overrightarrow{CD} = \begin{pmatrix} 4 \\ -2 \end{pmatrix}$, $\overrightarrow{DC} = \begin{pmatrix} -4 \\ 2 \end{pmatrix}$,
$\overrightarrow{EF} = \begin{pmatrix} -4 \\ -1 \end{pmatrix}$, $\overrightarrow{FE} = \begin{pmatrix} 4 \\ 1 \end{pmatrix}$
2. $\mathbf{b} = \mathbf{e} = \begin{pmatrix} -2 \\ -5 \end{pmatrix}$,
$\mathbf{c} = \mathbf{n} = \begin{pmatrix} -2 \\ -3 \end{pmatrix}$,
$\mathbf{d} = \mathbf{g} = \begin{pmatrix} -4 \\ 1 \end{pmatrix}$
3. (a) $\begin{pmatrix} -4 \\ -3 \end{pmatrix}$ (b) $\begin{pmatrix} 2 \\ -5 \end{pmatrix}$
(c) $\begin{pmatrix} -7 \\ 9 \end{pmatrix}$ (d) $\begin{pmatrix} 1 \\ 3 \end{pmatrix}$
(e) $\begin{pmatrix} -p \\ -q \end{pmatrix}$
5. (a) 13 units (b) 10 units
(c) $\sqrt{29}$ units (d) $\sqrt{50}$ units
(e) 3 units
6. $p = \pm\sqrt{21}$
7. (a) 5 units (b) ±4
8. 13
9. (a) 4.47 units (b) 6
10. $\overrightarrow{PQ}$ and $\overrightarrow{RS}$ are in different directions
11. $s = -3$, $t = -4$
12. $p = 2$, $q = 1$
13. (a) (i) $\overrightarrow{IJ} = \overrightarrow{HK} = \overrightarrow{GL} = \overrightarrow{FE} = \overrightarrow{KB}$
(ii) $\overrightarrow{AJ} = \overrightarrow{CL} = \overrightarrow{DE}$
(iii) $\overrightarrow{HI} = \overrightarrow{GH} = \overrightarrow{FG} = \overrightarrow{KJ} = \overrightarrow{LK} = \overrightarrow{EL}$
(iv) $\overrightarrow{BC} = \overrightarrow{AB} = \overrightarrow{CD}$
(v) $\overrightarrow{AK} = \overrightarrow{JH} = \overrightarrow{KG} = \overrightarrow{CE}$
(vi) $\overrightarrow{LB} = \overrightarrow{FL}$
(b) (i) $\overrightarrow{LB}$ (ii) $\overrightarrow{KJ}$
(iii) $\overrightarrow{KB}$
(c) (i) $\overrightarrow{AB}$ and $\overrightarrow{DE}$ are not parallel
(ii) Length *AK* ≠ Length *AB* or $\overrightarrow{AK}$ and $\overrightarrow{AB}$ are not parallel
14. (a) $\overrightarrow{KL}$
(b) $\overrightarrow{RQ} = \overrightarrow{TU}$, $\overrightarrow{QP} = \overrightarrow{ST}$
(c) $\overrightarrow{AB} = \overrightarrow{DC}$, $\overrightarrow{BC} = \overrightarrow{AD}$
(d) $\overrightarrow{LM} = \overrightarrow{QP}$, $\overrightarrow{MN} = \overrightarrow{RQ}$, $\overrightarrow{NO} = \overrightarrow{SR}$, $\overrightarrow{OP} = \overrightarrow{LS}$
15. (a) $\begin{pmatrix} 2 \\ -3 \end{pmatrix}$ (b) $\begin{pmatrix} 1 \\ 4 \end{pmatrix}$
(c) $\begin{pmatrix} -3 \\ -1 \end{pmatrix}$
(d) Yes. $\overrightarrow{PQ} \neq \overrightarrow{PR}$ because they are in opposite directions.

Exercise 3b

1. (c) $\overrightarrow{ML}$
2. (a) $\begin{pmatrix} 10 \\ 1 \end{pmatrix}$ (b) $\begin{pmatrix} 10 \\ -1 \end{pmatrix}$
(c) $\begin{pmatrix} 8 \\ -6 \end{pmatrix}$
3. (a) $\begin{pmatrix} 6 \\ 8 \end{pmatrix}$ (b) $\begin{pmatrix} 5 \\ 1 \end{pmatrix}$
(c) $\begin{pmatrix} -3 \\ 3 \end{pmatrix}$ (d) $\begin{pmatrix} 1 \\ 7 \end{pmatrix}$
4. (a) $\begin{pmatrix} 10 \\ 9 \end{pmatrix}$ (b) $\begin{pmatrix} 10 \\ 9 \end{pmatrix}$
(c) $\begin{pmatrix} 5 \\ 11 \end{pmatrix}$ (d) $\begin{pmatrix} 5 \\ 11 \end{pmatrix}$
Commutative and associative laws of vector addition.
5. (a) $\overrightarrow{PR}$ (b) $\overrightarrow{SR}$
(c) $\overrightarrow{SR}$ (d) $\overrightarrow{ST}$
(e) $\overrightarrow{PR}$ (f) $\overrightarrow{RS}$
6. (a) $\overrightarrow{AC}$ (b) $\overrightarrow{AD}$ (c) $\overrightarrow{AD}$
(d) **0**
7. (a) $\begin{pmatrix} 3 \\ 9 \end{pmatrix} + \begin{pmatrix} -3 \\ -9 \end{pmatrix} = \begin{pmatrix} 0 \\ 0 \end{pmatrix}$
(b) $\begin{pmatrix} 5 \\ -7 \end{pmatrix} + \begin{pmatrix} -5 \\ 7 \end{pmatrix} = \begin{pmatrix} 0 \\ 0 \end{pmatrix}$
(c) $\begin{pmatrix} x \\ -y \end{pmatrix} + \begin{pmatrix} -x \\ y \end{pmatrix} = \begin{pmatrix} 0 \\ 0 \end{pmatrix}$
9. (a) **p** − **q** (b) **q** − **p**
(c) **b** − **a** (d) **a** + **b**
(e) **s** − **r** (f) **r** + **s**
(g) −**m** − **n** (h) **n** − **m**
10. (a) $\overrightarrow{AC}$
(b) cannot simplify
(c) $\overrightarrow{CB}$ (d) $\overrightarrow{RQ}$
(e) $\overrightarrow{QN}$ (f) $\overrightarrow{QM}$
(e) $\overrightarrow{DF}$ (f) $\overrightarrow{FE}$
11. (a) (i) $\overrightarrow{PR}$ (ii) $\overrightarrow{RQ}$
(iii) $\overrightarrow{PQ}$
(b) (i) $\overrightarrow{OP}$ (ii) $\overrightarrow{OR}$
(iii) $\overrightarrow{RS}$ (iv) $\overrightarrow{RP}$
(v) $\overrightarrow{QR}$ (vi) $\overrightarrow{PQ}$
(c) (i) **a** (ii) **a** + **b**
(iii) **a** − **b**

12. **(a)** $\overrightarrow{KS}$ **(b)** $\overrightarrow{QS}$
(c) $\overrightarrow{PR}$ **(d)** $\overrightarrow{PS}$
(e) $\overrightarrow{PR}$ **(f)** **0**

13. **(a)** **b** **(b)** **v**
(c) **–u** **(d)** **c**

14. **(a)** $\begin{pmatrix}3\\2\end{pmatrix}$ **(b)** $\begin{pmatrix}4\\6\end{pmatrix}$
(c) $\begin{pmatrix}2\\0\end{pmatrix}$ **(d)** $\begin{pmatrix}9\\0\end{pmatrix}$

15. **(a)** $\begin{pmatrix}3\\-3\end{pmatrix}$ **(b)** $\begin{pmatrix}-2\\-5\end{pmatrix}$
(c) $\begin{pmatrix}6\\-4\end{pmatrix}$

16. **(a)** $\begin{pmatrix}8\\9\end{pmatrix}$ **(b)** $\begin{pmatrix}6\\-5\end{pmatrix}$
(c) $\begin{pmatrix}10\\1\end{pmatrix}$

17. **(a)** $\begin{pmatrix}2\\2\end{pmatrix}$ **(b)** $\begin{pmatrix}5\\0\end{pmatrix}$
(c) $\begin{pmatrix}5\\1\end{pmatrix}$ **(d)** $\begin{pmatrix}-1\\3\end{pmatrix}$

18. $a = c$ and $b = d$

19. **(a)** $a = 7, b = -1$
(b) $a = 2, b = -1$
(c) $a = 1, b = 4$

20. **(a)** $\begin{pmatrix}4\\-1\end{pmatrix}$ **(b)** $\begin{pmatrix}0\\6\end{pmatrix}$
(c) $\begin{pmatrix}-5\\2\end{pmatrix}$

21. **(a)** $x = 3, y = 5$
(b) $x = -4, y = -6$
(c) $x = -4, y = 6$
(d) $x = 3, y = 5$

Exercise 3c

2. (a), (b), (d), (e), (f)
3. These answers are just some examples.
(a) $\begin{pmatrix}4\\2\end{pmatrix}, \begin{pmatrix}-2\\-1\end{pmatrix}$
(b) $\begin{pmatrix}-6\\-4\end{pmatrix}, \begin{pmatrix}3\\2\end{pmatrix}$
(c) $\begin{pmatrix}16\\-10\end{pmatrix}, \begin{pmatrix}-8\\5\end{pmatrix}$
(d) $\begin{pmatrix}-14\\8\end{pmatrix}, \begin{pmatrix}7\\-4\end{pmatrix}$
(e) $\begin{pmatrix}-1\\4\end{pmatrix}, \begin{pmatrix}1\\-4\end{pmatrix}$
(f) $\begin{pmatrix}9\\2\end{pmatrix}, \begin{pmatrix}-9\\-2\end{pmatrix}$

4. 8
5. $-1\frac{1}{2}$
6. –4
8. $\frac{1}{4}, \begin{pmatrix}16\\-12\end{pmatrix}$
9. $\frac{2}{5}, \begin{pmatrix}-30\\12\frac{1}{2}\end{pmatrix}$
10. $-\frac{1}{2}, \begin{pmatrix}-14\\-48\end{pmatrix}$

11. **(a)** $\begin{pmatrix}-10\\1\end{pmatrix}$ **(b)** $\begin{pmatrix}-2\\10\end{pmatrix}$
(c) $\begin{pmatrix}10\\11\end{pmatrix}$ **(d)** $\begin{pmatrix}10\\-5\end{pmatrix}$
(e) $\begin{pmatrix}5\\-16\end{pmatrix}$ **(f)** $\begin{pmatrix}24\\-9\end{pmatrix}$

12. **(a)** $\begin{pmatrix}2\\4\end{pmatrix}$ **(b)** $\begin{pmatrix}-18\\18\end{pmatrix}$
(c) $\begin{pmatrix}-32\\-33\end{pmatrix}$ **(d)** $\begin{pmatrix}5\\16\end{pmatrix}$

13. **(a)** $x = 2, y = 1$
(b) $x = -7, y = 4$
(c) $x = 3, y = 1$

14. **(a)** $\begin{pmatrix}16\\-15\end{pmatrix}$
2(b) (i) 13 units
(ii) 18 units
(c) –48

15. **(a)** $\begin{pmatrix}-1\\30\end{pmatrix}$ **(b)** –4.5
(c) $\overrightarrow{CD} = 4\,\overrightarrow{PQ}$

Exercise 3d

1. $\overrightarrow{AB} = 2\mathbf{u} + 3\mathbf{v}$
$\overrightarrow{MN} = 3\mathbf{u} - 4\frac{1}{2}\mathbf{v}$
$\overrightarrow{PQ} = 5\frac{1}{2}\mathbf{v} - 2\mathbf{u}$

2. $\overrightarrow{LM} = 2\frac{1}{4}\mathbf{a} + 1\frac{1}{4}\mathbf{b}$
$\overrightarrow{PR} = -1\frac{1}{4}\mathbf{a} + 1\frac{3}{4}\mathbf{b}$
$\overrightarrow{ST} = 2\mathbf{a} + 2\mathbf{b}$
$\overrightarrow{XY} = 2\frac{5}{8}\mathbf{a} - 1\frac{7}{8}\mathbf{b}$

3. **(a)** $\mathbf{a} + 2\mathbf{b}$ **(b)** $-\frac{8}{3}\mathbf{b}$
(c) $\frac{2}{3}\mathbf{b} - \mathbf{a}$

4. **(a)** $-\frac{1}{2}\mathbf{q}$ **(b)** $\mathbf{p} - \mathbf{q}$
(c) $\mathbf{p} + \frac{1}{2}\mathbf{q}$ **(d)** $\frac{1}{2}\mathbf{q} - \mathbf{p}$

5. **(a)** $\frac{4}{3}\mathbf{q}$ **(b)** $\mathbf{q} - \mathbf{p}$
(c) $\mathbf{p} - \frac{4}{3}\mathbf{q}$

6. **(a)** $\mathbf{v} - \mathbf{u}$ **(b)** $\frac{1}{2}\mathbf{u}$
(c) $\frac{1}{2}\mathbf{v}$
(d) $\frac{1}{2}(\mathbf{v} - \mathbf{u})$
$\overrightarrow{BC}$ and $\overrightarrow{MN}$ are parallel;
$BC = 2MN$

7. **(a)** $\mathbf{v} - \mathbf{u}$ **(b)** $\frac{2}{5}(\mathbf{v} - \mathbf{u})$
(c) $\frac{3}{2}\mathbf{u} + \mathbf{v}$
(d) $\frac{1}{5}(3\mathbf{u} + 2\mathbf{v})$
(e) $\frac{1}{2}\mathbf{u} + \mathbf{v}$

8. **(a)** $\mathbf{u} + \frac{3}{2}\mathbf{v}$ **(b)** $\mathbf{u} + \frac{1}{2}\mathbf{v}$
(c) $\frac{1}{8}(2\mathbf{u} + 9\mathbf{v})$
(d) $\frac{1}{8}(9\mathbf{v} - 2\mathbf{u})$

9. **(a)** **(i)** $\frac{2}{3}\mathbf{b}$ **(ii)** $\frac{2}{3}\mathbf{a}$
(iii) $\frac{2}{3}\mathbf{a} + \mathbf{b}$
(iv) $\mathbf{a} - \mathbf{b}$
(v) $\frac{1}{3}(\mathbf{a} - \mathbf{b})$
(b) **(i)** $\frac{1}{3}$ **(ii)** $\frac{1}{18}$

10. (a) (i) $-3\mathbf{a} - 7\mathbf{b}$
(ii) $-2\mathbf{a} - 8\mathbf{b}$
(iii) $\mathbf{a} - 11\mathbf{b}$
(c) $4\mathbf{b} - 4\mathbf{a}$
(d) (i) $\frac{3}{4}$ (ii) $\frac{3}{4}$
(iii) $\frac{1}{3}$

11. (a) (i) $2\mathbf{b} - 2\mathbf{a}$ (ii) $\mathbf{b} - \mathbf{a}$
(iii) $\frac{12}{7}(\mathbf{a} + \mathbf{b})$ (iv) $3\mathbf{a}$
(v) $4\mathbf{b}$
(b) $4\mathbf{b} - 3\mathbf{a}$ (c) $\frac{3}{7}$
(e) (i) $\frac{3}{7}$ (ii) $\frac{2}{7}$

Exercise 3e

1. (a) $\begin{pmatrix} 4 \\ 7 \end{pmatrix}$ (b) $\begin{pmatrix} -2 \\ 5 \end{pmatrix}$
(c) $\begin{pmatrix} 6 \\ -1 \end{pmatrix}$ (d) $\begin{pmatrix} -4 \\ -9 \end{pmatrix}$

2. (a) $\begin{pmatrix} -1 \\ -2 \end{pmatrix}$ (b) $\begin{pmatrix} 0 \\ 7 \end{pmatrix}$
(c) $\begin{pmatrix} 1 \\ -5 \end{pmatrix}$

3. (a) $\begin{pmatrix} -4 \\ 6 \end{pmatrix}$ (b) $\begin{pmatrix} 2 \\ 5 \end{pmatrix}$
(c) $\begin{pmatrix} 6 \\ -1 \end{pmatrix}$

4. (a) $Q(-3, 8)$, $R(-1, 10)$
(b) 1, $\begin{pmatrix} 2 \\ 2 \end{pmatrix}$

5. (a) $B(1, 4)$, $D(3, -6)$
(b) $\overrightarrow{BC} = \begin{pmatrix} 6 \\ 0 \end{pmatrix}$, $\overrightarrow{CD} = \begin{pmatrix} -4 \\ -10 \end{pmatrix}$

6. (a) $\begin{pmatrix} 6 \\ -10 \end{pmatrix}$ (b) (7, –8)
(c) (2, 5)

7. (a) $\begin{pmatrix} 4 \\ 6 \end{pmatrix}$ (b) (3, –2)

8. (a) $\begin{pmatrix} t + 3 \\ 4 \end{pmatrix}$ (b) 29
(c) –10 or 4

9. (a) (2, 2) (b) (0, –2)

10. (a) $\begin{pmatrix} 2 \\ 8 \end{pmatrix}$ (b) $\begin{pmatrix} 5 \\ -1 \end{pmatrix}$
(c) (3, 10)

11. $\frac{1}{2}\mathbf{a} - \mathbf{b}$

12. $\frac{1}{8}(3\mathbf{a} + 2\mathbf{b})$

13. $\frac{1}{5}(3\mathbf{a} + 2\mathbf{b})$

14. (a) $15\mathbf{b} - 15\mathbf{a}$ (b) $\frac{15}{4}(\mathbf{b} - \mathbf{a})$
(c) $\frac{15}{4}(3\mathbf{a} + \mathbf{b})$
(d) $15\mathbf{a} + 5\mathbf{b}$

15. (a) $4\mathbf{a} + 4\mathbf{b}$ (b) $2\mathbf{a} + 4\mathbf{b}$
(c) $8\mathbf{b} - 4\mathbf{a}$

16. (a) $20\mathbf{q} - 8\mathbf{p}$ (b) $5\mathbf{q} - 2\mathbf{p}$
(c) $6\mathbf{p} + 5\mathbf{q}$ (d) $6\mathbf{p} - 3\mathbf{q}$

17. (a) (i) $\frac{2}{3}\mathbf{b}$ (ii) $\frac{2}{3}\mathbf{b} - 2\mathbf{a}$
(iii) $\frac{1}{2}(\mathbf{a} + \mathbf{b})$
(iv) $\frac{1}{2}\mathbf{a} - \frac{1}{6}\mathbf{b}$
(b) $\frac{3}{1}$ or 3

18. (a) (i) $4\mathbf{q} - 3\mathbf{p}$
(ii) $4\mathbf{q} - 4\mathbf{p}$
(iii) $\mathbf{p} + \mathbf{q}$ (iv) $3\mathbf{q} - 4\mathbf{p}$
(v) $\frac{3}{4}(4\mathbf{p} - 3\mathbf{q})$
(c) (i) $\frac{3}{4}$ (ii) $\frac{9}{16}$

19. (a) (i) $\begin{pmatrix} 1 \\ -3 \end{pmatrix}$ (ii) $\begin{pmatrix} 1 \\ -1 \end{pmatrix}$
(iii) $\begin{pmatrix} 3 \\ 1 \end{pmatrix}$ (iv) $\begin{pmatrix} 6 \\ 2 \end{pmatrix}$
(b) $\frac{1}{2}$

Review Questions 3

1. (a) $\begin{pmatrix} 6 \\ 1 \end{pmatrix}$ (b) $\begin{pmatrix} 12 \\ 2 \end{pmatrix}$
(c) $\begin{pmatrix} 0 \\ 5 \end{pmatrix}$ (d) $\begin{pmatrix} 8 \\ -2 \end{pmatrix}$
(e) $\begin{pmatrix} -6 \\ -1 \end{pmatrix}$ (f) $\begin{pmatrix} 9 \\ -1 \end{pmatrix}$

2. (a) (i) $\begin{pmatrix} 4 \\ -1 \end{pmatrix}$ (ii) $\begin{pmatrix} 3 \\ -5 \end{pmatrix}$
(iii) $\begin{pmatrix} 1 \\ 4 \end{pmatrix}$
(b) $\begin{pmatrix} 5 \\ 3 \end{pmatrix}$
(c) (i) 4.12 units
(ii) 5.83 units

3. (a) ±4 (b) 4, 16

4. (a) (i) $\begin{pmatrix} 5 \\ 3 \end{pmatrix}$, 5.83 units
(ii) $\begin{pmatrix} 1 \\ 4 \end{pmatrix}$, 4.12 units
(iii) $\begin{pmatrix} -4 \\ 1 \end{pmatrix}$, 4.12 units
(b) $\triangle ABC$ is isosceles.

5. $a = -6$, $b = 8$

6. (a) $2(k - 1)\mathbf{p}$ (b) $10\mathbf{p} + 3\mathbf{q}$

7. (a) $4\mathbf{b} - 3\mathbf{a}$ (b) $\mathbf{b} - 3\mathbf{a}$
(c) $\frac{1}{3}(3\mathbf{a} + 2\mathbf{b})$ (d) $\frac{2}{3}(3\mathbf{a} + 2\mathbf{b})$

8. (a) $3\mathbf{p} + \mathbf{q}$ (b) $4\mathbf{q} - 4\mathbf{p}$
(c) $\frac{1}{2}(7\mathbf{q} - 3\mathbf{p})$
(d) $7\mathbf{q} - 3\mathbf{p}$

9. (a) 6 units
(b) (i) $\begin{pmatrix} -2 \\ -4 \end{pmatrix}$ (ii) $\begin{pmatrix} 4 \\ 0 \end{pmatrix}$
(iii) $\begin{pmatrix} 1 \\ -2 \end{pmatrix}$

10. (a) (i) $-\mathbf{p}$ (ii) $\mathbf{q} - \mathbf{p}$
(b) $\sqrt{2}$ units (c) $\frac{1}{\sqrt{2}}\mathbf{q}$

11. (a) (i) $\mathbf{p} - \mathbf{q}$
(ii) $\frac{2}{5}(\mathbf{p} - \mathbf{q})$
(iii) $\frac{1}{5}(2\mathbf{p} + 3\mathbf{q})$
(iv) $\frac{1}{10}(9\mathbf{q} - 4\mathbf{p})$
(b) (ii) R, S and T are collinear; $RS : ST = 2 : 3$.

12. (a) (i) $2\mathbf{p} - \mathbf{q}$
(ii) $3\mathbf{p}$
(iii) $3\mathbf{p} - 2\mathbf{q}$
(iv) $6\mathbf{p} - 4\mathbf{q}$
(b) S, R and T are collinear; $SR = RT$ (or $ST = 2SR$).
(c) $\frac{1}{2}$

Exercise 4a

1. (a) 2.17 (b) 1
2. (a) 6 (b) 3.43
3. 25
4. $2.08
5. 45.8
6. 59.25 km/h

Exercise 4b

1. (a) 3.02 (b) 4.02
   (c) 11.1 (d) 9.35
2. 66, 6.20
3. 38.5 g, 12.1
4. $144.67, 25.0
5. (a) School *X*: 44.8 kg, 5.56
   School *Y*: 45.8 kg, 10.8
   (b) 45.3 kg, 8.58
6. (a) *A*: 5.23, 1.42
   B: 4.93, 1.69
   (b) *B*
7. 12, 3.74
8. 19, 5.69, Alan is the best.
9. (a) *A*: 0.528, 0.155
   B: 0.498, 0.167
10. 5, $x = 1$, $y = 4$ or $x = 4$, $y = 1$

Review Questions 4

1. (a) $x > 7$ or $x \geq 8$
   (b) 6, 7, 8, 9, 10, 11, 12
   (c) 9
2. (b) 59.8, 6.00
3. (c) *A*: 66.75, 24.11
   B: 67, 9.67
4. (a) 15.4, 7.23 (b) 12.4, 7.23
   (c) fall alseep less during holiday. Same SD, so the spread is the same.
5. (a) 3, 4, 3, 2 (b) 49.25, 7.63
   (c) On Saturday, cars drove slower, but on Monday, car's speeds sprend wider.
6. (a) (i) 9.7 (ii) 4.18
   (b) *x* has greater spread of marks.
7. (a) $p = 989.5$, $q = 141.4$
   $r = 24$, $t = 176.6$
   (b) Factory *XYZ* has a greater spread.
8. (a) (i) *A*: 51, *B*: 48.1
   (ii) *A*: 5.2, *B*: 6.19
   (b) *A*, higher mean.
   (c) *B*, higher *SD*, greater spread.
9. (a) (i) *A*: 25, *B*:17.5
   (ii) *A*: 14.9, *B*:12.5
   (b) Bush, consistent in spread of data.
   (c) Bush, smaller mean.
10. (a) (i) 25 (ii) 2
    (b) The mean waiting time is the same but the spread of waiting time at SUSA Hospital is greater implying that some of patients either have shorter or longer waiting time.

Exercise 5a

1. (a) 13 (b) 12
   (c) 82%
2. (a) 58 (ii) $\frac{5}{32}$
   (c) 41
3. (a) 10 (b) $\frac{4}{5}$
   (c) 46
4. (b) (i) 33 (ii) 6
   (iii) 450.7
5. (a) Soil *A*: (i) 125
   (ii) 9%
   (iii) 42
   Soil *B*: (i) 90
   (ii) 3%
   (iii) 46
   (b) *A*
   (c) (i) 36% (ii) 24%
6. (a) 200 (b) $\frac{1}{5}$
   (c) 21

Exercise 5b

1. (a) 8, 4, 6, 8, 4
   (b) 29, 58.5, 65, 71, 12.5
   (c) 31, 12, 18, 29.5, 17.5
   (d) 164, 102, 166, 207, 105
   (e) 19.7, 5.8, 10.4, 14.1, 8.3
2. (a) (i) $44.50, $36.50, $51.50
   (ii) $15
   (b) (i) $34.50 (ii) $57.50
   (c) 30%
3. (a) (i) 42 (ii) 58
   (b) (i) 26 (ii) 24
   (c) (i) 50 (ii) 76
   (d) School *B*, the median is higher.
4. (a) 10.5, 13, 17.5
   (b) 27 (c) 9.5
   (d) 33.3%
   (e) Agree, the median is higher.
5. (a) (ii) 65, 105
   (ii) 46, 101.5
   (iii) 42, 35
   (b) City *Y*
   (c) The air pollution in City *Y* is very bad.
6. (a) (i) 35.5 mm
   (ii) 5.5 mm
   (b) 34.25 mm
   (c) 180, 240, 80, 20

Exercise 5c

1. (a) 19, 21,25 (b) 11
2. (a) 0.05, 0.07, 0.086,
   (b) greater spread
3. (a) 158, 188.5, 195, 199, 213
   (b) 10.5, interquartile range
   (c) 55, range
4. (a) 169 (b) 23
   (c) Lowest 25% of patients has greater spread in alcohol contents than highest 25%
5. (a) (i) *A* (ii) *C*
   (b) *B* (c) *B*
6. (a) (i) 63 (ii) 8
   (b) Well spread, median 68 kg.
   (c) Yes, higher median.
7. (a) (i) 49 (ii) 45
   (b) 27
   (c) 68, 30, Fermat performed better.
8. (a) (i) 45 (ii) 8
   (iii) 6
   (b) (i) 34 (ii) 24
   (c) Teenagers spent more time watching TV in general and greater spread in time.
9. (a) (i) 40.5 (ii) 5
   (b) (i) 50 (ii) 9
   (c) *XYZ*
   (d) *ABC* Club's members are younger in general. *XYZ* Club has greater spread in ages.

Review Questions 5

1. (a) (i) 51 (ii) 60
   (iii) 28 (iv) 180
   (v) 45
   (b) sch *A* 34%, sch *B* 14%
   (c) Yes, higher median, higher distinction.
2. (a) 50% (b) 5, 56
   (c) 13.2, 15, 16
   (d) 2.8, interquartile range
3. (a) (i) 23.5 (ii) 26.5
   (iii) 6.5 (iv) 16
   (b) 25.5
   (c) (i) Greater median for IQ quiz (37), Greater spread for IQ quiz (Range = 30, rather than 20).
   (ii) No, higher median or upper quartile for IQ quiz.
4. (a) (i) 54.5 g (ii) 7.5 g
   (iii) Grade 1: 20%
   Grade 2: 65%
   Grade 3: 15%

(b) (i) 50 g, 7 g
(ii) Rainbow produced better quality eggs, higher median, higher % in Grade 1's eggs.

5. (a) (i) 51 cm (ii) 58 cm
(iii) 40 cm (iv) 16
(v) 46 cm
(b) 50 cm (c) 6, 12, 20, 10

6. (a) (i) 21 (ii) 6
(iii) 2.71
(b) (i) 0.5, 1, 3
(ii) median, upperquartile
(iii) 2.5

7. (a) Set X: (i) 30
(ii) 40
(iii) 20
Set Y: (i) 21
(ii) 25
(iii) 7
(b) X (c) X
(d) Y (e) B

8. (a) 20 (b) 30.2
(c) (i) 30.2, 40.4, 45.6, 50.6
(ii) 10.2, interquartile range
(d) (i) 4.6 kg
(ii) after 3 months
(iii) No

9. (a) 46 (b) 11.25%
(c) School B achieved better because the median mark of the students from school B is higher.

Exercise 6a

1. $\frac{1}{5}$ 2. $\frac{1}{2}$
3. $\frac{5}{6}$ 4. $\frac{23}{25}$
5. $\frac{1}{2}$ 6. $\frac{2}{5}$
7. 12 8. $\frac{1}{3}, \frac{11}{17}$

9. (a) $\frac{31}{40}$ (b) $\frac{3}{20}$
(c) $\frac{13}{40}$ (d) $\frac{3}{5}$

10. (a) $\frac{1}{52}$ (b) $\frac{1}{26}$
(c) $\frac{1}{4}$ (d) $\frac{1}{2}$
(e) $\frac{3}{13}$ (f) $\frac{5}{52}$

11. (a) $\frac{7}{10}$ (b) $\frac{7}{30}$
(c) $\frac{1}{6}$ (d) $\frac{1}{6}$
(e) $\frac{7}{30}$

12. $x = 11$
(a) $\frac{19}{28}$ (b) $\frac{11}{56}$

13. (a) $\frac{1}{6}$ (b) $\frac{1}{10}$
(c) 0 (d) $\frac{3}{10}$

14. (a) 1 (b) $\frac{1}{10}$
(c) 0 (d) $\frac{1}{2}$

Exercise 6b

1. $S = \{76, 77, 78, ..., 98, 99\}$
(a) $\frac{1}{2}$ (b) $\frac{1}{8}$ (c) $\frac{1}{2}$

2. $S = \{13, 17, 18, 31, 37, 38, 71, 73, 78, 81, 83, 87\}$
(a) $\frac{7}{12}$ (b) $\frac{1}{4}$ (c) 0
(d) $\frac{2}{3}$

3. S = {H1, H2, H3, H4, H5, H6, H7, H8, H9, H10, HJ, HQ, HK, T1, T2, T3, T4, T5, T6, T7, T8, T9, T10, TJ, TQ, TK}
(a) $\frac{1}{2}$ (b) $\frac{1}{26}$ (c) $\frac{3}{26}$
(d) $\frac{3}{26}$ (e) 0

4. S = {HHH, HHT, HTH, HTT, TTT, TTH, THT, THH)
(a) $\frac{3}{8}$ (b) $\frac{1}{8}$ (c) $\frac{3}{8}$

5. S = {RB, RR, BB, BR, WB, WR}
(a) $\frac{1}{3}$ (b) $\frac{1}{3}$ (c) $\frac{2}{3}$

6. S = {BBB, BBG, BGB, BGG, GGG, GGB, GBG, GBB}
(a) $\frac{1}{8}$ (b) $\frac{3}{8}$ (c) $\frac{3}{8}$

Exercise 6c

1. (b) (i) $\frac{1}{6}$ (ii) $\frac{5}{6}$
(iii) $\frac{1}{4}$ (iv) $\frac{3}{4}$
(v) $\frac{5}{12}$

2. (a) 12, 13, 12, 13, 14, 13, 15; 28, 35, 32, 48, 36, 45, 54
(b) (i) $\frac{2}{9}$ (ii) $\frac{7}{9}$
(iii) $\frac{5}{9}$
(c) (i) $\frac{4}{9}$ (ii) $\frac{2}{3}$
(iii) $\frac{8}{9}$

3. (b) 36
(c) (i) $\frac{1}{9}$ (ii) $\frac{17}{36}$
(iii) $\frac{19}{36}$ (iv) $\frac{1}{2}$
(v) $\frac{1}{2}$
(d) sum of 7

4. (a) 25
(b) (i) $\frac{1}{5}$ (ii) $\frac{1}{5}$
(iii) $\frac{4}{5}$ (iv) $\frac{6}{25}$
(c) $\frac{2}{5}$

5. (a) 2, 3, 4, 5, 6, 2, 4, 8, 10, 12
(b) (i) $\frac{1}{4}$ (ii) $\frac{3}{4}$
(iii) $\frac{1}{3}$ (iv) $\frac{5}{6}$
(v) $\frac{1}{3}$

6. (a) 1, 2, 3, 4, 5, 1, 0, 2, 3, 2, 1, 0, 1, 2, 3, 3, 2, 1, 0, 1, 2, 4, 3, 2, 1, 0, 1, 5, 3, 2, 1
(b) (i) $\frac{5}{18}$ (ii) $\frac{5}{6}$
(iii) $\frac{1}{2}$ (iv) $\frac{4}{9}$
(v) $\frac{1}{3}$

Exercise 6d

1. (a) $\frac{1}{6}$ (b) $\frac{1}{3}$

2. (b) (i) $\frac{1}{6}$ (ii) $\frac{2}{3}$
(iii) $\frac{1}{2}$ (iv) $\frac{3}{4}$

(v) $\frac{2}{3}$ (vi) $\frac{5}{12}$

(vii) $\frac{1}{4}$ (viii) $\frac{1}{2}$

3. (a) $\frac{1}{8}$ (b) $\frac{1}{4}$ (c) $\frac{1}{2}$

(d) $\frac{1}{4}$ (e) $\frac{11}{16}$ (f) $\frac{3}{4}$

(g) $\frac{1}{4}$

4. (a) (i) $\frac{1}{4}$ (ii) $\frac{1}{2}$

5. (a) $\frac{5}{11}$ (b) $\frac{4}{11}$ (c) $\frac{9}{11}$

(d) $\frac{4}{11}$ (e) $\frac{7}{11}$ (f) $\frac{6}{11}$

(g) $\frac{3}{11}$ (h) $\frac{9}{11}$

6. (a) $\frac{7}{15}$ (b) $\frac{1}{3}$ (c) $\frac{4}{5}$

(d) $\frac{1}{5}$

7. (a) $\frac{3}{17}$ (b) $\frac{2}{17}$ (c) $\frac{5}{17}$

(d) $\frac{10}{17}$ (e) $\frac{13}{17}$ (f) $\frac{8}{17}$

8. (a) $\frac{1}{8}$ (b) $\frac{3}{8}$ (c) $\frac{1}{2}$

9. (a) $\frac{5}{6}$ (b) $\frac{1}{6}$

10. (a) $\frac{5}{14}$ (b) $\frac{11}{14}$ (c) $\frac{3}{14}$

11. (a) $\frac{7}{15}$ (b) $\frac{17}{30}$ (c) $\frac{8}{15}$

(d) $\frac{13}{30}$

Exercise 6e

1. (a) $\frac{5}{9}, \frac{5}{9}, \frac{4}{9}, \frac{5}{9}, \frac{4}{9}$

(b) (i) $\frac{20}{81}$ (ii) $\frac{40}{81}$

(iii) $\frac{5}{9}$

2. (a) $\frac{6}{10}, \frac{6}{10}, \frac{4}{10}; \frac{6}{10}, \frac{4}{10}$

(b) (i) $\frac{6}{10} \times \frac{6}{10}$

(ii) $2\left(\frac{6}{10} \times \frac{4}{10}\right)$

3. (a) $\frac{1}{4}, \frac{3}{4}; \frac{1}{2}, \frac{1}{4}, \frac{3}{4}; \frac{1}{4}, \frac{1}{4}, \frac{3}{4}$

(b) (i) $\frac{3}{4}$ (ii) $\frac{1}{4}$

(c) (i) $\frac{3}{8}$ (ii) $\frac{9}{16}$

(iii) $\frac{15}{16}$ (iv) $\frac{1}{16}$

4. (a) (i) $\frac{1}{15}$ (ii) $\frac{11}{30}$

(iii) $\frac{2}{5}$ (iv) $\frac{3}{10}$

(v) $\frac{7}{10}$

(b) $\frac{3}{10}, \frac{1}{2}; \frac{1}{3}, \frac{1}{5}, \frac{3}{10}, \frac{1}{2}; \frac{5}{12}, \frac{1}{5}, \frac{3}{10}, \frac{1}{2}$

(c) (i) $\frac{43}{120}$ (ii) $\frac{7}{60}$

(iii) $\frac{3}{8}$ (iv) $\frac{1}{5}$

5. (a) $\frac{1}{6}, \frac{1}{3}, \frac{1}{2}; \frac{5}{6}, \frac{1}{6}, \frac{5}{6}, \frac{1}{6}, \frac{5}{6}, \frac{1}{6}; \frac{5}{6}, \frac{1}{6}, \frac{5}{6}, \frac{1}{6}, \frac{5}{6}, \frac{1}{6}, \frac{5}{6}, \frac{1}{6}, \frac{5}{6}, \frac{1}{6}, \frac{5}{6}, \frac{1}{6}$

(b) (i) $\frac{5}{108}$ (ii) $\frac{1}{72}$

(iii) $\frac{1}{36}$ (iv) $\frac{5}{18}$

(v) $\frac{7}{24}$

6. $\frac{3}{8}$

(a) $\frac{2}{7}$

(b) $\frac{2}{7}, \frac{5}{7}; \frac{5}{8}, \frac{3}{7}, \frac{4}{7}$

(c) (i) $\frac{3}{28}$ (ii) $\frac{5}{14}$

(iii) $\frac{15}{28}$

7. (a) $\frac{7}{10}$

(b) (i) $\frac{2}{9}$ (ii) 0

(iii) $\frac{5}{12}$ (iv) $\frac{7}{15}$

8. (a) $\frac{5}{9}$ (b) $\frac{16}{81}$ (c) $\frac{40}{81}$

9. (a) $\frac{1}{5}$ (b) $\frac{3}{4}$

(c) (i) $\frac{1}{5}$ (ii) $\frac{7}{20}$

(iii) $\frac{13}{20}$ (iv) $\frac{19}{20}$

10. (a) $\frac{3}{5}$

(b) (i) $\frac{1}{3}$ (ii) $\frac{8}{15}$

(iii) $\frac{2}{3}$

11. (a) $\frac{2}{3}$ (b) $\frac{5}{22}$ (c) $\frac{5}{11}$

12. (a) (i) $\frac{7}{30}$ (ii) $\frac{2}{5}$

(iii) $\frac{11}{30}$

(b) $\frac{1}{10}$

13. (a) (i) $\frac{3}{7}$ (ii) $\frac{10}{21}$

(b) (i) $\frac{5}{21}$ (ii) $\frac{20}{273}$

14. (a) $\frac{3}{10}$ (b) $\frac{1}{15}$

(c) $\frac{2}{15}$ (d) $\frac{1}{9}$

15. (a) $\frac{1}{5}$

(b) (i) $\frac{1}{10}$ (ii) $\frac{2}{5}$

(iii) $\frac{3}{10}$ (iv) $\frac{3}{5}$

16. (a) $\frac{2}{3}$

(b) (i) $\frac{1}{15}$ (ii) $\frac{1}{6}$

(iii) $\frac{1}{30}$

17. (a) (i) $\frac{3}{11}$ (ii) $\frac{21}{110}$

(b) $\frac{7}{55}$

Review Questions 6

1. (a) $\frac{1}{6}$ (b) $\frac{1}{4}$ (c) $\frac{1}{4}$

(d) $\frac{1}{2}$

2. (a) $\frac{1}{12}$ (b) $\frac{1}{4}$

3. (a) $\frac{1}{26}$ (b) $\frac{1}{104}$

4. (a) $\frac{1}{26}$ (b) $\frac{1}{26}$ (c) $\frac{1}{24}$

5. (a) $\frac{6}{7}$ (b) $\frac{1}{49}$

(c) $\frac{12}{49}$ (d) $\frac{216}{343}$

6. (a) $\frac{4}{5}$ (b) $\frac{2}{15}$ (c) $\frac{1}{5}$

7. (a) (i) $\frac{40}{87}$ (ii) $\frac{38}{87}$

(b) (i) $\frac{1}{3}$ (ii) $\frac{8}{15}$

(iii) $\frac{13}{15}$

8. (a) $\frac{3}{10}$ (b) $\frac{31}{45}$ (c) $\frac{11}{120}$

(d) $\frac{5}{36}$ (e) $\frac{1}{24}$

9. (a) 1, 1; 3, $\frac{3}{4}$; $\frac{1}{3}$, $\frac{2}{3}$

(b) $\frac{5}{9}$

10. (a) $\frac{1}{2}$ (b) $\frac{1}{8}$ (c) $\frac{7}{16}$

(d) $\frac{7}{64}$

11. (a) (i) $\frac{5}{8}$ (ii) $\frac{3}{8}$

(b) (i) $\frac{1}{16}$ (ii) $\frac{1}{64}$

(iii) $\frac{7}{32}$ (iv) $\frac{17}{32}$

(v) $\frac{7}{16}$

12. (a) $\frac{27}{55}$ (b) $\frac{18}{55}$

13. $\frac{2}{3}$

14. $\frac{13}{81}$

15. $\frac{1}{9}$

16. $\frac{5}{132}$

17. $\frac{133}{1150}$

Revision Exercise 7a

1. (a) 0.03 (b) 0.034 6
   (c) 3.456×10^{-2}
2. (a) 4.0 (b) 4.03
3. (a) 0.000 074 (b) 7.4×10^{-5}
4. (a) 173 min
   (b) 01 08 the next day
5. (a) 1.556×10^{6}
   (b) $2.386\ 8 \times 10^{6}$
   (c) 2×10^{2}
   (d) $1.216\ 8 \times 10^{10}$
   (e) $4.745\ 52 \times 10^{13}$
   (f) 2×10^{-2}
6. 0.3
7. 1.4×10^{6}
8. (a) 1.92 (b) 10.90
   (c) 63.17
9. (a) 4.80×10^{-7}
   (b) 3.72×10^{-7}
10. (a) 3.82×10^{11}
    (b) 7.48%
    (c) 2.706 times
11. $220
12. $85
13. $25
14. $308
15. 386
16. (a) 34 (b) $171.30
17. 62.9%
18. $408, $640
19. 20%
20. (a) 16.1% (b) 87.3%
    (c) 69.8%
21. (a) 108.6° (b) –34.9°
22. 100 000 tonnes, 125 000 tonnes
23. (a) $3 \times 5^2 \times 7$ (b) 21, 25
    (c) 21
24. 4% decrease
25. $440
26. $4140

Revision Exercise 7b

1. 20%
2. 6%
3. $3\frac{1}{3}$ days
4. $7\frac{1}{5}$ days
5. 9 km/h
6. 90
7. 700 boys, 500 girls
8. $7\frac{1}{2}$ days
9. $120, $48, $12
10. (a) 270 (b) $7\frac{1}{2}$
    (c) $y = 3\frac{1}{2}x^{\frac{2}{3}}$, $31\frac{1}{2}$
11. $4\frac{1}{2}$
12. $y = \frac{7}{8}$, $y = \frac{7}{z^3}$
13. $1\frac{7}{9}$, 2, $y = \frac{16}{x^2}$
14. $2\frac{1}{2}$, –3
15. $y = \frac{32}{27}(x + 1)^2$, $18\frac{26}{27}$
16. (a) 10 km (b) 50 cm²
17. (a) 4 km (b) 7 km²
18. (a) 4.8 m (b) 250 cm²
    (c) 240 litres
19. (a) 24 000 m (b) 4 000 000
20. (a) $3\frac{1}{2}x - 4\frac{1}{2}$
    (b) $3x + 3$ (c) 48 km
    (d) $13\frac{5}{7}$ km/h
21. (a) 70 km (b) 49.4 km/h
22. (a) $4\frac{8}{11}$ km/h
    (b) 46 km/h
23. $7.74 billion
24. (a) $y = \frac{9}{4}(x + 1)^2$
    (b) 36
25. (a) 2.98×10^{5} km/s
    (b) 1.25×10^{-6}s

Revision Exercise 7c

1. $3\frac{1}{3}$%
2. S$3158
3. $14 100
4. $874.18
5. 10.5%
6. $27 318
7. (a) $50
   (b) (i) $60 (ii) $80
   (c) (i) $460 (ii) $610
   (d) 20
   (e) No
   (f) $88 700
8. (a) $181.32 (b) $130.23
   (c) $188.27
9. (a) 250 000
   (b) 3000, 100, 5
   (c) 2400, 80, 4
   (d) 100 000
   (e) 1436, 48
10. (a) S$31 000 (b) S$34 720
    (c) RM78 022.50
    (d) gain 56%
11. $2076.50; 24.2%
12. (a) (i) $224 (ii) $1.50
    (iii) $50 (iv) $8.40
    (b) $8; $42\frac{1}{2}$%
13. (a) (i) $1320 (ii) $396

(b) \$2856
(c) \$12 282.50
(d) \$3268
(e) \$741, \$54.60
(f) \$12 400

Revision Exercise 7d

1. (a) (i) $3x + 4$
(ii) $3x + 2k$
(b) $3x$ (c) $5x$
2. (a) (i) $5x$ (ii) kx
(b) (i) $8x + 0.8$
(ii) $hx + 0.1\,h$
(c) $yx + zx + 0.1z$
3. $\frac{10}{v}$ h (b) $\frac{x}{v}$ h
(c) $\frac{y}{1000\,v}$ h
4. (a) $\frac{1}{x}$ (b) $\frac{4}{x+6}$
(c) $\frac{2(x+3)}{x(x+6)}$
5. (a) $2x + 25$ (b) $x + 28$
(c) $-23x - 3$ (d) $18x - 1$
(e) $18a + 9$ (f) $-7k - 26$
(g) $9c - 21a + 5$
(h) $7q$ (i) $4y^2 - 3x^2$
(j) $8ab$
6. (a) $2a + 12$ (b) $4y - x + 3z$
(c) $4x - 4y - 3z$
(d) $-8a + 4b - 2c$
(e) $10b - 11a$
(f) $8z - 5y$
(g) $2ab + 3ac - 3bc - 5a^2$
(h) $11ab - 4ac - 2a + 2b - 2c - bc$
(i) $ab + 5bc$
(j) $22b - 3c - 9a$
7. (a) -4 (b) 3 (c) -5
8. (a) $-1\frac{1}{9}$ (b) $-5\frac{1}{2}$
(c) 12 (d) $\frac{7}{9}$
(e) $-5\frac{1}{5}$ (f) -14
(g) $\frac{9}{13}$ (h) 5
(i) 45 (j) $2\frac{9}{10}$
(k) $5\frac{3}{4}$ (l) $8\frac{9}{11}$
9. (a) (2, 3) (b) (2, -1)
(c) $\left(\frac{1}{2}, \frac{1}{3}\right)$ (d) (1, -1)
(e) (-1, -2) (f) (5, -1)
(g) (3, -2) (h) (4, -3)
10. (a) $8x(x + 2)$
(b) $(x - 12)(x + 12)$
(c) $(x - 2y)^2$
(d) $3xy(x^2 - 3y)$
(e) $(5 - 8k)(5 + 8k)$
(f) $(3x + 4y - 3z)(3x + 4y + 3z)$
(g) $(a - b + x - y)(a - b - x + y)$
(h) $(x + 3)(x - 17)$
(i) $(2a - 1)(a + 2)$
(j) $(3a - 2)(a + 3)$
(k) $(4k - 7)(k + 2)$
(l) $(5x + 1)(x + 2)$
(m) $(3a - 5)(2a - 7)$
(n) $(7a - 1)(a + 10)$
11. (a) $(x + 3)(x + y)$
(b) $(a - c)(b - c)$
(c) $(x - b)(a + k)$
(d) $(3 + c)(x + c)$
(e) $(a - k)(x - h)$
(f) $(5x + y)(a + b)$
(g) $(3x + 2)(y - 4)$
(h) $(5c - d)(4a - 3k)$
(i) $(2a + b)(3a - 4k)$
(j) $(2a - 1)(a^3 + 2)$
12. 70¢, \$1.80
13. (a) (10, 32) (b) (3, -1)
(c) (7, -13) (d) (5, 6)
(e) $\left(3, -\frac{1}{2}\right)$ (f) (56, -17)
(g) (8, -10) (h) (-1, -1)
14. $\frac{100y + z}{x}$, $\frac{100kx}{100y + z}$
15. (a) $x = 3$, $y = 1$
(b) they are parallel lines
16. (a) 10 (b) 242 (c) 5
(d) $-9\frac{1}{2}$ (e) $-8\frac{6}{7}$
17. $6\frac{4}{5}$

Revision Exercise 7e

1. (a) $21x^7$ (b) $6x^{\frac{5}{6}}$
(c) $8x^{7\frac{1}{2}}$ (d) $4x^4$
(e) $3x^{4\frac{1}{2}}$ (f) $2x^{19}$
(g) $49x^{-2}$ (h) $\frac{1}{8}x^4$
(i) $21x^3$ (j) $x^{\frac{1}{3}}y^{\frac{1}{4}}$
(k) $x^{\frac{1}{3}}y^{4\frac{1}{2}}$ (l) $2x^7y$
2. (a) $\frac{1}{9}$ (b) 8
(c) $\frac{1}{16}$ (d) $\frac{1}{243}$
(e) 1 (f) 125
(g) $2\frac{10}{27}$ (h) $\frac{1}{16}$
(i) 9 (j) $\frac{1}{216}$
(k) 4 (l) $\frac{5}{32}$
(m) 416 (n) 9
(o) $4\frac{1}{2}$ (p) $\frac{2}{13}$
(q) 192 (r) $\frac{-88}{147}$
3. (a) $x = 21\frac{1}{2}$ (b) $k = 0$
4. (a) $\frac{17x}{14}$ (b) $\frac{7 - 2x}{12}$
(c) $\frac{43 - x}{20}$ (d) $\frac{5x - 6}{4x}$
(e) $\frac{5x - 7}{2x - 3}$ (f) $\frac{2(10a - 1)}{5(5a - 1)}$
(g) $\frac{5x + 1}{(x - 1)(x + 2)}$
(h) $\frac{7x - 8}{(x + 1)(2x - 1)}$
(i) $\frac{-a - 9}{(3a - 1)(2a - 3)}$
(j) $\frac{a^2 - 2a + 3}{(1 - 2a)(4 + a)}$
(k) $\frac{x^2 - 7x - 5}{(x + 1)(x - 2)}$
(l) $\frac{3x^2 + 14x - 6}{(x - 3)(x + 4)}$
(m) $\frac{5p^2 + p + 12}{(p - 3)(p + 1)}$
(n) $\frac{2a^2 - 2a + 1}{(2a - 3)(a + 1)}$
(o) $\frac{3y - x}{x(x - y)}$
(p) $\frac{15x^2 - 3xy - y^2}{(2x - y)(3x - y)}$
5. (a) 5 or -14 (b) 12 or -13
(c) 4 or 7 (d) $\frac{7}{3}$ or $\frac{23}{2}$
(e) 3 or -7 (f) 3 or 5
(g) 3 or 16 (h) 7 or 25
(i) 1 or 7 (j) -4 or -5
(k) $\frac{1}{2}$ or 4 (l) $\frac{1}{3}$ or 3

(m) $\frac{1}{4}$ or −2 (n) $-\frac{1}{5}$ or −5

(o) $\frac{4}{3}$ or $\frac{3}{2}$ (p) 2 or $-\frac{1}{9}$

6. (a) $1\frac{7}{9}$ (b) $\frac{17}{72}$

7. (a) $\frac{2}{5}$ (b) −3

(c) $\frac{1}{17}$

8. (a) $3\frac{1}{2}$ (b) $-\frac{4}{7}$

(c) $-\frac{1}{4}$ (d) −4

(e) $1\frac{1}{2}$ (f) 20

9. (a) $b = \frac{-c - ax^2}{x}$

(b) $l = \frac{8gt^2}{\pi^2}$

(c) $c = \frac{6a}{2ak - 2 - ab}$

(d) $x = \frac{-5k - 9}{12}$

(e) $u = \pm\sqrt{v^2 - 2as}$

(f) $a = \frac{bx^3}{1 + x^3}$

10. (a) $\frac{3}{x + 1}$

(b) $\frac{3x + 1}{x^2 - 4}$

(c) $\frac{x^2 - 5x + 8}{2x^2 + x - 6}$

(d) $\frac{5}{x^2 - x - 2}$

11. (a) 3 (b) $\frac{y^2 + a}{2}$

12. (a) $\pm\frac{1}{\sqrt{2}}$ (b) $\frac{y^2}{2(x + 1)}$

13. $y = \frac{k - 2a}{a - 3}$

14. (a) $\frac{16}{3}t - 3$

(b) $t = \frac{9}{16}, x = \frac{1}{8}, y = 2\frac{3}{8}$

15. (a) $12x$

(b) $x = \frac{1}{4}, a = 7\frac{3}{4}, b = -4\frac{1}{2}$

16. (a) $a = -13, b = 35$

(b) $6t^2 + 6t + 14$

17. (a) $-1\frac{2}{3}$ (b) $\frac{1 - y}{1 + y}$

18. $a = \frac{-7b}{11}$

19. $\frac{2ac}{3c - a}$

Revision Exercise 7f

1. (a) 7 (b) −2 (c) 7

2. 5

3. 4, 5, 6

4. (1, 2), (2, 1)

5. (a) 11 (b) −10

(c) 7

6. (a) $x \leqslant 2\frac{1}{9}$ (b) $x < 2\frac{1}{2}$

(c) $x \geqslant 5\frac{4}{5}$ (d) $x \geqslant \frac{3}{4}$

7. 5, 7, 9, 11

8. (a) 1.1 (b) 13

(c) 60 (d) −130

9. (a) 28 cm (b) 61.75 cm²

10. 5, 6, 7, 8, 9

11. −5, −3, −2

12. (a) 13 (b) 6

(c) $-4 \leqslant x \leqslant 4$

13. (a) 6 (b) −25

14. (a) $2.9x \leqslant 23.8$

(b) 8

15. (a) $-\frac{4}{5}$ (b) −5

Revision Exercise 7g

1. (a) −0.27, 3.77

(b) −1.70, 1.37

(c) 0.57, 2.18

(d) 0.23, 1.43

(e) −1.54, 0.87

(f) −0.87, 1.54

2. 17.56 cm

3. 1.94 cm

4. $x^2 + 3.4x - 125 = 0$, 13.01 cm

5. $5t^2 + 7t - 100 = 0$, 3.83 sec

6. $x^2 + 2.4x - 156 = 0$, 50.20 cm

7. 30 m/min

8. 32.23 km/h, 37.23 km/h

9. 4, 9

10. $\frac{3}{5}$

11. $\frac{380}{x}, \frac{380}{x - 5}, \frac{380}{x - 5} - \frac{380}{x} = \frac{5}{12}$

70 km/h, 65 km/h

12. 2 h

13. (a) (−3, 0), (−5, 0)

(b) (0, 1), (0, 15)

14. (a) $2r - 1$ (c) 3 cm

15. (a) $3782.76 (b) 31.4%

(c) (i) $12 841.34

(ii) $647.09

16. (a) 5 h 45 min

(b) RM6608, S$2891.90

(c) (i) $\frac{200}{x}$ (ii) $\frac{200}{x + 5}$

(iv) 30.9 km/h

Revision Exercise 7h

1. (a) 54°

(b) (i) 14 cm

(ii) 92.4 cm²

2. (a) 90°

(b) 41.2 cm, 92.4 cm²

3. (a) 201 cm² (b) 13 cm²

4. (a) (i) 134.1 cm

(ii) 4 289.9 cm²

(iii) 1 169.4 cm²

(b) 37 536.4 cm³

5. (a) 11 cm (b) 121 cm²

6. (a) 14.36 cm²

(b) 10.90 cm²

(c) 9.58 cm²

7. (a) 9 π cm² (b) 8

8. (a) 12.11 cm (b) 14 cm

(c) $51\frac{1}{3}$ cm²

9. 154 cm²

10. (a) $\frac{14}{17}$ rad (b) 6.24 cm

(c) 12.6 cm²

11. (a) 9.00 m (b) 1.79 cm²

12. (a) (i) $2r + r\theta$

(ii) $A = \frac{1}{2}r^2\theta$

(b) $A = \frac{r(3 - 2r)}{2}$

$\theta = 0.76$ rad

13. (a) 38.4 cm (b) 37.8 cm²

Revision Exercise 7i

1. (a) $6\frac{2}{3}$ cm³ (b) $\frac{\pi r^3}{48}$

2. 1983 cm³ ; 21 217 g

3. (a) 42.7 cm³ (b) 70.5°

4. 616 cm²

5. (a) (i) 880 cm²

(ii) 21.56 kg

(b) (i) 218 cm³

(ii) 7.54 litres

6. (a) 5.5 cm (b) 19.25 cm^2
(c) 154 cm^2 (d) 194.5 cm^2

7. (a) 1344 cm^3 (b) $436\frac{1}{3}$ m^3
(c) 385 m^3 (d) 2310 cm^3

8. (a) 1584 cm^3 (b) 6.9 cm
(c) 9 cm

9. (a) (i) 2.1 m^2
(ii) 340.3 kg
(b) 2.52 m^3 (c) 8.6 cm
(d) 5040 (e) $2.10

10. (a) 27 440 cm^3
(b) 52.4%
(c) 406

11. (a) 1742.8 cm^2
(b) 897.2 cm^2

12. (a) $\frac{1}{6}$ (b) 3.587 cm
(c) 78.77 cm^2 (d) 12.9 cm^3

13. (a) 39.79 cm
(b) 4.07 cm
(c) 10 h 46 min.

Revision Exercise 7j

1. (a) 1
(b) $y = 5x - 7$

2. $k = -1$, $y = -\frac{1}{2}x - 4\frac{1}{2}$

3. 10 units

4. (a) P (9,0), Q (0,6)
(b) 10.8 units
(c) $y = 3x - 10.5$

5. 7.21 units

6. (a) −17 (b) $\frac{2}{7}$
(c) $2y + x = 11$

7. (a) $-\frac{3}{4}$ (b) (5, 5)

8. (a) $3y + 4x = 12$
(b) $3y = 4x + 12$

9. $4y + 2x = -9$

10. (a) $k = 4$ (b) 9.49
(c) $3y = 2x - 12$

11. $5y = 7x + 14$

13. (a) $\sqrt{17}$, $\sqrt{68}$, $\sqrt{85}$
(b) 17 $units^2$ (c) 3.69
(d) 4.61 unit

14. $10y = 7x - 47$

15. (a) $h = -4$, $k = 10$
(b) $y + 2x = 9\frac{1}{3}$
(c) $21\frac{7}{9}$

16. (a) 15 units (b) (12, 9)
(c) 48 $units^2$ (d) 8.54 units

17. (a) (7.6, 0)
(b) $y = 1\frac{1}{2}x - 11\frac{2}{5}$
(c) $t = 11\frac{1}{10}$ (d) 22.8 $units^2$

18. (a) $B(0, 8)$, $Q(0, 16)$, $P(-15, 0)$
(b) $15y = 16x + 240$
(c) 21.93 units
(d) 10.94 units

Revision Exercise 7k

1. (a) 45° (b) 30° (c) 15°
2. (a) 120° (b) 144° (c) 156°
3. (a) 72 (b) 45 (c) 30
4. (a) 36 (b) 90 (c) 20
5. (a) 160° (b) 150°
6. 140°
7. 12
8. 36
9. (a) 90° (b) 40° (c) 62°
10. 129
12. (a) 41 (b) 105°
13. (a) 8 (b) 16
14. (a) 26° (b) 102° (c) 128°
15. (a) 72° (b) 66° (c) 66°
16. (a) 97° (b) 253°
17. (a) 56° (b) 62°
18. (a) 77° (b) 18°
19. (a) 38° (b) 79° (c) 71°
20. (a) 30° (b) 150°
21. (a) 108° (b) 60° (c) 120°
22. (a) 17 (b) 27
23. (a) 72° (b) 36°
24. (a) 9 (b) 20
25. (a) 36, 10; 30, 12
(b) 100 (c) 2°

Revision Exercise 7l

1. (a) 3 : 5 (b) 9 : 25
2. (a) $6\frac{1}{4}$ cm (b) 62.5 cm^3
3. (a) 4 : 1 (b) 420 litres
4. (a) 16 cm (b) $11\frac{23}{27}$ kg
5. (a) 17 cm
(b) 7812.5 cm^3
6. 432.64 cm^3
7. 1890 cm^3
8. 675 cm^2
9. (a) 3375 : 1
(b) 225 : 1; 75 000 kg
10. 3850 m^2, 616 cm^2, 25 : 4, 32 cm^2
11. 204 m; $1.44 million; 2 g
12. (a) 12 cm
(b) (i) 4 : 9 (ii) 8 : 27
(c) $3.24
13. (a) 73.5 cm^2 (b) 50 cm^2
14. (a) 9 cm
(b) (i) $\frac{1}{3}$ (ii) 16
15. (a) 45 cm^2 (b) 25 cm^2
16. 24 cm^2, $21\frac{3}{5}$ cm^2
17. 50 cm^2
18. (a) 2.4 cm (b) 3 : 2
(c) 9 : 16

Revision Exercise 7m

1. (a) 27° (b) 36° (c) 54°
2. (a) 61° (b) 96°
3. (a) 49° (b) 27°
4. (a) 43° (b) 47°
5. (a) 64° (b) 32°
(c) 32° (d) 26°
6. (a) 56° (b) 62° (c) 56°
7. (a) 132° (b) 26°
(c) 24° (d) 40°
8. (a) 32° (b) 124° (c) 24°
9. 2.31 cm
10. (a) 85 cm^2 (b) 12.85 cm
11. 13.23 cm
12. 9.60 cm
13. (a) 28° (b) 56°
(c) 86° (d) 28°
14. 3 cm
15. (a) 120° (b) 70°
(c) 20° (d) 40°
16. (a) 50° (b) 25°
17. 114°
18. 61°
19. (a) 96° (b) 84°
20. 62°
21. $x = 10$, $y = 5$; 50°
22. (a) 24° (b) 114° (c) 68°

Revision Exercise 7n

1. (a) $A(-1, 0)$, $B(0, 2)$, $C(2, 0)$
(b) $x = \frac{1}{2}$
3. (a) (0, −5) (b) $k = 2$
4. $k = -5$, $p = 4$
5. **a** = 19, **b** = 9
(a) 3.55 or −0.55
(b) 4.55 or −1.55, $x = 1$ or 3
6. (a) 5, 8, 8, 5
(c) 3.4 or −1.4

(d) 9 (e) $0 < x < 2$

7. (b) (i) 1.7 or –4.7
(ii) $-3 \le x \le 1$
(iii) 0.4 or –4.4
(c) (–1, –5)

8. (a) –3, –1, 9, 32
(c) 0.75 (d) $x = 1$
(e) $x = -1, 1, 2$

9. (a) 3, $\frac{11}{12}$, 1
(c) (i) 0.8 (ii) 1.15, 2.43
(d) 0.71 2.64

10. 4, 3.5, 4.7, 8, 9.8
(a) 1.4
(b) (i) 3.2 , 0.8
(ii) 1, 5

11. (a) –3.3 (b) 1.8

12. (a) $h = 3.7, k = 1.7$
(c) –1.9
(d) (i) 2.2 (ii) 1.4
(iii) 2.4 (iv) $x < 1.2$

Revision Exercise 7o

1. (a) 6 litres (b) 62.5 km
2. (a) (i) S$5.40
(ii) S$17.10
(b) (i) RM93.30
(ii) RM166.70
3. (a) 36.7 (b) 122
(c) 27.8
4. (a) $12.78 (b) 40
(c) 75
5. (a) 2 m/s (b) $\frac{1}{3}$ m/s^2
(c) 210 m
6. (a) 40 (b) –0.8 m/s^2
(c) 360 m
7. (b) 2 m/s^2, $4\frac{1}{2}$ m/s^2
(c) $15\frac{15}{44}$ m/s
8. (a) $\frac{3}{4}$ m/s^2 (b) 1125 m
(c) 1000 m (d) $t = 30$ s
9. (a) (i) 100 N (ii) 240 N
(b) 50 N
10. (a) 48 km (b) 2 h
(c) 28 km
(d) 09 00 to 10 00
(e) 8 km/h
11. (a) 0 m/s^2 (b) –4.8 m/s^2
(c) 242.24 m (d) 12.1 m/s
12. (a) 6.4 s (b) 0.68 m/s^2
13. (a) $\frac{35}{x^2}$
(c) 62.3, 55.7, 53, 59.3

(e) (i) 5.4 cm (ii) 51
(iii) 2.1 cm (iv) 60.6 cm^2

Revision Exercise 7p

1. (a) 5.20 cm (b) 10.39 cm
2. (a) $-\frac{7}{24}$ (b) $-\frac{24}{25}$
3. (a) 7.1 cm^2
(b) 32.61 cm, 521.8 cm^2
(c) 8.78 cm
4. (a) 17.5 cm (b) 74.5°
5. (a) 24 cm, 134.8
(b) 2.6 m
6. (a) $1\frac{12}{13}$ (b) $\frac{5}{13}$
7. (a) (i) 48.2° (ii) 8.94 m
(b) 38.7°
8. (a) 10 cm (b) 4.8 cm
9. (a) 8 cm (b) 33.7°
10. (a) 148 (b) $-\frac{4}{5}, -\frac{3}{4}$
11. (a) 209.2 m (b) 2.215 m
12. (a) 13 cm (b) 37.4 cm^2
13. (a) 12.65 cm (b) 103.3°
14. (a) 32.2° or 147.8°
(b) 3.20 cm or 10.57 cm
15. 10.46 cm, 33°, 17.79 cm
16. (a) 4.85 cm (b) 33.3°
17. (a) 8.94 cm (b) 83.6°
18. (a) 10 sin x
(b) 105 sin x, 44.4°
19. (a) (i) 52° (ii) 8.96 cm
(iii) 22.24 cm^2
(b) 30.59 cm^2
20. (a) 22.7 cm (b) 337.2 cm^2
21. (a) 32.3° (b) 9.0 cm
(c) 15.5 cm; 25.6 cm^2
22. (a) 59.7° (b) 120.3°

Revision Exercise 7q

1. (a) 54.1° (b) 7.53 cm
(c) 9.51cm, 3.54 cm
2. (a) 150° (b) 330°
(c) 2.85 km
3. (a) 102° (b) 162°
4. (a) 8.12 m (b) 13.3°
5. (a) 42 km (b) 82°
(c) 138.2°
6. 502.8 m, 153.5°
7. (a) 6.50 km (b) 334.4°
(c) 718.9 ha
8. (a) 056.1° (b) 12.7 m
(c) 56.0 m (d) 939.3 m^2
9. (a) 126.6 m (b) 39.7°
(c) 30.1° (d) 158.6°
(e) 9211 m^2
10. (a) 315° (b) 36.71 km
(c) 1645 (d) 33.46 km
(e) 024.3°
11. (a) 337.5° (b) 60.7 km
(c) 17 55 or 5.55 pm
(d) 43.4° (e) 41.9 km
(f) 2531 km^2
12. (a) 117.4° (b) 153.7°
(c) 5.52 km (d) 5.33 km
13. (a) 108.8 km
(b) 64.5 km; 59.6 km
14. (a) (i) 109.25 m (ii) 198°
(b) 7.3
15. (a) (i) 9.89 cm (ii) 12.0 cm
(iii) 50 cm^2
(b) 352.3°

Revision Exercise 7r

1. (a) 86, 80 (b) $(1 - n)^3$
2. (a) 35, 48
(b) $\sqrt{21}$, $\sqrt{34}$
(c) $1\frac{1}{6}$, $1\frac{5}{12}$
3. (a) $8^2 - 8 = 56$
(b) 11
4. (a) 93, 142 (b) $2^n + 1$
5. (a) $S_3 = 36 = 6^2$
$S_4 = 100 = 10^2$
$S_5 = 225 = 15^2$
(b) $S_n = \left[\frac{n(n+1)}{2}\right]^2$
(c) 20th square.
6. (a) $a = 8, b = 24, c = 24, d = 8$
(b) 8 (c) 27
(d) (i) $12(n - 2)$
(ii) $6(n - 2)^2$
(iii) $(n - 2)^3$
7. (a) $l = 60, m = 25, n = 36$
(b) $T = 2\sqrt{SP}$ or $T^2 = 4SP$ or $T = S + P - 1$
(c) 196
(d) 112 is not a perfect square.
(e) 4 442 is not a multiple of 4.
8. (a) $p = 4$, $q = 5$; p and q are the next two terms of the sequence 0, 1, 2, 3, ...
(b) $r = 14, s = 20$
(c) $v = n - 3$

(d) $d = \frac{nv}{2}$; $d = \frac{n(n-3)}{2}$

(e) 405

Revision Exercise 7s

1. (a) {7, 8} (b) 2

2. (a) (i) {c} (ii) {a, c, d, e}
(b) (i) 2 (ii) 2

3. (a) {2}
(b) {1, 2, 3, 5, 7, 9}
(c) {2, 5, 7}

4. (a) 18 (b) 12
(c) 7 (d) 9
(e) 7 (f) 5

5. $m = 2, c = 4$

6. (a) A (b) B

7. (a) 51 (b) 64, 81, 100
(c) 8, 9, 10

8. 2

9. (a) (i) {16, 17, ..., 24, 25}
(ii) ø
(b) (i) 9 (ii) 0

10. (a) {1, 2, 3, 4, 6, 12}
(b) {5, 7, 9, 11}
(c) {1, 2, 3, 4, 5, 6, 7, 9, 11, 12}

11. (a) {3, 6, 9, 12, 18, 36}
(b) {1, 2, 4}

12. (a) {1, 2, 3, 4, 5, 6, 10, 12, 15, 20}
(b) {2, 3, 5, 7, 11, 13, 17, 19}
(c) {2, 3, 5}

13. (a) {1, 2, 3, 4, 6, 8, 12, 24}
(b) {2, 3}
(c) {1, 2, 4, 8}
(d) {2, 5, 7, 11, 13, 17, 19, 23}

16. (a) $A \cap B'$ (b) $(A \cup B)'$
(c) $A \cap B'$ (d) $(A \cap B)'$

Revision Exercise 7t

1. (a) $\begin{pmatrix} 5 \\ -2 \\ -4 \end{pmatrix}$ (b) $\begin{pmatrix} 7 & 8 & 12 \\ 4 & -1 & 9 \end{pmatrix}$

(c) $\begin{pmatrix} 0 & 1 \\ 1 & -2 \\ 14 & 0 \end{pmatrix}$ (d) $\begin{pmatrix} 3 & 11 \\ 12 & 1 \end{pmatrix}$

2. (a) (5) (b) $\begin{pmatrix} -6 \\ 4 \end{pmatrix}$

(c) $\begin{pmatrix} 10 & 8 \\ 4 & 8 \\ 0 & 4 \end{pmatrix}$

(d) $(15 \quad 14 \quad 0)$

(e) $\begin{pmatrix} 36 & 160 \\ 12 & 80 \end{pmatrix}$ (f) $(37 \quad 1)$

(g) $\begin{pmatrix} -58 \\ -86 \end{pmatrix}$ (h) (88)

3. (a) $x = -4, y = -20$ (b) $x = 8, y = 8$
(c) $x = 5, y = -3$ (d) $x = 1, y = 1$
(e) $x = 1\frac{3}{4}, y = 1, z = -1\frac{5}{8}$
(f) $x = -4, y = 6$

4. (a) $x = 1, y = 2$ (b) $x = 3, y = -1$
(c) $x = -4, y = 4$

5. $A = \frac{1}{3}\begin{pmatrix} 3 & 1 \\ 10 & 11 \end{pmatrix}, B = \frac{1}{3}\begin{pmatrix} 3 & -4 \\ -1 & 7 \end{pmatrix}$

6. (a) $\begin{pmatrix} -22 & 3 \\ -6 & -21 \end{pmatrix}$ (b) $\begin{pmatrix} 37 & 279 \\ -558 & 130 \end{pmatrix}$ (c) $\begin{pmatrix} -42 & -33 \\ 66 & -53 \end{pmatrix}$

7. $a = -\frac{3}{4}, b = 12, c = 4$

8. $p = 0, q = 15$

9. (a) $\begin{pmatrix} 560 & 240 & 30 & 20 \\ 580 & 220 & 40 & 22 \\ 480 & 200 & 36 & 25 \\ 450 & 180 & 45 & 18 \\ 460 & 210 & 38 & 16 \\ 640 & 180 & 42 & 26 \end{pmatrix}\begin{pmatrix} 2.40 \\ 0.80 \\ 3.20 \\ 3.60 \end{pmatrix} = \begin{pmatrix} 1704 \\ 1775.20 \\ 1517.20 \\ 1432.80 \\ 1451.20 \\ 1908 \end{pmatrix}$

(b) $(1 \quad 1 \quad 1 \quad 1 \quad 1 \quad 1)\begin{pmatrix} 1704 \\ 1775.20 \\ 1517.20 \\ 1432.80 \\ 1451.20 \\ 1908 \end{pmatrix} = (9788.40)$

10. $\begin{pmatrix} 24 & 12 & 22 \\ 32 & 16 & 25 \\ 42 & 20 & 26 \\ 48 & 28 & 34 \end{pmatrix}\begin{pmatrix} 12 \\ 15 \\ 18 \end{pmatrix} = \begin{pmatrix} 864 \\ 1074 \\ 1272 \\ 1608 \end{pmatrix}$

$(46 \quad 58 \quad 65 \quad 34)\begin{pmatrix} 864 \\ 1074 \\ 1272 \\ 1608 \end{pmatrix} = (239 \quad 388)$

11. (a) $\begin{pmatrix} 12 & 8 & 11 \\ 18 & 11 & 7 \\ 8 & 9 & 15 \end{pmatrix}\begin{pmatrix} 48 \\ 32 \\ 26 \end{pmatrix} = \begin{pmatrix} 1118 \\ 1398 \\ 1062 \end{pmatrix}$

(b) $(9.80 \quad 10.40 \quad 9.90)\begin{pmatrix} 1118 \\ 1398 \\ 1062 \end{pmatrix} = (36009.40)$

Revision Exercise 7u

1. (a) $\overrightarrow{OM} = \begin{pmatrix}3\\4\end{pmatrix}$

   (b) $\overrightarrow{ON} = \begin{pmatrix}-1\\0\end{pmatrix}$

2. $\overrightarrow{PQ} = \begin{pmatrix}-1\\8\end{pmatrix}$, $\overrightarrow{RQ} = \begin{pmatrix}3\\1\end{pmatrix}$,

   $\overrightarrow{MN} = \begin{pmatrix}\frac{5}{2}\\\frac{7}{2}\end{pmatrix}$, $\overrightarrow{XY} = \begin{pmatrix}-\frac{5}{2}\\-\frac{7}{2}\end{pmatrix}$;

   $MN = XY$ and $MN \parallel YX$

3. (a) 8.25 (b) (6, 4)

   (c) 6.32

4. (a) 13 units (b) $\begin{pmatrix}2\\27\end{pmatrix}$

   (c) $p = 6.5, q = -5$

5. (a) $\begin{pmatrix}-9\\12\end{pmatrix}$

   (b) $\begin{pmatrix}5\\12\end{pmatrix}$, 13 units

   (c) $\begin{pmatrix}4\\-3\end{pmatrix}$ (d) $\begin{pmatrix}-5\\0\end{pmatrix}$

6. (a) 5 units

   (b) (i) $\begin{pmatrix}-1\\-5\end{pmatrix}$ (ii) $\begin{pmatrix}2\\0\end{pmatrix}$

   (iii) $\begin{pmatrix}-4\\0\end{pmatrix}$ (iv) $\begin{pmatrix}-6\\-10\end{pmatrix}$

7. (a) trapezium (b) $-(\mathbf{a} + \mathbf{b})$

8. (a) $\begin{pmatrix}3\\1\end{pmatrix}$ (b) (9, 5)

   (c) (i) $\sqrt{37}$ (ii) $-\frac{1}{6}$

   (iii) $y = -\frac{1}{6}x + 2$

   (iv) $\left(3, \frac{3}{2}\right)$

9. (a) $-\frac{3}{4}\mathbf{p}$

   (b) (i) $\frac{3}{4}\mathbf{p} + \mathbf{q}$

   (ii) $\mathbf{p} - \mathbf{q}$

   (iii) $\frac{1}{4}(\mathbf{p} + 3\mathbf{q})$

10. (a) (i) $\mathbf{b} - \mathbf{a}$ (ii) $\frac{1}{2}(\mathbf{b} - \mathbf{a})$

    (iii) $\frac{1}{2}(\mathbf{a} + \mathbf{b})$

    (c) (i) $\mathbf{a} + \mathbf{b}$

    (ii) $\mathbf{b}$

    (iii) $\mathbf{a}$; parallelogram

11. (b) $\overrightarrow{OP} = -2(\mathbf{t} + \mathbf{s})$,

    $\overrightarrow{OQ} = \frac{8}{3}\mathbf{t} - 2\mathbf{s}$,

    $\overrightarrow{OR} = -\mathbf{t} + 4\mathbf{s}$,

    $\overrightarrow{OU} = \frac{2}{3}\mathbf{t} - \frac{3}{2}\mathbf{s}$

12. (a) (i) $2(\mathbf{a} + 3\mathbf{b})$

    (ii) $\mathbf{a} + 3\mathbf{b}$

    (iii) $\frac{3}{2}(\mathbf{b} - \mathbf{a})$

    (iv) $\mathbf{b} - \mathbf{a}$

    (b) PN is parallel to ML

    (c) trapezium

    (d) (i) $\frac{1}{3}$ (ii) $\frac{9}{4}$

Revision Exercise 7v

1. (a) 27

   (b) (i) $13 500

   (ii) $3240

2. (a) 18 000 tonnes
3. 60, 35, 20, 5
4. (a) (i) 4 (ii) 5.5

   (iii) 7

   (b) $a = 33$

5. (a) 20, 25, 37

   (b) 62.6 cm (c) $\frac{17}{550}$

6. (b) (i) 6 marks

   (ii) 5 marks

   (iii) 4.44 marks

7. (b) 56.5
8. (a) 21 (c) 6
9. (b) 56.9 (c) 57
10. (a) 79 cents, 64 cents

    (b) (ii) 2 (iii) 45.5%

Revision Exercise 7w

1. (a) 27 km (b) 17 km

   (c) $\frac{9}{13}$

2. (a) (i) 80.4 mm

   (ii) 22 mm

   (b) $\frac{51}{100}$ (c) $\frac{11}{51}$

3. (a) 90

   (b) (i) 3.5 km (ii) 1.2 km

   (c) (i) $\frac{2}{7}$ (ii) 5

   (d) $\frac{1}{4900}$

4. (a) 76.6 kg

   (b) (i) 46% (ii) 984

5. 10.3 h
6. (a) 31, 27, 14.5

   (b) 56, 58, 34

7. (a) (i) 169 (ii) 36

   (iii) 189

   (b) 179 (c) $\frac{28}{45}$

Revision Exercise 7x

1. (a) $\frac{2}{15}$ (b) $\frac{2}{5}$ (c) $\frac{2}{5}$

   (d) $\frac{8}{15}$ (e) $\frac{8}{45}$

2. (b) $\frac{17}{24}$

3. $\frac{x}{x + 36}$, $x = 24$

4. (a) $\frac{41}{50}$ (b) $\frac{7}{50}$ (c) $\frac{7}{25}$

   (d) $\frac{17}{50}$

5. (a) $\frac{35}{88}$ (b) $\frac{23}{44}$ (c) $\frac{21}{44}$

6. (a) $\frac{1}{6}$ (b) $\frac{1}{4}$ (c) $\frac{1}{12}$

7. (a) 9, 12, 18, 21, 24

   12, 20, 24, 28, 32

   15, 20, 25, 35, 40

   24, 30, 36, 42, 48

   21, 28, 35, 42, 49

   24, 40, 48, 56, 64

   (b) (i) $\frac{1}{4}$ (ii) $\frac{1}{3}$

   (iii) 0 (iv) $\frac{1}{6}$

   (v) 1

8. (a) $\frac{8}{15}, \frac{7}{14}, \frac{4}{14}, \frac{3}{14}$; $\frac{8}{14}, \frac{3}{14}$;

   $\frac{3}{15}, \frac{8}{14}, \frac{4}{14}, \frac{2}{14}$

   (b) (i) $\frac{4}{35}$ (ii) $\frac{68}{105}$

   (iii) $\frac{4}{15}$ (iv) $\frac{13}{35}$

9. (a) (i) $\frac{1}{6}$ (ii) $\frac{1}{2}$

   (b) $\frac{11}{18}$ (c) $\frac{4}{15}$

10. $x = 12, y = 24$

    (a) $\frac{103}{295}$ (b) $\frac{24}{295}$